Differentiation Rules

$f(t)$	$\dfrac{df}{dt} = f(t)$
cu	$c\dot{u}$
$u + v$	$\dot{u} + \dot{v}$
uv	$u\dot{v} + v\dot{u}$
$\dfrac{u}{v}$	$\dfrac{v\dot{u} - u\dot{v}}{v^2}$
$u[v(t)]$	$\dot{u}[v(t)]\dot{v}(t)$

$$\frac{d}{dt}f[x(t), y(t)]$$

$$= \frac{\partial f}{\partial x}\dot{x} + \frac{\partial f}{\partial y}\dot{y}.$$

Differentiation Formulas

$f(t)$	$\dfrac{df}{dt} = f(t)$
c	0
t^α	$\alpha t^{\alpha-1}$
e^t	e^t
a^t	$(\ln a)a^t$
$\ln t$	$\dfrac{1}{t}$
$\sin t$	$\cos t$
$\cos t$	$-\sin t$
$\tan t$	$\sec^2 t$
$\cot t$	$-\csc^2 t$
$\sec t$	$\tan t \sec t$
$\csc t$	$-\cot t \csc t$
$\arcsin t$	$\dfrac{1}{\sqrt{1 - t^2}}$
$\arctan t$	$\dfrac{1}{1 + t^2}$
$\sinh t$	$\cosh t$
$\cosh t$	$\sinh t$
$\tanh t$	$\operatorname{sech}^2 t$

Polar Coordinates

$$\begin{cases} x = r\cos\theta \\ y = r\sin\theta \end{cases}$$

$$\begin{cases} x^2 + y^2 = r^2 \\ \cos\theta = x/r \\ \sin\theta = y/r \end{cases}$$

Integrals   (constant of integration omitted)

1. $\displaystyle\int u \, dv = uv - \int v \, du$

2. $\displaystyle\int \frac{dx}{x} = \ln|x|$

3. $\displaystyle\int \frac{dx}{a^2 + x^2} = \frac{1}{a}\arctan\left(\frac{x}{a}\right)$

4. $\displaystyle\int \frac{dx}{a^2 - x^2} = \frac{1}{2a}\ln\left|\frac{x + a}{x - a}\right|$

5. $\displaystyle\int \frac{dx}{(a^2 + x^2)^n} = \frac{x}{(2n - 2)a^2(a^2 + x^2)^{n-1}}$
$$+ \frac{2n - 3}{(2n - 2)a^2}\int \frac{dx}{(a^2 + x^2)^{n-1}} \qquad (n > 1)$$

6. $\displaystyle\int \frac{dx}{\sqrt{a^2 - x^2}} = \arcsin\left(\frac{x}{a}\right)$

7. $\displaystyle\int \sqrt{a^2 - x^2}\,dx = \frac{x}{2}\sqrt{a^2 - x^2} + \frac{a^2}{2}\arcsin\left(\frac{x}{a}\right)$

8. $\displaystyle\int \frac{dx}{\sqrt{x^2 \pm a^2}} = \ln|x + \sqrt{x^2 \pm a^2}|$

9. $\displaystyle\int \sqrt{x^2 \pm a^2}\,dx$
$$= \frac{x}{2}\sqrt{x^2 \pm a^2} \pm \frac{a^2}{2}\ln|x + \sqrt{x^2 \pm a^2}|$$

(continued inside back cover)

Vectors

$$\mathbf{u} = (a,b), \qquad \mathbf{v} = (c,d)$$
$$\mathbf{u} + \mathbf{v} = (a + c, b + d)$$
$$\mathbf{u} \cdot \mathbf{v} = ac + bd$$
$$\|\mathbf{u}\| = \sqrt{a^2 + b^2}$$

A First Course in Calculus with Analytic Geometry

Harley Flanders   Tel Aviv University

Robert R. Korfhage   Southern Methodist University

Justin J. Price   Purdue University

ACADEMIC PRESS   New York and London

A Subsidiary of Harcourt Brace Jovanovich, Publishers

ACADEMIC PRESS, INC.
111 Fifth Avenue, New York, New York 10003

United Kingdom Edition published by
ACADEMIC PRESS, INC. (LONDON) LTD.
24/28 Oval Road, London NW1

LIBRARY OF CONGRESS CATALOG CARD NUMBER: 72-88355

PRINTED IN THE UNITED STATES OF AMERICA

Contents

4. THE DERIVATIVE

5. APPLICATIONS OF DIFFERENTIATION

6. DIRECTION FIELDS AND MOTION

7. CIRCULAR FUNCTIONS

13. VOLUMES

14. INVERSE FUNCTIONS AND LOGARITHMS

15. TRIGONOMETRIC FUNCTIONS

16. TECHNIQUES OF INTEGRATION

21. CALCULUS THEORY

MATHEMATICAL TABLES

Preface

AIMS OF THIS BOOK

1. To introduce plane analytic geometry and single-variable calculus with a minimum of fuss—through practice, not theory.

2. To stress techniques, applications, and problem solving, rather than definitions, theorems, and proofs.

3. To emphasize numerical aspects such as approximations, order of magnitude, and concrete answers to problems.

4. To organize the topics consistent with the needs of students in their concurrent science and engineering courses.

5. To illustrate the usefulness of computers in applications of calculus.

6. To present the theory behind calculus after the student has developed technical skill and an intuitive appreciation of the usefulness of calculus.

The text is designed for a two-semester or three-quarter course.

WHY THIS APPROACH?

Calculus can be an exciting subject; no other gives so much new scope and power. Yet painful experience has shown that insistence on theory and rigor before the student is taught technique and application tend to stifle the excitement. The premature teaching of real variables to freshmen and sophomores has generally been a failure, a great disservice to students, and a source of well-deserved criticism from science and engineering departments.

Our presentation is informal except in two theory chapters; we reject the practice of writing calculus texts with the style and precision of research papers. Instead of formal definitions, theorems, and proofs, we include intuitive discussions, rules of procedure, and realistic problems. When pedagogically expedient, we allow a few circular arguments and slight inconsistencies; they are set right later. We omit technicalities that almost never occur in practice, rather than clutter the exposition "for the sake of completeness."

We stress explicit computation and, when appropriate, indicate the value of computers in numerical work. We believe that a modern calculus text must recognize the increasing importance of computers in all branches of science. (The material on computer applications can be omitted without loss of continuity.)

ORGANIZATION

This book presupposes reasonable skill in algebraic manipulation and familiarity with graphing, but there is some review in Chapter 1.

Chapters 2 and 3 present vectors and plane analytic geometry. Classes with previous work in analytic geometry can omit these chapters.

Chapters 4–10 cover differentiation, the exponential functions, and sine and cosine. If integration is desired earlier, Chapters 9 and 10 can be postponed until after Chapter 13.

Chapters 11–13 cover the concept of integration and basic applications. Chapters 14 and 15 cover inverse functions, logarithms, direct and inverse trigonometric functions, and hyperbolic functions. A feature is Sections 14.7 and 14.8 on growth rates of e^x and $\ln x$ at ∞. Chapters 16 and 17 cover techniques of integration. An unusual section is 17.5 on tricks with differentials.

Chapters 18 and 19 cover approximations of functions, of integrals, and of roots of equations. We introduce flow charts and discuss estimation of errors.

Chapter 20 contains a careful exposition of the theory of limits of sequences and of functions, and the fundamental properties of continuous functions. Chapter 21 contains the theory behind differential calculus, the Riemann integral developed by what we think is the briefest and clearest method available, and then a rigorous and natural development of the elementary transcendental functions. We take pains throughout to indicate the relations between the theory and the earlier intuitive presentation. There are numerous exercises in these chapters, many quite challenging.

EXAMPLES AND EXERCISES

The 250 worked examples are the core of the text. Many times, methods are explained more through choice examples than elaborate discussions. We are always result-oriented and insist on explicit numerical answers.

A number of topics are included as much because they are a source of meaningful, noncontrived problems as they are of interest in themselves.

Physical examples occur in some sections and in many exercises. The science or engineering student is usually impressed by this material, and motivated to learn it.

The exercises in the early chapters are easy and involve few steps. In the later chapters each exercise set begins with easy problems, but continues to harder ones. Altogether about 2450 exercises are included.

The exercise sets containing problems for the computer also contain parallel problems for hand computation.

We recommend use of a slide rule and a book of tables (such as the *C.R.C. Standard Mathematical Tables*). We include some tables on pages 588–594 and basic formulas on the inside covers.

ILLUSTRATIONS

To solve problems, the student must be able to make clear accurate drawings. We have purposely restricted the illustrations in this book to simple line drawings, the kind the student can make himself.

ACKNOWLEDGMENTS

We thank our typists Allene Fritsch, Shoshanna Kahn, Phyllis Mandel, Kathy Smith, Helen Sutton, and Elizabeth Young for their patience with draft after draft of the manuscript. Our reviewers, Peter Balise, John W. Fujii, Ettore Infante, Paul Mielke, and Robert E. Mosher, contributed numerous valuable improvements to the text.

We are also grateful to the staff of the Academic Press for an excellent production job, and to The Maple Press for the high quality of its typesetting and printing.

1. Functions and Graphs

1. INTRODUCTION

Everyone is familiar with the use of graphs to summarize data (Fig. 1.1)
The figure shows three typical graphs. There are many others; one sees
graphs concerning length, time, speed, voltage, blood pressure, supply, demand, etc.

All graphs have an essential common feature; they illustrate visually the
way one numerical quantity depends on (or varies with) another. In Fig. 1.1,

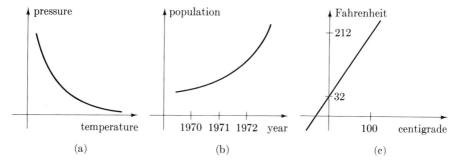

Fig. 1.1.   common graphs

(a) shows how the pressure in a physical experiment depends on the temperature, (b) shows how the population depends on (varies with) time, and
(c) shows how Fahrenheit readings depend on (are related to) centigrade
readings.

Graphs are pictures of **functions.** Roughly speaking, a function describes
the dependence of one quantity on another or the way in which one quantity
varies with another. We say, for instance, that pressure is a function of
temperature, or that population is a function of time, etc.

Functions lurk everywhere; they are the basic idea in almost every application of mathematics. Therefore, a great deal of study is devoted to their
nature and properties. This book is largely an introduction to the more common functions in mathematics.

As Fig. 1.1 illustrates, a graph is an excellent tool in understanding the nature of a function. For it is a kind of "life history" of a function, to be seen at a glance.

The functions and graphs we shall deal with concern quantities measured in the **real number system.** This consists of the familiar numbers of our experience. Before starting our study of functions and graphs, we shall devote a brief section to the real number system itself.

2. REAL NUMBERS

The real numbers are the common numbers of everyday life. Everyone is familiar with their arithmetic. In more advanced courses they are defined and developed rigorously. However, that is a deep and lengthy project, not in the spirit of this book. We shall be content to list the basic properties of real numbers for actual use.

First of all we can compute with real numbers, we can do arithmetic. In doing so we automatically make use of the basic rules listed below.

Associative laws

$$a + (b + c) = (a + b) + c \qquad a(bc) = (ab)c.$$

Commutative laws

$$a + b = b + a \qquad\qquad ab = ba.$$

Zero and unity laws

$$a + 0 = a \qquad\qquad a \cdot 1 = a.$$

Distributive laws

$$a(b + c) = ab + ac \qquad (a + b)c = ac + bc.$$

Inverse laws

If a is any real number, then there is a unique real number $-a$ such that	If a is any real number different from 0, then there is a unique real number a^{-1} such that
$$a + (-a) = 0.$$	$$a \cdot a^{-1} = 1.$$

Recall that we write $a - b = a + (-b)$, and $a/b = ab^{-1}$ if $b \neq 0$.

Besides satisfying these arithmetic rules, the real number system also carries an **order relation**; we can say that one number is greater or less than another. We write "$a < b$" or "$b > a$" to mean "a is less than b", or equivalently, "*b* is greater than *a*". Actually it is often more convenient to write "*a* ≤ *b*" meaning "*a* is less than or equal to *b*". Let us review the rules that govern the order relation.

Reflexivity

$$a \leq a$$

Anti-symmetry

If $a \leq b$ and $b \leq a$, then $a = b$.

Transitivity

If $a \leq b$ and $b \leq c$, then $a \leq c$.

There are important rules relating the algebraic operations and the order relation, but they have no common names:

If $a \leq b$, then $a + c \leq b + c$.

If $a \leq b$ and $c \geq 0$, then $ac \leq bc$.

If $a \leq b$, then $-b \leq -a$.

If $0 < a < b$, then $0 < b^{-1} < a^{-1}$.

If $a \leq b$, then $0 \leq b - a$;
 conversely, if $0 \leq b - a$, then $a \leq b$.

Absolute Values

We often need the relative size of a number, regardless of its sign. For instance, in some sense -10 is greater than 3, but we cannot write $-10 > 3$. For this reason we introduce the absolute value of a real number. We define the **absolute value** of a, written $|a|$, by:

$$|a| = \begin{cases} a & \text{if} \quad a \geq 0 \\ -a & \text{if} \quad a < 0. \end{cases}$$

Thus $|-10| = 10$, $|3| = 3$, $|0| = 0$. Now it is correct to write $|-10| > |3|$.
 Absolute values satisfy the following rules:

$|a| > 0$ if $a \neq 0$; $|a| = 0$ if $a = 0$.

If $a \leq b$ and $-a \leq b$, then $|a| \leq b$.

$|-a| = |a|$.

$|ab| = |a| \, |b|$.

$\left| \dfrac{a}{b} \right| = \dfrac{|a|}{|b|}, b \neq 0.$

$|a + b| \leq |a| + |b|$ (the triangle inequality).

Prove (using the rules):

1. $(a + b)(c + d) =$
   $da + cb + ac + bd$

2. $(a + b)(a - b) = a^2 - b^2$

3. $(a^2 + ab + b^2)(a - b) = a^3 - b^3$

4. $(a + a + a)(b + b + b + b) = 12ab$

5. if $a > 0$ and $b < 0$, then $ab < 0$

6. if $a < 0$ and $b < 0$, then $ab > 0$

7. if $a \neq 0$, then $a^2 > 0$

8. $-(a + b) = (-a) + (-b)$

9. $(-a)(-b) = ab$

10. $-(-a) = a$

11. if $ab \neq 0$, then $a \neq 0$ and $b \neq 0$

12. if $ab = 0$, then $a = 0$ or $b = 0$

13. if $a \neq 0$ and $b \neq 0$, then
    $(ab)^{-1} = a^{-1}b^{-1}$

14. if $b \neq 0$ and $d \neq 0$, then
    $(a/b)(c/d) = (ac)/(bd)$

15. if $b \neq 0$, $c \neq 0$, and $d \neq 0$, then
    $(a/b)/(c/d) = (ad)/(bc)$

16. if $b \neq 0$ and $d \neq 0$, then
    $$\frac{a}{b} + \frac{c}{d} = \frac{ad + bc}{bd}$$

17. if $a \neq 0$ and $b \neq 0$, then
    $(a/b)^{-1} = b/a$

18. if $0 < a < b$, then $0 < a/b < 1$

19. if a, b, c, d are not all zero, then $a^2 + b^2 + c^2 + d^2 > 0$

20. $\dfrac{1}{a^2 + b^2 + c^2 + d^2} = \left(\dfrac{a}{a^2 + b^2 + c^2 + d^2}\right)^2 + \cdots + \left(\dfrac{d}{a^2 + b^2 + c^2 + d^2}\right)^2$

21. $|ab| = |a||b|$

22. $\left|\dfrac{a}{b}\right| = \dfrac{|a|}{|b|}$ if $b \neq 0$

23. if a and b have the same sign, or if either is zero, then $|a + b| = |a| + |b|$

24*. if $a \leq b$ and $-a \leq b$, then $|a| \leq b$

25*. if a and b have opposite signs, then $|a + b| < |a| + |b|$

26*. (cont.) $|a| - |b| \leq |a - b| \leq |a| + |b|$.

Find all numbers a for which

27. $|a - 3| = 1$

28. $|a + 5| = 2$

29. $|a - 5| \leq 3$

30. $|a + 2| \leq 1$

31. $\left|\dfrac{a}{2}\right| \leq 1$

32. $|-4a| > 6$

33. $|a^2| = |a|^2$

34. $|a^3| = |a|^3$.

3. COORDINATES ON THE LINE AND PLANE

The real numbers provide labels for the points on a line. First, choose a point and mark it 0. Then choose a point to the right of 0 and mark it 1. In other words, choose a starting point, a unit length, and a positive direction (the direction from 0 towards 1). Then mark the points 2, 3, 4, $\cdots$ to the right and $-1, -2, -3, \cdots$ to the left (Fig. 3.1). (It is perfectly possible to take the positive direction to the left; perhaps that is the convention on some planet in some galaxy.)

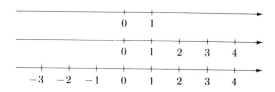

Fɪɢ. 3.1.   number line

Here we must make a fundamental assumption. We take it as an axiom that there is a perfect one-to-one correspondence between the points on the line and the system of real numbers. That means each point is assigned a unique real number label, and each real number labels exactly one point.

Because of this close association of the real number system and the set of points on a line, it is common to refer to a line "as" the real number system and to the real number system "as" a line. For instance, in a mathematical discussion, the real number 5.2 and the point labeled 5.2 might be considered the same. Although this is not correct logically, it almost never causes confusion; in fact it often sharpens our feeling for a problem.

Once the identification between real numbers and points on the line has been made, many arithmetic statements can be translated into geometric statements, and vice versa. Here are a few examples:

ARITHMETIC STATEMENT	GEOMETRIC STATEMENT
a is positive.	The point a lies to the right of the point 0.
$a > b$.	a lies to the right of b.
$a - b = c > 0$.	a lies c units to the right of b.
$a < b < c$.	b lies between a and c.
$\|3 - a\| < \frac{1}{2}$.	The point a is within $\frac{1}{2}$ unit of the point 3.
$\|a\| < \|b\|$.	The point a is closer to the origin than the point b is.

This close relationship between arithmetic and geometry is extremely important; often we can use arithmetical reasoning to solve geometrical problems or geometrical reasoning to solve arithmetical problems. Thus we may have two different ways of looking at a problem and, hence, increased chances of solving it.

If we denote a typical real number by x, we call the corresponding line the x-axis and draw Fig. 3.2.

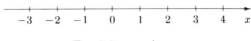

FIG. 3.2.   *x*-axis

If we are measuring time, we generally choose *t* for a typical real number and draw the *t*-axis (Fig. 3.3).

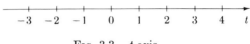

FIG. 3.3.   *t*-axis

Usually 0 on the *t*-axis represents the time when an experiment begins; negative numbers represent past time, positive numbers future time.

Coordinates in the Plane

When the points of a line are specified by real numbers, we say that the line is **coordinatized**: each point has a label or **coordinate**. It is possible also to label, or coordinatize, the points of a plane.

Draw two perpendicular lines in the plane. Mark their intersection *O* and coordinatize each line as shown in Fig. 3.4. By convention, call one line horizontal and name it the *x*-axis; call the other line vertical and name it the *y*-axis.

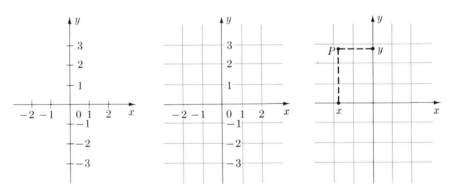

FIG. 3.4.   coordinate axes in the plane   FIG. 3.5.   rectangular grid   FIG. 3.6.   coordinates of a point

Consider all lines parallel to the *x*-axis and all lines parallel to the *y*-axis (Fig. 3.5). These two systems of parallel lines impose a rectangular grid on the whole plane. We use this grid to coordinatize the points of the plane.

Take any point *P* of the plane. Through *P* pass one vertical line and one horizontal line (Fig. 3.6). They meet the axes in points *x* and *y* respectively.

Associate with P the ordered pair (x, y); it completely describes the location of P.

Conversely, take any ordered pair (x, y) of real numbers. The vertical line through x on the x-axis and the horizontal line through y on the y-axis meet in a point P whose coordinates are precisely (x, y). Thus there is a one-to-one correspondence,

$$P \longleftrightarrow (x, y),$$

between the set of points of the plane and the set of all ordered pairs of real numbers. The numbers x and y are the **coordinates** of P. The point $(0, 0)$ is called the **origin**.

REMARK 1: The pair (x, y) is also sometimes called (ungrammatically) the coordinates of P.

REMARK 2: Some writers refer to the horizontal coordinate of a point as its **abscissa** and the vertical coordinate as its **ordinate**.

REMARK 3: The coordinate system we have introduced is called a **rectangular** or **cartesian** coordinate system.

The coordinate axes divide the plane into four quadrants which are numbered as in Fig. 3.7.

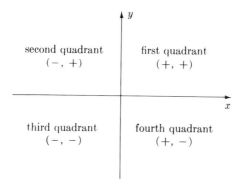

FIG. 3.7.   the four quadrants

Sometimes the two coordinate axes are used to represent incompatible physical quantities. When this is the case, there is no reason whatsoever for choosing equal unit lengths on the two axes; on the contrary, it is usually best to take different unit lengths, or scales. For example, Fig. 3.8 shows the distance y in miles covered by a car in t seconds moving in city traffic.

If we are interested in the car's progress for about one minute, a reasonable choice of unit on the t-axis is 10 sec. Since we expect the car's speed to be at most 40 mph (about 0.1 mi per 10 sec) a reasonable choice for the unit on the y-axis is 0.1 mi. If we choose 1 sec and 1 mi for units, the graph will be silly and impractical. Try it!

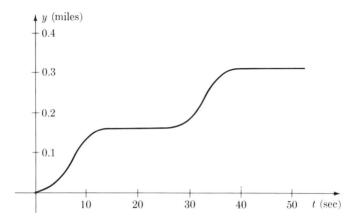

Fɪɢ. 3.8.   example of different scales on the axes

If, however, we wish to plot the car's progress for 10 or 15 min, then 10 sec would probably be too small as a unit of time. A more practical choice might be 1 min as the time unit and 0.5 mi as the distance unit.

EXERCISES

Plot and label the points on one graph:

1. $(-4, 1)$, $(3, 2)$, $(5, -3)$, $(1, 4)$ 2. $(0, -2)$, $(3, 0)$, $(-2, 2)$, $(1, -3)$
3. $(0.2, -0.5)$, $(-0.3, 0)$, $(-1.0, -0.1)$ 4. $(75, -10)$, $(-15, 60)$, $(95, 40)$.

Choose suitable scales on the axes and label the points:

5. $(150, 0.3)$, $(50, 0.6)$ 6. $(-0.02, 5)$, $(0.03, 12)$
7. $(0.1, -0.003)$, $(-0.3, 0.007)$ 8. $(-0.02, 35)$, $(0.00, -60)$.

Indicate on a suitable diagram all points (x, y) in the plane for which:

9. $x = -3$ 10. $y = 2$
11. x and y are positive   12. either x or y (or both) is zero
13. $1 \leq x \leq 3$ 14. $-1 \leq y \leq 2$
15. $-2 \leq x \leq 2$ and $-2 \leq y \leq 2$ 16. $x > 2$ and $y < 3$
17. both x and y are integers 18. $x^2 > 4$
19. $|x| \geq 1$ and $|y| \leq 2$ 20. $|x| \geq 2$ and $|y| \geq 2$
21. $xy > 0$ and $|x| \leq 3$ 22. $|x| + |y| > 0$.

Write the coordinates (x, y) of the

23. vertices of square centered at $(0, 0)$, sides of length 2 and parallel to the axes
24. vertices of a square centered at $(1, 3)$, sides of length 2, at $45°$ angles with the axes
25. vertices of a 3-4-5 right triangle in the first quadrant, right angle at $(0, 0)$, hypotenuse of length 15
26. vertices of an equilateral triangle, sides of length 2, base on the x-axis, vertex on the positive y-axis.

4. FUNCTIONS

Let the symbol x represent a real number, taken from a certain set D of real numbers. Suppose there is a rule that associates with each such x a real number y. Then this rule is called a **function** whose **domain** is D.

For instance, suppose that to each real x is assigned a number y by the rule $y = x^2$. Then this assignment is a function whose domain is the set of all real numbers.

As another example, take the assignment of $+ \sqrt{x}$ to each real number x which has a square root. This assignment is a function whose domain is the set of non-negative numbers.

Notation: The symbol x used to denote a typical real number in the domain of a function is sometimes called the **independent variable.** The symbol y used to denote the real number assigned to x is called the **dependent variable.**

Generally, but not always, variables are denoted by lowercase letters such as t, x, y, z. Functions are denoted by f, g, h and by capital letters.

If f denotes a function, x the independent variable, and y the dependent variable, then it is common practice to write "$y = f(x)$", read "y equals f of x" or "y equals f at x". This means that the function f assigns to each x in its domain a number $f(x)$ which is abbreviated by y.

There are several common variations of this notation. For instance, if f is the function that assigns to each real number its square, then we write "$f(x) = x^2$" or "$y = x^2$".

Warning 1: It is logically incorrect to say "the function $f(x)$", or "the function x^2", or the function "$y = f(x)$". The symbols "$f(x)$", "y", "x^2" represent numbers, the numbers assigned by the function f to the numbers x. A function is not a number, but an assignment of a number y or $f(x)$ to each number x in a certain domain. Nevertheless, these slight inaccuracies are so universal, we shall not try to avoid them.

Warning 2: A function is not a formula, and need not be specified by a formula. It is true that in practice most functions are indeed *computed* by formulas. For instance, f may assign to each real number x the real number y computed by formulas such as $y = x^2$, or $y = (\sqrt{x^2 + 1})/(1 + 7x^4)$, etc. Yet there are perfectly good functions not given by formulas. Here are a few examples:

(a) $f(x) = $ the largest integer (whole number) y for which $y \leq x$.

(b) $f(x) = \begin{cases} 1 & \text{if} \quad x > 0 \\ 0 & \text{if} \quad x = 0 \\ -1 & \text{if} \quad x < 0. \end{cases}$

(c) $f(x) = 1$ if x is an integer, $f(x) = -1$ if x is not an integer.

(d) $f(x)$ = number of letters in the English spelling of the rational number x in lowest terms. For example, $f(\frac{1}{2}) = 7$, $f(3) = 5$.

More on notation: Keep in mind that $f(x)$ is the *number* assigned to x by the function f. If, for instance, $f(x) = x^2 + 3$, then $f(1) = 4$, $f(2) = 7$, $f(3) = 12$. By the same token $f(x + 1) = (x + 1)^2 + 3$, $f(x^2) = (x^2)^2 + 3$ = $x^4 + 3$, etc. For this particular function, you must boldly square and add 3 to whatever appears in the window, no matter what it is called:

$$f(x + y) = (x + y)^2 + 3, \qquad f\left(\frac{1}{x}\right) = \left(\frac{1}{x}\right)^2 + 3,$$

$$f[f(x)] = [f(x)]^2 + 3 = (x^2 + 3)^2 + 3 = x^4 + 6x^2 + 12.$$

On domains of function: Most functions arising in practice have simple domains. The most common domains are the whole line, an interval (segment) $a \le x \le b$, a "half-line" such as $x \ge 0$ or $x < 2$ or some simple combination of these. Examples:

FUNCTION	DOMAIN
$f(x) = 2x + 1$	all real x (the whole line)
$f(x) = \sqrt{x + 2}$	$x \ge -2$ (half line)
$f(x) = \sqrt{1 - x^2}$	$-1 \le x \le 1$ (interval)
$f(x) = \dfrac{1}{x}$	all x except $x = 0$ (union of two half-lines)

Graphs of Functions

Given a real-valued function f, we construct its graph, a geometric picture of the function. Here is how we do it: for each real number x in the domain of f, we find the associated number $y = f(x)$ and plot the point (x, y). The locus (totality) of all such points is called the **graph** of $f(x)$.

EXAMPLE 4.1

Graph the (constant) function $f(x) = 2.5$.

Solution: The function is extremely simple; it assigns to each real number the same number, 2.5. The graph extends indefinitely in both directions, and we only show part of it (Fig. 4.1). It consists of all points of the form $(x, 2.5)$.

In general, when we construct a graph we indicate all points in the plane of a certain special type. Think of it this way: Imagine at each point of the plane a flag bearing the coordinates of the point (Fig. 4.2). Now to graph $f(x)$,

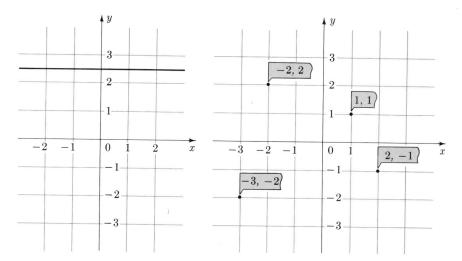

FIG. 4.1. graph of $f(x) = 2.5$ FIG. 4.2. flag at each point

knock down all of the flags except those that show (x, y) where $y = f(x)$.
What remains is a curve of flags standing over the graph of $f(x)$.

EXAMPLE 4.2

Graph the function $f(x) = x$.

Solution: For each x the corresponding y is $y = f(x) = x$. Thus if
$x = 0$ then $y = 0$, so $(0, 0)$ is on the graph. Likewise $(2.5, 2.5)$, $(1, 1)$,
$(-1.5, -1.5)$ are on the graph. We must knock down all flags except those
whose two numbers are equal. The result (Fig. 4.3) is a straight line through
the origin $(0, 0)$ at an angle 45° with the positive x-axis.

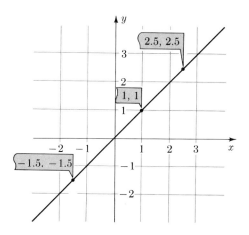

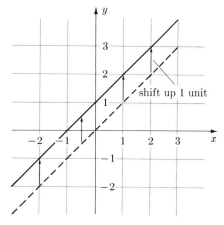

FIG. 4.3. graph of $f(x) = x$ FIG. 4.4. graph of $f(x) = x + 1$

EXAMPLE 4.3

Graph the function $f(x) = x + 1$.

Solution: For each x, we have $y = f(x) = x + 1$, so the corresponding point on the graph is $(x, x + 1)$. This point is one unit higher than the point (x, x) on the graph of the function $g(x) = x$. In other words, start with the graph in Fig. 4.3, and move each point up one unit. The result is Fig. 4.4.

Example 4.3 illustrates an important point. Adding a positive constant c to a function shifts its graph upwards c units. Similarly subtracting c shifts the graph downwards c units (Fig. 4.5).

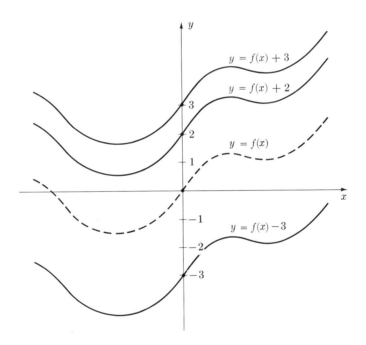

FIG. 4.5.   graph of $y = f(x) + c$

REMARK 1:   The following notation is convenient and common: Instead of writing "the graph of $f(x) = x + 1$", we often write "the graph of $y = x + 1$". Thus we say "graph $y = f(x)$" instead of "graph the function $f(x)$".

REMARK 2:   Not only does each function have a graph, but each graph defines a function. By a graph, we mean here, a collection of points (x, y) in the plane such that no two of the points have the same first coordinate (only one point can lie above a point on the x-axis). Such a graph automatically defines a function: to each x that occurs as a first coordinate of a point (x, y), it assigns the second coordinate y. In other words, $f(x)$ is the "height" of the graph above x.

The graphical definition of functions is standard procedure in science. For instance a scientific instrument recording temperature or blood pressure on a graph is defining a function of time. There is hardly ever an explicit formula for such a function.

EXERCISES

1. Let $f(x) = 2x + 5$. Compute:
   (a) $f(0)$ (b) $f(2)$ (c) $f(\frac{1}{2})$ (d) $f(1/x)$ (e) $f(x - 3)$.

2. Let $f(x) = x^2 + x + 1$. Compute:
   (a) $f(0)$ (b) $f(-x)$ (c) $f(x^2)$ (d) $f(\sqrt{x})$ (e) $f(x + h) - f(x)$.

Graph:

3. $f(x) = x + 2$ 4. $f(x) = x - 1$ 5. $f(x) = -x$

6. $f(x) = -x + 1$ 7. $f(x) = -17$ 8. $f(x) = 0.03$

9. $f(x) = x + 0.01$ 10. $f(x) = -x - 2.5$ 11. $f(x) = |x|$

12. $f(x) = |x - 1|$ 13. $f(x) = \begin{cases} 0, & x \le 0 \\ 2x, & x > 0 \end{cases}$ 14. $f(x) = \begin{cases} x - 1, & x \le 3 \\ 2, & x > 3 \end{cases}$

15. $f(x) = \begin{cases} 1, & x > 0 \\ 0, & x = 0 \\ -1, & x < 0 \end{cases}$ 16. $f(x) = \begin{cases} 1 & \text{if } x \text{ is an integer} \\ -1 & \text{if } x \text{ is not an integer.} \end{cases}$

Find the domain of $f(x)$:

17. $f(x) = 3x - 2$ 18. $f(x) = -7x + 6$ 19. $f(x) = 4x - 5$

20. $f(x) = 7 - x$ 21. $f(x) = 1/(2x - 3)$ 22. $f(x) = x/(x + 2)$

23. $f(x) = x/(3x - 5)$ 24. $f(x) = x/(x - 1)(x - 3)$ 25. $f(x) = \sqrt{x - 6}$

26. $f(x) = \sqrt{5 - 2x}$ 27. $f(x) = \sqrt{4 - 9x^2}$ 28. $f(x) = \sqrt{15x^2 + 11}$

29. $f(x) = \sqrt{2x - 3}$ 30. $f(x) = \dfrac{1}{\sqrt{x + 4}}$ 31. $f(x) = \sqrt{\frac{1}{4} - x^2}$

32. $f(x) = \sqrt{x^2 - 1}$ 33. $f(x) = \dfrac{}{\sqrt{(x - 1)(x - 4)}}$ 34. $f(x) = \sqrt{x^3 + 1}$.

5. CONSTRUCTION OF FUNCTIONS

There are several standard methods for building new functions out of old ones. We shall list the most common of these constructions.

1.   *Addition of functions.*   If f and g are functions of x defined on the same domain, then their **sum** $f + g$ is a function defined on the same domain by

$$[f + g](x) = f(x) + g(x).$$

For example, let $f(x) = 2x - 3$ and $g(x) = x^2 - x - 1$. Then

$$[f + g](x) = (2x - 3) + (x^2 - x - 1) = x^2 + x - 4.$$

2. *Multiplication of a function by a constant.* If c is a constant and f is a function, the function cf is defined by

$$[cf](x) = cf(x).$$

For example, if $f(x) = x^2 - 2x - 1$, then

$$[-5f](x) = (-5)(x^2 - 2x - 1) = -5x^2 + 10x + 5.$$

3. *Multiplication of functions.* If f and g are functions of x defined on the same domain, then their **product** fg is defined by

$$[fg](x) = f(x)g(x).$$

For example, if $f(x) = 2x - 1$ and $g(x) = 3x + 4$, then

$$[fg](x) = (2x - 1)(3x + 4) = 6x^2 + 5x - 4.$$

4. *Composition of functions.* If g is a function whose values lie in the domain of a second function f, then the **composite** $f \circ g$ of f and g is defined by the formula

$$[f \circ g](x) = f[g(x)].$$

Think of substituting one function into the other, or replacing the variable of f by the function g. Here are some examples:

1. $f(x) = x^2 + 2x, \quad g(x) = -3x.$

$$\begin{aligned}
[f \circ g](x) = f[g(x)] &= [g(x)]^2 + 2[g(x)] \\
&= (-3x)^2 + 2(-3x) \\
&= 9x^2 - 6x.
\end{aligned}$$

Note that the domain of f is all real numbers, hence the values of g certainly lie in the domain of f.

2. $f(x) = 3x - 4, \quad g(x) = 2x^2 - x + 1.$

$$\begin{aligned}
[f \circ g](x) = f[g(x)] &= 3g(x) - 4 \\
&= 3(2x^2 - x + 1) - 4 \\
&= 6x^2 - 3x - 1.
\end{aligned}$$

Again the domain of f is all real numbers.

3. $f(x) = \sqrt{x - 1}, \quad g(x) = -x^2.$

The domain of f is the set of real numbers x with $x \geq 1$. But $g(x) \leq 0$. Therefore the composition $f[g(x)]$ is not defined. Stated briefly, $\sqrt{-x^2 - 1}$ makes no sense.

If, however, $g(x) = 4x^2$, then $g(x) \geq 1$ provided $|x| \geq \frac{1}{2}$. Hence

$$[f \circ g](x) = \sqrt{4x^2 - 1}$$

is defined for $|x| \geq \frac{1}{2}$.

EXERCISES

Find $[f + g](x)$, and $[fg](x)$, where
1. $f(x) = 3x + 1, g(x) = -2$
2. $f(x) = 2x - 1, g(x) = 2x + 3$
3. $f(x) = x^2, g(x) = -2x + 1$
4. $f(x) = x^2 + 1, g(x) = -x^2 + x$
5. Does it make sense to add the functions $y = \sqrt{1 - x}$ and $y = \sqrt{x - 2}$?
6. A function f is called **strictly increasing** if whenever $x_1 < x_2$, then $f(x_1) < f(x_2)$. Show that the sum of two strictly increasing functions is strictly increasing.

Find $f \circ g$ and $g \circ f$, where
7. $f(x) = 3x + 1, g(x) = x - 2$
8. $f(x) = 2x - 1, g(x) = -x^2 + 3x$
9. $(fx) = 2x^2, g(x) = -x - 1$
10. $f(x) = x + 1, g(x) = -x + 1$
11. $f(x) = 2x, g(x) = -2x$
12. $f(x) = x + 3, g(x) = -x + 1$
13. $f(x) = x^2, g(x) = 3$
14. $f(x) = \pi x^2, g(x) = 2x + 5$.

15. If $f(x) = x$ and $g(x)$ is any function, find $f \circ g$.
16. If $g(x) = x$ and $f(x)$ is any function, find $f \circ g$.
17. Let $f(x) = 1 - x$. Compute $[f \circ f](x)$.
18. Let $f(x) = 1/x$ for $x \neq 0$. Compute $[f \circ f](x)$.
19. Find an example of a function $f(x)$ such that $f(x^2) \neq [f(x)]^2$.
20. Find an example of a function $f(x)$ such that $f(1/x) \neq 1/f(x)$.
21. Does it make sense to form $f \circ g$ if $f(x) = \sqrt{2x - 5}$ and $g(x) = 1 - x^2$?
22. Prove that if $f(x) = 3x - 5$, then

$$f\left(\frac{x_0 + x_1}{2}\right) = \frac{f(x_0) + f(x_1)}{2}.$$

23. (cont.) Is the same true for $f(x) = ax + b$?
24. (cont.) Is the same true for $f(x) = x^2$?
25. If $f(x) = 1/x$, show that

$$f\left(\frac{x_0 + x_1}{2}\right) = 2f(x_0 + x_1).$$

26. If $f(x) = 1/x^2$, show that $f(x_0 x_1) = f(x_0)f(x_1)$.

6. LINEAR FUNCTIONS

A function $f(x)$ is called **linear** if

$$f(x) = ax + b$$

for all real values of x, where a and b are constants. If $a = 0$, then $f(x) = b$ is a constant function; thus the class of linear functions includes the class of constant functions. Here are two basic facts about linear functions and their graphs:

> The graph of each linear function $y = ax + b$ is a non-vertical straight line.
>
> Conversely, each non-vertical straight line is the graph of a linear function.

(Thus the word "linear" is used because the graph of a linear function is a straight line.)

In order to prove the two assertions we shall first take the special case $b = 0$. We shall prove: (1) the graph of $y = ax$ is a non-vertical straight line through the origin, and (2) each non-vertical straight line through the origin is the graph of a linear function $y = ax$.

(1) Consider the graph of $y = ax$. First assume $a > 0$. The points $(0, 0)$ and $(1, a)$ are on the graph. Construct the line L through these points; it lies in the first and third quadrants (Fig. 6.1).

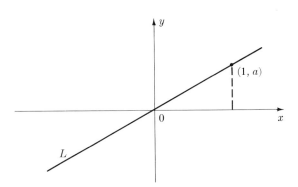

Fig. 6.1. line L through $(0, 0)$ and $(1, a)$

Each point (x, y) on this line L has the form (x, ax), and each point (x, ax) is on L. Why? Because the right triangles in Fig. 6.2 are all similar, hence the ratios of their corresponding legs are equal:

$$\frac{|y|}{|x|} = \frac{a}{1} = a.$$

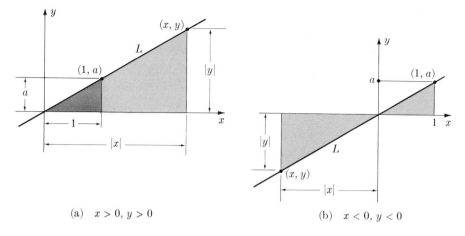

(a) $x > 0, y > 0$ (b) $x < 0, y < 0$

FIG. 6.2.   similar triangles: $a > 0$

Since (x, y) is in the first or third quadrant, x and y have the same sign. Hence $|y|/|x| = y/x$,

$$\frac{y}{x} = a, \qquad y = ax.$$

If $a < 0$, a similar argument applies, but we must be careful with signs (Fig. 6.3).

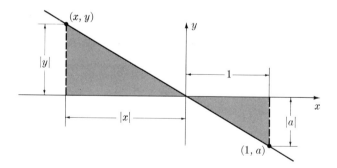

FIG. 6.3.   similar triangles: $a < 0$

This time L lies in the second and fourth quadrants, hence $|y|/|x| = -y/x$. Also $a < 0$, so $|a| = -a$. Therefore

$$\frac{|y|}{|x|} = \frac{|a|}{1}, \qquad -\frac{y}{x} = -\frac{a}{1}, \qquad \frac{y}{x} = a, \qquad y = ax.$$

If $a = 0$, the graph of $y = ax = 0$ is the x-axis. Thus in all cases the graph of $y = ax$ is a non-vertical straight line through $(0, 0)$.

(2)   Conversely, let L be any non-vertical line through $(0, 0)$. Then L passes through a point $(1, a)$, and the same reasoning shows that each point (x, y) on L satisfies $y = ax$.

In the general case $y = ax + b$, with $b \neq 0$, the graph is just the graph of $y = ax$ moved up or down $|b|$ units, hence a non-vertical straight line. Conversely each non-vertical straight line is parallel to a non-vertical straight line $y = ax$ through $(0, 0)$; hence it is the graph of $y = ax + b$ for a suitable constant b. See Fig. 6.4.

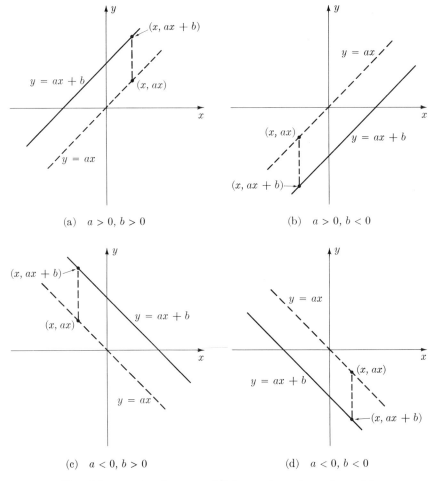

(a) $a > 0, b > 0$

(b) $a > 0, b < 0$

(c) $a < 0, b > 0$

(d) $a < 0, b < 0$

FIG. 6.4.   graphs of $y = ax + b$ for various signs of a and b

Knowing that the graph of a linear function is a line, it is easy to plot the graph. We simply find any two points on the graph and then draw the straight line through them.

EXAMPLE 6.1

Graph $y = 2x$ for $-1 \leq x \leq 1$.

Solution: If $x = -1$, then $y = 2(-1) = -2$, hence $(-1, -2)$ is a point on the graph. Similarly $(1, 2)$ is another point on the graph. Plot these two points, then join them by a line segment; it is the graph (Fig. 6.5).

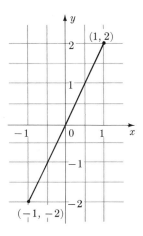

Fig. 6.5. graph of $y = 2x$ for $-1 \leq x \leq 1$	Fig. 6.6. graph of $y = \frac{1}{2}x - 1$ for $-1 \leq x \leq 3$

EXAMPLE 6.2

Graph $y = \frac{1}{2}x - 1$ for $-1 \leq x \leq 3$.

Solution: The values $x = -1$ and $x = 3$ yield the points $(-1, -\frac{3}{2})$ and $(3, \frac{1}{2})$ of the graph. Plot and connect them by a straight line (Fig. 6.6).

EXAMPLE 6.3

Graph $y = -x + 9$ for $8 \leq x \leq 10$.

Solution: The points $(8, 1)$ and $(10, -1)$ are on the graph. Plot and join them by a straight line (Fig. 6.7).

Slope

Examine the four lines in Fig. 6.8. The arrows indicate the direction of increasing x. Line C moves upwards steeply; line D moves upwards gently;

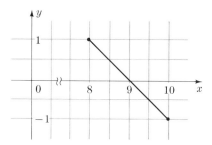

FIG. 6.7.   graph of $y = -x + 9$ for $8 \le x \le 10$

line B moves downwards steeply; line A moves downwards gently. We associate with each non-vertical line in the coordinate plane a measure of its steepness of climb or descent called its **slope**. More precisely, slope is a measure of the amount y changes relative to a change in x.

Look at Fig. 6.9. Choose two points on the line, (x_0, y_0) and (x_1, y_1). As x advances from x_0 to x_1, the variable y changes from y_0 to y_1, so the change in

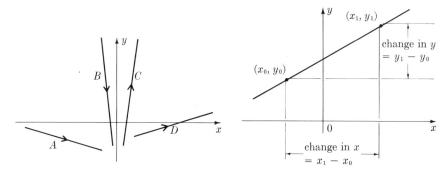

FIG. 6.8.   various degrees of steepness   FIG. 6.9.   changes in x and y

y is $y_1 - y_0$. The change in x is $x_1 - x_0$. The slope is the ratio of the change in y to the change in x:

$$\text{Slope} = \frac{y_1 - y_0}{x_1 - x_0}.$$

If the line rises steeply, then the change in y is greater than the change in x. Hence the slope is a large number. If the line rises slowly, the slope is a small number.

Notice that if the line falls as x increases, then $y_1 - y_0$ is *negative* while $x_1 - x_0$ is positive. Hence the slope is negative.

To compute the slope of the line $y = ax + b$, use *any* two points on the line; the answer is always the same:

$$\frac{y_1 - y_0}{x_1 - x_0} = \frac{(ax_1 + b) - (ax_0 + b)}{x_1 - x_0} = \frac{a(x_1 - x_0)}{x_1 - x_0} = a.$$

This simple calculation proves an important fact:

> The slope of the line $y = ax + b$ is a.

REMARK: The formula

$$\text{slope} = \frac{y_1 - y_0}{x_1 - x_0}$$

is valid whether $x_1 > x_0$ or $x_1 < x_0$, i.e., whether (x_1, y_1) is to the right of (x_0, y_0) or to the left of (x_0, y_0). That is because

$$\frac{y_1 - y_0}{x_1 - x_0} = \frac{y_0 - y_1}{x_0 - x_1}.$$

Of course, $x_1 = x_0$ is strictly forbidden!

Because the line $y = ax + b$ meets the y-axis at $(0, b)$, the number b is called the y-**intercept** of the line.

> The y-intercept of the line $y = ax + b$ is b.

EXAMPLE 6.4

Find the equation of the line with slope a through the point (x_0, y_0).

Solution: The equation is of the form $y = ax + b$, where b is the y-intercept. To compute b, use the fact that (x_0, y_0) satisfies the equation of the line:

$$y_0 = ax_0 + b, \qquad b = y_0 - ax_0.$$

Hence

$$y = ax + b = ax + y_0 - ax_0,$$

that is,

$$y - y_0 = a(x - x_0).$$

> *Answer:* $y = a(x - x_0) + y_0 = ax + (y_0 - ax_0)$.

EXAMPLE 6.5

Find the equation of the straight line passing through two given points (x_0, y_0) and (x_1, y_1). Assume $x_0 \neq x_1$.

Solution: The slope of the line is

$$a = \frac{y_1 - y_0}{x_1 - x_0}.$$

Therefore, by the answer to Example 6.4, the equation is

$$y - y_0 = a(x - x_0) = \frac{y_1 - y_0}{x_1 - x_0}(x - x_0),$$

that is,

$$\frac{y - y_0}{x - x_0} = \frac{y_1 - y_0}{x_1 - x_0}.$$

Answer: $y - y_0 = \left(\dfrac{y_1 - y_0}{x_1 - x_0}\right)(x - x_0)$, that is,

$y = ax + b$, where $a = \dfrac{y_1 - y_0}{x_1 - x_0}$ and $b = y_0 - ax_0$.

We have derived three useful formulas for a straight line:

Slope–intercept form:	$y = ax + b$
Point–slope form:	$y - y_0 = a(x - x_0)$
Two-point form:	$\dfrac{y - y_0}{x - x_0} = \dfrac{y_1 - y_0}{x_1 - x_0}.$

These formulas are used to obtain the equation of a given line. Conversely, given an equation in one of these forms, it represents a line which can be easily identified. For example, $y - 3 = 2(x - 1)$ is the equation of the line through $(1, 3)$ with slope 2.

Bear in mind that an equation $cx + dy + f = 0$ can be put in the slope–intercept form if $d \neq 0$. For example, $3x - 2y + 2 = 0$ can be written

$$y = \tfrac{3}{2}x + 1,$$

hence it represents a line of slope $\tfrac{3}{2}$ and y-intercept 1.

EXERCISES

Graph:

1. $y = 2x - 3, 0 \leq x \leq 4$ 2. $y = 2x - 3, -2 \leq x \leq 0$
3. $y = 2x + 9, 1 \leq x \leq 2$ 4. $y = -3x + 1, 0 \leq x \leq 1$
5. $y = -3x + 1, -5 \leq x \leq 5$ 6. $y = -2x + 1, -20 \leq x \leq -10$
7. $y = 3x + 40, 25 \leq x \leq 50$ 8. $y = 9x - 50, 100 \leq x \leq 200$
9. $y = 0.1x + 1.5, 2 \leq x \leq 3$ 10. $y = -0.3x + 0.2, -1 \leq x \leq 1.$

Graph; t in seconds, x in feet:

11. $x = 0.2t - 1, 0 \leq t \leq 5$ 12. $x = 25t + 15, 50 \leq t \leq 100$
13. $x = 9t - 9, 1 \leq t \leq 2$ 14. $x = -100t + 20, -1 \leq t \leq 1$
15. $x = -t + 10, 25 \leq t \leq 50$ 16. $x = 40t + 40, 0 \leq t \leq 100.$

Find the slope of the line through the given points:

17. $(0, 0)$, $(3, 4)$ 　　　18. $(0, 0)$, $(2, 6)$ 　　　19. $(-1, 2)$, $(1, 2)$
20. $(-1, 2)$, $(1, 0)$ 　　　21. $(0, 1)$, $(1, 2)$ 　　　22. $(0, -1)$, $(1, 2)$
23. $(-1, -1)$, $(1, 2)$ 　　24. $(-1, 2)$, $(2, -1)$ 　　25. $(-3, 1)$, $(-2, 2)$
26. $(-2, -2)$, $(3, -4)$.

Find the equation and y-intercept of the line with given slope a and passing through the given point:

27. $a = 1$, $(1, 2)$ 　　　28. $a = -1$, $(2, -1)$ 　　29. $a = 0$, $(4, 3)$
30. $a = 2$, $(1, 3)$ 　　　31. $a = \frac{1}{2}$, $(2, -2)$ 　　32. $a = \frac{2}{3}$, $(-1, 1)$.

Find the equation of the line through the two given points:

33. $(0, 0)$, $(1, 2)$ 　　　34. $(1, 0)$, $(3, 0)$ 　　　35. $(-1, 0)$, $(2, 4)$
36. $(-1, -1)$, $(2, 6)$ 　　37. $(\frac{1}{2}, 1)$, $(\frac{3}{2}, 2)$ 　　38. $(-2, 0)$, $(-\frac{1}{2}, -1)$
39. $(0.1, 3.0)$, $(0.3, 2.0)$ 　40. $(-2.01, 4.10)$, $(-2.00, 4.00)$.

Find the slope and y-intercept:

41. $3x - y - 7 = 0$ 　　　　　42. $x + 2y + 6 = 0$
43. $3(x - 2) + y + 5 = 2(x + 3)$ 　44. $2(x + y + 1) = 3x - 5$.

Find both intercepts:

45. $\dfrac{x}{2} + \dfrac{y}{3} = 1$ 　　　　　46. $\dfrac{x}{a} + \dfrac{y}{b} = 1$

47. $2x + 3y = 1$ 　　　　　48. $ax + by = 1$.

7. QUADRATIC FUNCTIONS

A function $f(x)$ is called **quadratic** if

$$f(x) = ax^2 + bx + c,$$

where a, b, and c are constants. A quadratic function is defined for all values of the independent variable x because $ax^2 + bx + c$ is a real number for each real number x. If $a = 0$, then $f(x) = bx + c$ is a linear function; thus the class of quadratic functions includes the class of linear functions.

Quadratic functions occur frequently in applications. For example, if a projectile is shot upwards with muzzle velocity v_0, then its height y at time t is given by

$$y = -\tfrac{1}{2}gt^2 + v_0 t,$$

where g is the constant of gravity.

We begin our study of quadratic functions by graphing $y = x^2$. First we consider only $x \geq 0$. When x is small, then x^2 is very small. For example

$(0.1)^2 = 0.01$, and $(0.001)^2 = 0.000001$. Thus $y = x^2$ rises very slowly from 0 as x increases from 0. See Fig. 7.1.

On the other hand, when x is large, x^2 is very large. For example $(10)^2 = 100$, $(1000)^2 = 1000000$. Thus $y = x^2$ rises very steeply as x gets larger and larger (Fig. 7.2).

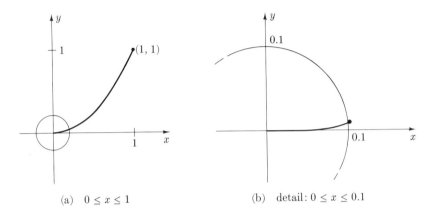

(a) $0 \le x \le 1$ (b) detail: $0 \le x \le 0.1$

FIG. 7.1. graph of $y = x^2$ for x small

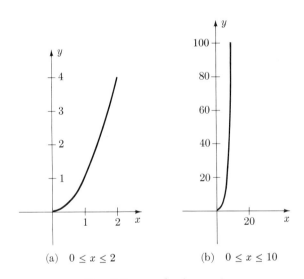

(a) $0 \le x \le 2$ (b) $0 \le x \le 10$

FIG. 7.2. graph of $y = x^2$

For $x < 0$, we use the fact that $(-x)^2 = x^2$. That means the value of y at $-x$ is the same as at x. So whenever (x, y) is on the graph, so is $(-x, y)$. Thus the graph of $y = x^2$ for $x < 0$ is the mirror image in the y-axis of the graph for $x > 0$. See Fig. 7.3.

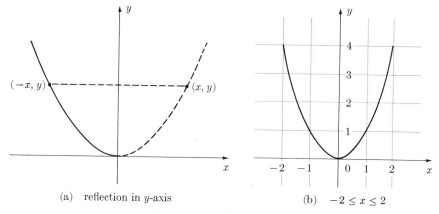

(a)   reflection in y-axis

(b) $-2 \leq x \leq 2$

FıG. 7.3.   graph of $y = x^2$

Next we graph $y = ax^2$, assuming first that $a > 0$. The graph of $y = ax^2$ can be obtained from the graph of $y = x^2$ in a simple way: Each point (x, y) on $y = x^2$ is changed to (x, ay), in other words, the graph $y = x^2$ is stretched (or shrunk) by the factor a in the y-direction only (Fig. 7.4).

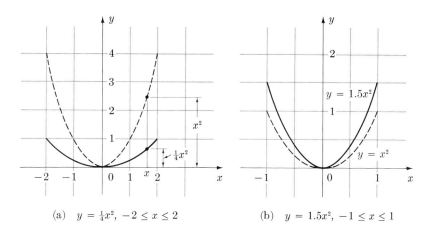

(a) $y = \frac{1}{4}x^2$, $-2 \leq x \leq 2$

(b) $y = 1.5x^2$, $-1 \leq x \leq 1$

FıG. 7.4.   graphs of $y = ax^2$ for $a > 0$

If $a < 0$, then $-a > 0$, and the graph of $y = ax^2$ is obtained from the graph of $y = (-a)x^2$ by changing each y to $-y$, that is, by forming a mirror image in the x-axis (Fig. 7.5).

Note that $(0, 0)$ is the lowest point on the graph of $y = ax^2$ if $a > 0$, and is the highest point on the graph if $a < 0$.

The graph of $y = ax^2 + c$ is obtained by shifting the graph of $y = ax^2$ up or down by $|c|$ units (Fig. 7.6).

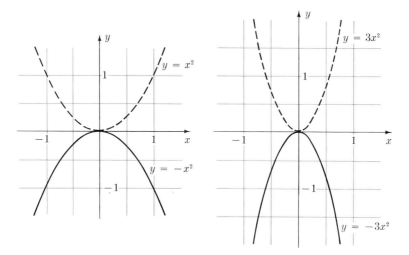

FIG. 7.5.   graphs of $y = ax^2$ for $a < 0$

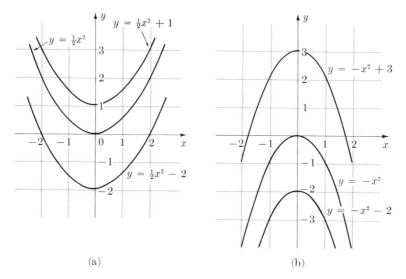

(a)   (b)

FIG. 7.6.   graphs of $y = ax^2 + c$

Completing the Square

To graph the most general quadratic function $y = ax^2 + bx + c$, we need an important technique called **completing the square**. (We can suppose $a \neq 0$, otherwise the function is linear.) We write

$$y = a\left(x^2 + \frac{b}{a}x + \frac{c}{a}\right)$$

and observe that the first two terms in the parentheses are part of a perfect square:

$$\left(x + \frac{b}{2a}\right)^2 = x^2 + \frac{b}{a} + \frac{b^2}{4a^2}.$$

We "complete the square" by inserting $b^2/4a^2$ in the parentheses, and then compensate by subtracting the same quantity:

$$y = a\left(x^2 + \frac{b}{a}x + \frac{b^2}{4a^2} + \frac{c}{a} - \frac{b^2}{4a^2}\right)$$

$$= a\left(x^2 + \frac{b}{a}x + \frac{b^2}{4a^2}\right) + a\left(\frac{c}{a} - \frac{b^2}{4a^2}\right)$$

$$= a\left(x + \frac{b}{2a}\right)^2 + \left(c - \frac{b^2}{4a}\right).$$

Hence for $a \ne 0$, the graph of $y = ax^2 + bx + c$ is the graph of

$$y = a\left(x + \frac{b}{2a}\right)^2 + \left(\frac{4ac - b^2}{4a}\right).$$

For each point (x, y) on this graph, the point $(x + b/2a, y)$ is on the graph of $y = ax^2 + c'$, where $c' = (4ac - b^2)/4a$. Therefore the graph of $y = ax^2 + bx + c$ is the graph of $y = ax^2 + c'$ shifted horizontally $|b/2a|$ units, shifted eft if $b/2a > 0$, shifted right if $b/2a < 0$. See Fig. 7.7.

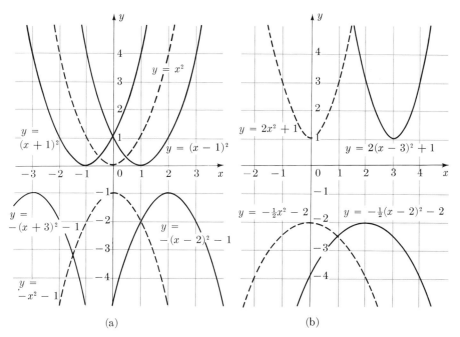

(a)   (b)

FIG. 7.7.   graphs of $y = a(x + h)^2 + c'$

Note that $(-h, c')$ is the lowest point on the graph of $y = a(x + h)^2 + c'$ if $a > 0$, and the highest point if $a < 0$.

EXAMPLE 7.1

Graph $y = x^2 + 2x + 4$.

Solution: Complete the square:

$$y = x^2 + 2x + 4 = (x^2 + 2x + 1) + 3 = (x + 1)^2 + 3.$$

Thus the graph is obtained by shifting the graph of $y = x^2$ one unit to the left, then three units up (Fig. 7.8).

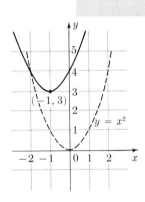

$(-1, 3)$

$y = x^2$

FIG. 7.8. Graph of $y = x^2 + 2x + 4$

EXAMPLE 7.2

Graph $y = x^2 - 6x$. Find the lowest point on the curve.

Solution: Complete the square:

$$y = x^2 - 6x = x^2 - 6x + 9 - 9 = (x - 3)^2 - 9.$$

If $x \neq 3$, then $(x - 3)^2 > 0$, so $y > -9$. Hence the lowest point is $(3, -9)$.

Answer: Fig. 7.9; $(3, -9)$.

EXAMPLE 7.3

Graph $y = -2x^2 - 4x + 1$ and find the highest point on the curve.

Solution: Complete the square:

$$y = -2x^2 - 4x + 1 = -2(x^2 + 2x) + 1$$
$$= -2(x^2 + 2x + 1) + 2 + 1 = -2(x + 1)^2 + 3.$$

If $x \neq -1$, then $(x + 1)^2 > 0$, hence $-2(x + 1)^2 < 0$, so $y < 3$. The highest point is $(-1, 3)$.

Answer: Fig. 7.10; $(-1, 3)$.

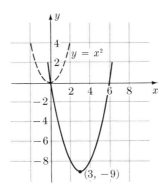

FIG. 7.9.   graph of $y = x^2 - 6x$

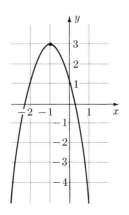

FIG. 7.10.   graph of $y = -2x^2 - 4x + 1$

EXERCISES

Graph:

1. $y = 2x^2$

2. $y = -2x^2$

3. $y = -\frac{1}{2}x^2$

4. $y = \frac{1}{2}x^2$

5. $y = x^2 + 3$

6. $y = -x^2 - 3$

7. $y = 2x^2 - 1$

8. $y = -2x^2 - 1$

9. $y = -\frac{1}{4}x^2 + 2$

10. $y = -\frac{1}{4}x^2 - 2$.

Graph on the indicated range (use different scales on the axes if necessary):

11. $y = 0.1x^2$, $0 \le x \le 100$

12. $y = -x^2$, $-0.1 \le x \le 0$.

Graph:

13. $y = x^2 - 4x + 1$ 14. $y = x^2 + 2x - 5$ 15. $y = x^2 + x + 1$

16. $y = x^2 - x + 1$ 17. $y = -x^2 - 2x$ 18. $y = -x^2 + 2x$

19. $y = -x^2 - 4x - 3$ 20. $y = -x^2 + 4x + 1$ 21. $y = 2x^2 - 6x + 1$

22. $y = 2x^2 + 4x$ 23. $y = 3x^2 + 12x - 8$ 24. $y = -3x^2 + 12x - 8$

25. $y = -2x^2 + 8x - 10$ 26. $y = -2x^2 + 12x$ 27. $y = -4x^2 + x$

28. $y = 2x^2 + 2x + 2$.

Find the lowest point on each graph:

29. $y = 2x^2 - 3x$ 30. $y = x^2 - 6x + 2$ 31. $y = x^2 + x - 4$

32. $y = 3x^2 + 3x$.

Find the highest point on each graph:

33. $y = -x^2 + x - 2$ 34. $y = -x^2 - 2x$ 35. $y = -2x^2 + x$

36. $y = -2x^2 - 6x + 1$.

37. Show that the graph of $y = ax^2 + bx$ passes through the origin for all choices of a and b.

38*. For what value of c does the lowest point of the graph of $y = x^2 + 6x + c$ fall on the x-axis?

39. Under what conditions is the lowest point of the graph of $y = x^2 + bx + c$ on the y-axis?

40*. What is the relation between the graph of $y = ax^2 + bx + c$ and that of $y = ax^2 - bx + c$?

2. Vectors

1. VECTOR ALGEBRA

Vector algebra is a powerful tool in formulating and solving problems in the plane and in space. A knowledge of vectors is indispensable in several-variable calculus, classical and modern physics, engineering, statistics, numerical analysis, and mathematical economics. Vectors have two properties: (a) length, (b) direction. So do many physical quantities such as force, velocity, acceleration, momentum, torque, heat flow, electric field, etc. This accounts for the frequent use of vectors in the physical sciences.

We choose once and for all a point **0** in the plane and call it the origin. A **vector** is a directed line segment from **0** to a point of the plane (Fig. 1.1a). The vector that goes from **0** to **0** (a degenerate line segment) we call the *vector* **0**.

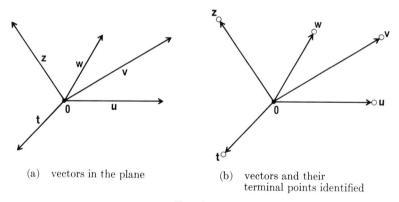

(a) vectors in the plane   (b) vectors and their
                                       terminal points identified

Fig. 1.1

The vector from **0** to a point **z** is completely determined by its terminal point. For this reason, we shall often identify a vector and its terminal point as one and the same thing (Fig. 1.1b).

We have defined vectors without reference to coordinate systems. This is as it should be, for in real life a force is a force and a velocity is a velocity, regardless of how we choose to set up coordinate axes. Nevertheless, to compute with vectors we shall need coordinates. Given a Cartesian coordinate system in the plane, we assign to each vector **v** the coordinates of its terminal point, and write

$$\mathbf{v} = (x, y).$$

Some examples are shown in Fig. 1.2.

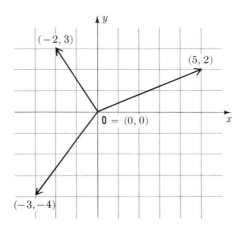

FIG. 1.2.   vectors in the coordinate plane

We must keep an open mind about coordinate systems, and never feel committed to a particular one. Even in the middle of a problem, it may be useful to switch from one coordinate system to another. Then the *same* vector will have *different* coordinates in the new system (Fig. 1.3).

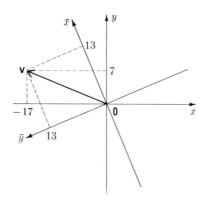

FIG. 1.3.   two coordinate representations of the same vector

Our first job is to introduce three basic algebraic operations on vectors: multiplication by a scalar and addition (this section), and inner product (Section 3).

Multiplication by a Scalar

In the context of vector algebra, the word **scalar** means real number. We combine a scalar a and a vector **v** to form a new vector a**v** called the scalar multiple of a and **v**.

If a is a scalar and **v** is a vector, then the **scalar multiple** a**v** is the vector defined by

$$a\mathbf{v} = \begin{cases} \mathbf{0} & \text{if } a = 0, \\[1em] \text{a vector in the same direction as } \mathbf{v} \text{ with length } a \\ \text{times the length of } \mathbf{v} & \text{if } a > 0, \\[1em] \text{a vector in the opposite direction as } \mathbf{v} \text{ with length } |a| \\ \text{times the length of } \mathbf{v} & \text{if } a < 0. \end{cases}$$

Examples of multiplication by a scalar are shown in Fig. 1.4.

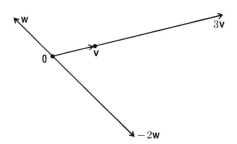

Fig. 1.4. scalar multiples of vectors

If **v** is expressed in coordinates, it is easy to express a**v** in coordinates. The rule seems very natural:

$$a(x, y) = (ax, ay).$$

To see why the rule holds, look at Fig. 1.5. If the new vector a**v** has coordinates (x_1, y_1), we must show that $x_1 = ax$ and $y_1 = ay$.

Project **v** and a**v** on the x-axis. By similar triangles,

$$\frac{|x_1|}{|x|} = \frac{\text{length of } a\mathbf{v}}{\text{length of } \mathbf{v}} = |a|.$$

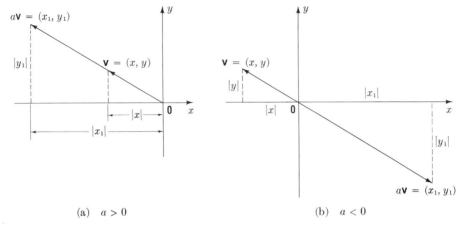

(a) $a > 0$ (b) $a < 0$

FIG. 1.5.   proof by similar triangle that $a(x, y) = (ax, ay)$

If $a > 0$, the terminal points of $\mathbf{v}$ and $a\mathbf{v}$ lie in the same quadrant, therefore $|x_1|/|x| = x_1/x$. Hence the absolute values can be dropped:

$$\frac{x_1}{x} = a, \qquad x_1 = ax.$$

If $a < 0$, the terminal points of $\mathbf{v}$ and $a\mathbf{v}$ lie in opposite quadrants, so $|x_1|/|x| = -x_1/x$. Hence

$$-\frac{x_1}{x} = |a| = -a, \qquad x_1 = ax.$$

Thus $x_1 = ax$ in all cases. A similar argument shows that $y_1 = ay$.
    Examples of scalar multiplication:

$$1(x, y) = (x, y) \qquad\qquad -3(5, -7) = (-15, 21)$$
$$3(0, 0) = (0, 0) = \mathbf{0} \qquad\qquad 0(5, -1) = \mathbf{0}$$
$$-2(1, 0) = (-2, 0) \qquad\qquad 2(3, -2) = (6, -4).$$

Two identities follow from the formula $a(x, y) = (ax, ay)$:

$$\boxed{(a + b)\mathbf{v} = a\mathbf{v} + b\mathbf{v} \qquad (ab)\mathbf{v} = a(b\mathbf{v}).}$$

One can interpret scalar multiplication physically in several ways. For example, a velocity vector $\mathbf{v}$ has direction and magnitude (speed). If the direction remains the same, but the speed triples, then the new velocity vector is $3\mathbf{v}$.

Addition

We now define the sum $\mathbf{v} + \mathbf{w}$ of two vectors $\mathbf{v}$ and $\mathbf{w}$. Draw a directed line segment parallel to $\mathbf{w}$, starting from the terminal point of $\mathbf{v}$. See Fig. 1.6a.

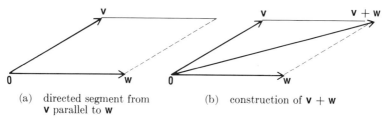

(a)   directed segment from
v parallel to **w**

(b)   construction of **v** + **w**

Fɪɢ. 1.6

By closing the parallelogram, we see that the roles of **v** and **w** can be interchanged in the definition (Fig. 1.7). The result is

$$\mathbf{v} + \mathbf{w} = \mathbf{w} + \mathbf{v}.$$

Probably the most intuitive physical interpretation of addition of vectors is in terms of force vectors. A force has magnitude and direction, hence is a

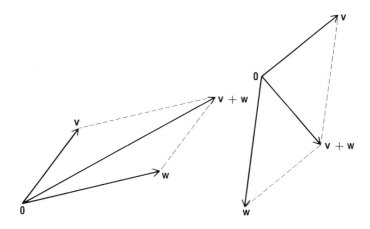

Fɪɢ. 1.7.   parallelograms of "forces"

vector. If two forces **v** and **w** are applied at the same point, the resultant force is **v** + **w**; that is the law of "parallelogram of forces".

Given **v** and **w** expressed in a coordinate system, how do we compute **v** + **w**? The answer is again quite natural:

$$(x_1, y_1) + (x_2, y_2) = (x_1 + x_2, y_1 + y_2).$$

We say vectors are added "componentwise" or "coordinatewise".

To verify the formula, let $\mathbf{v} = (x_1, y_1)$, $\mathbf{w} = (x_2, y_2)$, and $\mathbf{v} + \mathbf{w} = (x_3, y_3)$. We must show that $x_3 = x_1 + x_2$ and $y_3 = y_1 + y_2$. See Fig. 1.8.

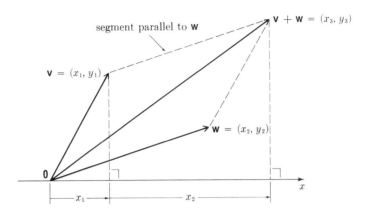

FIG. 1.8.   (sum of projections) = (projection of sum)

The projection on the x-axis of $\mathbf{v}$ is x_1. The projection on the x-axis of the directed segment parallel to $\mathbf{w}$ is a directed segment of length $|x_2|$. No matter what the sign of x_2 is, the terminal point of this segment is $x_1 + x_2$. But this point is the projection of $\mathbf{v} + \mathbf{w}$, that is, x_3. Hence $x_3 = x_1 + x_2$. Similarly $y_3 = y_1 + y_2$.

We denote by $-\mathbf{v}$ the vector $(-1)\mathbf{v}$, opposite to $\mathbf{v}$. Thus $-(3, -4) = (-3, 4)$.

The basic rules of vector algebra follow easily from the coordinate formulas for scalar multiplication and addition:

$$1 \cdot \mathbf{v} = \mathbf{v}$$
$$\mathbf{v} + (-\mathbf{v}) = \mathbf{0}$$
$$\mathbf{v} + \mathbf{w} = \mathbf{w} + \mathbf{v} \qquad \text{(commutative law)}$$
$$\mathbf{u} + (\mathbf{v} + \mathbf{w}) = (\mathbf{u} + \mathbf{v}) + \mathbf{w} \qquad \text{(associative law)}$$
$$\left. \begin{array}{l} a(\mathbf{v} + \mathbf{w}) = a\mathbf{v} + a\mathbf{w} \\ (a + b)\mathbf{v} = a\mathbf{v} + b\mathbf{v} \end{array} \right\} \qquad \text{(distributative laws)}$$
$$a(b\mathbf{v}) = (ab)\mathbf{v}.$$

We define the **difference** $\mathbf{v} - \mathbf{w}$ by

$$\mathbf{v} - \mathbf{w} = \mathbf{v} + (-\mathbf{w}).$$

In coordinates,

$$(x_1, y_1) - (x_2, y_2) = (x_1, y_1) + (-x_2, -y_2) = (x_1 - x_2, y_1 - y_2).$$

Examples of vector addition and subtraction:

$$(2, 7) + (1, 3) = (3, 10) \qquad (2, 7) - (1, 3) = (1, 4)$$
$$(2, 7) + (1, -3) = (3, 4) \qquad (2, 7) - (1, -3) = (1, 10)$$
$$(2, 7) + (-5, 0) = (-3, 7) \qquad (2, 7) - (-5, 0) = (7, 7).$$

Note the geometric interpretation of the difference of vectors. The directed line segment from **w** to **v** has the same length and direction as the vector **v** − **w**. See Fig. 1.9.

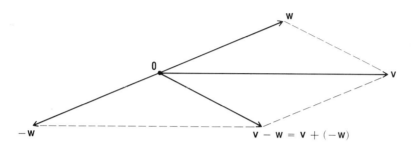

FIG. 1.9. difference of vectors

EXERCISES

Compute:

1. $3(0, 1)$
2. $-5(2, 0)$
3. $2(1, -1)$
4. $7(3, -2)$
5. $4(\frac{1}{2}, 3)$
6. $-\frac{1}{3}(4, -2)$
7. $(3, -1) + (0, 1)$
8. $(4, 2) + (3, 1)$
9. $(-1, 1) + (1, -1)$
10. $(2, -2) + (3, 3)$
11. $(4, -1) + (-3, 2)$
12. $(7, 11) + (11, 7)$
13. $3(1, 1) + (7, 1)$
14. $(2, -2) + 8(1, 2)$
15. $-2(1, 3) + 4(5, 4)$
16. $3(2, 0) + 2(4, 5).$

Plot the vectors and compute their sum graphically by the "parallelogram of forces." Check your answer:

17. $(4, 1) + (3, 2)$
18. $(-3, 2) + (4, 4)$
19. $(1, 5) + (-5, -1)$
20. $(2, -3) + (-1, -3).$

21. Find a vector parallel to and having the same length as the directed segment from $(-2, 4)$ to $(-1, -6)$.

22. Find a point **x** such that the directed segment from $(2, 3)$ to **x** is parallel to the directed segment from $(1, 1)$ to $(-4, 0)$ and of the same length.

Find a and b; check your answer graphically:

23. $(-4, 5) = a(2, 0) + b(0, 1)$
24. $(3, 3) = a(1, 0) - b(1, 1).$

Suppose **u** and **v** are vectors whose terminal points lie on the curve $y = x^2$:

25. Find **u** and **v** if **u** + **v** = $(0, 8)$.

26. When is the terminal point of **u** + **v** outside of the curve ? Inside?

2. LINES

In this section we obtain a vector equation for a line and derive a number of useful facts from it. All we need are the basic ideas of vector addition and multiplication by a scalar.

Parametric Vector Equation of a Line

Given a point $\mathbf{x}_0$ in the plane and a vector **v**, how can we describe the line that passes through $\mathbf{x}_0$ and is parallel to **v**? With vectors, it's very simple. We draw the vector $\mathbf{x}_0$, then add to it multiples of **v**. See Fig. 2.1a. If we add to $\mathbf{x}_0$ all possible multiples of **v**, we generate the points on the desired line. Conversely, Fig. 2.1b shows that each point **x** on the line has the form $\mathbf{x}_0 + t\mathbf{v}$ for a suitable real number t.

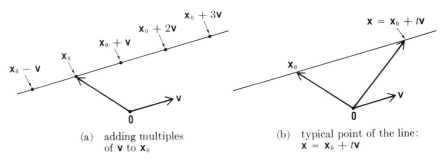

(a)   adding multiples of **v** to $\mathbf{x}_0$

(b)   typical point of the line:
      $\mathbf{x} = \mathbf{x}_0 + t\mathbf{v}$

Fig. 2.1

Given a point $\mathbf{x}_0$ in the plane, and a non-zero vector **v**, the line through $\mathbf{x}_0$ parallel to **v** consists of all points

(1) $\mathbf{x} = \mathbf{x}_0 + t\mathbf{v}$,

where t ranges over all real numbers.

Equation (1) is called a **parametric vector equation** for the line, and the variable t is called a **parameter.** Each real number t describes a point, yet t itself is not visible on the line. One interpretation of t is this: suppose a particle starts at $\mathbf{x}_0$ at time $t = 0$ and each second moves an amount indicated by the vector **v**. (We say the particle has the constant velocity vector **v**.) Then its position at time t is $\mathbf{x} = \mathbf{x}_0 + t\mathbf{v}$.

Equation (1) is not the only parametric equation of the line; there are many others. For instance, $\mathbf{x} = \mathbf{x}_0 + 2t\mathbf{v}$ represents the same line but traced out by a particle moving twice as fast. Also $\mathbf{x} = \mathbf{x}_0 + t^3\mathbf{v}$ represents the same line traced out by a particle that accelerates rapidly as time goes on.

Equation (1) is the basic equation of this section. We are going to derive several useful scalar equations for a line, all easy consequences of (1).

Scalar Equations of Lines

First, let us write equation (1) in coordinates. If $\mathbf{x} = (x, y)$, $\mathbf{x}_0 = (x_0, y_0)$, and $\mathbf{v} = (a, b)$, then (1) becomes

$$(x, y) = (x_0, y_0) + t(a, b) = (x_0 + ta, y_0 + tb).$$

Thus, the parametric vector equation is equivalent to the *pair* of **parametric scalar equations**

(2)
$$\begin{cases} x = x_0 + at \\ y = y_0 + bt. \end{cases}$$

Next, we obtain a **non-parametric scalar equation** for the line by eliminating the parameter t in (2). We multiply the first equation by b, the second by a, and subtract: $bx - ay = bx_0 - ay_0$, that is,

(3)
$$a(y - y_0) = b(x - x_0).$$

> **EXAMPLE 2.1**
>
> Find parametric and non-parametric scalar equations for the line through $(2, 0)$ parallel to the vector $(-3, 2)$.

Solution: A parametric vector equation (1) for this line is $\mathbf{x} = \mathbf{x}_0 + t\mathbf{v}$ where $\mathbf{x}_0 = (2, 0)$ and $\mathbf{v} = (-3, 2)$. Now change to coordinates:

$$(x, y) = (2, 0) + t(-3, 2) = (2 - 3t, 2t).$$

Hence parametric scalar equations are:

$$\begin{cases} x = 2 - 3t \\ y = 2t. \end{cases}$$

Now eliminate t. Multiply the first equation by 2, the second equation by 3 and add:

$$2x + 3y = 2(2 - 3t) + 3(2t) = 4.$$

> *Answer:* $x = 2 - 3t$, $y = 2t$; $2x + 3y = 4$.

Special Scalar Equations

Let us return to equation (3) for the line through the point (x_0, y_0) parallel to the vector (a, b). In Chapter 1, Section 6, we derived three useful scalar equations for lines. Now we show that these follow directly from (3). Thus all of our equations for lines follow from the basic equation (1).

The equation of a line through the point (x_0, y_0) with slope m. Such a line is parallel to the vector $(1, m)$. Set $(a, b) = (1, m)$ in (3):

(4) $$y - y_0 = m(x - x_0) \qquad (Point\text{-}slope\ form).$$

The equation of a line with y-intercept c and slope m. This is just a special case of (4) with $x_0 = 0$ and $y_0 = c$. The resulting equation is usually written

(5) $$y = mx + c \qquad (Slope\text{-}intercept\ form).$$

The equation of a line through two points (x_0, y_0) and (x_1, y_1). [Assume the line is non-vertical $(x_0 \neq x_1)$; otherwise an equation is simply $x = x_0$.] This again is a special case of (4) because the slope can be computed from the two points:

$$m = \frac{y_1 - y_0}{x_1 - x_0}.$$

The equation is usually written

(6) $$\frac{y - y_0}{x - x_0} = \frac{y_1 - y_0}{x_1 - x_0} \qquad (2\text{-}point\ form).$$

Division of a Segment

Suppose $\mathbf{v}$ and $\mathbf{w}$ are two points in the plane, and we want the point that is $\frac{3}{5}$ of the way from $\mathbf{v}$ to $\mathbf{w}$. By vectors, this is easy; just add $\frac{3}{5}$ of the vector $\mathbf{w} - \mathbf{v}$ to $\mathbf{v}$. The desired point is $\mathbf{v} + \frac{3}{5}(\mathbf{w} - \mathbf{v}) = \frac{2}{5}\mathbf{v} + \frac{3}{5}\mathbf{w}$. See Fig. 2.2.

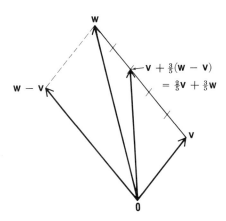

FIG. 2.2.   division of a segment: $\frac{3}{5}$ of the way from $\mathbf{v}$ to $\mathbf{w}$

The same reasoning applies in finding the point **x** that is a fractional part t of the way from **v** to **w**:

$$\mathbf{x} = \mathbf{v} + t(\mathbf{w} - \mathbf{v}) = t\mathbf{w} + (1 - t)\mathbf{v}.$$

This formula is a parametric representation of the line segment from **v** to **w**. As t runs from 0 to 1, we see that **x** traces the segment from **v** to **w**.

An important special case is the midpoint of the segment. The point **x** reaches the midpoint when $t = \frac{1}{2}$.

> The midpoint of the line segment between **v** and **w** is
> $$\frac{1}{2}\mathbf{v} + \frac{1}{2}\mathbf{w}.$$

This formula suggests that the midpoint is the "average" of the two points **v** and **w**. In fact we do get averages in the usual sense if we express the midpoint formula in coordinates. If $\mathbf{v} = (x_0, y_0)$ and $\mathbf{w} = (x_1, y_1)$, then

$$\frac{1}{2}(\mathbf{v} + \mathbf{w}) = \left(\frac{x_0}{2}, \frac{y_0}{2}\right) + \left(\frac{x_1}{2}, \frac{y_1}{2}\right) = \left(\frac{x_0 + x_1}{2}, \frac{y_0 + y_1}{2}\right).$$

> The midpoint of the segment joining (x_0, y_0) and (x_1, y_1) is
> $$\left(\frac{x_0 + x_1}{2}, \frac{y_0 + y_1}{2}\right).$$

Thus the coordinates of the midpoint are the averages of the coordinates of the points.

Similarly the coordinates of $\frac{2}{5}\mathbf{v} + \frac{3}{5}\mathbf{w}$ are $\frac{2}{5}x_0 + \frac{3}{5}x_1$ and $\frac{2}{5}y_0 + \frac{3}{5}y_1$. These numbers are **weighted averages.** If you want the point $\frac{3}{5}$ of the way from **v** to **w**, you must average the coordinates, giving a weight of $\frac{3}{5}$ to **w** and $\frac{2}{5}$ to **v**. (The desired point is closer to **w**, so **w** gets the larger weight.)

Here is an application of these ideas to a geometric problem.

EXAMPLE 2.2

Prove that the midpoints of the sides of any quadrilateral are the vertices of a parallelogram.

Solution: Denote the vertices of the quadrilateral by $\mathbf{v}_1, \mathbf{v}_2, \mathbf{v}_3, \mathbf{v}_4$ and the midpoints of the sides by $\mathbf{m}_1, \mathbf{m}_2, \mathbf{m}_3, \mathbf{m}_4$. See Fig. 2.3. Take either pair of opposite sides of the quadrilateral formed by the midpoints. It suffices to show that these sides are parallel and of equal length.

The side connecting $\mathbf{m}_1$ and $\mathbf{m}_2$ has the same length and direction as the vector $\mathbf{m}_1 - \mathbf{m}_2$. The side connecting $\mathbf{m}_3$ and $\mathbf{m}_4$ has the same length and direction as $\mathbf{m}_4 - \mathbf{m}_3$. But

$$\mathbf{m}_1 - \mathbf{m}_2 = \tfrac{1}{2}(\mathbf{v}_1 + \mathbf{v}_2) - \tfrac{1}{2}(\mathbf{v}_2 + \mathbf{v}_3) = \tfrac{1}{2}(\mathbf{v}_1 - \mathbf{v}_3),$$
$$\mathbf{m}_4 - \mathbf{m}_3 = \tfrac{1}{2}(\mathbf{v}_1 + \mathbf{v}_4) - \tfrac{1}{2}(\mathbf{v}_3 + \mathbf{v}_4) = \tfrac{1}{2}(\mathbf{v}_1 - \mathbf{v}_3).$$

These vectors are the same! Hence, two opposite sides are parallel and equal. Therefore the quadrilateral of midpoints is a parallelogram.

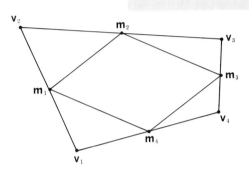

FIG. 2.3.   midpoints of a quadrilateral

Lines turn up in many locus problems. Here is an example.

EXAMPLE 2.3

Let $\mathbf{x} = \mathbf{x}_0 + t\mathbf{u}$ and $\mathbf{x} = \mathbf{y}_0 + t\mathbf{v}$ be two lines described by the same parameter t. Find the locus of the midpoints of corresponding points of the lines.

Solution: The midpoint is

$$\mathbf{x} = \tfrac{1}{2}(\mathbf{x}_0 + t\mathbf{u}) + \tfrac{1}{2}(\mathbf{y}_0 + t\mathbf{v}) = \tfrac{1}{2}(\mathbf{x}_0 + \mathbf{y}_0) + \tfrac{1}{2}t(\mathbf{u} + \mathbf{v}).$$

If $\mathbf{u} + \mathbf{v} = \mathbf{0}$, the locus is a single point, $\tfrac{1}{2}(\mathbf{x}_0 + \mathbf{y}_0)$. If $\mathbf{u} + \mathbf{v} \neq \mathbf{0}$, the locus is the line through $\tfrac{1}{2}(\mathbf{x}_0 + \mathbf{y}_0)$ parallel to $\tfrac{1}{2}(\mathbf{u} + \mathbf{v})$ or, what is the same thing, to $\mathbf{u} + \mathbf{v}$.

Answer: A line (usual case) or a point (exceptional case).

EXERCISES

Find a parametric vector equation, parametric scalar equations, and a scalar equation for the line through $\mathbf{x}_0$ parallel to $\mathbf{v}$:

1. $\mathbf{x}_0 = \mathbf{0}$, $\mathbf{v} = (1, 1)$
2. $\mathbf{x}_0 = \mathbf{0}$, $\mathbf{v} = (2, -1)$
3. $\mathbf{x}_0 = (1, 0)$, $\mathbf{v} = (0, 1)$
4. $\mathbf{x}_0 = (0, -1)$, $\mathbf{v} = (1, 0)$
5. $\mathbf{x}_0 = (2, 3)$, $\mathbf{v} = (2, -1)$
6. $\mathbf{x}_0 = (-1, 2)$, $\mathbf{v} = (-1, 2)$
7. $\mathbf{x}_0 = (3, 1)$, $\mathbf{v} = (4, 3)$
8. $\mathbf{x}_0 = (-1, -3)$, $\mathbf{v} = (-4, -3)$.

Find a scalar equation for the line through the given points:

9. $(0, 0)$, $(2, 0)$
10. $(0, 1)$, $(0, -1)$
11. $(1, 2)$, $(2, 1)$
12. $(0, 2)$, $(-3, 2)$
13. $(1, 4)$, $(1, -4)$
14. $(2, 3)$, $(-1, 0)$
15. $(-1, 2)$, $(-3, -1)$
16. $(3, 1)$, $(4, -3)$.

Find a scalar equation for the line through the given point with given slope:

17. $(0, 0)$, 0
18. $(0, 0)$, -1
19. $(1, 0)$, 1
20. $(0, 1)$, -1
21. $(2, 1)$, -2
22. $(-1, 2)$, 3
23. $(-1, 1)$, 3
24. $(1, -4)$, 4.

Determine whether the two lines are the same or different:

25. $\begin{cases} x = 2t + 1 \\ y = -3t + 2 \end{cases}$ $\begin{cases} x = 2t + 3 \\ y = -3t - 1 \end{cases}$

26. $\begin{cases} x = t - 1 \\ y = -t + 1 \end{cases}$ $\begin{cases} x = 2t - 1 \\ y = -2t + 1 \end{cases}$

27. $\begin{cases} x = t - 1 \\ y = 2t - 1 \end{cases}$ $\begin{cases} x = 3t - 1 \\ y = 6t - 1 \end{cases}$

28. $\begin{cases} x = t - 2 \\ y = 3t + 1 \end{cases}$ $\begin{cases} x = 2t - 4 \\ y = 6t - 5. \end{cases}$

Find the midpoint of the segment with given endpoints:

29. $(2, 0)$, $(0, 4)$
30. $(1, -2)$, $(3, 1)$
31. $(-1, 3)$, $(3, -1)$
32. (a, b), (b, a).

Find the point $\frac{1}{5}$ of the way from the first point to the second:

33. $(0, 0)$, $(10, 15)$
34. $(2, 3)$, $(-1, 7)$
35. $(-1, -1)$, $(-3, 5)$
36. $(-1, 5)$, $(9, 20)$.

37. Prove that $\frac{1}{3}(\mathbf{u} + \mathbf{v} + \mathbf{w})$ is the intersection of the medians of the triangle with vertices $\mathbf{u}$, $\mathbf{v}$, $\mathbf{w}$.

38. Let $\mathbf{u}$, $\mathbf{v}$, $\mathbf{w}$, $\mathbf{z}$ be the vertices of a parallelogram, taken counterclockwise. Prove that $\mathbf{u} + \mathbf{w} = \mathbf{v} + \mathbf{z}$.

39. Write the equations of the medians of the triangle with vertices $(0, 0)$, $(3, 4)$, $(5, 10)$.

40. Write the scalar equation of the most general line through $(-1, 2)$.

41. Write the most general scalar equation of a line parallel to the vector $(3, -2)$.

42. Let L be a fixed line and c a fixed positive scalar. Find the locus of $c\mathbf{x}$ as $\mathbf{x}$ varies over L.

43. Let L be a fixed line and $\mathbf{c}$ a fixed vector. Find the locus of $\mathbf{x} + \mathbf{c}$ as $\mathbf{x}$ varies over L.

44*. Let $\mathbf{abc}$ be a fixed triangle. Each line L parallel to $\mathbf{bc}$ meets $\mathbf{ab}$ in a point $\mathbf{b}'$ and $\mathbf{ac}$ in a point $\mathbf{c}'$. Let $\mathbf{p}$ be the intersection of $\mathbf{b}'\mathbf{c}$ and $\mathbf{bc}'$. Prove that the locus of $\mathbf{p}$ as L varies in a line. [*Hint:* Place $\mathbf{a}$ at the origin.]

3. LENGTH AND INNER PRODUCT

Distances and Angles

Given two points (x_1, y_1) and (x_2, y_2) in the coordinate plane, what is the distance between them? We show several cases in Fig. 3.1. In each case we introduce an auxilliary point (x_2, y_1) forming a right triangle as shown. The legs have lengths $|x_2 - x_1|$ and $|y_2 - y_1|$, so by the Pythagorean theorem,

$$d^2 = |x_2 - x_1|^2 + |y_2 - y_1|^2 = (x_2 - x_1)^2 + (y_2 - y_1)^2.$$

> The distance between two points
>
> $\quad (x_1, y_1) \qquad$ and $\qquad (x_2, y_2)$
>
> is
>
> $$\sqrt{(x_2 - x_1)^2 + (y_2 - y_1)^2}.$$

If the points (x_1, y_1) and (x_2, y_2) lie on the same horizontal line or the same vertical line, the distance is $|x_1 - x_2|$ or $|y_1 - y_2|$; there is no need to introduce an auxiliary point. Nevertheless, the distance formula still yields the correct answer.

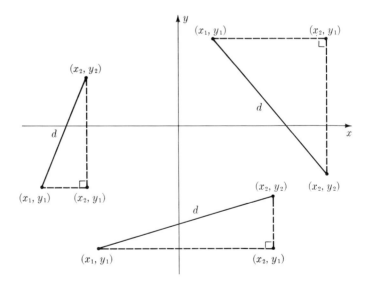

FIG. 3.1.   distance between points

The Unit Circle

The locus of all points one unit from the origin is a circle of radius 1, called the **unit circle.** By the distance formula, a point (x, y) is on the circle if and only if $(x - 0)^2 + (y - 0)^2 = 1^2$,

$$x^2 + y^2 = 1.$$

This formula is the **equation of the unit circle.**

The unit circle consists of all points (x, y) in the plane that satisfy the condition

$$x^2 + y^2 = 1.$$

The equation is simply a restatement of the Pythagorean theorem for right triangles of hypotenuse 1. See Fig. 3.2.

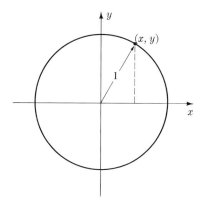

FIG. 3.2.   unit circle, $x^2 + y^2 = 1$

Length

We start with some basic properties of the length of a vector. We denote the length of **v** by $\|\mathbf{v}\|$.

If $\mathbf{v} = (x, y)$, then

(1) $\|\mathbf{v}\|^2 = \|(x, y)\|^2 = x^2 + y^2$,

(2) $\|\mathbf{0}\| = 0$, $\|\mathbf{v}\| > 0$ if $\mathbf{v} \neq \mathbf{0}$,

(3) $\|a\mathbf{v}\| = |a| \cdot \|\mathbf{v}\|$,

(4) $\|\mathbf{v} + \mathbf{w}\| \leq \|\mathbf{v}\| + \|\mathbf{w}\|$ (triangle inequality).

The first property comes directly from the distance formula, and the second follows from the first. The third is also proved by direct calculation:

$$\|a(x, y)\|^2 = \|(ax, ay)\|^2 = (ax)^2 + (ay)^2 = a^2(x^2 + y^2) = a^2\|(x, y)\|^2,$$

therefore
$$\|a\mathbf{v}\|^2 = a^2\|\mathbf{v}\|^2, \qquad \|a\mathbf{v}\| = |a| \cdot |\mathbf{v}|.$$

A useful fact: if $\mathbf{v}$ is any non-zero vector, then $\mathbf{v}/\|\mathbf{v}\|$ is a unit vector (length 1) in the same direction. Just apply (3) with $a = 1/\|\mathbf{v}\|$.

The triangle inequality (4) expresses a basic geometric fact: the length of each side of a triangle cannot exceed the sum of the lengths of the other two sides (Fig. 3.3).

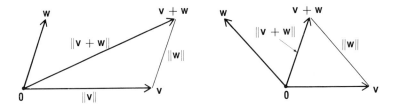

Fig. 3.3.   geometric proof that $\|\mathbf{v} + \mathbf{w}\| \leq \|\mathbf{v}\| + \|\mathbf{w}\|$

REMARK: The inequality between real numbers

$$|a + b| \leq |a| + |b|,$$

mentioned in Chapter 1, Section 2, is called "the triangle inequality" because of its close resemblance to the triangle inequality for vectors.

Inner Product

We now define the third basic operation on vectors, the **inner product** (also called **dot product**). The inner product combines two vectors to produce a scalar. Suppose $\mathbf{v}$ and $\mathbf{w}$ are non-zero vectors, and $\cos \theta$ is the cosine of the angle between them. We define

$$\boxed{\mathbf{v} \cdot \mathbf{w} = \|\mathbf{v}\| \cdot \|\mathbf{w}\| \cdot \cos \theta.}$$

Note: There are four possibilities for "the angle between $\mathbf{v}$ and $\mathbf{w}$". If one is θ, then the others are $-\theta$, $2\pi - \theta$, and $\theta - 2\pi$. But

$$\cos \theta = \cos(-\theta) = \cos(2\pi - \theta) = \cos(\theta - 2\pi),$$

so there is only one possibility for "the cosine of the angle between **v** and **w**". See Fig. 3.4. If either **v** = **0** or **w** = **0**, the angle between **v** and **w** is not defined. In this case we define

$$\mathbf{0} \cdot \mathbf{w} = \mathbf{v} \cdot \mathbf{0} = 0.$$

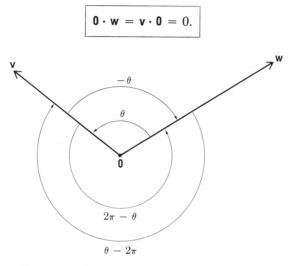

FIG. 3.4. The four angles have equal cosines.

Notice that the inner product of two vectors is a *real number*, not a vector.

Three special cases that arise all the time follow directly from the definition of inner product:

(1) $$\mathbf{v} \cdot \mathbf{v} = \|\mathbf{v}\|^2.$$

(2) Vectors **v** and **w** are perpendicular if and only if $\mathbf{v} \cdot \mathbf{w} = 0$.

(3) If **v** and **w** are unit vectors ($\|\mathbf{v}\| = \|\mathbf{w}\| = 1$), then $\mathbf{v} \cdot \mathbf{w} = \cos \theta$.

Some examples of dot products are shown in Fig. 3.5.

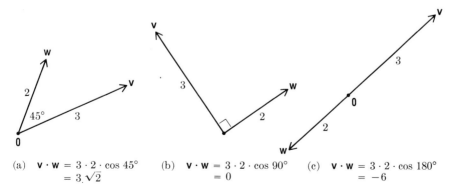

(a) $\mathbf{v} \cdot \mathbf{w} = 3 \cdot 2 \cdot \cos 45°$
$= 3 \sqrt{2}$

(b) $\mathbf{v} \cdot \mathbf{w} = 3 \cdot 2 \cdot \cos 90°$
$= 0$

(c) $\mathbf{v} \cdot \mathbf{w} = 3 \cdot 2 \cdot \cos 180°$
$= -6$

FIG. 3.5. examples of dot products

There is another important geometric interpretation of the inner product. Suppose $\mathbf{v}$ and $\mathbf{w}$ are non-zero vectors and θ is the angle between them (we can always take θ so that $0 \leq \theta \leq \pi$). See Fig. 3.6. The quantity $\|\mathbf{v}\| \cdot \cos\theta$ is the length of the projection of $\mathbf{v}$ on $\mathbf{w}$ if $0 \leq \theta \leq \frac{1}{2}\pi$ and the negative of the length if $\frac{1}{2}\pi \leq \theta \leq \pi$. We call $\|\mathbf{v}\| \cdot \cos\theta$ the **signed projection** of $\mathbf{v}$ on $\mathbf{w}$. Its sign is $+$ when $\mathbf{v}$ projects directly onto $\mathbf{w}$, and $-$ when $\mathbf{v}$ projects onto $\mathbf{w}$ extended backwards. Since $\mathbf{v} \cdot \mathbf{w} = (\|\mathbf{v}\| \cos\theta) \cdot \|\mathbf{w}\| = (\|\mathbf{w}\| \cos\theta) \cdot \|\mathbf{v}\|$,

$$
\begin{aligned}
\mathbf{v} \cdot \mathbf{w} &= \text{(signed projection of } \mathbf{v} \text{ on } \mathbf{w}) \cdot \|\mathbf{w}\| \\
&= \text{(signed projection of } \mathbf{w} \text{ on } \mathbf{v}) \cdot \|\mathbf{v}\|.
\end{aligned}
$$

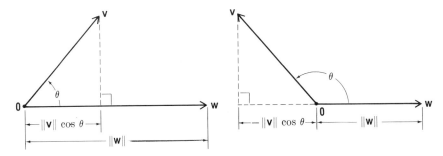

FIG. 3.6. $\mathbf{v} \cdot \mathbf{w} = \text{(signed projection of } \mathbf{v} \text{ on } \mathbf{w}) \cdot \|\mathbf{w}\|$

Computations with Inner Products

How do we compute the inner product of two vectors given their coordinates? We use the following formula, a consequence of the law of cosines:

$$
(x_1, y_1) \cdot (x_2, y_2) = x_1 x_2 + y_1 y_2.
$$

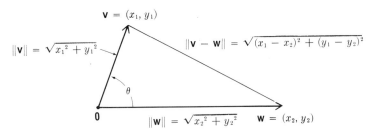

FIG. 3.7.   computation of $\|\mathbf{v} - \mathbf{w}\|$ by the law of cosines

Consider the triangle shown in Fig. 3.7. By the law of cosines,

$$
\|\mathbf{v} - \mathbf{w}\|^2 = \|\mathbf{v}\|^2 + \|\mathbf{w}\|^2 - 2\|\mathbf{v}\| \cdot \|\mathbf{w}\| \cdot \cos\theta = \|\mathbf{v}\|^2 + \|\mathbf{w}\|^2 - 2\mathbf{v} \cdot \mathbf{w}.
$$

Hence

$$\mathbf{v} \cdot \mathbf{w} = \tfrac{1}{2}(\|\mathbf{v}\|^2 + \|\mathbf{w}\|^2 - \|\mathbf{v} - \mathbf{w}\|^2)$$
$$= \tfrac{1}{2}[\|(x_1, y_1)\|^2 + \|(x_2, y_2)\|^2 - \|(x_1 - x_2, y_1 - y_2)\|^2]$$
$$= \tfrac{1}{2}[(x_1^2 + y_1^2) + (x_2^2 + y_2^2) - (x_1 - x_2)^2 - (y_1 - y_2)^2]$$
$$= \tfrac{1}{2}[x_1^2 + y_1^2 + x_2^2 + y_2^2 - (x_1^2 - 2x_1x_2 + x_2^2) - (y_1^2 - 2y_1y_2 + y_2^2)]$$
$$= x_1x_2 + y_1y_2.$$

This formula for inner products provides an explicit expression for the cosine of the angle between two vectors.

If $\mathbf{v} = (x_1, y_1)$ and $\mathbf{w} = (x_2, y_2)$ are non-zero vectors and θ is the angle between them, then

$$\cos \theta = \frac{\mathbf{v} \cdot \mathbf{w}}{\|\mathbf{v}\| \cdot \|\mathbf{w}\|} = \frac{x_1x_2 + y_1y_2}{\sqrt{x_1^2 + y_1^2} \cdot \sqrt{x_2^2 + y_2^2}}.$$

EXAMPLE 3.1

Find the cosine of the angle between the vectors $(4, 3)$ and $(1, 5)$.

Solution: Set $\mathbf{v} = (4, 3)$ and $\mathbf{w} = (1, 5)$. Then

$$\|\mathbf{v}\|^2 = 4^2 + 3^2 = 25, \qquad \|\mathbf{w}\|^2 = 1^2 + 5^2 = 26,$$
$$\mathbf{v} \cdot \mathbf{w} = 4 \cdot 1 + 3 \cdot 5 = 19,$$
$$\cos \theta = \frac{\mathbf{v} \cdot \mathbf{w}}{\|\mathbf{v}\| \cdot \|\mathbf{w}\|} = \frac{19}{5\sqrt{26}}.$$

Answer: $\cos \theta = 19/5\sqrt{26}.$

Here are the main properties of the inner product:

(1)	$\mathbf{v} \cdot \mathbf{w} = \mathbf{w} \cdot \mathbf{v}$	
(2)	$(a\mathbf{v}) \cdot \mathbf{w} = \mathbf{v} \cdot (a\mathbf{w}) = a(\mathbf{v} \cdot \mathbf{w})$	
(3)	$(\mathbf{u} + \mathbf{v}) \cdot \mathbf{w} = \mathbf{u} \cdot \mathbf{w} + \mathbf{v} \cdot \mathbf{w}$	
(4)	$\mathbf{u} \cdot (\mathbf{v} + \mathbf{w}) = \mathbf{u} \cdot \mathbf{v} + \mathbf{u} \cdot \mathbf{w}.$	

Property (1) simply says that $x_1x_2 + y_1y_2 = x_2x_1 + y_2y_1$. Property (2) is nearly as easy; it says $(ax_1)x_2 + (ay_1)y_2 = x_1(ax_2) + y_1(ay_2) = a(x_1x_2 + y_1y_2)$.

In view of (1), relations (3) and (4) are equivalent to each other, so it suffices to prove (3). We have

$$(\mathbf{u} + \mathbf{v}) \cdot \mathbf{w} = [(x_1, y_1) + (x_2, y_2)] \cdot (x_3, y_3)$$
$$= (x_1 + x_2, y_1 + y_2) \cdot (x_3, y_3) = (x_1 + x_2)x_3 + (y_1 + y_2)y_3$$
$$= (x_1 x_3 + y_1 y_3) + (x_2 x_3 + y_2 y_3)$$
$$= (x_1, y_1) \cdot (x_3, y_3) + (x_2, y_2) \cdot (x_3, y_3)$$
$$= \mathbf{u} \cdot \mathbf{w} + \mathbf{v} \cdot \mathbf{w}.$$

Perpendicular Vectors

If $\mathbf{v} = (a, b)$ is a non-zero vector, then $(-b, a)$ is perpendicular to $\mathbf{v}$ and has the same length as $\mathbf{v}$:

$$(a, b) \cdot (-b, a) = -ab + ba = 0,$$
$$\|(-b, a)\| = \sqrt{(-b)^2 + a^2} = \sqrt{a^2 + b^2} = \|(a, b)\|.$$

Therefore $(-b, a)$ is one of the two vectors shown in Fig. 3.8a.

A direct check of the 4 quadrants shows that $(-b, a)$ is *always* $\frac{1}{2}\pi$ forward of $\mathbf{v}$. See Fig. 3.8b.

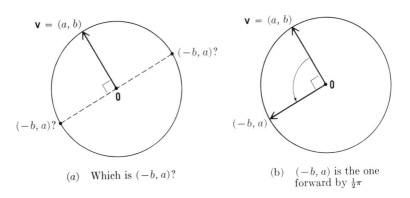

(a) Which is $(-b, a)$?

(b) $(-b, a)$ is the one forward by $\frac{1}{2}\pi$

FIG. 3.8

The result of rotating a vector $\mathbf{v} = (a, b)$ counterclockwise $\frac{1}{2}\pi$ radians is $(-b, a)$.

EXERCISES

Compute:

1. $(2, 0) \cdot (3, 1)$
2. $(-1, -1) \cdot (1, 1)$
3. $(4, 1) \cdot (-1, 4)$
4. $(2, 2) \cdot (-1, 2)$
5. $(0, 3) \cdot (1, 1)$
6. $(2, 3) \cdot (-3, -1)$.

Compute in two ways:

7. $(2, 3) \cdot [(1, 4) + (2, 2)]$

8. $(-1, 2) \cdot [(1, 3) + (1, 4)]$.

9. Prove $\|\mathbf{v} + \mathbf{w}\|^2 = \|\mathbf{v}\|^2 + 2\mathbf{v} \cdot \mathbf{w} + \|\mathbf{w}\|^2$

10. Prove $\|\mathbf{v} + \mathbf{w}\|^2 + \|\mathbf{v} - \mathbf{w}\|^2 = 2\|\mathbf{v}\|^2 + 2\|\mathbf{w}\|^2$

11. Prove $\|\mathbf{v} + \mathbf{w}\|^2 - \|\mathbf{v} - \mathbf{w}\|^2 = 4\mathbf{v} \cdot \mathbf{w}$

12. Prove $|\mathbf{v} \cdot \mathbf{w}| \leq \|\mathbf{v}\| \cdot \|\mathbf{w}\|$.

Compute the smallest positive angle (at least its cosine) between the vectors:

13. $(3, 4), (-4, 3)$ 14. $(1, -2), (-2, 1)$ 15. $(1, 3), (3, 1)$

16. $(1, -3), (3, 6)$ 17. $(1, 1), (-1, 7)$ 18. $(3, 4), (-5, -2)$.

19. Prove that the diagonals of a rhombus are perpendicular.

20. Prove Schwarz's Inequality: If a_1, a_2, b_1, b_2 are any real numbers, then $(a_1 a_2 + b_1 b_2)^2 \leq (a_1^2 + a_2^2)(b_1^2 + b_2^2)$. [*Hint:* Interpret in terms of lengths and inner products.]

21. Find a vector perpendicular to $(9, -1)$.

22. (cont.) Find a parametric equation for the line tangent to the circle $x^2 + y^2 = 25$ at the point $(3, 4)$.

23. Find a parametric equation for the perpendicular bisector of the line segment from $(1, 1)$ to $(5, 3)$.

24*. Show that the result of rotating (x, y) through angle $\frac{1}{4}\pi$ is $(1/\sqrt{2})(x - y, x + y)$.

4. NORMAL FORM

Using inner products, we shall obtain a useful and simple vector equation for a straight line, different from the parametric equations in Section 2. Take any line L_0 that passes through $\mathbf{0}$. There are two unit vectors perpendicular to L_0; choose either one and call it $\mathbf{n}$. See Fig. 4.1. A point $\mathbf{x}$ is on L_0 if and only if the vector $\mathbf{x}$ is perpendicular to the vector $\mathbf{n}$, that is, if and only if

$$\mathbf{x} \cdot \mathbf{n} = 0.$$

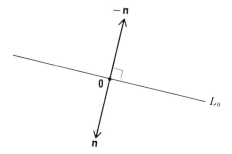

Fig. 4.1.   the two unit vectors perpendicular to a line

This is the equation for L_0. How much simpler could it be?

Each line through **0** is the locus of an equation

$$\mathbf{x} \cdot \mathbf{n} = 0.$$

Conversely, each such equation (with **n** non-zero) determines the line through **0** perpendicular to **n**.

The equation $\mathbf{x} \cdot \mathbf{n} = 0$ makes good sense in coordinates. Write $\mathbf{x} = (x, y)$ and $\mathbf{n} = (a, b)$. Then the equation becomes

$$ax + by = 0,$$

the general scalar equation for a line through the origin.

REMARK: It is handy to remember that the expression $ax + by$ can be written $(x, y) \cdot (a, b)$. Given $ax + by = 0$, you can tell at a glance that the equation is satisfied by all vectors (x, y) perpendicular to the fixed vector (a, b).

Now take any line L not passing through **0** and choose a unit vector **n** perpendicular to L. The point on L closest to **0** is $p\mathbf{n}$ where p is a scalar (Fig. 4.2a). Subtract the vector $p\mathbf{n}$ from each point of L, shifting L to a line L_0 through **0**. See Fig. 4.2b. A point $\mathbf{x}$ is on L if and only if the point $\mathbf{x} - p\mathbf{n}$ is on L_0. But $\mathbf{x} - p\mathbf{n}$ is on L_0 if and only if

$$(\mathbf{x} - p\mathbf{n}) \cdot \mathbf{n} = 0.$$

This is the vector equation for L. Simplify it by the rules for inner product and the fact that $\|\mathbf{n}\|^2 = \mathbf{n} \cdot \mathbf{n} = 1$:

$$\mathbf{x} \cdot \mathbf{n} - p\mathbf{n} \cdot \mathbf{n} = 0, \qquad \mathbf{x} \cdot \mathbf{n} = p.$$

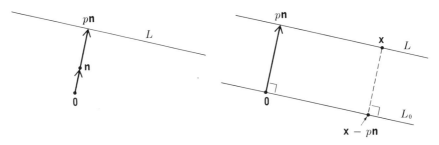

(a)   The point on L (b)   Shift L to position L_0.
      nearest to **0** is $p\mathbf{n}$

FIG. 4.2

Each line in the plane is the locus of an equation

$$\mathbf{x} \cdot \mathbf{n} = p,$$

where $\mathbf{n}$ is a unit vector and p is a scalar. This equation is called the **normal form** of the line.

Conversely, each equation $\mathbf{x} \cdot \mathbf{n} = p$, where $\mathbf{n}$ is a unit vector, describes the line perpendicular to $\mathbf{n}$ passing through the point $p\mathbf{n}$.

REMARK: Actually each line has two normal forms because there are two choices, $\mathbf{n}$ and $-\mathbf{n}$, for the unit perpendicular vector, hence two equivalent equations

$$\mathbf{x} \cdot \mathbf{n} = p \qquad \text{and} \qquad \mathbf{x} \cdot (-\mathbf{n}) = -p.$$

We try to ignore this ambiguity and we refer (incorrectly) to either as "the" normal form of the line.

Here is another derivation of the normal form. For simplicity choose $\mathbf{n}$ pointing from $\mathbf{0}$ towards the line L. A point $\mathbf{x}$ is on L if and only if the signed projection of $\mathbf{x}$ on $\mathbf{n}$ is p. (See the right triangle in Fig. 4.3.) Since

$$\mathbf{x} \cdot \mathbf{n} = (\text{signed projection of } \mathbf{x} \text{ on } \mathbf{n}) \cdot \|\mathbf{n}\|$$

and $\|\mathbf{n}\| = 1$, the point $\mathbf{x}$ is on L if and only if $\mathbf{x} \cdot \mathbf{n} = p$.

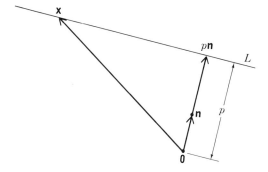

FIG. 4.3. $\mathbf{x}$ is on L when its signed projection on $\mathbf{n}$ is $p\mathbf{n}$, that is, when $\mathbf{x} \cdot \mathbf{n} = p$.

The vector equation $\mathbf{x} \cdot \mathbf{n} = p$ becomes a scalar equation, $ax + by = p$, when we substitute $\mathbf{x} = (x, y)$ and $\mathbf{n} = (a, b)$.

Each line in the plane is the locus of an equation

$$ax + by = p, \qquad a^2 + b^2 = 1.$$

This scalar equation is also called the **normal form** of the line.

Conversely, each equation of this type describes the line perpendicular to (a, b) passing through the point (pa, pb).

Examples (Fig. 4.4):

(a) $x = 3,$ $(a, b) = (1, 0),$ $p = 3;$

(b) $-y = \frac{1}{2},$ $(a, b) = (0, -1),$ $p = \frac{1}{2};$

(c) $-\dfrac{x}{\sqrt{2}} - \dfrac{y}{\sqrt{2}} = -1,$ $(a, b) = \left(\dfrac{-1}{\sqrt{2}}, \dfrac{-1}{\sqrt{2}}\right),$ $p = -1.$

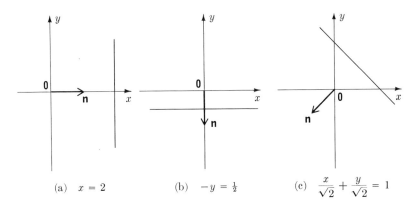

(a) $x = 2$ (b) $-y = \frac{1}{2}$ (c) $\dfrac{x}{\sqrt{2}} + \dfrac{y}{\sqrt{2}} = 1$

FIG. 4.4. straight lines in normal form

A unit vector (a, b) is a point on the unit circle, hence we have (a, b) $= (\cos \theta, \sin \theta)$ for some θ. Therefore the normal form is often written

$$\boxed{x \cos \theta + y \sin \theta = p.}$$

To convert an equation $ax + by = c$, into normal form we divide by $\sqrt{a^2 + b^2}$ (assuming not both a and b are zero):

$$\frac{a}{\sqrt{a^2 + b^2}} x + \frac{b}{\sqrt{a^2 + b^2}} y = \frac{c}{\sqrt{a^2 + b^2}}.$$

But

$$\left(\frac{a}{\sqrt{a^2 + b^2}}\right)^2 + \left(\frac{b}{\sqrt{a^2 + b^2}}\right)^2 = 1,$$

so there is an angle θ satisfying

$$\frac{a}{\sqrt{a^2 + b^2}} = \cos \theta, \qquad \frac{b}{\sqrt{a^2 + b^2}} = \sin \theta,$$

and we have

$$x \cos \theta + y \sin \theta = p, \qquad p = c/\sqrt{a^2 + b^2}.$$

EXAMPLE 4.1

Find the normal form of the lines

(a) $3x + 2y = 1$ (b) $y = 2x + 7$.

Solution: (a) Divide by $\sqrt{3^2 + 2^2} = \sqrt{13}$:

$$\frac{3}{\sqrt{13}} x + \frac{2}{\sqrt{13}} y = \frac{1}{\sqrt{13}}.$$

(b) Transpose first. Write $2x - y = -7$. Divide by $\sqrt{2^2 + (-1)^2} = \sqrt{5}$:

$$\frac{2}{\sqrt{5}} x - \frac{1}{\sqrt{5}} y = \frac{-7}{\sqrt{5}}.$$

Answer: (a) $\dfrac{3}{\sqrt{13}} x + \dfrac{2}{\sqrt{13}} y = \dfrac{1}{\sqrt{13}}$;   (b) $\dfrac{2}{\sqrt{5}} x - \dfrac{1}{\sqrt{5}} y = \dfrac{-7}{\sqrt{5}}$.

REMARK: When we put $ax + by = c$ in normal form, we obtain a *unit* normal vector $\mathbf{n} = (a^2 + b^2)^{-1/2}(a, b)$. But if we need only *some* vector perpendicular to the line, we can drop the scalar $(a^2 + b^2)^{-1/2}$ and simply take (a, b).

Distance from a Point to a Line

Problem: Given a point $\mathbf{x}_0$ in the plane and a line L, compute the distance from $\mathbf{x}_0$ to L. There is a neat solution in terms of the normal form of L:

Suppose $\mathbf{x} \cdot \mathbf{n} = p$ is the normal form of a line L, and $\mathbf{x}_0$ is a point of the plane. Then the distance from $\mathbf{x}_0$ to L is

$$|p - \mathbf{x}_0 \cdot \mathbf{n}|.$$

If $ax + by = p$ is the normal form in coordinates, then the distance is

$$|p - ax_0 - by_0|.$$

It is easy to apply this rule. Just write the normal form as $0 = p - \mathbf{x} \cdot \mathbf{n}$. Then take the absolute value of the right-hand side with $\mathbf{x}$ replaced by $\mathbf{x}_0$.

In order to prove the rule, we consider the family of parallel lines $\mathbf{x} \cdot \mathbf{n} = p$ for various values of p. See Fig. 4.5a. As is seen in Fig. 4.5b, the distance between two lines $\mathbf{x} \cdot \mathbf{n} = p$ and $\mathbf{x} \cdot \mathbf{n} = q$ is $|p - q|$.

Now let $\mathbf{x}_0$ be a fixed point in the plane. It lies on one of the parallel lines, say on $\mathbf{x} \cdot \mathbf{n} = q$, so $\mathbf{x}_0 \cdot \mathbf{n} = q$. The distance from $\mathbf{x}_0$ to the line $\mathbf{x} \cdot \mathbf{n} = p$ is the same as the distance between the lines $\mathbf{x} \cdot \mathbf{n} = p$ and $\mathbf{x} \cdot \mathbf{n} = q$. But this distance is $|p - q| = |p - \mathbf{x}_0 \cdot \mathbf{n}|$, as we wished to prove.

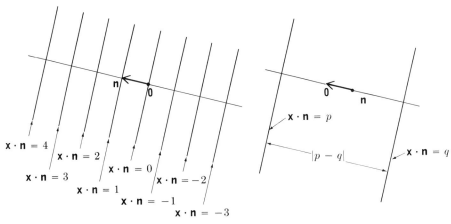

(a)   family of lines $\mathbf{x} \cdot \mathbf{n} = p$ (b)   distance between two
                                                                  of the lines

FIG. 4.5

EXAMPLE 4.2

Find the distance from $(4, -1)$ to the lines

(a) $\frac{3}{5}x - \frac{4}{5}y = 1$ (b) $y = 3x - 1$.

Solution: (a) Since $\mathbf{n} = (\frac{3}{5}, -\frac{4}{5})$ is a unit vector, the equation *is* the normal form of a line. Therefore the distance from $(4, -1)$ to the line is

$$|1 - [\tfrac{3}{5}(4) - \tfrac{4}{5}(-1)]| = |1 - \tfrac{16}{5}| = \tfrac{11}{5}.$$

(b)   First convert the equation to normal form. Write $0 = 1 - 3x + y$ and divide by $\sqrt{3^2 + 1^2} = \sqrt{10}$:

$$0 = \frac{1 - 3x + y}{\sqrt{10}}.$$

Now substitute $(4, -1)$ on the right side and take the absolute value:

$$\text{distance} = \frac{|1 - 3(4) + (-1)|}{\sqrt{10}} = \frac{|-12|}{\sqrt{10}}.$$

Answer: (a) $\dfrac{11}{5}$;   (b) $\dfrac{12}{\sqrt{10}}$.

Angle between Lines

Problem: Find the angles between intersecting lines. As Fig. 4.6a shows, intersecting lines form two angles, θ and $\pi - \theta$; it suffices to find either one. Suppose $\mathbf{m}$ and $\mathbf{n}$ are unit vectors, each perpendicular to one of the lines. Then the smaller angle between **m** and **n** is either θ or $\pi - \theta$. See Fig. 4.6b. Therefore $\mathbf{m} \cdot \mathbf{n} = \cos\theta$ or $\cos(\pi - \theta)$.

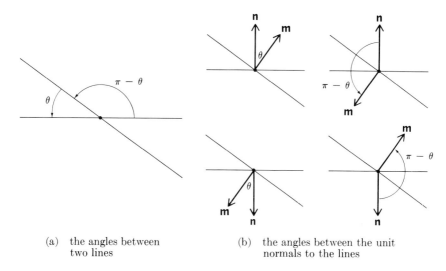

(a)   the angles between
two lines

(b)   the angles between the unit
normals to the lines

Fɪɢ. 4.6

If $\mathbf{x} \cdot \mathbf{m} = p$ and $\mathbf{x} \cdot \mathbf{n} = q$ are two lines in normal form, then

$$\mathbf{m} \cdot \mathbf{n} = \cos\theta \qquad \text{or} \qquad \mathbf{m} \cdot \mathbf{n} = \cos(\pi - \theta),$$

where θ is one of the angles of intersection of the lines.

Rᴇᴍᴀʀᴋ: If the lines are parallel, or are the same line, then $\mathbf{m} = \pm\mathbf{n}$, and $\mathbf{m} \cdot \mathbf{n} = \pm 1$. Therefore the result is correct in this case also, provided we interpret $\theta = 0$ or π to mean parallel (or the same).

Since $\mathbf{m} \cdot \mathbf{n} = \cos\theta$, lines are perpendicular if and only if $\mathbf{m} \cdot \mathbf{n} = 0$. This criterion is often expressed in terms of slopes:

The graphs of two linear functions

$$y = mx + b, \qquad y = nx + c$$

are perpendicular if and only if

$$n = -\frac{1}{m}.$$

Stated in other terms, two non-vertical lines are perpendicular if and only if their slopes are negative reciprocals of each other.

Proof: Write the two linear equations in the form:

$$-mx + y = b, \qquad -nx + y = c.$$

By inspection, the vector $(-m, 1)$ is perpendicular to the first line, and $(-n, 1)$ to the second. Hence the lines are perpendicular, if and only if these two vectors are perpendicular:

$$(-m, 1) \cdot (-n, 1) = 0, \qquad mn + 1 = 0, \qquad n = -\frac{1}{m}.$$

Example: The line through the origin perpendicular to $y = 3x + 1$ is $y = -\frac{1}{3}x$, because $-\frac{1}{3}$ is the negative reciprocal of 3.

EXERCISES

Give the normal form of each line:

1. $y = 3x$ 2. $y = -x$ 3. $y = x - 2$
4. $y = 3x + 1$ 5. $y = -2x - 1$ 6. $y = -4x + 2$
7. $y = -x + 3$ 8. $y = 4$ 9. $3x - 4y = 0$
10. $3x - 4y = 5$ 11. $12x + 5y = 1$ 12. $-12x + 5y = 3$.

Find the distance from **0** to the line:

13. $x + 2y = 1$ 14. $y = x + 4$ 15. $3x - 4y = 6$

16. $x = 2y - 1$ 17. $y = ax + b$ 18. $\dfrac{x}{a} + \dfrac{x}{b} = 1$.

Find the distance, point to line:

19. $(1, 0), \ y = -2$ 20. $(0, -1), \ x = 3$
21. $(1, 0), \ x + y = 2$ 22. $(1, -1), \ 3x - 4y = 1$
23. $(-2, -3), \ 3x + 4y = 5$ 24. $(1, 3), \ -5x + 12y = 1$.

Show that the lines are parallel and find the distance between them:

25. $x - 2y = -1, \ x - 2y = 3$ 26. $3x - 4y = 5, \ -6x + 8y = 1$.

Find the angles between the lines:

27. $x + y = 1, \ x - y = 1$ 28. $y = x, \ y = 0$
29. $y = \frac{1}{2}x, \ y = 2x$ 30. $y = 3x, \ y = -x$

31. $x + y = 0, \ x + \dfrac{y}{\sqrt{3}} = 1$ 32. $-\dfrac{x}{\sqrt{3}} + y = 0, \ x + y = 1$.

Find the equation of the line:

33. through $(1, 0)$ and perpendicular to $x - 2y = 6$.

34. through $(-2, -3)$ and perpendicular to the line through $(1, 0)$ and $(5, 4)$.

35. Find the equation of the perpendicular bisector of the line segment between $(0, 1)$ and $(5, -2)$.

36. (cont.) Do Exercise 35 another way, using the distance formula.

37. Prove that the perpendicular bisector of any chord of a circle passes through the center of the circle.

38*. Prove that the triangle formed by the points $(0, 0)$, (a, b), and (x_0, y_0) has area $\frac{1}{2}|ay_0 - bx_0|$.

39*. Let $\mathbf{x} \cdot \mathbf{m} = p$ and $\mathbf{x} \cdot \mathbf{n} = q$ be lines in normal form, not parallel. Show that the two lines through their intersection bisecting their angles of intersection are $\mathbf{x} \cdot \mathbf{m} - p = \pm(\mathbf{x} \cdot \mathbf{n} - q)$.

40. Let $\mathbf{a}_1, \mathbf{a}_2, \cdots, \mathbf{a}_r$ be fixed points in the plane. Consider all lines in normal form $\mathbf{x} \cdot \mathbf{n} = p$ such that $(\mathbf{a}_1 \cdot \mathbf{n} - p) + (\mathbf{a}_2 \cdot \mathbf{n} - p) + \cdots + (\mathbf{a}_r \cdot \mathbf{n} - p) = 0$. Show that these lines all pass through a common point. What point?

Harder Problems

41*. Let $\mathbf{v}_1, \mathbf{v}_2, \mathbf{v}_3$ be the vertices of a triangle and a_1, a_2, a_3 the lengths of the opposite sides. Prove that the **incenter** (intersection of angle bisectors = center of inscribed circle) is

$$\mathbf{p} = \frac{a_1\mathbf{v}_1 + a_2\mathbf{v}_2 + a_3\mathbf{v}_3}{a_1 + a_2 + a_3}.$$

42*. (cont.) Show that the **excenters** (centers of the three circles that are tangent externally to all three sides of the triangle extended) are

$$\frac{a_1\mathbf{v}_1 + a_2\mathbf{v}_2 - a_3\mathbf{v}_3}{a_1 + a_2 - a_3}, \quad \frac{a_1\mathbf{v}_1 - a_2\mathbf{v}_2 + a_3\mathbf{v}_3}{a_1 - a_2 + a_3}, \quad \text{and} \quad \frac{-a_1\mathbf{v}_1 + a_2\mathbf{v}_2 + a_3\mathbf{v}_3}{-a_1 + a_2 + a_3}.$$

43*. Let L and M be fixed lines not passing through $\mathbf{0}$. Let $\mathbf{u}$ be a variable unit vector. If $a\mathbf{u}$ is on L and $b\mathbf{u}$ is on M, choose x so that $2x^{-1} = a^{-1} + b^{-1}$ and set $\mathbf{x} = x\mathbf{u}$. Prove that the locus of $\mathbf{x}$ is part of a line in general. [Hint: Use the normal forms of L and M.]

44*. (cont.) Let $L_1, L_2, \cdots, L_r$ be fixed lines, none passing through $\mathbf{0}$. For each unit vector $\mathbf{u}$, let $a_i\mathbf{u}$ be the intersection of L_i and the line $t\mathbf{u}$. Define x by $rx^{-1} = a_1^{-1} + a_2^{-1} + \cdots + a_r^{-1}$ and set $\mathbf{x} = x\mathbf{u}$. Prove that as $\mathbf{u}$ varies the locus of $\mathbf{x}$ lies on a line.

45*. Prove that the three altitudes of a triangle intersect in a common point (the **orthocenter**). [Hint: Let the vertices be $\mathbf{0}$, $\mathbf{x}$, and $\mathbf{y}$. Choose unit vectors $\mathbf{u}$ and $\mathbf{v}$ so that $\mathbf{x} \cdot \mathbf{u} = \mathbf{y} \cdot \mathbf{v} = 0$. The intersection of two of the altitudes is $\mathbf{p} = \mathbf{y} + a\mathbf{u} = \mathbf{x} + b\mathbf{v}$. Prove that $\mathbf{p} \cdot (\mathbf{y} - \mathbf{x}) = 0$.]

46*. Let L and M be fixed perpendicular lines. The line N through $\mathbf{0}$ meets L in $\mathbf{a}$. The line N' through $\mathbf{0}$ perpendicular to N meets M in $\mathbf{b}$. Find the locus of $\mathbf{x} = \frac{1}{3}\mathbf{a} + \frac{2}{3}\mathbf{b}$ as N varies.

47*. Let L_1, L_2, M be three lines. For each point $\mathbf{v}$ on M, let $\mathbf{p}_1$ and $\mathbf{p}_2$ be the feet of the perpendiculars dropped from $\mathbf{v}$ to L_1 and L_2. Let $\mathbf{x}$ be the midpoint of $\mathbf{p}_1$ and $\mathbf{p}_2$. Prove the locus of $\mathbf{x}$ is a line or a point. [Hint: Take L_1 and L_2 in normal form and M in parametric form, the origin at the intersection of L_1 and L_2.]

48*. (cont.) Suppose instead, $\mathbf{x} = c\mathbf{p}_1 + (1 - c)\mathbf{p}_2$ where c is fixed. Does the conclusion hold?

3. Analytic Geometry

1. TRANSLATION OF AXES

In working problems, it is often convenient to introduce new coordinate axes parallel to the given ones. This operation is called **shifting** or **translating** the axes. A translation is described by a single vector directed from the old origin to the new origin (Fig. 1.1).

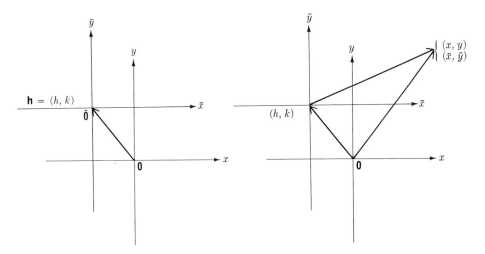

FIG. 1.1. new origin at (h, k) FIG. 1.2. relation between old and new coordinates:

$$(x, y) = (\bar{x}, \bar{y}) + (h, k)$$

When new axes are introduced, each point of the plane acquires new coordinates. What is the relation between the original coordinates (x, y) of a point and its new coordinates $(\bar{x}, \bar{y})$? See Fig. 1.2. Suppose the new origin is the point with old coordinates (h, k). From the triangle in Fig. 1.2, we see that $\mathbf{x} = \bar{\mathbf{x}} + \mathbf{h}$, or $(x, y) = (\bar{x}, \bar{y}) + (h, k) = (\bar{x} + h, \bar{y} + k)$.

If the coordinate axes are translated so that the origin is moved to (h, k), then the new coordinates $(\bar{x}, \bar{y})$ and the old coordinates (x, y) of a point are related by the equations

$$\begin{cases} x = \bar{x} + h \\ y = \bar{y} + k \end{cases} \qquad \begin{cases} \bar{x} = x - h \\ \bar{y} = y - k. \end{cases}$$

To get the signs right in this relation, just remember that $\bar{x} = 0$ and $\bar{y} = 0$ when $x = h$ and $y = k$.

Translation of axes is helpful in simplifying equations and computations. For example, take the equation $y + 3 = (x - 2)^2$. If we introduce a new coordinate system with origin at $(2, -3)$, then $x - 2 = \bar{x}$ and $y + 3 = \bar{y}$. Therefore the equation becomes $\bar{y} = \bar{x}^2$ in the new coordinates. Thus the graph of $y + 3 = (x - 2)^2$ is just the familiar quadratic curve $y = x^2$, but with its vertex shifted (Fig. 1.3).

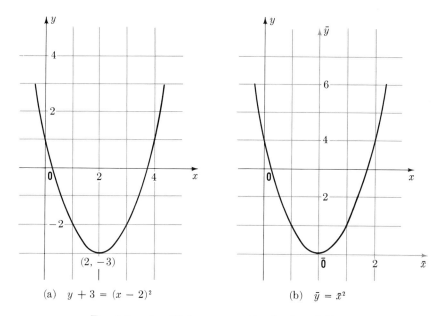

(a)　$y + 3 = (x - 2)^2$　　　　(b)　$\bar{y} = \bar{x}^2$

FIG. 1.3.　simplifying an equation by translation

In general, given an equation in x and y and new axes with origin at (h, k), it is easy to write the equation in $\bar{x}$ and $\bar{y}$ that describes the same locus. Simply substitute $x = \bar{x} + h$ and $y = \bar{y} + k$ for x and y in the given equation. For example, the equation of the line $ax + by = c$ is transformed into the equation $a(\bar{x} + h) + b(\bar{y} + k) = c$, that is

$$a\bar{x} + b\bar{y} = c - (ah + bk).$$

Note that the equation of the line is the same in either coordinate system except for the constant on the right side. Can you explain why geometrically?

An $\bar{x}$, $\bar{y}$-coordinate system is introduced with its origin at $(-5, 2)$. Find the $\bar{x}$, $\bar{y}$-coordinates of the point (x, y):

1. $(1, 6)$ 2. $(5, 4)$ 3. $(0, 0)$

4. $(-8, 1)$ 5. $(-5, -6)$ 6. $(0, 2)$.

With the $\bar{x}$, $\bar{y}$-coordinate system as above, find the x, y-coordinates of the point:

7. $(\bar{x}, \bar{y}) = (1, 3)$ 8. $(\bar{x}, \bar{y}) = (4, -2)$ 9. $(\bar{x}, \bar{y}) = (-6, -7)$

10. $(\bar{x}, \bar{y}) = (0, 3)$.

11. Show that the distance formula gives the same distance between two points regardless of whether the computation is performed in x, y-coordinates or in $\bar{x}$, $\bar{y}$-coordinates.

12. Let $\mathbf{u}$ and $\mathbf{v}$ be vectors. Show that computing $\mathbf{u} - \mathbf{v}$ in either x, y-coordinates or $\bar{x}$, $\bar{y}$-coordinates yields the same answer.

Describe a translation of axes that converts the first equation into the second:

13. $3x - 2y = 1$, $3\bar{x} - 2\bar{y} = 0$ 14. $x + 2y = 5$, $\bar{x} + 2\bar{y} = 0$

15. $y = x^2 + 2x + 2$, $\bar{y} = \bar{x}^2 + 1$ 16. $y = 3 + \dfrac{x - 1}{1 + (x - 1)^2}$, $\bar{y} = \dfrac{\bar{x}}{1 + \bar{x}^2}$

17. $y = \sin(x - \frac{1}{6}\pi) - 1$, $\bar{y} = \sin \bar{x}$

18. $y = \cos x + \cos(x + \frac{2}{3}\pi) + \cos(x + \frac{2}{3}\pi)$,
    $\bar{y} = \cos(\bar{x} - \frac{1}{3}\pi) + \cos \bar{x} + \cos(\bar{x} + \frac{1}{3}\pi)$.

Suppose the normal form of a line is $\mathbf{x} \cdot \mathbf{n} = p$.

19. If the origin is translated to the point $\mathbf{h}$, find the normal form in the new coordinates.

20. (cont.) Describe all translations which convert the normal form to $\bar{\mathbf{x}} \cdot \mathbf{n} = 0$. Interpret geometrically.

2. THE CIRCLE

A circle of radius r is the locus of all points at distance r from a fixed point, its center. If the center is the origin, the equation of the circle is $x^2 + y^2 = r^2$. If the center is at (a, b), the equation is similar:

> The equation of the circle with center (a, b) and radius r is
> $$(x - a)^2 + (y - b)^2 = r^2.$$

This is simply the equation $\bar{x}^2 + \bar{y}^2 = r^2$ relative to axes centered at (a, b).

The equation can also be derived directly from the definition of the circle. If the center is at $\mathbf{a} = (a, b)$, then the circle consists of precisely those points $\mathbf{x} = (x, y)$ for which $\|\mathbf{x} - \mathbf{a}\| = r$. This vector equation is equivalent to an ordinary equation:

$$\|(x, y) - (a, b)\|^2 = \|(x - a, y - b)\|^2 = r^2,$$
$$(x - a)^2 + (y - b)^2 = r^2.$$

When we expand the squares in this equation, we get

$$(x^2 - 2ax + a^2) + (y^2 - 2by + b^2) = r^2,$$
$$x^2 + y^2 - 2(ax + by) + (a^2 + b^2 - r^2) = 0.$$

Conversely, suppose we start with an equation of the form

$$x^2 + y^2 - 2(ax + by) + c = 0;$$

what is the locus of all points (x, y) that satisfy it? (Of course we suspect the locus is a circle.) We complete the squares for both the x and the y term

$$(x^2 - 2ax + a^2) + (y^2 - 2by + b^2) + c = a^2 + b^2,$$
$$(x - a)^2 + (y - b)^2 = a^2 + b^2 - c.$$

Now here is a hitch: the left side is a sum of squares, hence non-negative. But the right side is not guaranteed to be non-negative! We are forced to consider 3 cases:

(1) $a^2 + b^2 - c < 0$. Then no point (x, y) satisfies the equation; the locus is empty.

(2) $a^2 + b^2 - c = 0$. Then only $(x, y) = (a, b)$ satisfies the equation because the left side is positive for any other point; the locus is the single point (a, b).

(3) $a^2 + b^2 - c > 0$. Then we set $r = \sqrt{a^2 + b^2 - c}$, and the equation becomes

$$(x - a)^2 + (y - b)^2 = r^2.$$

The locus in this case is an honest circle.

EXAMPLE 2.1

Describe the set of points (x, y) that satisfy

(a) $x^2 + y^2 - 2x + 4y - 4 = 0,$

(b) $x^2 + y^2 - 2x + 4y + 5 = 0,$

(c) $x^2 + y^2 - 2x + 4y + 6 = 0.$

Solution: Complete the squares in x and y:

$$x^2 - 2x + y^2 + 4y = (x - 1)^2 + (y + 2)^2 - 5.$$

Hence, the three cases become

(a) $(x - 1)^2 + (y + 2)^2 = 9 = 3^2$

(b) $(x - 1)^2 + (y + 2)^2 = 0$

(c) $(x - 1)^2 + (y + 2)^2 = -1.$

> *Answer:*   (a)   circle; center $(1, -2)$, radius 3;
> (b)   single point: $(1, -2)$;
> (c)   empty locus.

Intersection of Line and Circle

Given a circle and a line, there are three possibilities: (1) they do not intersect, (2) they have exactly one common point—the line is a **tangent** to the circle, (3) they intersect in two distinct points.

From the equations of the circle and line, we can find explicitly the intersections (if any). The algebra is simplest if the circle has its center at the origin. Otherwise, we make a preliminary translation to move the origin to the center.

Suppose the equations are

$$\begin{cases} x^2 + y^2 = r^2 \\ ax + by = c, \quad a^2 + b^2 > 0. \end{cases}$$

We must solve the two equations simultaneously for their common solutions (x, y).

Either $a \neq 0$ or $b \neq 0$; assume $a \neq 0$ and multiply the first equation by a^2:

$$a^2x^2 + a^2y^2 = a^2r^2.$$

Substitute $c - by$ for ax; this eliminates x:

$$(c - by)^2 + a^2y^2 = a^2r^2, \quad (a^2 + b^2)y^2 - 2bcy + (c^2 - a^2r^2) = 0.$$

This is a quadratic equation for y; it has 0, 1, or 2 solutions, depending on the discriminant Δ.

If $\Delta < 0$, then there are no real solutions, hence no points of intersection. If $\Delta \geq 0$, solve for y by the quadratic formula, then find x from the relation $ax = c - by$. Note that if $\Delta = 0$, there is one point of intersection (tangency), and if $\Delta > 0$, there are two points of intersection. (In case $a = 0$, then $b \neq 0$ and a similar argument applies.)

> **EXAMPLE 2.2**
>
> Find the intersections of $x^2 + y^2 = 4$ and $x + 2y = 1$.

Solution: Replace x^2 by $(1 - 2y)^2$:

$$(1 - 2y)^2 + y^2 = 4, \quad 1 - 4y + 5y^2 = 4, \quad 5y^2 - 4y - 3 = 0.$$

The discriminant of the quadratic equation is

$$\Delta = (-4)^2 - 4(5)(-3) = 16 + 60 = 76 > 0.$$

There are two solutions:

$$y = \frac{4 \pm \sqrt{76}}{10} = \frac{4 \pm 2\sqrt{19}}{10} = \frac{2 \pm \sqrt{19}}{5}.$$

The corresponding values of x are

$$x = 1 - 2y = 1 - \tfrac{1}{5}(4 \pm 2\sqrt{19}) = \tfrac{1}{5}(1 \mp 2\sqrt{19}).$$

See Fig. 2.1.

Answer: $\tfrac{1}{5}(1 - 2\sqrt{19}, 2 + \sqrt{19})$; $\tfrac{1}{5}(1 + 2\sqrt{19}, 2 - \sqrt{19})$.

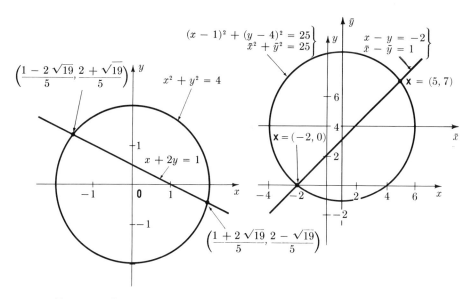

FIG. 2.1.   See Example 2.2.   FIG. 2.2.   See Example 2.3.

EXAMPLE 2.3

Find the intersection of $(x - 1)^2 + (y - 4)^2 = 25$ and $x - y = -2$.

Solution: Set $\bar{x} = x - 1$, $\bar{y} = y - 4$. Then the new equation of the circle is $\bar{x}^2 + \bar{y}^2 = 25$, and the new equation of the line is

$$(\bar{x} + 1) - (\bar{y} + 4) = -2; \quad \text{that is,} \quad \bar{x} - \bar{y} = 1.$$

Now solve the system of equations

$$\begin{cases} \bar{x}^2 + \bar{y}^2 = 25 \\ \bar{x} - \bar{y} = 1. \end{cases}$$

Eliminate $\bar{x}$:

$$(\bar{y} + 1)^2 + \bar{y}^2 = 25, \qquad 2\bar{y}^2 + 2\bar{y} - 24 = 0, \qquad \bar{y}^2 + \bar{y} - 12 = 0,$$
$$(\bar{y} + 4)(\bar{y} - 3) = 0, \qquad \bar{y} = -4, \qquad \bar{y} = 3.$$

The corresponding values of $\bar{x} = \bar{y} + 1$ are $\bar{x} = -3$ and $\bar{x} = 4$, so the two points of intersection are $(\bar{x}, \bar{y}) = (-3, -4), (4, 3)$. The (x, y) coordinates of these points are

$$(x, y) = (\bar{x} + 1, \bar{y} + 4) = (-2, 0), (5, 7).$$

See Fig. 2.2.

> *Answer:* $(-2, 0), (5, 7).$

REMARK: Example 2.3 can be solved without shifting axes. For instance x can be eliminated from the original pair of equations and the resulting quadratic solved for y. The computations involved are a bit longer.

Intersection of Two Circles

Given two non-concentric circles, find their intersection. To solve this problem, we shall reduce it to the previous problem of the intersection of a circle and a line. Let the equations of the circles be

(1) $$x^2 + y^2 - 2a_1 x - 2b_1 y = c_1,$$

(2) $$x^2 + y^2 - 2a_2 x - 2b_2 y = c_2.$$

The centers are (a_1, b_1) and (a_2, b_2) respectively, as can be seen by completing the squares. Subtract the two equations:

(3) $$2(a_1 - a_2)x + 2(b_1 - b_2)y = c_1 - c_2.$$

Because the circles are not concentric, $(a_1, b_1) \neq (a_2, b_2)$; hence $a_1 - a_2$ and $b_1 - b_2$ are not both 0, so (3) is the equation of a line L.

This line L intersects either circle in precisely the same points where the circles intersect each other. Why? Because the intersections of the circles are the simultaneous solutions of the equations (1) and (2). The intersections of L and the first circle are the simultaneous solutions of equations (1) and (3). In either case the answers are the same. For if (x, y) satisfies both (1) and (2), then (x, y) also satisfies (3), the difference of (1) and (2). Likewise if (x, y) satisfies (1) and (3), then (x, y) also satisfies (2), the difference of (1) and (3). Similarly, the intersections of L and the second circle are the same points.

Thus finding the intersection of two circles is equivalent to finding the intersection of a circle and a line. But we know how to do that!

EXAMPLE 2.4

Find the intersections of the circles

$$x^2 + y^2 = 25, \qquad x^2 + y^2 + 2x + 2y = 31.$$

Solution: Subtract the equations:

$$2x + 2y = 31 - 25 = 6, \qquad x + y = 3.$$

This is the equation of a line. To obtain its intersection with the first circle, solve the system

$$\begin{cases} x^2 + y^2 = 25 \\ x + y = 3. \end{cases}$$

Eliminate y:

$$x^2 + (3 - x)^2 = 25, \qquad 2x^2 - 6x - 16 = 0,$$

$$x^2 - 3x - 8 = 0, \qquad x = \tfrac{1}{2}(3 \pm \sqrt{41}).$$

The corresponding values of $y = 3 - x$ are $y = \tfrac{1}{2}(3 \mp \sqrt{41})$.

$$Answer: \quad \tfrac{1}{2}(3 + \sqrt{41}, 3 - \sqrt{41});$$
$$\tfrac{1}{2}(3 - \sqrt{41}, 3 + \sqrt{41}).$$

EXERCISES

Write the equation of the circle:

1. center $(1, 3)$, radius 6
2. center $(5, 12)$, radius 13
3. center $(-4, 3)$, radius 5
4. center $(-2, -1)$, radius 1
5. center $(1, 5)$, through $(0, 0)$
6. center $(3, 3)$, through $(-2, -4)$.
7. center $(-5, 2)$, tangent to y-axis
8. center $(1, 2)$, tangent to x-axis
9. diameter from $(0, 1)$ to $(3, 3)$
10. diameter from $(-2, -3)$ to $(4, 1)$.

Write the equation for the most general circle:

11. radius 3, tangent to x-axis
12. center in first quadrant, tangent to both axes
13. passing through $(0, 0)$
14. tangent to the line $y = 3$.

Describe the locus:

15. $x^2 + y^2 - 4x - 4y = 0$
16. $x^2 + y^2 - 6x = 0$
17. $x^2 + y^2 + 2x + 6y = 26$
18. $x^2 + y^2 - x + y = \frac{33}{2}$
19. $x^2 + y^2 - x + 2y = 0$
20. $x^2 + y^2 + 6x - 8y = 25$
21. $2x^2 + 2y^2 - 3x - 5y + 1 = 0$
22. $3x^2 + 3y^2 - x - y = 0$.

Find the intersection of the circle and the line:

23. $x^2 + y^2 = 9$, $y = x + 1$ 24. $x^2 + y^2 = 10$, $x + y = 1$

25. $x^2 + y^2 = 5$, $x + 2y = 5$ 26. $x^2 + y^2 = 6$, $y = 2x - 7$

27. $x^2 + y^2 - 4y - 2y + 4 = 0$,   28. $x^2 + y^2 + 4x + 5y = 0$,
     $2x - 5y = 6$ $x - 4y = 1$

29. circle with center $(1, 1)$ and radius 5, line through $(0, 2)$ and $(4, 0)$

30. circle with center at $(3, 4)$ and passing through $(0, 0)$, line through $(1, 1)$ parallel to $y = 3x$.

Find the point or points of intersection (if any) of the circles:

31. $x^2 + y^2 = 9$, $x^2 + y^2 + 8x + 12 = 0$

32. $x^2 + y^2 - 2x - 2y = 0$, $(x - 2)^2 + (y - 3)^2 = 4$

33. $x^2 + y^2 - 10x + 6y + 33 = 0$, $x^2 + y^2 + 2x + 4y - 4 = 0$

34. $(x - 1)^2 + (y - 2)^2 = \frac{5}{4}$, $(x - 3)^2 + (y - 6)^2 = \frac{45}{4}$.

For additional exercises on conics, see Section 9.

3. TANGENTS AND LOCI

Tangents

    A line tangent to a circle is perpendicular to the radius at the point of contact. This simple fact makes it easy to find the equation of the tangent to a circle at one of its points.

> **EXAMPLE 3.1**
>
> Find the equation of the tangent to the circle $x^2 + y^2 = 25$ at the point $(4, 3)$.

    Solution: The radius at the point of contact is the line segment from $(0, 0)$ to $(4, 3)$. It slope is $\frac{3}{4}$; the slope of the tangent is the negative reciprocal, $-\frac{4}{3}$. Thus the tangent passes through $(4, 3)$ and has slope $-\frac{4}{3}$. By the point-slope form, its equation is $y - 3 = -\frac{4}{3}(x - 4)$.

> *Answer:* $y = -\frac{4}{3}x + \frac{25}{3}$.

    The problem of finding the two tangent lines to a circle from an external point is slightly harder, but the basic idea is the same.

> **EXAMPLE 3.2**
>
> Find the two tangents to the circle $x^2 + y^2 = 4$ from the point $(3, 0)$.

    Solution: Suppose a tangent meets the circle at (x, y). Then the vectors (x, y) and $(x, y) - (3, 0)$ are perpendicular (Fig. 3.1).

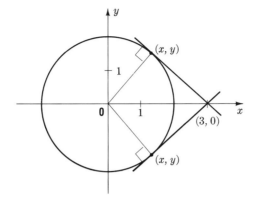

Fɪɢ. 3.1.   finding tangents from an external point

Hence

$$(x, y) \cdot [(x, y) - (3, 0)] = (x, y) \cdot (x - 3, y) = 0, \qquad x^2 + y^2 = 3x.$$

Therefore the points of contact satisfy two equations:

$$x^2 + y^2 = 4, \qquad x^2 + y^2 = 3x.$$

Subtract: $3x = 4$, $x = \frac{4}{3}$. Hence $y^2 = 4 - (\frac{4}{3})^2 = \frac{36}{9} - \frac{16}{9} = \frac{20}{9}$, $y = \pm \frac{2}{3}\sqrt{5}$.

Each tangent passes through $(3, 0)$ and one of the two points $(\frac{4}{3}, \pm \frac{2}{3}\sqrt{5})$. By the two-point form, the two equations are

$$\frac{y - 0}{x - 3} = \frac{\pm \frac{2}{3}\sqrt{5}}{\frac{4}{3} - 3} = \frac{\pm \frac{2}{3}\sqrt{5}}{-\frac{5}{3}} = \mp \frac{2}{5}\sqrt{5}.$$

Answer: $y \pm \frac{2}{5}\sqrt{5}(x - 3).$

REMARK: The algebra in the solution of Example 3.2 turned out to be fairly simple because $(3, 0)$ is on the x-axis. For an external point off the axes, the algebra will involve a quadratic equation for y.

Locus

Often a geometric figure is described as the set of all points that satisfy a certain condition. A figure specified in this way is called a **locus** (plural, **loci**). For example the locus of all points at a distance 3 from a fixed point **p** is a circle of radius 3 centered at **p**. The locus of all points equidistant from fixed points **p** and **q** is the perpendicular bisector of the segment **pq**. The locus of all points (x, y) for which $y = f(x)$ is the graph of the function $f(x)$.

EXAMPLE 3.3

Let **p** be a point and C a circle in the plane. Find the locus of the midpoint of the segment **pz** as **z** traces C.

Solution: The midpoint of **pz** is $\mathbf{x} = \frac{1}{2}(\mathbf{p} + \mathbf{z})$. It follows that $\mathbf{z} = 2\mathbf{x} - \mathbf{p}$. But **z** satisfies the equation of the circle, $\|\mathbf{z} - \mathbf{a}\| = r$, where **a** is the center and r the radius. Hence **x** satisfies $\|(2\mathbf{x} - \mathbf{p}) - \mathbf{a}\| = r$. Rearrange the left side and factor out 2:

$$\|(2\mathbf{x} - \mathbf{p}) - \mathbf{a}\| = \|2\mathbf{x} - (\mathbf{p} + \mathbf{a})\| = 2\|\mathbf{x} - \tfrac{1}{2}(\mathbf{p} + \mathbf{a})\| = r.$$

Hence

$$\|\mathbf{x} - \tfrac{1}{2}(\mathbf{p} + \mathbf{a})\| = \tfrac{1}{2}r.$$

> *Answer:*   A circle of radius $\frac{1}{2}r$ with center the midpoint of **ap**, where r is the radius and **a** the center of C. See Fig. 3.2.

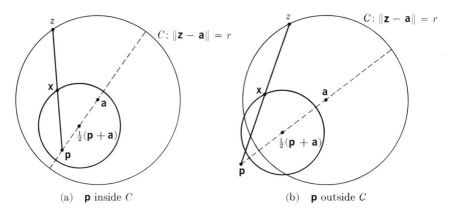

(a)   **p** inside C (b)   **p** outside C

FIG. 3.2.   locus of $\mathbf{x} = \frac{1}{2}(\mathbf{p} + \mathbf{z})$, for **z** on C

REMARK: Example 3.3 illustrates a basic technique in locus problems. The point **x** that generates the locus is usually related to a point **z** that satisfies a known equation (locus). Express **z** in terms of **x**, then substitute into the equation for **z**. This yields an equation for **x**.

> **EXAMPLE 3.4**
>
> Let **z** trace the curve $y = x^2$. Find the locus of the point **x** that is $\frac{1}{3}$ of the way from $(-6, 0)$ to **z**.

Solution: This is precisely the kind of situation we just discussed. Here **z** traces the curve $y = x^2$, so we can write $\mathbf{z} = (z, w)$, where $w = z^2$. We write $\mathbf{x} = (x, y)$ and seek the relation between x and y. [Note carefully the change in notation. You cannot write *both* $\mathbf{x} = (x, y)$ *and* $\mathbf{z} = (x, y)$ because **x** and **z** are completely different points. So if you want the answer in x and y, you *must* give the coordinates of **z** some other names.] By the rule for division of a segment (p. 40),

$$\mathbf{x} = \tfrac{2}{3}(-6, 0) + \tfrac{1}{3}\mathbf{z},$$

hence

$$\mathbf{z} = 3\mathbf{x} - 2(-6, 0), \qquad (z, w) = 3(x, y) - 2(-6, 0),$$

$$z = 3x + 12, \qquad w = 3y.$$

Now substitute into $w = z^2$:

$$3y = (3x + 12)^2 = 9(x + 4)^2, \qquad y = 3(x + 4)^2.$$

Answer: The curve $y = 3(x + 4)^2$.

EXAMPLE 3.5

Let **p** lie inside a circle C. Find the locus of the midpoints of all chords through **p**.

Solution: Take axes so that **p** is at the origin and C is the circle $(x - a)^2 + y^2 = r^2$ with $0 < a < r$. A chord through **0** meets the circle at two points (x_1, y_1) and (x_2, y_2). Its midpoint is $(\frac{1}{2}(x_1 + x_2), \frac{1}{2}(y_1 + y_2))$. See Fig. 3.3a.

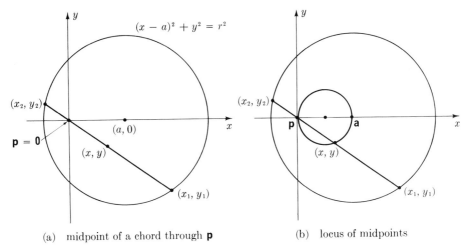

(a)   midpoint of a chord through **p**   (b)   locus of midpoints

Fɪɢ. 3.3

A typical line through **0** is $y = mx$. Hence (x_1, y_1) and (x_2, y_2) are solutions of the system

$$\begin{cases} y = mx \\ (x - a)^2 + y^2 = r^2. \end{cases}$$

Substitute the first equation into the second and rearrange:

$$(x - a)^2 + m^2 x^2 = r^2, \qquad (1 + m^2)x^2 - 2ax + (a^2 - r^2) = 0.$$

Since we do not need x_1 and x_2 separately but only their sum, we use the fact that the sum of the roots of $ax^2 + bx + c = 0$ is $-b/a$, as follows from the quadratic formula. Apply this to the quadratic above:

$$x_1 + x_2 = \frac{2a}{1 + m^2}.$$

Since $y = mx$,

$$y_1 + y_2 = m(x_1 + x_2) = \frac{2am}{1 + m^2}.$$

Therefore, for each real number m, the chord through **0** has midpoint

$$(x, y) = \left(\frac{x_1 + x_2}{2}, \frac{y_1 + y_2}{2}\right) = \left(\frac{a}{1 + m^2}, \frac{am}{1 + m^2}\right).$$

To find the locus of (x, y) eliminate the parameter m. The quickest way is to observe that

$$x^2 + y^2 = \frac{a^2 + (am)^2}{(1 + m^2)^2} = \frac{a^2(1 + m^2)}{(1 + m^2)^2} = a\frac{a}{1 + m^2} = ax,$$

$$x^2 + y^2 - ax = 0.$$

Complete the square:

$$(x - \tfrac{1}{2}a)^2 + y^2 = (\tfrac{1}{2}a)^2.$$

Answer: The circle with diameter **pa**, where **a** is the center of the given circle C. See Fig. 3.3b.

EXERCISES

Find the tangent to $x^2 + y^2 = 1$ at

1. $(-1, 0)$ 2. $(0, -1)$ 3. $(\tfrac{1}{2}\sqrt{2}, -\tfrac{1}{2}\sqrt{2})$
4. $(-\tfrac{1}{2}\sqrt{2}, -\tfrac{1}{2}\sqrt{2})$ 5. $(\tfrac{1}{2}\sqrt{3}, \tfrac{1}{2})$ 6. $(-\tfrac{1}{2}, \tfrac{1}{2}\sqrt{3})$.

7. Find the tangents to $(x - 1)^2 + (y - 2)^2 = 1$ that pass through $(0, 0)$.
8. Find the tangents to $x^2 + y^2 = 1$ that pass through $(2, 2)$.
9. Find the tangents to $x^2 + y^2 = 13$ that pass through $(-5, 1)$.
10. Find the tangents to $(x - 1)^2 + y^2 = 1$ that pass through $(0, -2)$.
11. Show that the circles $x^2 + y^2 - 2x - 4y - 6\tfrac{1}{4} = 0$ and $x^2 + y^2 - 6x - 12y + 43\tfrac{3}{4} = 0$ are tangent. [Hint: compute the distance between their centers.]
12*. Find all common tangents to the circles $x^2 - 2x + y^2 = 0$ and $x^2 + 4x + y^2 = 0$.
13. Show that the tangent to the circle $x^2 + y^2 = r^2$ at a point (x_0, y_0) on the circle is $x_0 x + y_0 y = r^2$.
14. (cont.) Show that the tangent to $(x - a)^2 + (y - b)^2 = r^2$ at a point (x_0, y_0) on the circle is $(x_0 - a)(x - a) + (y_0 - b)(y - b) = r^2$.
15. Let **a** and **b** be points and c a positive number. Show that the vector equation $(\mathbf{x} - \mathbf{a}) \cdot (\mathbf{x} - \mathbf{b}) = c^2$ defines a circle. Find its center and radius.

16. Let $\mathbf{a}_1$, $\mathbf{a}_2$, $\mathbf{a}_3$, $\mathbf{a}_4$ be points and c a number. Show that

$$\|\mathbf{x} - \mathbf{a}_1\|^2 + \|\mathbf{x} - \mathbf{a}_2\|^2 + \|\mathbf{x} - \mathbf{a}_3\|^2 + \|\mathbf{x} - \mathbf{a}_4\|^2 = c^2$$

is the equation of a circle provided c is sufficiently large. Find the center of the circle.

17. A 10-ft ladder leans against a wall, and its foot slides along the floor as its top slides down the wall. Find the locus of its midpoint.

18. Find the locus of the midpoints of all chords of length 6 of a circle of radius 5.

19. At each point of a circle of radius 1 is drawn a segment of length 3, tangent at one end to the circle. Find the locus of the other ends of the segments.

20. Find the locus of all points whose distance from $(0,0)$ is twice the distance from $(3, 4)$.

4. POLAR COORDINATES

There are situations with radial symmetry for which the usual rectangular coordinate system is less useful than another coordinate system called **polar coordinates.**

In a rectangular coordinate system, two families of grid lines, $x = $ constant and $y = $ constant, fill the plane. Each point $\mathbf{x}$ is the intersection of two of these lines, $x = a$ and $y = b$, and receives the coordinates (a, b). See Fig. 4.1.

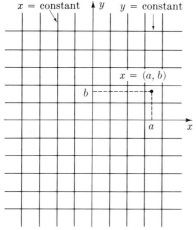

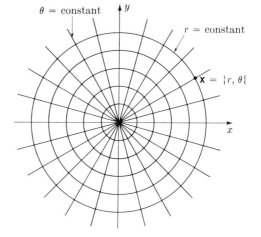

Fig. 4.1.   two families of grid lines:
$x = $ constant and
$y = $ constant

Fig. 4.2.   two families of grid lines:
$r = $ constant and
$\theta = $ constant

Polar coordinates work on a similar principle. The grid lines are (1) all circles centered at **0**, and (2) all rays from **0**. See Fig. 4.2. Each point $\mathbf{x}$

different from **0** is the intersection of one circle and one ray. The circle is identified by a positive number r, its radius, and the ray is identified by a real number θ, its angle in radians from the positive x-axis. Thus **x** is assigned the **polar coordinates** $\{r, \theta\}$. Since θ is determined only up to a multiple of 2π, we agree that

$$\{r, \theta + 2\pi n\} = \{r, \theta\} \qquad (n \text{ any integer}).$$

The point **0** does not determine an angle θ. Nonetheless, it is customary to say that *any* pair $\{0, \theta\}$ represents **0**.

The idea of polar coordinates is quite natural. You identify a point by telling how far it is from here, and in what direction. (This is the principle of the radar screen.)

Given the polar coordinates $\{r, \theta\}$ of a point, what are its rectangular coordinates? The point lies on the circle $x^2 + y^2 = r^2$ in the direction θ. Hence $x = r \cos \theta$, $y = r \sin \theta$. See Fig. 4.3a.

Conversely, given the rectangular coordinates (x, y), what are the polar coordinates? Figure 4.3b shows that $r = \sqrt{x^2 + y^2}$, and that $\cos \theta = x/r$ and $\sin \theta = y/r$.

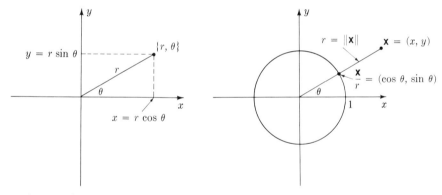

(a) $\{r, \theta\}$ determines x and y (b)   **x** determines r and $(\cos \theta, \sin \theta)$

FIG. 4.3

Polar to rectangular	Rectangular to polar
$\begin{cases} x = r \cos \theta \\ y = r \sin \theta \end{cases}$	$\begin{cases} r = \sqrt{x^2 + y^2} \\ \cos \theta = \dfrac{x}{\sqrt{x^2 + y^2}} = \dfrac{x}{r} \\ \sin \theta = \dfrac{y}{\sqrt{x^2 + y^2}} = \dfrac{y}{r} \end{cases}$

EXAMPLE 4.1

(a) Convert $(2, -2\sqrt{3})$ to polar coordinates.
(b) Convert $\{3, \frac{1}{6}\pi\}$ to rectangular coordinates.

Solution: (a) $r^2 = 4 + 12 = 16, r = 4.$ Also $\cos\theta = \frac{2}{4} = \frac{1}{2}$ and $\sin\theta = \frac{1}{4}(-2\sqrt{3}) = -\frac{1}{2}\sqrt{3},$ so $\theta = \frac{5}{3}\pi.$

(b) $x = r\cos\theta = 3\cos\frac{1}{6}\pi = \frac{3}{2}\sqrt{3},$ and $y = r\sin\theta = 3\sin\frac{1}{6}\pi = \frac{3}{2}.$

Answer: (a) $\{4, \frac{5}{3}\pi\},$ (b) $(\frac{3}{2}\sqrt{3}, \frac{3}{2}).$

Negative r

In applications it is convenient to allow points $\{r, \theta\}$ with $r < 0.$ For example, consider a ray and a point $\{r, \theta\}$ on the ray (Fig. 4.4a). Suppose the point moves towards **0**, through **0**, and keeps on going! Then r decreases, becomes 0, but then what? So that θ won't jump abruptly to $\theta + \pi$, we agree that θ remains constant, but r becomes negative. This amounts to agreeing that

$$\{-r, \theta\} = \{r, \theta + \pi\}.$$

See Fig. 4.4b.

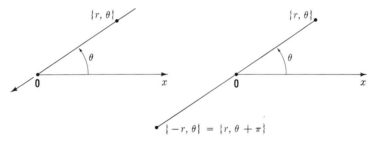

(a) Hold θ fixed and move $\{r, \theta\}$ through the origin.

(b) Identify $\{-r, \theta\}$ and $\{r, \theta + \pi\}.$

Fɪɢ. 4.4

Graphs of Equations

Each curve $r = c$ is a circle with center **0**, except for $c = 0.$ Each curve $\theta = \theta_0$ is a line through the origin (Fig. 4.5).

What is the equation in polar coordinates for a line not necessarily through the origin? Take a line in normal form

$$x\cos\alpha + y\sin\alpha = p.$$

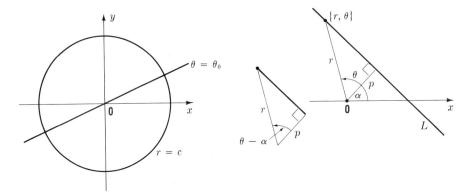

F<small>IG</small>. 4.5.   graphs of $r = c$ and
$\theta = \theta_0$

F<small>IG</small>. 4.6.   The projection of the typical point $\{r, \theta\}$ of L on the perpendicular is $p = r \cos(\theta - \alpha)$.

Replace x by $r \cos \theta$ and y by $r \sin \theta$:

$$r \cos \theta \cos \alpha + r \sin \theta \sin \alpha = p.$$

But $\cos \theta \cos \alpha + \sin \theta \sin \alpha = \cos(\theta - \alpha)$, therefore:

> The equation in polar coordinates of the general straight line is
> $$r \cos(\theta - \alpha) = p.$$

This result makes sense geometrically; Fig. 4.6 shows the case $p > 0$. Note that the line is perpendicular to the ray $\theta = \alpha$.

R<small>EMARK</small>:   From the right triangle in Fig. 4.6 we have $r \cos(\theta - \alpha) = p$. As noted above, we also have $r(\cos \theta \cos \alpha + \sin \theta \sin \alpha) = p$. Combined, these facts provide a proof of the addition formula for the cosine.

Consider next the circle of radius a and center $(a, 0)$. Its Cartesian equation is

$$(x - a^2) + y^2 = a^2,$$

that is,

$$x^2 + y^2 = 2ax.$$

Substitute $x = r \cos \theta$ and $y = r \sin \theta$:

$$r^2 = 2ar \cos \theta.$$

If $r \neq 0$, then $r = 2a \cos \theta$. But $r = 0$ represents only the point $\mathbf{0}$, which is already on the locus $r = 2a \cos \theta$ for $\theta = \tfrac{1}{2}\pi$. Hence canceling r does not change the locus, so

$$r = 2a \cos \theta$$

is the polar equation of the given circle. The right triangle in Fig. 4.7 shows that the relation $r = 2a \cos \theta$ is satisfied by every point on the circle.

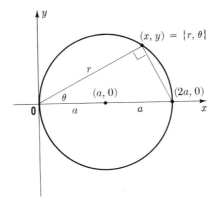

FIG. 4.7. circle of radius a, tangent to the y-axis at **0**

How does $\{r, \theta\}$ move on the circle $r = 2a \cos \theta$ as θ makes a complete revolution? If θ starts at 0, then r starts at $2a$. If θ increases to $\frac{1}{2}\pi$, then r decreases to 0. (Think of an arm rotating counterclockwise and shrinking.) Hence $\{r, \theta\}$ traces the upper half of the circle (Fig. 4.8a).

If θ increases from $\frac{1}{2}\pi$ to π, then r decreases from 0 to $-2a$. Since r is negative, the point $\{r, \theta\}$ is measured "backwards" and moves through the *fourth* quadrant, tracing the lower half of the circle (Fig. 4.8b).

Thus the full circle is described as θ runs from 0 to π. As θ runs from π to 2π, the same circle is traced again. For when θ is in the third quadrant, $r < 0$, so $\{r, \theta\}$ describes the semicircle in the first quadrant; when θ is in the fourth quadrant $r > 0$, so $\{r, \theta\}$ describes the semicircle in the fourth quadrant. Therefore, in one complete revolution of θ, the circle is traced twice.

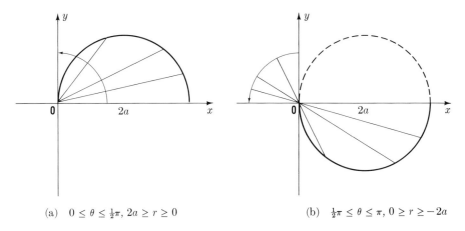

(a) $0 \le \theta \le \frac{1}{2}\pi, 2a \ge r \ge 0$ (b) $\frac{1}{2}\pi \le \theta \le \pi, 0 \ge r \ge -2a$

FIG. 4.8. circle traced by $\{r, \theta\}$ in a half revolution of θ

The graph of the equation

$$r = 2a \cos \theta$$

is a circle of radius a and center $\{a, 0\}$. The circle is traced twice as θ makes a complete revolution.

Graphs of Functions

Graphing a function $r = f(\theta)$ in polar coordinates is tricky at first, because you must change your point of view. For $y = f(x)$, you think of x running along the horizontal axis, with the corresponding point (x, y) measured above or below. Basically your mental set is "left–right" and "up–down".

In polar coordinates, however, you must think of the angle θ swinging around (like a radar scope) and repeating after 2π. For each θ, you must measure forward from the origin a distance $f(\theta)$, or backward if $f(\theta) < 0$. Your mental set must be "round and round", "in and out", "forward or backward".

Because of the special nature of points $\{r, \theta\}$ where $r < 0$, pay close attention to the sign of $f(\theta)$ and be sure to plot points "backwards" if $f(\theta) < 0$.

Look for symmetries and periodicity. For example if $f(\theta + 2\pi) = f(\theta)$, the polar graph $r = f(\theta)$ will repeat after 2π. There are many symmetries possible; we mention only two, $f(\theta)$ even and $f(\theta)$ odd. If $f(\theta)$ is even, that is, $f(-\theta) = f(\theta)$, then the point $\{r, -\theta\}$ is on the graph whenever $\{r, \theta\}$ is.

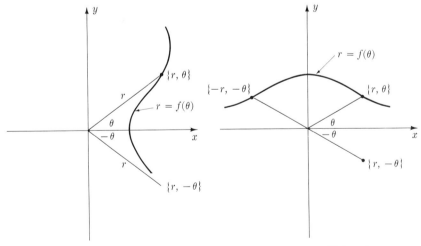

(a) graph of an even function:
$f(-\theta) = f(\theta)$

(b) graph of an odd function:
$f(-\theta) = -f(\theta)$

Fig. 4.9

The curve is symmetric in the x-axis (Fig. 4.9a). If $f(\theta)$ is odd, $f(-\theta) = -f(\theta)$, then the point $\{-r, -\theta\}$ is on the graph whenever $\{r, \theta\}$ is. The curve is symmetric in the vertical axis (Fig. 4.9b).

EXAMPLE 4.2

Graph the "spiral of Archimedes" $r = \theta$.

Solution: As θ increases from 0 we see that r increases steadily. Hence the locus goes round and round, its distance from **0** greater and greater. The result is a spiral (Fig. 4.10a). Since $f(\theta) = \theta$ is an odd function, we obtain the locus for $\theta < 0$ by reflection in the vertical axis (Fig. 4.10b).

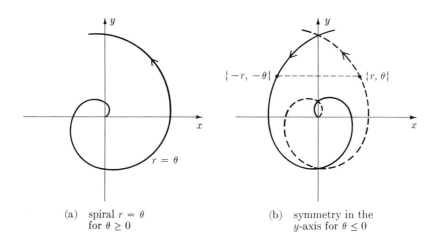

(a) spiral $r = \theta$
    for $\theta \geq 0$

(b) symmetry in the
    y-axis for $\theta \leq 0$

FIG. 4.10

EXAMPLE 4.3

Graph the "rose" $r = a \cos 2\theta$ where $a > 0$.

Solution: Since $\cos 2(\theta + 2\pi) = \cos 2\theta$, the curve repeats every 2π, so we need plot it only for $0 \leq \theta \leq 2\pi$.

Since the sign of $\cos 2\theta$ fluctuates, it is advisable to make a preliminary sketch showing the proper sign (Fig. 4.11a). As θ starts at 0 and increases to $\frac{1}{4}\pi$, we see that $\cos 2\theta$ starts at 1 and decreases to 0. Since $\cos 2\theta$ is an even function, this part of the graph is repeated below forming a loop (Fig. 4.11b).

As θ increases from $\frac{1}{4}\pi$ to $\frac{1}{2}\pi$ to $\frac{3}{4}\pi$, we see that $\cos 2\theta$ is negative and goes from 0 to -1 and back to 0. Thus we get another loop, but between $\frac{3}{4}\pi$ and $\frac{1}{4}\pi$. See Fig. 4.12a. For θ going from $\frac{3}{4}\pi$ to $\frac{5}{4}\pi$, we get a third loop plotted forward, and from $\frac{5}{4}\pi$ to $\frac{7}{4}\pi$ a fourth loop plotted backwards. The complete graph is shown in Fig. 4.12b.

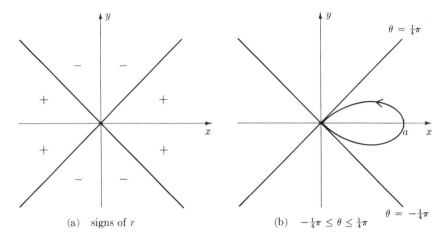

(a)   signs of r (b) $-\frac{1}{4}\pi \le \theta \le \frac{1}{4}\pi$

Fɪɢ. 4.11.   partial graph of $r = a \cos 2\theta$

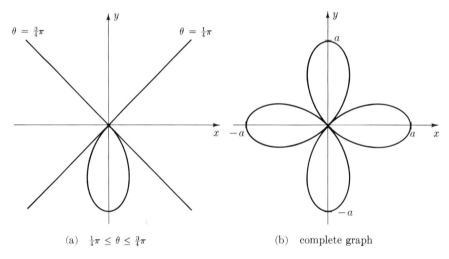

(a) $\frac{1}{4}\pi \le \theta \le \frac{3}{4}\pi$ (b)   complete graph

Fɪɢ. 4.12.   continuation of $r = a \cos 2\theta$

Hindsight: It is necessary to plot only one of the petals in Fig. 4.12b. Since $\cos(\theta + \pi) = -\cos \theta$, we have $\cos 2(\theta + \frac{1}{2}\pi) = -\cos 2\theta$. Thus $\cos 2\theta$ repeats itself negatively after $\frac{1}{2}\pi$. We conclude that the first loop we plotted (for $-\frac{1}{4}\pi \le \theta \le \frac{1}{4}\pi$) is repeated negatively as θ continues from $\frac{1}{4}\pi$ to $\frac{3}{4}\pi$. In other words, rotate the first loop *backwards* by $\frac{1}{2}\pi$; the result is another loop of the curve. Rotate again, and once again, and you have generated the whole curve.

For an accurate picture of the petals, plot some points. One thing we can say without plotting; the petals are rounded at their ends, not pointed.

That stems from a property of the cosine: for small angles, $\cos 2\theta$ is very close to 1. Hence for θ small (near the tip of the petal to the right) the curve $r = a \cos 2\theta$ looks like the circle $r = a$.

Rotation

Rotation is much easier in polar coordinates than in rectangular coordinates. If the polar axis is rotated through an angle α, a point $\{r, \theta\}$ acquires new polar coordinates $\{r', \theta'\}$. The relation between the new and old coordinates of a point are seen directly from Fig. 4.13.

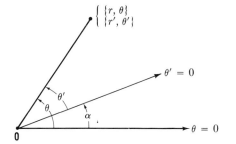

FIG. 4.13.   rotation of polar axis   FIG. 4.14.   polar equation of line

Since **0** is unchanged, $r' = r$. From Fig. 4.13 we see that $\theta' = \theta - \alpha$.

> If the polar axis is rotated by an angle α, a point $\{r, \theta\}$ acquires the new coordinates $\{r', \theta'\}$, where
> $$r' = r, \qquad \theta' = \theta - \alpha.$$

As an application, let us find the polar equation of the line L that is p units from the origin, perpendicular to the ray $\theta = \alpha$. See Fig. 4.14. Relative to the tilted axis, the line has equation $x' = p$ or $r' \cos \theta' = p$. Its r, θ-equation therefore is $r \cos(\theta - \alpha) = p$. This is a quick derivation of the result given on p. 76.

EXERCISES

Express in rectangular coordinates:

1. $\{1, \frac{1}{2}\pi\}$ 2. $\{1, -\frac{1}{2}\pi\}$ 3. $\{1, -\frac{1}{6}\pi\}$

4. $\{1, \frac{1}{3}\pi\}$ 5. $\{2, -\frac{3}{4}\pi\}$ 6. $\{2, \frac{5}{4}\pi\}$.

Express in polar coordinates:

7. $(1, 1)$ 8. $(0, -1)$ 9. $(-1, 1)$

10. $(-\frac{1}{2}, \frac{1}{2}\sqrt{3})$ 11. $(\sqrt{3}, -1)$ 12. $(\sqrt{2}, -\sqrt{2})$.

Find the equation in polar coordinates:

13. line through **0** and $\{3, \frac{1}{4}\pi\}$ 14. circle, center **0**, radius 5

15. line through $\{1, 0\}$ and $\{1, \frac{1}{2}\pi\}$ 16. line perpendicular to $\theta = \frac{3}{4}\pi$, tangent to circle $r = 1$

17. circle, center $\{a, \pi\}$, radius a 18. circle, center $\{a, \frac{1}{2}\pi\}$, radius a

19. circle through **0**, center $\{1, \frac{1}{2}\pi\}$ 20. circle through **0**, center $\{2, \frac{1}{4}\pi\}$.

Graph:

21. $r = 2 \sin 2\theta$ 22. the "rose" $r = \sin 5\theta$

23. $r = \cos 3\theta$ 24. $r = -\cos 4\theta$

25. $r = \theta^2$ 26. the "lemniscate" $r^2 = \cos 2\theta$

27. the "cissoid" $r = \sec \theta - \cos \theta$ 28. the "strophoid" $r = \cos 2\theta \sec \theta$
    $= \sin \theta \tan \theta$

29. the "cardioid" $r = 1 - \cos \theta$ 30. the "limaçon" $r = 2 + \cos \theta$

31. the "limaçon" $r = 1 + 2 \cos \theta$.   32*. Discuss the general case of
$$r = a + b \cos \theta, \quad a > 0, \quad b > 0.$$
$$[Hint: \text{ Use Exs. 30, 31.}]$$

33. Graph the "conchoid" $r = \csc \theta - 2$ 34. Graph the "bifolium" $r = \sin \theta \cos^2 \theta$.
    for $0 < \theta < \pi$.

35. Use trigonometry to prove
$$\|\{r_1, \theta_1\} - \{r_2, \theta_2\}\|^2 = r_1{}^2 + r_2{}^2 - 2r_1 r_2 \cos(\theta_1 - \theta_2).$$

36. (cont.) Use the distance formula to do Ex. 35.

5. CONICS; THE PARABOLA

The ancient Greek geometers discovered that on cutting a right circular cone by various planes, they obtained three types of remarkable curves called **conic sections,** or **conics.** Please look at Fig. 5.1.

A special case of the ellipse is a circle, obtained by cutting the cone by a plane parallel to its base.

A section of the cone by a plane through its apex is called a **degenerate conic** (Fig. 5.2).

It is possible to define the conic sections as certain geometric loci. We shall do so because this is less complicated than starting from plane sections of a cone.

The Parabola

A **parabola** is the locus of all points equidistant from a fixed line D and a fixed point **p** not on D. We call D the **directrix** and **p** the **focus** of the parabola.

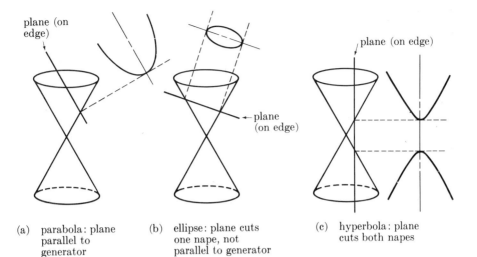

(a) parabola: plane parallel to generator

(b) ellipse: plane cuts one nape, not parallel to generator

(c) hyperbola: plane cuts both napes

Fɪɢ. 5.1.   conic sections (conics)

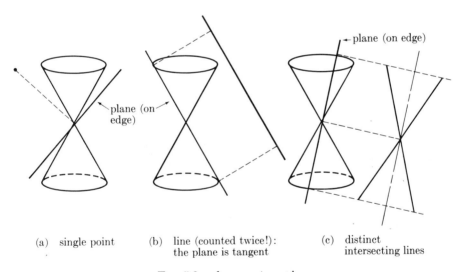

(a)   single point

(b)   line (counted twice!): the plane is tangent

(c)   distinct intersecting lines

Fɪɢ. 5.2.   degenerate conics

To find the equation of a parabola, choose the coordinate system (Fig. 5.3a) so that $\mathbf{p} = (0, p)$ and D is the line $y = -p$.

By definition, a point (x, y) is on the parabola if and only if

$$\|(x, y) - (0, p)\| = \|(x, y) - (x, -p)\|.$$

Carry out the subtractions and square:

$$\|(x, y - p)\|^2 = \|(0, y + p)\|^2, \qquad x^2 + (y - p)^2 = (y + p)^2,$$

$$x^2 + y^2 - 2py + p^2 = y^2 + 2py + p^2, \qquad x^2 = 4py.$$

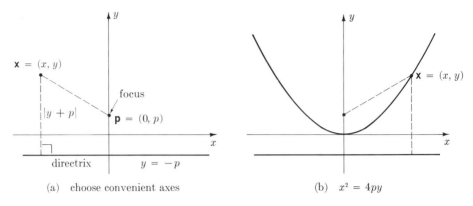

(a)   choose convenient axes   (b) $x^2 = 4py$

FIG. 5.3.   equation of parabola

The steps can be read backwards; therefore if $x^2 = 4py$, then (x, y) is a point of the parabola.

> The equation of the parabola with focus $(0, p)$ and directrix $y = -p$ is
>
> $$y = \frac{1}{4p} x^2.$$

The curve is shown in Fig. 5.3b.

We see from the equation that for our choice of axes, the parabola is the graph of a quadratic polynomial. Conversely, the graph of any quadratic polynomial $y = ax^2 + bx + c$ (with $a \neq 0$) is a parabola. To prove this, complete the square:

$$y = a(x - h)^2 + k,$$

where h and k are easily determined. Then translate axes by $\bar{x} = x - h$, $\bar{y} = y - k$. The result is $\bar{y} = a\bar{x}^2$, a parabola with $4p = 1/a$.

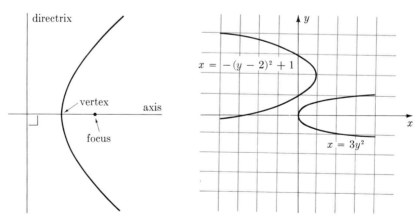

FIG. 5.4.   axis and vertex   FIG. 5.5.   parabolas with horizontal axes

The line through the focus perpendicular to the directrix is called the **axis** of the parabola. The point of intersection of the axis with the parabola is the **vertex** of the parabola (Fig. 5.4).

By interchanging the roles of x and y, we see that a parabola whose axis is parallel to the x-axis is the locus of an equation $x = ay^2 + by + c$. Some examples are shown in Fig. 5.5.

REMARK: If the inside of a parabola is a mirror, then each ray from the focus will be reflected to a ray parallel to the axis. This important focal property explains why headlight reflectors, telescope mirrors, and directional antennas are parabolic.

Parabolas arise in many locus problems. Here is an example.

EXAMPLE 5.1

Find the locus of all points **x** whose distance to the y-axis equals the length of the tangent(s) from **x** to the circle $(x - 1)^2 + y^2 = 1$.

Solution: Draw a careful figure (Fig. 5.6). The condition on the distances is

$$\sqrt{[(x - 1)^2 + y^2] - 1} = x.$$

Simplify:

$$(x - 1)^2 + y^2 - 1 = x^2, \qquad -2x + y^2 = 0, \qquad y^2 = 2x.$$

Answer: The parabola $y^2 = 2x$

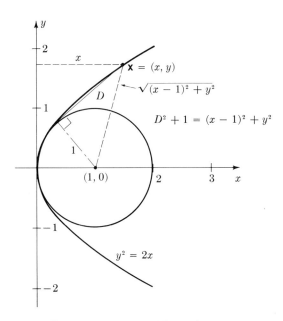

FIG. 5.6. set-up for Example 5.1

Sketch the parabola and locate the focus, directrix, axis, and vertex:

1. $y = x^2$
2. $x = 2y^2$
3. $x = -3y^2$
4. $y = -\frac{1}{2}x^2$
5. $x - 3 = 3y^2$
6. $x + 2 = -y^2$
7. $x = 2(y + 1)^2$
8. $2y = -3(x - 2)^2$
9. $x^2 + 4x - 6y = 0$
10. $2y^2 - 4y + x + 2 = 0$.

Find the equation of the parabola:

11. vertex $(0, 0)$, through the point $(1, 3)$, axis vertical
12. vertex $(0, 0)$, through the point $(6, -1)$, axis vertical
13. vertex $(1, 2)$, through the point $(-3, 4)$, axis horizontal
14. vertex $(-5, 0)$, through the point $(C, 8)$, axis horizontal
15. vertex $(2, -3)$, focus $(2, 1)$
16. vertex $(2, -3)$, focus $(10, -3)$.

17. The line $y - 1 = -2(x - 1)$ intersects the parabola $y = x^2$ in two points. One of them is $(1, 1)$; find the other.

18. Does the point $(3, 7)$ lie inside or outside the parabola $y = x^2$? How can you tell without plotting the point?

19. Sketch the family of parabolas $4py = x^2 - 4p^2$ for $p > 0$. Locate their foci. Now sketch the family for $p < 0$.

20. (cont.) Show that no two of the curves for $p > 0$ intersect.

21. Let (x_0, y_0) be a point on the parabola $4ay = x^2$. Show that the line $2a(y + y_0) = x_0 x$ meets the parabola only in (x_0, y_0). Interpret.

22. Find the locus of $(x, y) = (2at, at^2)$, where $-\infty < t < \infty$.

23. Show that the equation in polar coordinates of the parabola with focus at $\mathbf{0}$ and directrix $x = -p$ is $r(1 - \cos \theta) = p$.

24. (cont.) Find the polar equation of the parabola with focus at $\mathbf{0}$ and directrix $x + y = -1$.

25. A shell fired with speed v_0 ft/sec at angle α with the ground will have coordinates

$$x = (v_0 \cos \alpha)t, \qquad y = (v_0 \sin \alpha)t - 16t^2$$

after t seconds (if air drag is ignored). Show that the trajectory is a parabolic arc.

26. (cont.) Find the highest point on the trajectory.

6. THE ELLIPSE

An **ellipse** is the locus of all points $\mathbf{x}$ such that the sum of the distances of $\mathbf{x}$ from two fixed points $\mathbf{p}$ and $\mathbf{q}$ is a constant greater than $\|\mathbf{p} - \mathbf{q}\|$. The points $\mathbf{p}$ and $\mathbf{q}$ are the **foci** (plural of focus) of the ellipse.

To find an equation for the ellipse, choose axes so $\mathbf{p} = (-c, 0)$ and $\mathbf{q} = (c, 0)$, and let the distance sum by $2a$. (Because $\mathbf{p}, \mathbf{q}, \mathbf{x}$ form a triangle, $2a > \|\mathbf{p} - \mathbf{q}\| = 2c$, so $a > c$.) See Fig. 6.1.

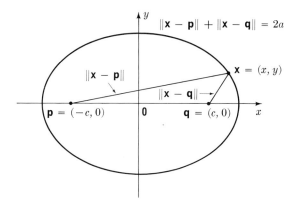

$$\|\mathbf{x} - \mathbf{p}\| + \|\mathbf{x} - \mathbf{q}\| = 2a$$

FIG. 6.1.   definition of ellipse

A point $\mathbf{x}$ is on the ellipse if and only if

$$\|\mathbf{x} - \mathbf{p}\| + \|\mathbf{x} - \mathbf{q}\| = 2a,$$

that is,

$$\sqrt{(x + c)^2 + y^2} + \sqrt{(x - c)^2 + y^2} = 2a.$$

To simplify this equation, set

$$\sqrt{(x + c)^2 + y^2} - \sqrt{(x - c)^2 + y^2} = 2k.$$

Multiply the two preceding equations, then add them:

$$\left\{ \begin{array}{l} [(x + c)^2 + y^2] - [(x - c)^2 + y^2] = 4ak, \\ \qquad 2\sqrt{(x + c)^2 + y^2} = 2(a + k). \end{array} \right.$$

From the first result,

$$4cx = 4ak, \qquad k = \frac{cx}{a}.$$

From the second,

$$\sqrt{(x + c)^2 + y^2} = a + k = a + \frac{cx}{a} = \frac{a^2 + cx}{a}.$$

Multiply by a, square, and simplify:

$$a^2[(x + c)^2 + y^2] = (a^2 + cx)^2,$$
$$a^2(x^2 + 2cx + c^2 + y^2) = a^4 + 2a^2cx + c^2x^2,$$
$$a^2x^2 + a^2c^2 + a^2y^2 = a^4 + c^2x^2,$$
$$(a^2 - c^2)x^2 + a^2y^2 = a^4 - a^2c^2 = a^2(a^2 - c^2).$$

Define a positive number b by $a^2 = b^2 + c^2$. This is possible because $a > c$.

Then the last formula becomes

$$b^2x^2 + a^2y^2 = a^2b^2, \qquad \frac{x^2}{a^2} + \frac{y^2}{b^2} = 1.$$

The equation of the ellipse with foci $(-c, 0)$ and $(c, 0)$ and length sum $2a$ is

$$\frac{x^2}{a^2} + \frac{y^2}{b^2} = 1,$$

where $b^2 = a^2 - c^2$.

We have proved only part of this statement: if (x, y) is a point on the ellipse, then (x, y) satisfies the equation. It is not obvious that the proof can be reversed, because one step required squaring; taking square roots might introduce an incorrect sign. (Because $1^2 = (-1)^2$ we do *not* deduce $1 = -1$.) However, with care the proof can be reversed; we postpone this until Exs. 23–26.

Let us carefully examine the locus of

$$\frac{x^2}{a^2} + \frac{y^2}{b^2} = 1 \qquad (a^2 = b^2 + c^2).$$

The equation implies

$$\frac{x^2}{a^2} \le 1, \qquad x^2 \le a^2; \qquad \frac{y^2}{b^2} \le 1, \qquad y^2 \le b^2.$$

Therefore the curve lies in the box $-a \le x \le a$, $-b \le y \le b$. See Fig. 6.2. The points $(\pm a, 0)$ and $(0, \pm b)$ are called the **vertices** of the ellipse.

The numbers a and b are known (historically) by the names **semi-major axis** and **semi-minor axis**. The midpoint of the foci is called the **center** of the ellipse. (It is the origin in our example.)

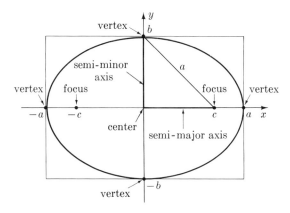

FIG. 6.2.   geometry of the ellipse

Note from Fig. 6.2, that the distance from a focus to one of the points $(0, \pm b)$ is a; that is because $a^2 = b^2 + c^2$.

If $a = b$, the equation becomes

$$\frac{x^2}{a^2} + \frac{y^2}{a^2} = 1, \qquad x^2 + y^2 = a^2,$$

a circle of radius a. Thus a circle can be considered as a limiting (extreme) case of an ellipse, where $c = 0$. (The foci come together at one point, the center.)

If $a < b$, then

$$\frac{x^2}{a^2} + \frac{y^2}{b^2} = 1$$

is an ellipse with major axis along the y-axis instead of the x-axis. To see why, interchange the roles of x and y in the previous argument.

By a translation of axes, we get

$$\frac{(x - h)^2}{a^2} + \frac{(y - k)^2}{b^2} = 1,$$

the equation of an ellipse centered at (h, k).

REMARK 1: To construct an ellipse, tie a string of length $2a$ to two fixed pins $2c$ units apart $(a > c)$. Place your pencil against the string and move it so the string is taut. The locus generated is an ellipse, Why? If the pins are moved closer and closer together $(c \longrightarrow 0)$, the ellipse becomes more and more like a circle.

REMARK 2: It is possible to prove that on an elliptical billiard table, a ball shot in any direction from one focus will bounce once and pass through the other focus. (This accounts for the name focus, or focal point.) Whispering galleries are constructed in an elliptical shape because of this property.

Parameterization of the Ellipse

Consider again the ellipse

$$\frac{x^2}{a^2} + \frac{y^2}{b^2} = 1, \qquad \text{where} \quad a \geq b.$$

Since

$$\left(\frac{x}{a}\right)^2 + \left(\frac{y}{b}\right)^2 = 1,$$

there is an angle θ such that $x/a = \cos \theta$ and $y/b = \sin \theta$, so

$$(x, y) = (a \cos \theta, b \sin \theta).$$

As θ makes a complete revolution, the point $(a \cos \theta, b \sin \theta)$ traverses the ellipse once. See Fig. 6.3. Note that θ is *not* the polar angle of (x, y).

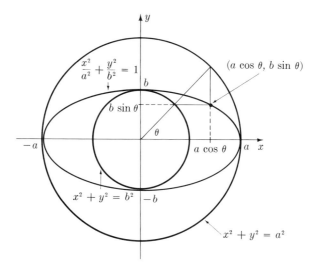

FIG. 6.3.   parameterization of the ellipse

Polar Form and Eccentricity

The orbit of a planet around a fixed star is an ellipse with the star at one focus. Because in astronomy one measures angles rather than distances, it is natural to study the polar equation of an ellipse with one focus at the origin.

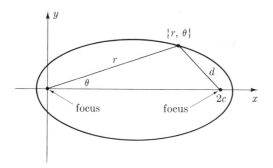

FIG. 6.4.   polar form of ellipse

Place the axes as in Fig. 6.4. By definition of the ellipse, $r + d = 2a$, hence $d^2 = (2a - r)^2$. On the other hand, by the law of cosines,

$$d^2 = r^2 + (2c)^2 - 2r(2c) \cos \theta = r^2 + 4c^2 - 4rc \cos \theta.$$

Equate the two expressions for d^2:

$$(2a - r)^2 = r^2 + 4c^2 - 4rc \cos \theta, \qquad 4a^2 - 4ar = 4c^2 - 4rc \cos \theta.$$

Solve for r:

$$r(a - c \cos \theta) = a^2 - c^2 = b^2, \qquad r\left(1 - \frac{c}{a} \cos \theta\right) = \frac{b^2}{a}.$$

Define the **eccentricity** of the ellipse to be the number $e = c/a$. Since $c < a$, it follows that $0 < e < 1$. Define also $p = b^2/ae$. Then the polar equation is

$$\boxed{r(1 - e \cos \theta) = ep.}$$

The eccentricity determines the shape of the ellipse. If e is near zero, then c is small compared to a. That means the foci are close together relative to the semi-major axis, hence the ellipse is circle-like. If e is near 1, the foci are relatively far apart and the ellipse is cigar-shaped. See Fig. 6.5. Once e is given, the scale factor p determines the size of the ellipse (as the radius does for a circle).

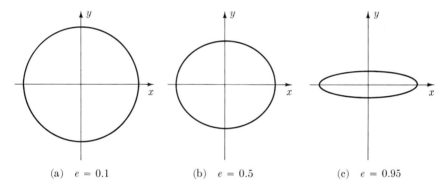

   (a) $e = 0.1$ (b) $e = 0.5$ (c) $e = 0.95$

FIG. 6.5.   ellipses of various eccentricities

EXERCISES

Give the center, foci, major and minor semi-axes (a and b), and vertices, and sketch:

1. $x^2/25 + y^2/9 = 1$ 2. $x^2 + 4y^2 = 4$
3. $2(x + 1)^2 + (y - 2)^2 = 2$ 4. $4x^2 + y^2 - 2y = 0$
5. $2x^2 + y^2 - 12x - 4y = -21$ 6. $x^2 + 2y^2 + 8y = 0.$

Write the equation of the ellipse:

7. center at $(1, 4)$, vertices at $(10, 4)$ and $(1, 2)$
8. center at $(-2, -3)$, vertices at $(7, -3)$ and $(-2, -7)$
9. foci at $(2, 0)$ and $(8, 0)$, vertices at $(0, 0)$ and $(10, 0)$
10. foci at $(0, 3)$ and $(0, -3)$, semi-major axis $= 10$
11. foci at $(-1, 0)$, $(3, 0)$, eccentricity $= \frac{1}{2}$
12. vertices at $(0, 2)$, $(0, 6)$, eccentricity $= \frac{3}{4}$, major axis vertical.

13. Let an ellipse have eccentricity e, and write $e = \cos \theta$ with $0 < \theta < 90°$. Then we speak of a "$\theta°$ ellipse". Interpret geometrically. Draw ellipses of 15°, 30°, 45°, and 60°.

14. Fix p and e with $0 < p$ and $0 < e < 1$. Find the locus of all points $\mathbf{x}$ whose distance from $\mathbf{0}$ is e times its distance from the line $x = -p$. [*Hint:* Use polar coordinates.]

15. Prove that the points on an ellipse farthest from its center are the two vertices on the major axis.

16. Prove that the points on an ellipse nearest to its center are the two vertices on the minor axis.

17. The orbit of the earth is approximately an ellipse with the sun at one focus and semi-major and semi-minor axes 9.3×10^7 and 9.1×10^7 miles respectively. Compute the eccentricity of the orbit.

18. (cont.) Find the distance from the sun to the other focus of the ellipse.

19. Let $\mathbf{p}$ be one end of the major axis of an ellipse. Find the locus of the midpoint of $\mathbf{pq}$ as $\mathbf{q}$ traces the ellipse.

20. A 9-ft ladder slides along the floor as its top slides down a wall. If $\mathbf{x}$ is the point on the ladder $\frac{1}{3}$ of the way from its top, find the path of $\mathbf{x}$.

21. A rod moves with one end on the x-axis and the other on the y-axis. If P is a point on the rod, prove that the locus of P is an ellipse.

22*. Let E be an ellipse and L a line. Prove that the midpoints of all chords of E parallel to L are collinear.

The following four exercises are intended to show that each point (x, y) that satisfies $x^2/a^2 + y^2/b^2 = 1$ does lie on the ellipse discussed in the text.

23*. Suppose $a > b > 0$ and $x^2/a^2 + y^2/b^2 = 1$. Set $c^2 = a^2 - b^2$, $c > 0$. Prove $a^2 + cx > 0$ and $a^2 - cx > 0$. [*Hint:* Use $(c \pm x)^2 \geq 0$, $c^2 < a^2$, and $x^2 \leq a^2$.]

24*. (cont.) Define $\lambda > 0$ and $\mu > 0$ by $\lambda^2 = (x + c)^2 + y^2$, $\mu^2 = (x - c)^2 + y^2$. Prove that $(a^2 + cx)^2 = a^2\lambda^2$ and $(a^2 - cx)^2 = a^2\mu^2$.

25*. (cont.) Prove that $a^2 + cx = a\lambda$ and $a^2 - cx = a\mu$.

26*. (cont.) Prove that $\lambda + \mu = 2a$. Conclude that (x, y) lies on the ellipse with foci $(\pm c, 0)$ and length sum $2a$.

7. THE HYPERBOLA

A **hyperbola** is the locus of all points $\mathbf{x}$ such that the absolute value of the difference of the distances of $\mathbf{x}$ from two fixed points $\mathbf{p}$ and $\mathbf{q}$, called the **foci**, is a constant, $2a$. Because $\mathbf{p}$, $\mathbf{q}$, and $\mathbf{x}$ form a triangle, $2a < \|\mathbf{p} - \mathbf{q}\|$. See Fig. 7.1.

To find the equation of the hyperbola, choose axes so that $\mathbf{p} = (-c, 0)$ and $\mathbf{q} = (c, 0)$. Then $\|\mathbf{p} - \mathbf{q}\| = 2c$ and $a < c$. A point $\mathbf{x}$ is on the hyperbola if and only

$$\|\mathbf{x} - \mathbf{p}\| - \|\mathbf{x} - \mathbf{q}\| = \pm 2a.$$

The same steps that led to the equation of the ellipse, except for a few

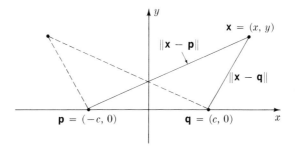

FIG. 7.1.   definition of the hyperbola: $\big|\,\|\mathbf{x} - \mathbf{p}\| - \|\mathbf{x} - \mathbf{q}\|\,\big| = 2a$

sign changes, lead to the equation

$$\frac{x^2}{a^2} - \frac{y^2}{b^2} = 1, \qquad (a^2 + b^2 = c^2).$$

As with the ellipse, it is necessary to prove that any point (x, y) that satisfies the equation actually is on the hyperbola. See Exs. 29–32.

The equation of the hyperbola with foci $(-c, 0)$ and $(c, 0)$ and absolute length difference $2a$ is

$$\frac{x^2}{a^2} - \frac{y^2}{b^2} = 1,$$

where $b^2 = c^2 - a^2$.

Note: For the hyperbola, $a^2 = c^2 - b^2$ unlike for the ellipse, where $a^2 = b^2 + c^2$. Therefore both $a > b$ and $a \le b$ are possible for the hyperbola, not just $a > b$ as for the ellipse.

Let us sketch the hyperbola

$$\frac{x^2}{a^2} - \frac{y^2}{b^2} = 1.$$

We first note symmetry; if (x, y) satisfies this equation, then so do $(-x, y)$, $(x, -y)$, and $(-x, -y)$. Therefore the curve is symmetric in both axes and in the origin; we need plot it only in the first quadrant, then extend the curve to the other quadrants by symmetry.

We solve for y:

$$y = \frac{b}{a}\sqrt{x^2 - a^2}.$$

(The positive square root applies for the first quadrant.) The locus is defined only for $x \ge a$. When x starts at a and increases, y starts at 0 and increases. When x is very large, we suspect that y is slightly less than bx/a. To confirm this suspicion, we write

$$
\frac{b}{a}x - y = \frac{b}{a}(x - \sqrt{x^2 - a^2}) = \frac{b}{a}(x - \sqrt{x^2 - a^2})\,\frac{x + \sqrt{x^2 - a^2}}{x + \sqrt{x^2 - a^2}}
$$

$$
= \left(\frac{b}{a}\right)\frac{x^2 - (x^2 - a^2)}{x + \sqrt{x^2 - a^2}} = \frac{ab}{x + \sqrt{x^2 - a^2}} < \frac{ab}{x}\,.
$$

It follows that $(b/a)x - y$ is positive, but becomes smaller and smaller as x becomes larger and larger. This means the curve approaches the line $y = bx/a$ (from below) as x increases; the line is an asymptote of the hyperbola.

We sketch the curve in the first quadrant, then extend by symmetry to the other quadrants (Fig. 7.2a).

In dealing with hyperbolas, the following terminology is customary. A hyperbola consists of two **branches:** one where $\|\mathbf{x} - \mathbf{p}\| - \|\mathbf{x} - \mathbf{q}\| = 2a$, and the other where $\|\mathbf{x} - \mathbf{q}\| - \|\mathbf{x} - \mathbf{p}\| = 2a$. The point half-way between the foci is the **center** of a hyperbola. The line through the foci is the **principal axis,** and the line through the center perpendicular to the principal axis is the **conjugate axis.** The points where the hyperbola meets its principal axes are its **vertices.** See Fig. 7.2b.

The lines $y = \pm bx/a$ are the asymptotes of the hyperbola. A neat way to remember this fact is to write

$$
\frac{x^2}{a^2} - \frac{y^2}{b^2} = \left(\frac{x}{a} + \frac{y}{b}\right)\left(\frac{x}{a} - \frac{y}{b}\right).
$$

The expression on the left is zero if and only if one of the factors on the right is zero, that is, if and only if $y = \pm bx/a$.

The asymptotes of the hyperbola

$$
\frac{x^2}{a^2} - \frac{y^2}{b^2} = 1
$$

are the lines

$$
y = \frac{b}{a}x \qquad \text{and} \qquad y = -\frac{b}{a}x,
$$

or equivalently, the locus of the equation

$$
\frac{x^2}{a^2} - \frac{y^2}{b^2} = 0.
$$

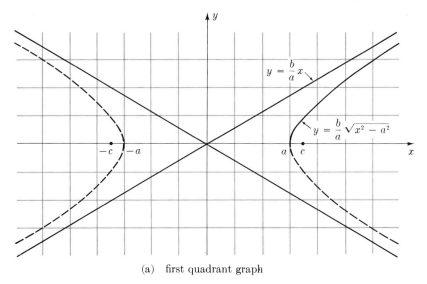

(a)   first quadrant graph

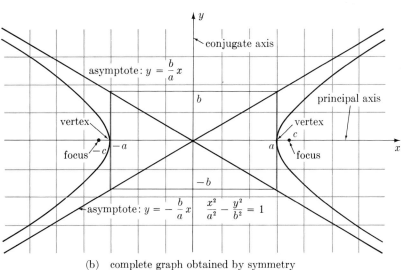

(b)   complete graph obtained by symmetry

Fig. 7.2.   graph of hyperbola, showing asymptotes

A hyperbola is called **rectangular** if its asymptotes are perpendicular. This happens when the slopes of the two asymptotes are negative reciprocals of each other:

$$\left(\frac{b}{a}\right)\left(-\frac{b}{a}\right) = -1, \qquad b^2 = a^2, \qquad b = a.$$

Thus the locus of

$$x^2 - y^2 = a^2$$

is a rectangular hyperbola.

By translation,

$$\frac{(x-h)^2}{a^2} - \frac{(y-k)^2}{b^2} = 1$$

is the equation of a hyperbola with center at (h, k) and horizontal principal axis.

By interchanging the roles of x and y, we see that the equation

$$-\frac{x^2}{a^2} + \frac{y^2}{b^2} = 1$$

defines a hyperbola with center at the origin, vertical principal axis, and foci at $(0, \pm c)$.

REMARK: The equations

$$\frac{x^2}{a^2} + \frac{y^2}{b^2} = 1 \qquad \text{and} \qquad \frac{x^2}{a^2} - \frac{y^2}{b^2} = 1$$

differ by a little minus sign, but that makes all the difference in the world. The first equation, where the sign is plus, requires $x^2 \leq a^2$ and $y^2 \leq b^2$; the locus is confined. The second imposes no such restriction; x^2/a^2 and y^2/b^2 can both be enormous, yet differ by 1.

EXERCISES

Find the center, foci, and asymptotes, and sketch:

1. $x^2/4 - y^2/9 = 1$
2. $x^2/9 - y^2/4 = 1$
3. $-x^2/9 + y^2/4 = 1$
4. $-x^2/4 + y^2/9 = 1$
5. $(x + 1)^2 - (y - 1)^2 = 1$
6. $-(x - 2)^2 + 4(y + 1)^2 = 4$
7. $x^2 - y^2 = 0$
8. $-2x^2 + y^2 = 0$.
9. $4x^2 - y^2 - 24x - 2y + 31 = 0$
10. $3x^2 - 3y^2 - 3x - 2y = 31/12$.

Write the equation of the hyperbola:

11. foci $(0, \pm 5)$, vertices $(0, \pm 4)$
12. center $(0, 0)$, vertices $(\pm 3, 0)$, foci $(\pm 5, 0)$
13. center $(0, 0)$, asymptotes $y = \pm 2x$, vertices $(\pm 2, 0)$
14. center $(1, 2)$, foci $(1, 7)$, $(1, -3)$, vertices $(1, 6)$, $(1, -2)$
15. asymptotes $y = \pm (x - 1)$, curve passes through $(3, 1)$.
16. asymptotes $y = \pm 2x$, curve passes through $(1, 1)$.

17. Show that $x^2 - y^2 + ax + by + c = 0$ represents a rectangular hyperbola.
18. Show that $3x^2 - y^2 + ax + by + c = 0$ represents a hyperbola whose asymptotes form a 60° angle.
19. Sketch the region $x^2/a^2 + y^2/b^2 < 1$ and the region $x^2/a^2 + y^2/b^2 > 1$.

20. Sketch the region $x^2/a^2 - y^2/b^2 < 1$ and the region $x^2/a^2 - y^2/b^2 > 1$.

21. Let C_1 and C_2 be circles external to each other. Prove that the locus of the center of a circle that touches C_1 and C_2 externally is either a branch of a hyperbola or a line.

22. A rifle at point **a** on level ground is shot at a target at point **b**. Find the locus of all observers who hear the shot and the impact of the shell simultaneously.

23. The foci of a hyperbola are **0** and $(2c, 0)$. Show that its equation in polar coordinates has the form

$$r(1 \pm e \cos \theta) = \pm ep,$$

where $e = c/a > 1$ and $eap = b^2 = c^2 - a^2$.

24. (cont.) Fix $p > 0$ and $e > 1$. Find the locus of all points **x** whose distance from **0** is e times its distance from the line $x = -p$. [*Hint:* Use polar coordinates.]

25*. Suppose $a > 0$, $b > 0$, $c > 0$, and $a^2 + b^2 = c^2$. Also suppose

$$\sqrt{(x + c)^2 + y^2} - \sqrt{(x - c)^2 + y^2} = \pm 2a.$$

Prove that

$$\sqrt{(x + c)^2 + y^2} + \sqrt{(x - c)^2 + y^2} = \pm 2\frac{cx}{a}.$$

[*Hint:* see p. 87.]

26*. (cont.) Complete the proof that $x^2/a^2 - y^2/b^2 = 1$.

The following four exercises are intended to show that each point (x, y) that satisfies $x^2/a^2 - y^2/b^2 = 1$ does lie on the hyperbola discussed in the text.

27*. Suppose $a > 0$, $b > 0$, and $x^2/a^2 - y^2/b^2 = 1$. Define $c > 0$ by $c^2 = a^2 + b^2$. Prove that $(a^2 + cx)(a^2 - cx) < 0$.

28*. Define $\lambda > 0$ and $\mu > 0$ by

$$\lambda^2 = (x + c)^2 + y^2, \qquad \mu^2 = (x - c)^2 + y^2.$$

Prove that $(a^2 + cx)^2 = a^2\lambda^2$ and $(a^2 - cx)^2 = a^2\mu^2$.

29*. (cont.) Prove that $a^2 + cx = \pm a\lambda$ and $a^2 - cx = \mp a\mu$, with the *opposite* choice of signs.

30*. (cont.) Prove that $|\lambda - \mu| = 2a$. Conclude that (x, y) is on the hyperbola with foci $(\pm c, 0)$ and absolute length difference $2a$.

8. ROTATION OF AXES [Optional]

Suppose the plane is rotated through an angle α about the origin. The x- and y-axes rotate to two new (perpendicular) lines we call the $\bar{x}$- and $\bar{y}$-axes (Fig. 8.1). They define a new rectangular coordinate system.

A point **p** in the plane now has x, y-coordinates (x, y) and $\bar{x}$, $\bar{y}$-coordinates $(\bar{x}, \bar{y})$. It is important to know the relations between the numbers x, y, $\bar{x}$, $\bar{y}$, and α. If we know α and (x, y), we should be able to compute $(\bar{x}, \bar{y})$. Conversely, if we know α and $(\bar{x}, \bar{y})$, we should be able to compute (x, y).

We can solve the problem neatly using vectors. Let **i** denote the unit

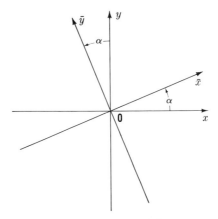

FIG. 8.1.   rotation of coordinate axes

vector with $(x, y) = (1, 0)$ and $\mathbf{j}$ the unit vector with $(x, y) = (0, 1)$. See
Fig. 8.2a. Then the point $\mathbf{p}$ with x, y-coordinates (x, y) can be written

$$\mathbf{p} = (x, y) = x(1, 0) + y(0, 1) = x\mathbf{i} + y\mathbf{j}.$$

Similarly, let $\bar{\mathbf{i}}$ denote the unit vector with $(\bar{x}, \bar{y}) = (1, 0)$ and let $\bar{\mathbf{j}}$ denote
the unit vector with $(\bar{x}, \bar{y}) = (0, 1)$. Then in the $\bar{x}$, $\bar{y}$-coordinate system,

$$\mathbf{p} = (\bar{x}, \bar{y}) = \bar{x}(1, 0) + \bar{y}(0, 1) = \bar{x}\bar{\mathbf{i}} + \bar{y}\bar{\mathbf{j}}.$$

Thus we have

$$\mathbf{p} = x\mathbf{i} + y\mathbf{j} = \bar{x}\bar{\mathbf{i}} + \bar{y}\bar{\mathbf{j}}.$$

To solve our problem, we express $\bar{\mathbf{i}}$ and $\bar{\mathbf{j}}$ in terms of $\mathbf{i}$, $\mathbf{j}$, and α, then
substitute.

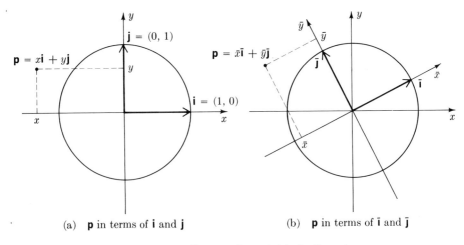

(a) $\mathbf{p}$ in terms of $\mathbf{i}$ and $\mathbf{j}$ (b) $\mathbf{p}$ in terms of $\bar{\mathbf{i}}$ and $\bar{\mathbf{j}}$

FIG. 8.2.   coordinates of a point in both systems

Look at Fig. 8.3a. It is obvious that the (x, y)-coordinates of $\mathbf{i}$ are $(\cos \alpha, \sin \alpha)$, because $\mathbf{i}$ is a unit vector making angle α with the positive x-axis. Now look at Fig. 8.3b. The unit vector $\mathbf{j}$ makes angle $\alpha + \frac{1}{2}\pi$ with the positive x-axis, so its (x, y)-coordinates are

$$(\cos(\alpha + \tfrac{1}{2}\pi),\ \sin(\alpha + \tfrac{1}{2}\pi)) = (-\sin \alpha,\ \cos \alpha).$$

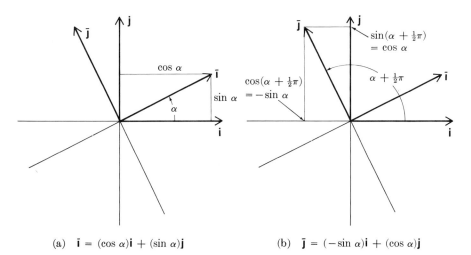

(a) $\mathbf{i} = (\cos \alpha)\mathbf{i} + (\sin \alpha)\mathbf{j}$ (b) $\mathbf{j} = (-\sin \alpha)\mathbf{i} + (\cos \alpha)\mathbf{j}$

FIG. 8.3

Therefore

$$\mathbf{i} = (\cos \alpha)\mathbf{i} + (\sin \alpha)\mathbf{j}, \qquad \mathbf{j} = (-\sin \alpha)\mathbf{i} + (\cos \alpha)\mathbf{j}.$$

Substitute into $\mathbf{p} = x\mathbf{i} + y\mathbf{j} = \bar{x}\mathbf{i} + \bar{y}\mathbf{j}$:

$$x\mathbf{i} + y\mathbf{j} = \bar{x}[(\cos \alpha)\mathbf{i} + (\sin \alpha)\mathbf{j}] + \bar{y}[(-\sin \alpha)\mathbf{i} + (\cos \alpha)\mathbf{j}]$$
$$= (\bar{x} \cos \alpha - \bar{y} \sin \alpha)\mathbf{i} + (\bar{x} \sin \alpha + \bar{y} \cos \alpha)\mathbf{j}.$$

We conclude that

$$x = \bar{x} \cos \alpha - \bar{y} \sin \alpha, \qquad y = \bar{x} \sin \alpha + \bar{y} \cos \alpha.$$

These formulas express x and y in terms of $\bar{x}$, $\bar{y}$, and α. Conversely, how do we express $\bar{x}$ and $\bar{y}$ in terms of x, y, and α? The simplest way is to notice that the x, y-axes are obtained from the $\bar{x}$, $\bar{y}$-axes by a rotation of $-\alpha$, so the formulas above apply with the substitutions

$$
\begin{array}{ccccc}
x & y & \bar{x} & \bar{y} & \alpha \\
\downarrow & \downarrow & \downarrow & \downarrow & \downarrow \\
\bar{x} & \bar{y} & x & y & -\alpha.
\end{array}
$$

Since $\cos(-\alpha) = \cos \alpha$ and $\sin(-\alpha) = -\sin \alpha$, the result is

$$\bar{x} = x \cos \alpha + y \sin \alpha, \qquad \bar{y} = -x \sin \alpha + y \cos \alpha.$$

Suppose the plane is rotated through angle α and the x- and y-axes, under this rotation, go to the $\bar{x}$- and $\bar{y}$-axes. Then the x, y-coordinates and $\bar{x}$, $\bar{y}$-coordinates of any point are related by

$$\begin{cases} x = \bar{x}\cos\alpha - \bar{y}\sin\alpha \\ y = \bar{x}\sin\alpha + \bar{y}\cos\alpha \end{cases} \qquad \begin{cases} \bar{x} = x\cos\alpha + y\sin\alpha \\ \bar{y} = -x\sin\alpha + y\cos\alpha. \end{cases}$$

For example, if $\alpha = 45°$, then

$$x = \tfrac{1}{2}\sqrt{2}\,(\bar{x} - \bar{y}), \qquad y = \tfrac{1}{2}\sqrt{2}\,(\bar{x} + \bar{y}).$$

For another example, if $\alpha = -30°$ then $\cos\alpha = \tfrac{1}{2}$ and $\sin\alpha = -\tfrac{1}{2}\sqrt{3}$; hence

$$x = \tfrac{1}{2}(\bar{x} + \sqrt{3}\,\bar{y}), \qquad y = \tfrac{1}{2}(-\sqrt{3}\,\bar{x} + \bar{y}).$$

Conics

We have learned how to graph quadratic equations of the form

(1) $ax^2 + cy^2 + dx + ey + f = 0 \qquad (a^2 + c^2 > 0).$

By completing squares, we generally obtain one of the conic sections (sometimes a degenerate conic, or no locus at all). Now we tackle the most general quadratic equation

(2) $ax^2 + bxy + cy^2 + dx + ey + f = 0.$

It is the term bxy that makes life difficult. Where does it come from and how can we get rid of it? We can learn a good deal from two experiments.

EXAMPLE 8.1

Find the equation of the ellipse

$$\frac{x^2}{9} + \frac{y^2}{4} = 1$$

in the $\bar{x}$, $\bar{y}$-coordinate system that results from a $\tfrac{1}{4}\pi$ rotation of the x, y-coordinate system.

Solution: The rotation formulas are

$$x = \tfrac{1}{2}\sqrt{2}\,(\bar{x} - \bar{y}), \qquad y = \tfrac{1}{2}\sqrt{2}\,(\bar{x} + \bar{y}).$$

Substitute:

$$\frac{x^2}{9} + \frac{y^2}{4} = \frac{1}{2}\left[\frac{(\bar{x} - \bar{y})^2}{9} + \frac{(\bar{x} + \bar{y})^2}{4}\right] = \frac{1}{2}\left[\frac{13}{36}\bar{x}^2 + \frac{10}{36}\bar{x}\bar{y} + \frac{13}{36}\bar{y}^2\right].$$

Answer: $\dfrac{13}{72}\bar{x}^2 + \dfrac{10}{72}\bar{x}\bar{y} + \dfrac{13}{72}\bar{y}^2 = 1$; see Fig. 8.4.

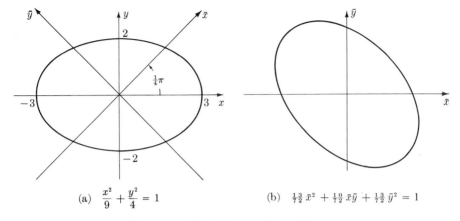

(a) $\dfrac{x^2}{9} + \dfrac{y^2}{4} = 1$ (b) $\tfrac{13}{72}\,\bar{x}^2 + \tfrac{10}{72}\,\bar{x}\bar{y} + \tfrac{13}{72}\,\bar{y}^2 = 1$

FIG. 8.4. ellipse in rotated coordinates

The experiment suggests that the $\bar{x}\bar{y}$ term is due to the tilt of the coordinate axes relative to the axes of the ellipse. The same should be true for hyperbolas and parabolas. Let us try a parabola.

EXAMPLE 8.2

Apply the rotation of Example 8.1 to the parabola $y = x^2$.

Solution: Substitute $x = \tfrac{1}{2}\sqrt{2}\,(\bar{x} - \bar{y})$ and $y = \tfrac{1}{2}\sqrt{2}\,(\bar{x} + \bar{y})$:

$$\tfrac{1}{2}\sqrt{2}\,(\bar{x} + \bar{y}) = [\tfrac{1}{2}\sqrt{2}\,(\bar{x} - \bar{y})]^2 = \tfrac{1}{2}(\bar{x}^2 - 2\bar{x}\bar{y} + \bar{y}^2),$$
$$\sqrt{2}\,(\bar{x} + \bar{y}) = \bar{x}^2 - 2\bar{x}\bar{y} + \bar{y}^2.$$

Answer: $\bar{x}^2 - 2\bar{x}\bar{y} + \bar{y}^2 - \sqrt{2}\,\bar{x} - \sqrt{2}\,\bar{y} = 0$; see Fig. 8.5.

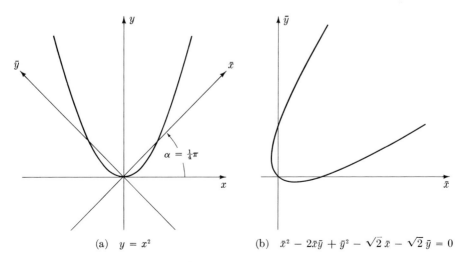

(a) $y = x^2$ (b) $\bar{x}^2 - 2\bar{x}\bar{y} + \bar{y}^2 - \sqrt{2}\,\bar{x} - \sqrt{2}\,\bar{y} = 0$

FIG. 8.5. parabola in rotated coordinates

Examples 8.1 and 8.2 suggest that an xy term occurs when the axes are "incorrectly" placed. We suspect it can be eliminated by rotating the axes through a cleverly chosen angle. Let us look for a suitable angle.

Now the most general rotation of coordinates is

$$\begin{cases} x = \bar{x} \cos \alpha - \bar{y} \sin \alpha \\ y = \bar{x} \sin \alpha + \bar{y} \cos \alpha. \end{cases}$$

This rotation changes a linear polynomial $dx + ey + f$ in x and y into a linear polynomial in $\bar{x}$ and $\bar{y}$. Of more interest to us is what happens to the quadratic part, $ax^2 + bxy + cy^2$ of (2). Substitute:

$$\begin{aligned} ax^2 + bxy + cy^2 = {} & a(\bar{x} \cos \alpha - \bar{y} \sin \alpha)^2 \\ & + b(\bar{x} \cos \alpha - \bar{y} \sin \alpha)(\bar{x} \sin \alpha + \bar{y} \cos \alpha) \\ & + c(\bar{x} \sin \alpha + \bar{y} \cos \alpha)^2. \end{aligned}$$

Multiply out and collect terms in $\bar{x}^2$, $\bar{x}\bar{y}$, and $\bar{y}^2$.

Under a rotation through an angle α, the quadratic polynomial

$$ax^2 + bxy + cy^2 + dx + ey + f$$

is changed into

$$\bar{a}\bar{x}^2 + \bar{b}\bar{x}\bar{y} + \bar{c}\bar{y}^2 + \bar{d}\bar{x} + \bar{e}\bar{y} + \bar{f},$$

where

$$\begin{cases} \bar{a} = a \cos^2 \alpha + b \cos \alpha \sin \alpha + c \sin^2 \alpha \\ \bar{b} = 2(c - a)\sin \alpha \cos \alpha + b(\cos^2 \alpha - \sin^2 \alpha) \\ \bar{c} = a \sin^2 \alpha - b \sin \alpha \cos \alpha + c \cos^2 \alpha. \end{cases}$$

For our purposes the most interesting of these formulas is the one for $\bar{b}$, which we can write in the form

$$\bar{b} = (c - a)\sin 2\alpha + b \cos 2\alpha.$$

From this formula we see that it is always possible to choose the rotation angle α so that $\bar{b} = 0$, that is,

(3) $$(c - a)\sin 2\alpha + b \cos 2\alpha = 0.$$

For if $c = a$, then $\alpha = \pm\frac{1}{4}\pi$ satisfies (3). If $c \neq a$, we choose α so that

$$\tan 2\alpha = \frac{b}{a - c};$$

then α satisfies (3).

A quadratic locus

$$ax^2 + bxy + cy^2 + dx + ey + f = 0$$

is changed into a quadratic locus

$$\bar{a}x^2 + \bar{c}y^2 + \bar{d}x + \bar{e}y + \bar{f} = 0$$

without an $\bar{x}\bar{y}$ term by rotating the axes through angle α, where

$$\alpha = \pm\tfrac{1}{4}\pi \qquad \text{if} \quad a = c,$$

$$\tan 2\alpha = \frac{b}{a - c} \qquad \text{if} \quad a \neq c.$$

Because the tangent has period π, the angle 2α is determined up to a multiple of π, hence α is determined only up to a multiple of $\tfrac{1}{2}\pi$. Therefore we can always choose α in the first quadrant.

In numerical examples, we must compute $\bar{a}$ and $\bar{c}$, having a, b, c, and $\tan 2\alpha$. We write the formulas for $\bar{a}$ and $\bar{c}$ in the form

(4)
$$\begin{cases} \bar{a} = a \cos^2 \alpha + \tfrac{1}{2}b \sin 2\alpha + c \sin^2 \alpha \\ \bar{c} = a \sin^2 \alpha - \tfrac{1}{2}b \sin 2\alpha + c \cos^2 \alpha. \end{cases}$$

From $\tan 2\alpha$ we can find $\sin 2\alpha$ and $\cos 2\alpha$:

$$\sin 2\alpha = \frac{\pm \tan 2\alpha}{\sqrt{1 + \tan^2 2\alpha}}, \qquad \cos 2\alpha = \frac{\pm 1}{\sqrt{1 + \tan^2 2\alpha}}.$$

From $\cos 2\alpha$ we can find $\cos^2 \alpha$ and $\sin^2 \alpha$:

$$\cos^2 \alpha = \tfrac{1}{2}(1 + \cos 2\alpha), \qquad \sin^2 \alpha = \tfrac{1}{2}(1 - \cos 2\alpha).$$

Everything ties together neatly.

EXAMPLE 8.3

Describe the locus of $xy = 1$.

Solution: In this case $a = c = 0$, $b = 1$. Therefore we choose $\alpha = \tfrac{1}{4}\pi$ to make $\bar{b} = 0$. The rotation is

$$x = \tfrac{1}{2}\sqrt{2}\,(\bar{x} - \bar{y}), \qquad y = \tfrac{1}{2}\sqrt{2}\,(\bar{x} + \bar{y}),$$

so by direct computation,

$$xy = \tfrac{1}{2}(\bar{x} - \bar{y})\,(\bar{x} + \bar{y}) = \tfrac{1}{2}(\bar{x}^2 - \bar{y}^2).$$

The locus is $\tfrac{1}{2}(\bar{x}^2 - \bar{y}^2) = 1$.

Answer: rectangular hyperbola; see Fig. 8.6.

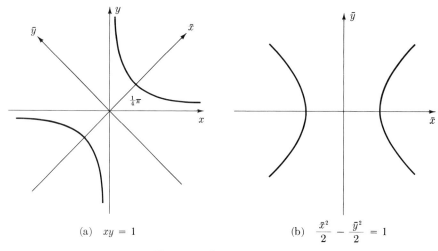

(a) $xy = 1$ (b) $\dfrac{\bar{x}^2}{2} - \dfrac{\bar{y}^2}{2} = 1$

FIG. 8.6.   locus of $xy = 1$

EXAMPLE 8.4

Describe the locus of $x^2 - 2xy + 3y^2 = 1$.

Solution: Rotate the axes through angle α where

$$\tan 2\alpha = \frac{b}{a - c} = \frac{-2}{-2} = 1,$$

$$2\alpha = \tfrac{1}{4}\pi, \qquad \alpha = \tfrac{1}{8}\pi.$$

In this case, $\sin 2\alpha = \cos 2\alpha = \tfrac{1}{2}\sqrt{2}$,

$$\cos^2 \alpha = \tfrac{1}{2}(1 + \tfrac{1}{2}\sqrt{2}), \qquad \sin^2 \alpha = \tfrac{1}{2}(1 - \tfrac{1}{2}\sqrt{2}).$$

Substitute these values with $a = 1$, $b = -2$, $c = 3$ into (4):

$$\begin{cases} \bar{a} = \tfrac{1}{2}(1 + \tfrac{1}{2}\sqrt{2}) - \tfrac{1}{2}\sqrt{2} + \tfrac{3}{2}(1 - \tfrac{1}{2}\sqrt{2}) = 2 - \sqrt{2}, \\ \bar{c} = \tfrac{1}{2}(1 - \tfrac{1}{2}\sqrt{2}) + \tfrac{1}{2}\sqrt{2} + \tfrac{3}{2}(1 + \tfrac{1}{2}\sqrt{2}) = 2 + \sqrt{2}. \end{cases}$$

Therefore, in the $\bar{x}$, $\bar{y}$-coordinate system, the locus is

$$(2 - \sqrt{2})\bar{x}^2 + (2 + \sqrt{2})\bar{y}^2 = 1.$$

Because $2 - \sqrt{2}$ and $2 + \sqrt{2}$ are both positive, this is an ellipse in standard form. We may write

$$\frac{\bar{x}^2}{A^2} + \frac{\bar{y}^2}{B^2} = 1,$$

where $A^2 = 1/(2 - \sqrt{2})$ and $B^2 = 1/(2 + \sqrt{2})$.

Answer: ellipse with semi-axes $\dfrac{1}{\sqrt{2 + \sqrt{2}}}$, $\dfrac{1}{\sqrt{2 - \sqrt{2}}}$; see Fig. 8.7.

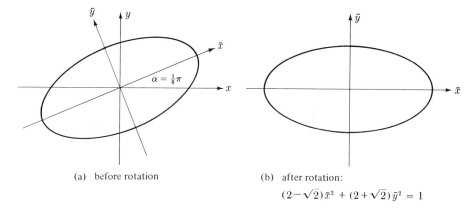

(a) before rotation

(b) after rotation:

$$(2-\sqrt{2})\bar{x}^2 + (2+\sqrt{2})\bar{y}^2 = 1$$

FIG. 8.7. locus of $x^2 - 2xy + 3y^2 = 1$

EXERCISES

1. Solve the system of linear equations

$$x = \bar{x}\cos\alpha - \bar{y}\sin\alpha, \qquad y = \bar{x}\sin\alpha + \bar{y}\cos\alpha$$

for $\bar{x}$ and $\bar{y}$. Explain your answer.

2. Let $x = \bar{x}\cos\alpha - \bar{y}\sin\alpha$ and $y = \bar{x}\sin\alpha + \bar{y}\cos\alpha$. Compute $x^2 + y^2$. Explain your answer.

3. Let (x_1, y_1) and (x_2, y_2) be two points in the x, y-coordinate system. Let $(\bar{x}_1, \bar{y}_1)$ and $(\bar{x}_2, \bar{y}_2)$ be their coordinates in the $\bar{x}$, $\bar{y}$-coordinate system obtained by a rotation. Compute $x_1x_2 + y_1y_2$ in terms of $\bar{x}_1, \bar{x}_2, \bar{y}_1, \bar{y}_2$, and α, the angle of rotation. Explain your answer.

4. Follow a rotation through angle α by a rotation through angle β. The result is obviously a rotation through angle $\alpha + \beta$. Use this observation and the rotation formulas to prove the addition laws for sine and cosine.

5. Let $(x, y) = (\cos\theta, \sin\theta)$ be a point on the unit circle. Rotate the axes by an angle α and show geometrically that $(\bar{x}, \bar{y}) = (\cos(\theta - \alpha), \sin(\theta - \alpha))$.

6. (cont.) Combine this result with the rotation formulas to get a new proof of the addition laws for the sine and cosine.

Make a suitable rotation and write the $\bar{x}$, $\bar{y}$-equation (without an $\bar{x}\bar{y}$ term):

7. $x^2 - xy = 1$

8. $xy - y^2 = 1$

9. $xy + y^2 = 1$

10. $2xy + y^2 = 1.$

Determine the type the conic and the directions of its principal axes:

11. $x^2 + xy + y^2 = 1$

12. $x^2 - xy + y^2 = 1$

13. $x^2 + xy - y^2 = 1$

14. $x^2 - xy - y^2 = 1$

15. $x^2 + xy + 2y^2 = 1$

16. $x^2 - xy + 2y^2 = 1$

17. $x^2 - 2xy + y^2 = 2y$

18. $x^2 - 4xy + 4y^2 = x$

19. $2x^2 - 6xy + y^2 = 1$

20. $x^2 + 3xy - y^2 = 1.$

Suppose a rotation converts $ax^2 + bxy + cy^2$ into $\bar{a}\bar{x}^2 + \bar{b}\bar{x}\bar{y} + \bar{c}\bar{y}^2$. Prove:

21. $a + c = \bar{a} + \bar{c}$ 22*. $4ac - b^2 = 4\bar{a}\bar{c} - \bar{b}^2$.

9. ADDITIONAL EXERCISES ON CONICS [Optional]

Circles and Loci

1. Let $\|\mathbf{x} - \mathbf{a}\|^2 = r^2$ and $\|\mathbf{x} - \mathbf{b}\|^2 = s^2$ be two non-concentric circles. The **radical axis** of the two circles is the locus of $\|\mathbf{x} - \mathbf{a}\|^2 - \|\mathbf{x} - \mathbf{b}\|^2 = r^2 - s^2$.
   Prove that the radical axis is a line perpendicular to the line joining $\mathbf{a}$ and $\mathbf{b}$.

2. (cont.) Suppose the circles intersect in two points. Prove that the radical axis is the line through these points.

3. (cont.) Suppose the circles are tangent. Prove that the radical axis is their common tangent line.

4. (cont.) Suppose the circles do not meet. Prove that the radical axis is the locus of all points $\mathbf{x}$ such that the tangents from $\mathbf{x}$ to the two circles all have the same length.

5. Find conditions on $\mathbf{a}$, $\mathbf{b}$, r, s so that the circles $\|\mathbf{x} - \mathbf{a}\| = r$ and $\|\mathbf{x} - \mathbf{b}\| = s$ intersect at right angles.

6*. Let $\mathbf{z}$ trace a circle passing through $\mathbf{0}$. Prove that the locus of $\mathbf{x} = \mathbf{z}/\|\mathbf{z}\|^2$ is a line. [*Hint:* First show that $\mathbf{z} = \mathbf{x}/\|\mathbf{x}\|^2$.]

7*. Let $\mathbf{z}$ trace a line L not through $\mathbf{0}$. Prove that the locus of $\mathbf{x} = \mathbf{z}/\|\mathbf{z}\|^2$ is a circle through $\mathbf{0}$. [*Hint:* Use normal form and the previous hint.]

8*. Let C_1 and C_2 be circles through $\mathbf{0}$. Each line L through $\mathbf{0}$ meets C_1 in a second point $\mathbf{x}_1$ and C_2 in another point $\mathbf{x}_2$. Find the locus of the midpoint of $\mathbf{x}_1$ and $\mathbf{x}_2$ as L varies.

9*. Let $\mathbf{p}$ be a point outside of the unit circle. Prove that the midpoint of the two points of contact of the tangents from $\mathbf{p}$ is $\mathbf{p}/\|\mathbf{p}\|^2$.

10*. A point $\mathbf{x}_1$ moves uniformly counterclockwise around a circle C_1, completing a revolution in time 2π. A second point $\mathbf{x}_2$ moves uniformly counterclockwise around another circle C_2, completing a revolution in the same time. Find the locus of the midpoint of $\mathbf{x}_1$ and $\mathbf{x}_2$.

11*. Let C_1 and C_2 be two circles that are external to each other, and let $a > 0$. Find the locus of all points $\mathbf{x}$ such that the length of the tangents from $\mathbf{x}$ to C_1 is a times the length of the tangents from $\mathbf{x}$ to C_2.

12*. For each (a, b) satisfying $a^{-2} + b^{-2} = 1$, let $\mathbf{x}$ be the point on the line $x/a + y/b = 1$ nearest $\mathbf{0}$. Find the locus of $\mathbf{x}$.

Parabolas

1. A circle C and a line L are given. Find the locus of all points $\mathbf{x}$ whose distance from L equals the length of the tangents from $\mathbf{x}$ to C. Discuss the case in which L passes through the center of C.

2*. Let P be a parabola with vertex $\mathbf{v}$. Let $\mathbf{x}_1$ and $\mathbf{x}_2$ be variable points of P such that $\angle\, \mathbf{x}_1\mathbf{v}\mathbf{x}_2$ is a right angle. Prove that the chords $\mathbf{x}_1\mathbf{x}_2$ all have a common point.

3*. (cont.) Prove that the locus of the midpoint of $\mathbf{x}_1\mathbf{x}_2$ is another parabola.

4. For each m, the line $y - 1 = m(x - 1)$ intersects the parabola $y = x^2$ in $(1, 1)$ and another point. Find a value of m for which the second point coincides with $(1, 1)$. Interpret.

5*. Each line through the focus $(0, 1)$ of the parabola $4y = x^2$ meets the parabola in the end points of a segment. Show that the locus of the midpoints of these segments is the parabola $2y = x^2 + 2$.

6*. Let **ab** be a chord through the focus of a parabola. Show that the circle with diameter **ab** is tangent to the directrix.

7*. Let **x** be any point on the parabola $x^2 = 4py$ and let **p** be the focus. Prove that the circle with diameter **px** is tangent to the x-axis.

8*. Suppose a circle C meets $x^2 = 4py$ in four points (x_i, y_i), $i = 1, 2, 3, 4$. Prove that $x_1 + x_2 + x_3 + x_4 = 0$.

9*. Let P be a parabola and L a line. Prove that the locus of all midpoints of chords of P parallel to L lie on a line parallel to the axis of P.

10*. A circle C and a line L are given. Prove that the locus of the centers of all circles tangent both to C and to L consists of two parabolas.

Ellipses

1. Show that

$$x = \frac{1 - t^2}{1 + t^2}, \qquad y = \frac{2t}{1 + t^2},$$

parameterizes the unit circle by *rational* functions.

2*. (cont.) Can you parametrize the ellipse $x^2/a^2 + y^2/b^2 = 1$ by rational functions? [*Hint:* Intersect the ellipse with the line $y = t(x + a)$. One intersection is $(-a, 0)$; express the other in terms of t.]

3*. Let $\mathbf{x}_1$ and $\mathbf{x}_2$ be two points of the ellipse $x^2/a^2 + y^2/b^2 = 1$ such that $\mathbf{x}_1 \cdot \mathbf{x}_2 = 0$. Prove that $\|\mathbf{x}_1\|^{-2} + \|\mathbf{x}_2\|^{-2}$ is constant.

4*. (cont.) Prove that the line $\mathbf{x}_1\mathbf{x}_2$ is a constant distance from **0**.

5*. Fix c and consider various values of $\lambda > 0$. Draw the family of ellipses

$$\frac{x^2}{\lambda + c^2} + \frac{y^2}{\lambda^2} = 1.$$

Prove they all have the same foci and no two intersect. Describe the ellipses as $\lambda \longrightarrow \infty$ and as $\lambda \longrightarrow 0+$. (This is called a family of **confocal ellipses**.)

6*. Let (x_0, y_0) be a point on the ellipse $x^2/a^2 + y^2/b^2 = 1$. Show that the line $x_0x/a^2 + y_0y/b^2 = 1$ meets the ellipse only in the point (x_0, y_0). Interpret.

Hyperbolas

1. Prove that the equation of the rectangular hyperbola with foci at (c, c) and $(-c, -c)$ is $2xy = c^2$.

2*. Let H be a hyperbola and L a line. Prove that the locus of the midpoints of all chords of H parallel to L is part of a line.

3*. Let L and M be fixed perpendicular lines and **p** a fixed point. A variable line through **p** meets L in **a** and M in **b**. Prove that the locus of $\mathbf{x} = \frac{1}{2}(\mathbf{a} + \mathbf{b})$ is a hyperbola with asymptotes parallel to L and M.

4*. Let H be a hyperbola with center $\mathbf{0}$ and let $\mathbf{p}$ be a fixed point. Prove that the locus of all midpoints of chords of H through $\mathbf{p}$ is a hyperbola with center $\frac{1}{2}\mathbf{p}$.

5*. Let $\mathbf{p}$ be a focus of a hyperbola H, and let $\mathbf{xy}$ be any chord of H through $\mathbf{p}$ with $\mathbf{x}$ and $\mathbf{y}$ on the same branch of H. Prove that $\|\mathbf{x} - \mathbf{p}\|^{-1} + \|\mathbf{y} - \mathbf{p}\|^{-1}$ is constant. [*Hint:* Use Ex. 23 of Section 7.]

6*. Show that the result of Ex. 5 also holds for parabolas and ellipses. [*Hint:* Use polar form.]

7*. Fix $c > 0$. Sketch the family of confocal hyperbolas

$$\frac{x^2}{c^2 - \lambda} - \frac{y^2}{\lambda} = 1 \qquad (0 < \lambda < c^2).$$

Describe the hyperbolas as $\lambda \longrightarrow 0+$ and as $\lambda \longrightarrow c^2-$.

8*. (cont.) Prove the curves have the same foci and that no two of them intersect.

9*. Find the locus of $\mathbf{x} = (a \tan(\theta + \alpha), b \tan(\theta + \beta))$, where a, b, α, β are fixed and θ is variable.

10*. Prove that the curve $ax^2 + bxy + cy^2 = 1$ is an ellipse if $a > 0$ and $4ac - b^2 > 0$, and is a hyperbola if $4ac - b^2 < 0$. What happens if $4ac - b^2 = 0$? [*Hint:* Use Exs. 21, 22 of Section 8.]

4. The Derivative

1. INTRODUCTION

The processes of nature are dynamic. Living matter grows; a planet moves in its orbit; a chemical reaction occurs at a certain rate; a rocket accelerates; a heavy object falls at increasing speed; a quantity of radioactive matter decays; a particle of fluid in a stream flows along its path with varying speed. Differential Calculus is the precise scientific theory that unifies the study of most situations in which there is dynamic change. It is indispensable for your further study of mathematics, physics, chemistry, engineering, modern biology, economics, virtually every exact science, both the theory and the application.

The main objects of study in Differential Calculus are functions. A function is a law which tells how one variable quantity is related to another. Given a particular function, Differential Calculus shows us the precise *rate of change* of the dependent variable relative to change in the independent variable. For example, if the dependent variable x is the distance a particle moves in time t, where t is the independent variable, then $x = x(t)$ is the law of motion of the particle; Calculus tells us the rate of change of distance per unit time, or instantaneous speed. As another example, the pressure P (dependent variable) of a gas confined in a cylinder of variable volume V (independent variable) varies according to the gas law

$$P = \frac{c}{V} \qquad (c \text{ a constant}).$$

From Calculus we learn the rate at which the pressure P changes relative to change in the volume V.

2. SLOPE

Differential Calculus deals with functions whose graphs are smooth curves. The graph of such a function $y = f(x)$ is usually drawn on rectangular graph paper (Fig. 2.1).

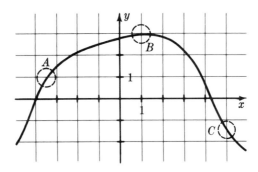

FIG. 2.1

Look at several portions of this graph through a microscope. If the magnification is sufficiently great, small portions appear to be almost straight (Fig. 2.2). Between P and Q in Detail A, the function y increases 0.005 units

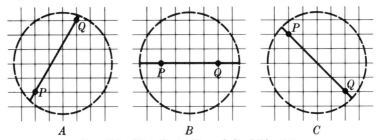

FIG. 2.2   Details A, B, and C of Fig. 2.1.

as x increases 0.003 units. It is reasonable to say that the rate of increase of the function is approximately

$$\frac{0.005}{0.003} = \frac{5}{3}.$$

In Detail B there is no increase in y as x increases 0.004, so the rate of change is approximately 0. Finally, in Detail C the function actually decreases 0.004 as x increases 0.004. In this case the approximate rate of increase is

$$\frac{-0.004}{0.004} = -1.$$

Here is the first idea for finding the rate of growth of a function at a point P. Magnify a small vicinity of P until the curve appears to be almost a straight line. Then define the rate of growth of the function at P to be the rate of change of this line.

In case the graph *is* a straight line, its rate of growth or change is the same at all points. This rate is called the **slope** of the line. It represents the change in y per unit change in x. The slope of a (nonvertical) line is easy to compute. Given any two points (x_0, y_0) and (x_1, y_1) on the line,

$$\text{slope} = \frac{y_1 - y_0}{x_1 - x_0}.$$

This number is the ratio of change in y to change in x. By similar triangles, this ratio depends only on the line, not on the particular pair of points (Fig. 2.3).

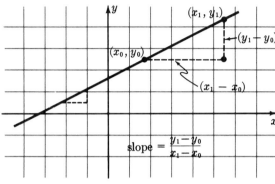

FIG. 2.3

The graph of a linear function

$$f(x) = mx + b$$

is a straight line (Fig. 2.4). Its slope is the coefficient m; let us check this.

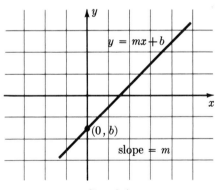

FIG. 2.4

Take any two points (x_0, y_0) and (x_1, y_1) on the graph. Then

$$y_1 = mx_1 + b, \qquad y_0 = mx_0 + b,$$

$$\frac{y_1 - y_0}{x_1 - x_0} = \frac{(mx_1 + b) - (mx_0 + b)}{x_1 - x_0} = \frac{mx_1 - mx_0}{x_1 - x_0} = m.$$

Note the special case $m = 0$. Then the function is

$$f(x) = b,$$

a constant function. Its slope is 0. No amount of change in x can produce any change whatever in y, so naturally the rate of change of y with respect to x is 0. See Fig. 2.5.

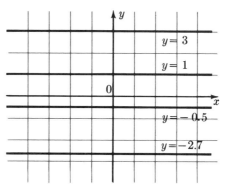

FIG. 2.5   Constant functions.

It is important to have a feeling for the magnitude of slope. Study Fig. 2.6 so you realize how slowly a line of slope $\frac{1}{10}$ grows and how quickly a line of slope 12 grows. Try to imagine slopes of 100 and of 10^{-3}.

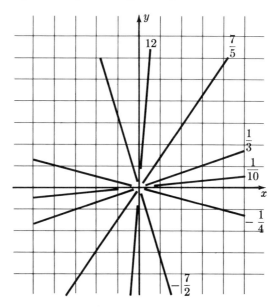

FIG. 2.6   Various slopes.

Plot the points and find the slope of the line segment joining them:

1. $(1, \frac{1}{4})$, (4, 1)
2. (2, 1), (5, 5)
3. $(-1, 2)$, $(3, -4)$
4. $(-30, 1)$, (30, 1).

Give the slope of the line:

5. $y = 2x + 3$
6. $y = -7x + 1$
7. $12y - 4x = 3$
8. $\dfrac{y + 1}{x - 1} = 2.$

Write the equation of the line:

9. through the points (3, 3), (0, 0)
10. through the points $(-4, -4)$, $(-1, -1)$
11. through the points (2, 0), $(0, -3)$
12. through the points $(-3, 4)$, (1, 2)
13. through the point (0, 3) with slope $m = 1$
14. through the point (0, 1) with slope $m = -7$
15. through the point (4, 3) with slope $m = 5$
16. through the point $(-1, 7)$ with slope $m = -\frac{4}{3}$.
17. A straight line rises 1 inch in 1 mile. What is its slope?
18. A 48-ft-wide highway is sloped for drainage. It is 3 in. higher along the center line than along the edges. What is the slope of the road on each side of the center line?
19. If a small part of the circle $x^2 + y^2 = 1$ near the point (0, 1) is viewed under a microscope, what does it look like?
20. Plot the graph and give the equation of a line that passes through (0, 3) and is parallel to $y = -2x$.

3. THE DERIVATIVE

A function $y = f(x)$ is under scrutiny. Perhaps it arises in a physical situation. Its graph is a smooth curve (Fig. 3.1).

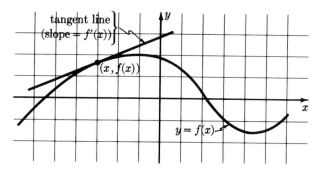

Fɪɢ. 3.1

Place a powerful microscope over a point $(x, y) = (x, f(x))$ of the graph. Under high magnification the graph looks nearly straight. Under higher magnification, the graph looks even straighter. Try to imagine the magnification increased indefinitely. The resulting ultimate view is a straight line called the **tangent line** to the graph. Its slope is called the **derivative of** $f(x)$ **at** x and is written

$$f'(x).$$

Thus the tangent line is the straight line through the point $(x, f(x))$ with slope $f'(x)$.

You know one derivative, that of a linear function

$$f(x) = mx + b.$$

Its derivative at each x is

$$f'(x) = m,$$

the slope of the graph.

To find the value of the derivative of any function $y = f(x)$ at $x = a$, you must find the slope of the tangent line to the graph at $(a, f(a))$. See Fig. 3.2.

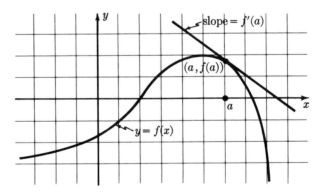

FIG. 3.2

The **slope of a graph** at a point is the slope of its tangent line at the point.

You **differentiate** a function $f(x)$ to form its derivative $f'(x)$. This process of forming the derivative is called **differentiation.** Thus differentiation of $f(x) = 2x - 1$ yields its derivative $f'(x) = 2$; differentiation of $f(x) = -3x$ yields its derivative $f'(x) = -3$.

Fortunately almost every function which occurs in real life can be differentiated. This is important because the derivative turns out to be so useful in applications.

In the following sections you will see the derivative computed in a number of particular cases. In each case the derivative is computed by a sequence of approximations. Each approximation is the slope of a secant to the graph through the point at $x = a$ and a nearby point at $x = a + h$. See Fig. 3.3. As h gets smaller and smaller, the secant is a better and better approximation to the tangent.

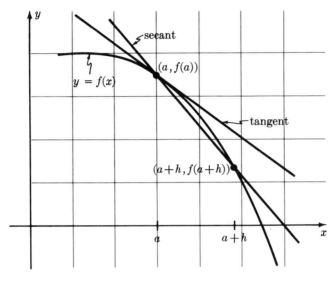

FIG. 3.3

Now please reread this short section several times. It contains the basic idea of Differential Calculus.

4. DERIVATIVE OF f(x) = x²

For a linear function $f(x) = mx + b$, the rate of change of $f(x)$ is constant. For the function $f(x) = x^2$, however, the rate of change is not constant. Graph $y = x^2$. See Fig. 4.1. Near the origin a small change in x produces a small change in y. Farther from the origin, the same change in x causes a larger change in y. For example, as x changes from 0 to 0.1, y increases by $(0.1)^2 - 0^2 = 0.01$, but as x changes from 3 to 3.1, y increases by

$$(3.1)^2 - 3^2 = 0.61.$$

Let us see precisely how the function is changing at various points. First take $x = 0$. The corresponding point of the graph is $(0, 0)$. A nearby point is (h, h^2). The line (secant) through these points has slope

$$\frac{h^2 - 0}{h - 0} = h.$$

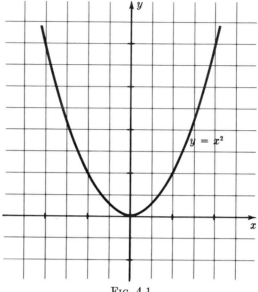

FIG. 4.1

When $h = 0.5$, the slope of the secant is 0.5; when $h = 0.1$, the slope is 0.1. See Fig. 4.2. The smaller h is, the closer the slope of the secant is to 0.

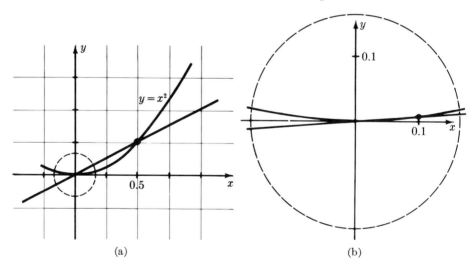

(a)   (b)

FIG. 4.2   (a) Graph of $y = x^2$.   (b) Detail of (a).

Conclusion: the slope of the curve at $(0, 0)$ is 0. Write

$$f(x) = x^2, \qquad f'(0) = 0.$$

Next, try a value different from 0, say $x = a$. Examine the slope of the secant through (a, a^2) and a nearby point $(a + h, (a + h)^2)$:

$$(\text{slope of secant}) = \frac{(a+h)^2 - a^2}{(a+h) - a} = \frac{(a+h)^2 - a^2}{h}.$$

Some values for $a = 1$ are tabulated:

h	1	0.5	0.1	0.001
slope	3	2.5	2.1	2.001

The values of the slope seem to approach the value 2 as h decreases. Try $h = 0.000001$; the new slope is 2.000001, still closer to 2.

Here are similar tables computed for $a = 2$

h	1	0.5	0.1	0.001
slope	5	4.5	4.1	4.001

and $a = 10$:

h	1	0.5	0.1	0.001
slope	21	20.5	20.1	20.001

The data suggest the following conclusions:

a	Slope = $f'(a)$
0	0
1	2
2	4
10	20

In each case the slope is $2a$. See Fig. 4.3. In general,

$$(\text{slope of secant}) = \frac{(a+h)^2 - a^2}{h}$$

$$= \frac{(a^2 + 2ah + h^2) - a^2}{h}$$

$$= \frac{2ah + h^2}{h}$$

$$= 2a + h.$$

Thus

$$(\text{slope of secant}) = 2a + h.$$

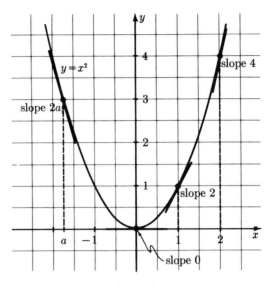

Fɪɢ. 4.3

As h becomes smaller and smaller, the slope of the secant more closely approximates $2a$. We conclude that the slope of the tangent line at (a, a^2) is $2a$. This means if $f(x) = x^2$, then $f'(a) = 2a$, or in general, $f'(x) = 2x$.

> The derivative of x^2 is $2x$.

Notation

Another notation for the operation of differentiation with respect to x is

$$\frac{d}{dx}.$$

It is applied to a function $y = f(x)$ as follows:

$$\frac{d}{dx} f(x) = f'(x).$$

Also the symbols

$$\frac{df}{dx} \quad \text{and} \quad \frac{dy}{dx}$$

denote $f'(x)$.

Examples.

$$\frac{d}{dx} (mx + b) = m.$$

$$y = x^2, \qquad \frac{dy}{dx} = 2x.$$

$$f(x) = 3x - 1, \qquad \frac{df}{dx} = 3.$$

The notation

$$\frac{dy}{dx}$$

does not indicate the point where the derivative is evaluated. When it is necessary to show the value of the derivative at $x = a$, the following notation is used:

$$\frac{dy}{dx}\bigg|_{x=a} \qquad \text{or simply} \qquad \frac{dy}{dx}\bigg|_{a}.$$

Example.

$$y = x^2, \qquad a = 3.$$

$$\frac{dy}{dx} = 2x,$$

$$\frac{dy}{dx}\bigg|_{x=3} = 2 \cdot 3 = 6.$$

Similarly,

$$\frac{dy}{dx}\bigg|_{-2} = 2(-2) = -4.$$

EXERCISES

Find:

1. $\dfrac{dy}{dx}$, for $y = x^2$

2. $\dfrac{dV}{dP}$, where $V = P^2$

3. $\dfrac{dy}{dx}$, for $y = -4(x - 5)$

4. $\dfrac{ds}{dt}$, where $s = -3(4 - 5t)$

5. $\dfrac{d}{dx}(x)$

6. $\dfrac{d}{dx}(x^2)$

7. $\dfrac{df}{dx}$, for $f(x) = 3x + 2$

8. $\dfrac{df}{dx}$, where $f(x) = 12x - 7$

9. $f'(x)$, where $f(x) = 8x$

10. $F'(z)$, for $F(z) = z^2$.

Evaluate:

11. $\dfrac{d}{dx}(x^2)$, at $x = 3, 7, 11$

12. $\dfrac{d}{dP}(P^2)$, at $P = -1, 1, 0$

13. $\dfrac{d}{dx}(13x + 5)$, at $x = 2$

14. $\dfrac{d}{dt}(-13t + v_0)$, for $t = 0$

15. $\left.\dfrac{dy}{dx}\right|_{x=3}$, $y = x^2$

16. $\left.\dfrac{dR}{dI}\right|_{I=-2}$, where $R = I^2$

17. $\left.\dfrac{dv}{dt}\right|_9$, $v = -32t + 200$

18. $\left.\dfrac{ds}{dt}\right|_{10}$, $s = t^2$.

Calculate:

19. $f'(-6)$, $f'(12)$, $f'(1)$, where $f(x) = x^2$

20. $G'(-1)$, $G'(0)$, $G'(1)$, if $G(x) = x^2$.

Compute the slope of the secant to $y = x^2$ through (a, a^2) and $(a + h, (a + h)^2)$:

21. for $a = -2$; $h = 1, 0.5, 0.1, 0.001$

22. for $a = 1$; $h = -1, -0.5, -0.1, -0.001$.

23. Find all points on $y = x^2$ where the tangent has slope 6.

24. Find a point on $y = x^2$ where the tangent is parallel to the line $x + 2y + 7 = 0$.

5. DERIVATIVE OF $f(x) = x^3$

Take a point (a, a^3) on the graph (Fig. 5.1) of the function

$$y = f(x) = x^3.$$

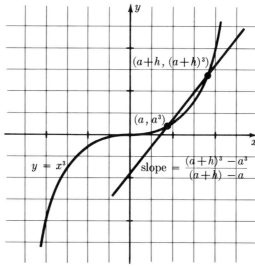

FIG. 5.1

Compute the slope of the secant through (a, a^3) and the nearby point $(a + h, (a + h)^3)$ of the graph:

$$(\text{slope of secant}) = \frac{(a + h)^3 - a^3}{(a + h) - a}.$$

The numerator is

$$(a + h)^3 - a^3 = (a^3 + 3a^2h + 3ah^2 + h^3) - a^3$$
$$= 3a^2h + 3ah^2 + h^3,$$

and the denominator is

$$(a + h) - a = h.$$

Hence

$$\text{(slope of secant)} = \frac{3a^2h + 3ah^2 + h^3}{h} = 3a^2 + 3ah + h^2.$$

Taking h smaller and smaller forces the slope of the secant closer and closer to $3a^2$. Conclusion:

$$\text{(slope of tangent)} = 3a^2.$$

Expressed in derivative notation,

$$\frac{d}{dx}(x^3) = 3x^2.$$

There is another instructive way to do the above computation. This time call the nearby point (x, x^3), but remember that x is close to a. See Fig. 5.2.

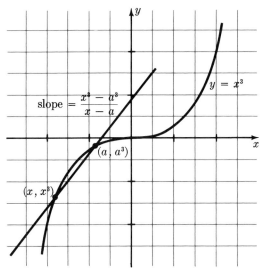

FIG. 5.2

For x near a,

$$\text{(slope of secant)} = \frac{x^3 - a^3}{x - a}.$$

From algebra, $x - a$ is a factor of $x^3 - a^3$:

$$x^3 - a^3 = (x - a)(x^2 + ax + a^2).$$

Hence

$$(\text{slope of secant}) = x^2 + ax + a^2.$$

Now let x approach closer and closer to a. Write

$$x \longrightarrow a$$

to abbreviate this "closer and closer" statement. Then

$$ax \longrightarrow a \cdot a = a^2,$$
$$x^2 = x \cdot x \longrightarrow a \cdot a = a^2,$$

and therefore

$$(\text{slope of secant}) \longrightarrow a^2 + a^2 + a^2 = 3a^2.$$

Conclusion:

$$\frac{d}{dx}(x^3) = 3x^2.$$

Similarly we can derive

$$\frac{d}{dx}(x^4) = 4x^3,$$

$$\frac{d}{dx}(x^5) = 5x^4,$$

and so on. However, we postpone doing so until we actually need these formulas.

EXERCISES

Use differentiation to find:

1. $\dfrac{dy}{dx}$, if $y = x^3$

2. $\dfrac{dF}{dx}$, if $F(x) = x^3$

3. $\dfrac{d}{dx}(4^3)$

4. $\dfrac{d}{dt}(5)\Big|_{t=1}$

5. $\dfrac{dy}{dx}$ at $x = 0, 3, -3$, if $y = x^3$

6. $\dfrac{ds}{dt}$ for $t = 0, 1, 2, 3$ if $s = t^3$

7. $\dfrac{dG}{dz}\Big|_6$, $G(z) = z^3$

8. $\dfrac{dy}{dx}\Big|_{-4}$, $y = x^3$

9. $V'(4)$, $V'(a)$, if $V(P) = P^3$

10. $s'(5)$, $s'(t_0)$, if $s(t) = t^3$.

Compute the slope of the secant to $y = x^3$ through (a, a^3) and $(a + h, (a + h)^3)$:

11. for $a = 1$; $h = 1, 0.5, 0.1, 0.001$

12. for $a = 1$; $h = -1, -0.5, -0.1, -0.001$.

Compute the slope of the secant to the curve $y = x^3$ through (a, a^3) and (x, x^3):

13. for $a = 2$; $x = 3, 2.5, 2.1, 2.001$

14. for $a = 2$; $x = 1, 1.5, 1.9, 1.99$.

15. Find all points on the curve $y = x^3$ where the slope is 12.

16. Is the graph of $y = x^3$ ever horizontal?

17. Show there do not exist points on the curve $y = x^3$ where the tangent is parallel to the line $x + y + 1 = 0$.

18. Find which of the two curves $y = x^2$ and $y = x^3$ is steeper at $x = \frac{1}{2}$, at $x = 1$, at $x = 2$.

19. Find all positive values of x where $y = x^2$ is steeper than $y = x^3$.

20. Find all positive values of x where $y = x^3$ is steeper than $y = x^2$.

6. DERIVATIVE OF $f(x) = 1/x$

We seek the derivative of the function

$$f(x) = \frac{1}{x},$$

whose graph is shown in Fig. 6.1.

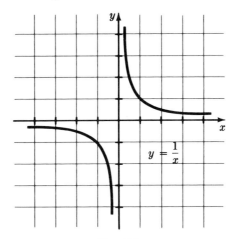

FIG. 6.1

Fix $x_0 \neq 0$. The slope of the secant through $(x_0, f(x_0))$ and a nearby point $(x_0 + h, f(x_0 + h))$ is

$$(\text{slope of secant}) = \frac{f(x_0 + h) - f(x_0)}{(x_0 + h) - x_0}$$

$$= \frac{1}{h} [f(x_0 + h) - f(x_0)]$$

$$= \frac{1}{h} \left[\frac{1}{x_0 + h} - \frac{1}{x_0} \right] = \frac{1}{h} \left[\frac{x_0 - (x_0 + h)}{(x_0 + h)x_0} \right]$$

$$= \frac{1}{h} \left[\frac{-h}{(x_0 + h)x_0} \right] = \frac{-1}{(x_0 + h)x_0}.$$

Let $h \longrightarrow 0$. Then

$$(x_0 + h) \longrightarrow x_0,$$

$$(x_0 + h)x_0 \longrightarrow x_0 \cdot x_0 = x_0{}^2,$$

$$(\text{slope of secant}) \longrightarrow \frac{-1}{x_0{}^2}.$$

Conclusion:

$$\frac{d}{dx}\left(\frac{1}{x}\right) = \frac{-1}{x^2}.$$

The derivative is negative since the function decreases as x increases.

EXERCISES

Differentiate:

1. $y = 1/x$

2. $F(t) = 1/t$.

Calculate:

3. $f'(-1)$, $f'(1)$, $f'(a)$, $f'(-a)$, where $f(x) = 1/x$

4. $f'(-\frac{1}{2})$, $f'(\frac{1}{2})$, $f'(2)$, $f'(3)$, if $f(x) = 1/x$

5. $\dfrac{dy}{dx}\bigg|_{x=a}$ and $\dfrac{dy}{dx}\bigg|_{x=1/a}$, if $y = \dfrac{1}{x}$

6. $\dfrac{dV}{dP}\bigg|_{P=1/4}$ and $\dfrac{dV}{dP}\bigg|_{P-1}$, if $V = \dfrac{1}{P}$

7. $\dfrac{d}{ds}\left(\dfrac{1}{s}\right)\bigg|_{b}$

8. $\dfrac{d}{dx}\left(\dfrac{1}{x}\right)\bigg|_{t}$.

9. Find where the curve $y = 1/x$ has slope $-\frac{1}{2}$.

10. Is the curve $y = 1/x$ ever horizontal?

11. Do the curves $y = 1/x$ and $y = x^3$ ever have the same slope?

Let $f(x) = 1/x$. Find the slope of the secant:

12. through $(1, f(1))$ and $(2, f(2))$ 13. through $(10, f(10))$ and $(11, f(11))$

14. through $(100, f(100))$ and $(101, f(101))$.

7. THE TANGENT LINE

Take a point $(a, f(a))$ on the graph of a function $y = f(x)$. The tangent line at this point (Fig. 7.1) has slope $f'(a)$. Its equation is found by the point-slope formula:

$$y - f(a) = f'(a)(x - a),$$

or

$$y = f(a) + f'(a)(x - a).$$

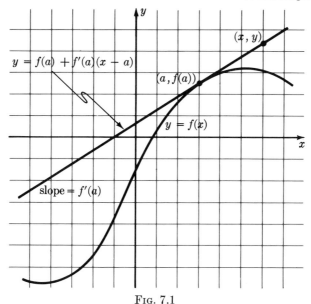

FIG. 7.1

EXAMPLE 7.1

Find the equation of the tangent line to the curve $y = x^2$ at $x = -2$.

Solution: At $x = -2$, $y = (-2)^2 = 4$, and the derivative is

$$\frac{dy}{dx}\bigg|_{-2} = 2x\bigg|_{-2} = 2(-2) = -4.$$

Thus the tangent line passes through $(-2, 4)$ and has slope -4. Its equation is

$$y - 4 = -4(x + 2).$$

Hence

$$y = 4 - 4(x + 2)$$
$$= -4x - 4.$$

Answer: $y = -4x - 4$.

EXAMPLE 7.2

Find where the tangent line to the curve $y = 1/x$ at $x = 3$ meets the x-axis.

Solution: When $x = 3$, $y = \tfrac{1}{3}$. Set $f(x) = 1/x$. Then

$$f'(x) = -\frac{1}{x^2}, \qquad f'(3) = -\frac{1}{9}.$$

The tangent line has slope $-\frac{1}{9}$ and passes through $(3, \frac{1}{3})$. Its equation is

$$y - \frac{1}{3} = -\frac{1}{9}(x - 3),$$

that is,

$$y = -\frac{1}{9}x + \frac{2}{3}.$$

It crosses the x-axis where $y = 0$, i.e.,

$$-\frac{1}{9}x + \frac{2}{3} = 0.$$

Hence

$$x = 6.$$

> *Answer:*   The tangent line meets
> the x-axis at $(6, 0)$.

The tangents at certain points of a curve may be vertical; at such points the derivative is undefined. However, the equation of the tangent is then simply $x = $ constant.

EXERCISES

Write the equation of the tangent to the curve:

1. $y = x^2$, through $(2, 4)$ 2. $y = x^3$, through $(2, 8)$
3. $y = 1/x$, through $(-1, -1)$ 4. $y = 1/x$, through $(2, \frac{1}{2})$.

Write the equation of the tangent to the curve:

5. $y = x^2$, at $x = -1$ 6. $y = x^3$, at $x = -1$
7. $y = 1/x$, at $x = -3$ 8. $y = 1/x$, at $x = 4$.

Find the equation(s) of the tangent(s) to the curve:

9. $y = x^2$, at all points where the slope is 10
10. $y = x^3$, at all points where the slope is 27
11. $y = x^2$, if the tangent crosses the y-axis at $y = -16$
12. $y = x^3$, if the tangent crosses the y-axis at $y = -128$.

Find the equation(s) of the tangent line(s) to the curve and determine where each crosses the coordinate axes if:

13. the curve is $y = x^2$ and the tangent is at the point $(10, 100)$
14. the tangent is determined by the curve $y = x^3$ and the point $(10, 1000)$
15. the curve is defined by the function $F(x) = 1/x$ and the tangent has slope -81
16. the curve is defined by the function $f(x) = 1/x$ and the tangent has slope -6.

Find the area of the triangle bounded by the coordinate axes and the line tangent to $y = 1/x$:

17. at $x = 2$ 18. at $x = a$, where $a \neq 0$.

19. Show that the tangents to the parabola $y = x^2$ at $(3, 9)$ and $(-3, 9)$ cross on the y-axis. Where?

20. Exactly one of the lines $y = 3x + b$ is tangent to the parabola $y = x^2$. Which one?

21. Which of the lines $y = -9x + b$ is tangent to the curve $y = 1/x$?

8. RULES FOR DIFFERENTIATING

You know these derivatives:

$$\frac{d}{dx}(mx + b) = m, \qquad \frac{d}{dx}\left(\frac{1}{x}\right) = \frac{-1}{x^2},$$

$$\frac{d}{dx}(x^2) = 2x, \qquad \frac{d}{dx}(x^3) = 3x^2.$$

By learning a few simple rules, you will be able to differentiate all sorts of functions constructed from the ones you already know, for example,

$$\frac{3}{x - 1}, \qquad x^3 + x - \frac{1}{x}, \qquad 5x^3 + 2x^2, \; \ldots \;.$$

First the rules will be stated with examples. Then the rules will be justified.

Sum Rule   The derivative of the sum of two functions is the sum of the individual derivatives:

$$\frac{d}{dx}[f(x) + g(x)] = \frac{d}{dx}f(x) + \frac{d}{dx}g(x).$$

EXAMPLE 8.1

Differentiate $x^2 + \dfrac{1}{x}$.

Solution:

$$\frac{d}{dx}\left(x^2 + \frac{1}{x}\right) = \frac{d}{dx}(x^2) + \frac{d}{dx}\left(\frac{1}{x}\right)$$

$$= 2x - \frac{1}{x^2}.$$

Answer: $2x - \dfrac{1}{x^2}$.

EXAMPLE 8.2

Differentiate $x^3 - 8x + 5$.

Solution:

$$\frac{d}{dx}(x^3 - 8x + 5) = \frac{d}{dx}(x^3) + \frac{d}{dx}(-8x + 5) = 3x^2 - 8.$$

Answer: $3x^2 - 8.$

Constant-multiple Rule If a function is multiplied by a constant, its derivative is also multiplied by that constant:

$$\frac{d}{dx}[kf(x)] = kf'(x).$$

EXAMPLE 8.3

Differentiate $8x^3$.

Solution: By the Constant-multiple Rule,

$$\frac{d}{dx}(8x^3) = 8\frac{d}{dx}(x^3) = 8(3x^2).$$

Answer: $24x^2.$

EXAMPLE 8.4

Differentiate $4x^2 - 3x + \dfrac{5}{x}$·

Solution: First apply the Sum Rule, then the Constant-multiple Rule:

$$\frac{d}{dx}\left(4x^2 - 3x + \frac{5}{x}\right) = \frac{d}{dx}(4x^2) + \frac{d}{dx}(-3x) + \frac{d}{dx}\left(\frac{5}{x}\right)$$

$$= 4\frac{d}{dx}(x^2) - 3\frac{d}{dx}(x) + 5\frac{d}{dx}\left(\frac{1}{x}\right)$$

$$= 4(2x) - 3(1) + 5\left(\frac{-1}{x^2}\right)·$$

Answer: $8x - 3 - \dfrac{5}{x^2}$·

With a little practice, it becomes easy to do problems like the last one by inspection.

EXAMPLE 8.5

Differentiate $2x^3 + 5x^2 - 7x$.

Answer: $6x^2 + 10x - 7.$

> **Shifting Rule**   If $g(x) = f(x + c)$, then
>
> $$\frac{d}{dx} g(x) = \frac{df}{dx}\bigg|_{x+c} = f'(x + c).$$

EXAMPLE 8.6

Find $\dfrac{d}{dx}\left(\dfrac{1}{x + 2}\right)$.

Solution: Set

$$f(x) = \frac{1}{x}$$

and

$$g(x) = f(x + 2) = \frac{1}{x + 2}.$$

Then

$$f'(x) = \frac{-1}{x^2};$$

by the Shifting Rule,

$$g'(x) = f'(x + 2) = \frac{-1}{(x + 2)^2}.$$

Answer: $\dfrac{-1}{(x + 2)^2}.$

The next example shows how the Shifting Rule is used in practice.

EXAMPLE 8.7

Differentiate $(x - 1)^2$.

Solution:

$$\frac{d}{dx}(x^2) = 2x, \qquad \frac{d}{dx}[(x - 1)^2] = 2(x - 1).$$

CHECK:

$$(x - 1)^2 = x^2 - 2x + 1.$$

By the Sum Rule,

$$\frac{d}{dx}[(x - 1)^2] = \frac{d}{dx}(x^2) + \frac{d}{dx}(-2x + 1)$$

$$= 2x - 2 = 2(x - 1).$$

Answer: $2(x - 1).$

The following example illustrates a technique used over and over in Calculus.

EXAMPLE 8.8

Differentiate $\dfrac{1}{3x - 5}$.

Solution: By the Shifting Rule,

$$\frac{d}{dx}\left(\frac{1}{x - c}\right) = \frac{-1}{(x - c)^2}, \qquad c \text{ constant.}$$

Our problem, however, has $3x$ in the denominator, so this formula does not apply. We can *make* it apply by dividing the denominator by 3:

$$\frac{1}{3x - 5} = \frac{1}{3}\left(\frac{1}{x - \dfrac{5}{3}}\right).$$

Apply first the Constant-multiple Rule, then the Shifting Rule:

$$\frac{d}{dx}\left(\frac{1}{3x - 5}\right) = \frac{1}{3}\frac{d}{dx}\left(\frac{1}{x - \dfrac{5}{3}}\right) = \frac{1}{3}\left[\frac{-1}{\left(x - \dfrac{5}{3}\right)^2}\right]$$

$$= \frac{-1}{3\left(x - \dfrac{5}{3}\right)^2} = \frac{-3}{(3x - 5)^2}.$$

Answer: $\dfrac{-3}{(3x - 5)^2}.$

REMARK: If you cannot differentiate an expression, try writing it in an equivalent algebraic form; for example, try factoring, multiplying out factors, combining terms, etc.

Scale Rule   If $g(x) = f(kx)$, then

$$\frac{d}{dx}g(x) = k\left.\frac{df}{dx}\right|_{kx} = kf'(kx).$$

EXAMPLE 8.9

Differentiate $(2x)^3$.

Solution: If $f(x) = x^3$, then $f'(x) = 3x^2$. Set $g(x) = f(2x) = (2x)^3$.

By the Scale Rule with $k = 2$,

$$\frac{d}{dx} g(x) = 2f'(2x),$$

$$\frac{d}{dx} (2x)^3 = 2 \cdot 3(2x)^2.$$

Answer: $24x^2$.

REMARK: Compare Example 8.9 with Example 8.3.

EXAMPLE 8.10

Differentiate $\dfrac{1}{3x - 5}$.

Solution: Set

$$f(x) = \frac{1}{x - 5} \quad \text{and} \quad g(x) = f(3x) = \frac{1}{3x - 5}.$$

Then

$$f'(x) = \frac{-1}{(x - 5)^2},$$

so by the Scale Rule,

$$\frac{d}{dx} \left(\frac{1}{3x - 5} \right) = \frac{d}{dx} g(x) = 3f'(3x) = 3 \left[\frac{-1}{(3x - 5)^2} \right].$$

Answer: $\dfrac{-3}{(3x - 5)^2}$.

REMARK: Compare Example 8.10 with Example 8.8.

The Shifting Rule and the Scale Rule are special cases of a more general rule to be derived in Chapter 9:

Chain Rule   If $y = f[g(x)]$, then

$$\frac{dy}{dx} = f'[g(x)] \frac{dg}{dx}.$$

EXAMPLE 8.11

Differentiate $y = (5x - 1)^3 + 4(5x - 1)^2$ by the Chain Rule.

Solution: Set

$$f(x) = x^3 + 4x^2 \quad \text{and} \quad g(x) = 5x - 1.$$

Then

$$f'(x) = 3x^2 + 8x \quad \text{and} \quad \frac{dg}{dx} = 5.$$

Note that $y = f[g(x)]$. Therefore by the Chain Rule,

$$\frac{dy}{dx} = f'(5x - 1) \cdot 5$$
$$= [3(5x - 1)^2 + 8(5x - 1)] \cdot 5$$
$$= 5(5x - 1)(15x + 5).$$

Answer: $25(5x - 1)(3x + 1).$

EXERCISES

Find the derivative:

1. $y = x^3 + \dfrac{1}{x}$

2. $f(x) = x^3 + x^2 + \dfrac{1}{x}$

3. $f(x) = x^2 + 4x + 3$

4. $g(x) = x^3 + x^2 + 5x - 1$

5. $y = \dfrac{1}{x + 1}$

6. $g(x) = \dfrac{1}{x - 4}$

7. $s(t) = (t - 8)^2$

8. $y = (x - 5)^3$

9. $y = 3x^2$

10. $y = -\dfrac{3}{x}.$

Calculate the derivative:

11. $y = x^3 - 2x^2$

12. $y = x^3 - \dfrac{8}{x}$

13. $F(x) = 2x^3 - 5x^2 + 2x + 7$

14. $f(x) = \frac{1}{3}x^3 + \frac{1}{2}x^2 + x + 1$

15. $y = \dfrac{1}{2x - 1}$

16. $g(x) = \dfrac{3}{5x - 2}$

17. $f(x) = (36x - 2)^2$

18. $F(x) = (96x - 9)^3$

19. $\dfrac{d}{dr}(2\pi r^2 + 2\pi r)$

20. $\dfrac{d}{dr}\left(\dfrac{4}{3}\pi r^3 - 3\pi r^2\right).$

21. Use the identity $\dfrac{1}{x(x + 1)} = \dfrac{1}{x} - \dfrac{1}{x + 1}$ to find $\dfrac{d}{dx}\left[\dfrac{1}{x(x + 1)}\right].$

22. Use the identity $\dfrac{x + 2}{x + 1} = \dfrac{x + 1 + 1}{x + 1} = 1 + \dfrac{1}{x + 1}$ to find $\dfrac{d}{dx}\left(\dfrac{x + 2}{x + 1}\right).$

Use the methods of Exs. 21 and 22 to evaluate:

23. $\dfrac{d}{dx}\left[\dfrac{-1}{x(x - 1)}\right]$

24. $\dfrac{d}{dx}\left(\dfrac{x}{x + 1}\right)$

25. $\dfrac{d}{dx}\left[\dfrac{x + 2}{x(x + 1)}\right]$

26. $\dfrac{d}{dx}\left(\dfrac{2x + 1}{4x + 8}\right).$

27. Find the equation of the tangent to $y = x^3 - 3x + 1$ at $x = 2$.

28. Find the equation of the tangent to $y = 4x^3 - 12x$ at $x = \frac{1}{2}$.

29. The path of an electron in a certain magnetic field is the curve $y = 1 - 2x^2$. When $x = 3$ the electron flies off tangentially. Find the equation of its line of travel.

30. An object, moving from left to right, travels along the path $y = 3x^2$. When $x = 2$ the object escapes the path tangentially. Along what line does it travel? Find its position when $x = 3$.

31. The resistance of a certain resistor as a function of temperature is $R = 40(2 + 0.41T + 0.001T^2)$. Find the rate of change of resistance with respect to temperature (in ohms per degree Kelvin) when the temperature is $15°\text{K}$.

32. A ball is thrown straight up. Its height at time t is $s = -16t^2 + 96t + 4$. What is the rate of change of height with respect to time (in ft/sec) after 1 sec, after 3 sec, after 5 sec? How high is the ball at these times?

9. REASONS FOR THE RULES

The Sum Rule is true for linear functions. This is easy to see by direct calculation: if

$$f(x) = mx + b \quad \text{and} \quad g(x) = nx + c,$$

then $f(x) + g(x) = (m + n)x + (b + c)$. The slope of $f(x)$ is m; the slope of $g(x)$ is n; the slope of $f(x) + g(x)$ is $(m + n)$. Thus

$$\frac{d}{dx}[f(x) + g(x)] = m + n = \frac{d}{dx}[f(x)] + \frac{d}{dx}[g(x)].$$

Consequently, for a pair of linear functions, the slope of the sum function is the sum of the two slopes.

Why is the Sum Rule true for any pair of functions?

Graph two functions $y = f(x)$ and $y = g(x)$, and their sum $y = f(x) + g(x)$. Inspect these graphs near $x = a$. See Fig. 9.1. Under a sufficiently

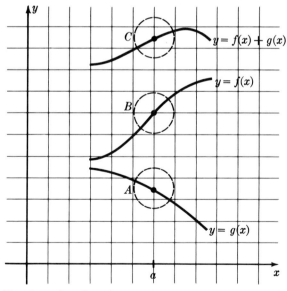

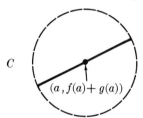

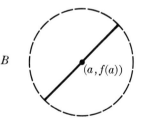

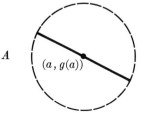

FIG. 9.1 Graphs of $y = g(x)$, of $y = f(x)$, and of $y = f(x) + g(x)$.
A. Detail of $y = g(x)$ with slope $= g'(a)$.
B. Detail of $y = f(x)$ with slope $= f'(a)$.
C. Detail of $y = f(x) + g(x)$ with slope $= f'(a) + g'(a)$.

high-powered microscope, the graphs appear to be straight. Indeed, they are indistinguishable from graphs of linear functions. The function shown in Detail C is the sum of the functions shown in Details A and B. But for all practical purposes these are linear functions, and for linear functions the Sum Rule is true.

The Constant-multiple Rule is true for linear functions. If $g(x) = mx + b$, then $g'(x) = m$. But $kg(x) = (km)x + (kb)$;

$$\frac{d}{dx}[kg(x)] = km = k\frac{d}{dx}[g(x)].$$

A function $f(x)$ looks like a linear function $g(x)$ under a microscope; the constant multiple $kf(x)$ looks like the linear function $kg(x)$. Since the Constant-multiple Rule is true for $g(x)$ it is true for $f(x)$.

The Constant-multiple Rule makes sense if you interpret it this way. If y is changing m times as fast as x, then ky is changing km times as fast as x.

Example.

$$\frac{d}{dx}\left(\frac{1}{x}\right) = \frac{-1}{x^2}, \qquad \frac{d}{dx}\left(\frac{3}{x}\right) = \frac{-3}{x^2}.$$

Figure 9.2 makes this appear plausible.

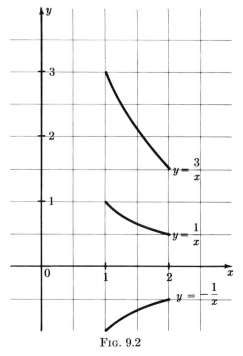

FIG. 9.2

NOTE: k can be negative. On the same figure a portion of the graph of $y = -1/x$ is plotted; it is a reflected image of the graph of $y = 1/x$ in the

x-axis. At each point its slope is

$$\frac{d}{dx}\left(\frac{-1}{x}\right) = -\frac{d}{dx}\left(\frac{1}{x}\right) = \frac{1}{x^2}.$$

The Constant-multiple Rule can be interpreted in terms of a change of units on the y-axis. For example, since one yard equals three feet, a speed of m yd/sec (derivative of distance with respect to time) is the same as a speed of $3m$ ft/sec.

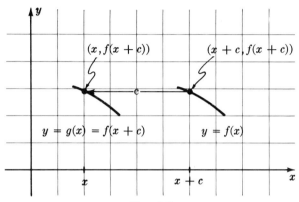

FIG. 9.3

The Shifting Rule is obvious when you look carefully at a graph (Fig. 9.3). The graph of $y = f(x)$ is shifted c units to the left (when c is positive) to form the graph of $y = g(x) = f(x + c)$. The slope of the graph $y = f(x)$ at $x + c$ is the same as the slope of the graph $y = g(x) = f(x + c)$ at x. Examples are shown in Fig. 9.4 and Fig. 9.5.

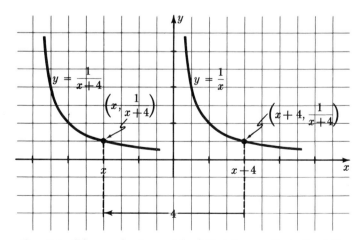

FIG. 9.4   The graph of $y = 1/x$ shifted four units to the left.

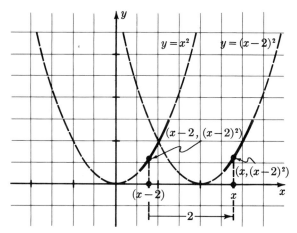

Fɪɢ. 9.5   The graph of $y = x^2$ shifted two units to the right.

The Scale Rule for a positive scale factor k is seen by comparing slopes in Fig. 9.6. Look at the curve on the left, the graph of $y = g(x) = f(kx)$. An increase in x from a to $a + h$ produces an increase in y from $g(a) = f(ka)$ to $g(a + h) = f[k(a + h)]$. Precisely the same increase in y is produced on the graph of $y = f(x)$ by increasing x from ka to $k(a + h)$.

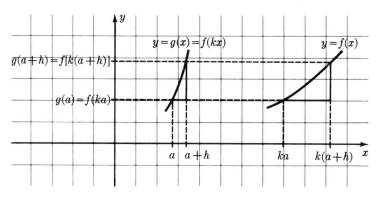

Fɪɢ. 9.6

For the curve on the left, the slope at $x = a$ is approximately

$$\frac{g(a + h) - g(a)}{h} = \frac{f[k(a + h)] - f(ka)}{h}.$$

For the curve on the right, the slope at $x = ka$ is approximately

$$\frac{f[k(a + h)] - f(ka)}{kh},$$

which is the preceding expression divided by k. Consequently,

$$\frac{1}{k}\frac{d}{dx}g(x)\bigg|_{x=a} = \frac{1}{k}\frac{d}{dx}f(kx)\bigg|_{x=a} = \frac{d}{dx}f(x)\bigg|_{x=ka}.$$

Hence

$$\frac{d}{dx}g(x) = k\frac{df}{dx}\bigg|_{kx}.$$

The special case $k = -1$ is illustrated in Fig. 9.7. The graph of $y = g(x) = f(-x)$ is the reflection of the graph of $y = f(x)$ in the y-axis. The slope of $g(x) = f(-x)$ at $x = a$ is the negative of the slope of $f(x)$ at $x = -a$.

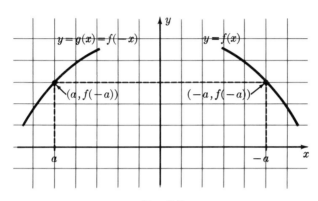

FIG. 9.7

The Scale Rule can be interpreted in terms of a change of units on the x-axis. For example, since one minute equals sixty seconds, a speed of m ft/sec is the same as a speed of $60m$ ft/min.

EXERCISES

Plot the curves. Where more than one equation occurs, plot all curves on the same coordinate axes:

1. $y = \frac{1}{2}x$, $y = x$, $y = 2x$
2. $y = x^2$, $y = -x^2$
3. $y = x^3$, $y = -x^3$
4. $y = \frac{1}{2}x^2$, $y = x^2$, $y = 3x^2$
5. $y = (x - 2)^2$
6. $y = (x + 1)^3$
7. $y = \dfrac{1}{x - 4}$
8. $y = 2x$, $y = 2(x - 3)$
9. $y = x^2$, $y = (x - 1)^2$, $y = -(x - 1)^2$, where $x \geq 0$
10. $y = x^3$, $y = (x + 3)^3$, $y = -(x + 3)^3$, where $x \geq 0$
11. $y = f(x)$, $y = f(-x)$, if $f(x) = (x - 3)^2$ and $x \geq 3$
12. $y = g(x)$, $y = g(-x)$, if $g(x) = (x - 1)^3$ and $x \geq 1$.

Plot the curve $y = f(x) + g(x)$:

13. $f(x) = x$ and $g(x) = 1/x$ 14. $f(x) = 5x$ and $g(x) = 4/x$.

[*Hint:* First plot the curves $y = f(x)$ and $y = g(x)$ on the coordinate axes, then use these curves to locate points on $y = f(x) + g(x)$.]

10. SECOND DERIVATIVE

Start with a function $y = f(x)$. It has a derivative

$$\frac{dy}{dx} = f'(x),$$

which itself is a function. Since the derivative is a function, it also has a derivative,

$$\frac{d}{dx}[f'(x)].$$

This is called the **second derivative** of f and is written

$$\frac{d^2y}{dx^2} \quad \text{or} \quad f''(x).$$

Example.

$$f(x) = x^3 - 3x.$$
$$f'(x) = 3x^2 - 3,$$
$$f''(x) = \frac{d}{dx}(3x^2 - 3) = 6x.$$

Example.

$$H = 4(T + 2)^3.$$
$$\frac{dH}{dT} = 12(T + 2)^2,$$
$$\frac{d^2H}{dT^2} = 24(T + 2).$$

Example.   Let $L = L(t)$ be a function whose first derivative is

$$\frac{dL}{dt} = \frac{1}{t + 1}.$$

Find $\dfrac{d^2L}{dt^2}$.

Solution: $\dfrac{d^2L}{dt^2} = \dfrac{d}{dt}\left(\dfrac{dL}{dt}\right) = \dfrac{d}{dt}\left(\dfrac{1}{t+1}\right) = \dfrac{-1}{(t+1)^2}.$

EXERCISES

Find the first and second derivatives:

1. $y = 5x^2 - 3$

2. $f(x) = 3x^2 - 2x + 1$

3. $y = 7x^3 + 4x^2 - 3x + 2$

4. $F(x) = \frac{1}{3}x^3 + \frac{1}{2}x^2 + x + 1$

5. $V(P) = P^3 - 7$

6. $s(t) = t^2(1 - t)$

7. $f(x) = (x - 2)^3$

8. $y = (8 - x)^2$

9. $y = (3x)^2$

10. $s(t) = -32t^2 + 96t + 4.$

11. Find $f'(1)$, $f'(3)$, $f''(1)$, $f''(3)$, where $f(x) = 3x^2 - x.$

12. Find $f'(2)$, $f'(3)$, $f''(1)$, $f''(2)$, where $f(x) = 4x^3 - x.$

Evaluate:

13. $\dfrac{d^2}{dx^2}(4x^2 + 3)\bigg|_{x=2}$

14. $\dfrac{d^2}{dt^2}(5 - 7t^3)\bigg|_{t=-2}$

15. $\dfrac{d}{dt}\left(\dfrac{dL}{dt}\right)$, where $\dfrac{dL}{dt} = \dfrac{1}{3t - 1}$

16. $F''(2)$, where $\dfrac{dF}{dt} = \dfrac{3}{t} - 7t^2$

17. $\dfrac{d^2V}{dr^2}\bigg|_{r=3}$, where $V = \frac{4}{3}\pi r^3 - \frac{1}{2}\pi r^2$

18. $\dfrac{dv}{dt}$, where $v = \dfrac{ds}{dt}$ and $s = -\frac{1}{2}gt^2 + v_0 t + s_0$

19. $\dfrac{d^2y}{dx^2}$, where $y = -3x + 7.$

Review Exercises

Find all values of x at which the curves have equal slope:

20. $y = -\dfrac{27}{x}$, $\quad y = x^3$

21. $y = 2x^3 - x^2$, $\quad y = x^2 - 4$

22. $y = -3x + 2$, $\quad y = x^3 + 5x^2$

23. $y = \dfrac{1}{2x - 1}$, $\quad y = x^2 - x.$

24. For what values of x are the first and second derivatives of $x^3 - 2x^2 - x$ equal?

25. For what values of x is $x^3 + 6x + 1$ equal to its second derivative?

26. Where does the tangent to the curve $y = kx^2$ at (a, ka^2) meet the x-axis? Assume $k \neq 0$.

27. Show that the tangents to the curve $y = x^2$ at (a, a^2) and at $(a + 1, (a + 1)^2)$ intersect on the curve $y = x^2 - \frac{1}{4}$.

28. For what values of x do $2x^3 + 15x - 1$ and $-3/x$ have the same derivative?

29. Find where the tangent line to $y = 1/(2x - 5)$ at $x = 2$ crosses the line $x = -1$.

5. Applications of Differentiation

1. CURVE SKETCHING

The derivative of a function gives the slope of the tangent to its graph. This information is of great help in sketching curves.

EXAMPLE 1.1

Sketch the curve $y = x^3 - 3x + 1$.

Solution: Examine the derivative:

$$y' = 3x^2 - 3 = 3(x^2 - 1).$$

$$y' > 0 \quad \text{if} \quad x^2 > 1,$$

$$y' < 0 \quad \text{if} \quad x^2 < 1,$$

$$y' = 0 \quad \text{if} \quad x = \pm 1.$$

The curve increases and decreases as indicated below.

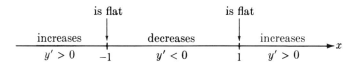

There is a high point on the curve at $x = -1$ and a low point at $x = +1$. Plot the points. At

$$x = -1, \quad y = (-1)^3 - 3(-1) + 1 = 3;$$

at

$$x = +1, \quad y = (1)^3 - 3(1) + 1 = -1.$$

Since it is so easy, plot also the point where $x = 0$. At

$$x = 0, \quad y = (0)^3 - 3(0) + 1 = 1.$$

Now sketch the curve, using the information about its increasing and decreasing sections (Fig. 1.1).

Since $y' = 3(x^2 - 1)$, the slope increases as x increases indefinitely (written $x \longrightarrow \infty$). Similarly, the slope increases as $x = \longrightarrow -\infty$. This is why the curve is progressively steeper to the right and to the left.

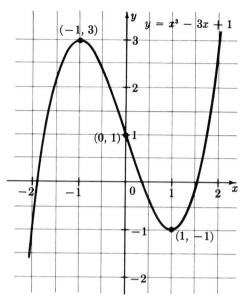

Fɪɢ. 1.1

EXAMPLE 1.2

Sketch $y = 0.75 - 0.25x - 0.25x^3$.

Solution:

$$y' = -0.25 - 0.75x^2.$$

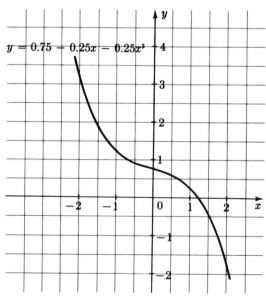

Fɪɢ. 1.2

The derivative is always negative. Hence the graph falls steadily from left to right; there are no high points or low points. Notice that as $x \longrightarrow \infty$ or as $x \longrightarrow -\infty$, the slope y' becomes more and more negative. Hence the curve gets steeper and steeper. If you are alert, you will see that the slope is least negative where $x = 0$. There the slope is -0.25. From this information a reasonable sketch of the graph is easily made (Fig. 1.2).

EXERCISES

Sketch the parabola:

1. $y = x^2 - 2x + 1$

2. $y = 4x^2 + 8x + 4$

3. $y = -x^2 + 6x - 9$

4. $y = -x^2 - 4x - 4$

5. $y = x^2 - 2x + 2$

6. $y = x^2 + 4x + 7$

7. $y = -3x^2 - 6x - 1$

8. $y = 12x - 3x^2$.

Sketch the curve:

9. $y = x^3 - 12x$

10. $y = 9x - x^3$

11. $y = 2x^3 - 9x^2 + 12x$

12. $y = x^3 + 9x^2 + 24x$

13. $y = 2x^3 - 9x^2 + 4$

14. $y = -x^3 + 3x^2 + 9x - 1$

15. $y = 16x^3 - 12x^2 + 1$

16. $y = -2x^3 + 15x^2 - 24x - 6$.

Sketch the graph:

17. $f(x) = x^3 + 3x + 2$

18. $f(x) = 1 - 3x - 2x^3$

19. $f(x) = \dfrac{1}{4x + 5}$

20. $f(x) = \dfrac{3}{2x - 1}$

21. $f(x) = 2x - \dfrac{1}{x}$

22. $f(x) = x^2 + \dfrac{1}{4x}$.

2. USE OF THE SECOND DERIVATIVE

The derivative of $f'(x)$ is $f''(x)$. If $f''(x) > 0$, then $f'(x)$ has a positive derivative. Therefore, $f'(x)$ is increasing, which means the slope of the graph $y = f(x)$ is increasing. In Fig. 2.1a, the slope increases from small

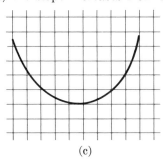

(a)   (b)   (c)

FIG. 2.1   Concave upwards.

positive values to large positive values. In Fig. 2.1b, the slope *increases* from large negative values to small negative values. (Going from -10 to -2 is an increase.) In Fig. 2.1c, the slope increases from large negative to small negative values, to zero, to small positive, to large positive values. The shape illustrated in Fig. 2.1 is called **concave upwards**.

If $f''(x) < 0$, then $f'(x)$ has a negative derivative. Therefore, $f'(x)$ itself is decreasing. The curve will have one of the shapes in Fig. 2.2. Check

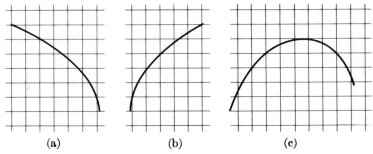

(a)   (b)   (c)

Fɪɢ. 2.2 Concave downwards.

for yourself that in each case the slope of the tangent is decreasing. The shape illustrated in Fig. 2.2 is called **concave downwards**.

Knowledge of concavity helps in curve sketching. Look at Example 1.1. That curve was plotted with the information that $y' = 3(x^2 - 1)$. Now take the second derivative, $y'' = 6x$:

$$y'' > 0 \quad \text{if} \quad x > 0,$$
$$y'' < 0 \quad \text{if} \quad x < 0,$$
$$y'' = 0 \quad \text{if} \quad x = 0.$$

The graph cannot look like Fig. 2.3.

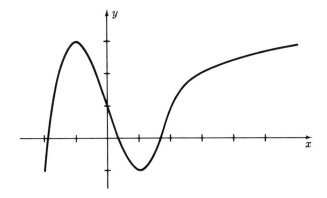

Fɪɢ. 2.3

By the sign of y'', the curve is concave upwards when $x > 0$, concave downwards when $x < 0$, and the concavity reverses at $x = 0$. The graph must have the shape shown in Fig. 1.1. It cannot have the shape shown in Fig. 2.3 because the curve sketched there is not always concave upwards when $x > 0$.

Look at Example 1.2. There $y' = -0.25 - 0.75x^2$. The second derivative is $y'' = -1.5x$.

	Second derivative	Concavity
$x < 0$	positive	upwards
$x = 0$	zero	reverses
$x > 0$	negative	downwards

Without this knowledge of the concavity, there might be a temptation to draw the curve as in Fig. 2.4 since you know from the first derivative

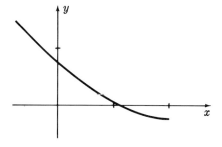

Fɪɢ. 2.4

that the graph is always falling. But the sketch is wrong; it shows a curve always concave upwards, whereas the true graph is concave downwards for $x > 0$.

See Chapter 21, Section 3 for the theory of convex and concave graphs.

Inflection Points

Correct concavity makes a sketch more accurate. Changes of concavity are especially noteworthy.

> A point on a curve at which the concavity reverses is called an **inflection point**.

The graph of $y = f(x)$ has an inflection point where y'' changes from positive to negative, or vice versa.

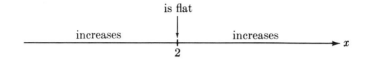

EXAMPLE 2.1

Sketch $y = (x - 2)^3 + 1$.

Solution: By the Shifting Rule, $y' = 3(x - 2)^2$. Hence $y' > 0$ for all x except $x = 2$. There $y' = 0$.

```
                              is flat
                                 |
        increases                ↓         increases
_____ x
                                 2
```

By the Shifting Rule again, $y'' = 3 \cdot 2(x - 2)$.

	Second derivative	Concavity
$x < 2$	negative	downwards
$x = 2$	zero	reverses
$x > 2$	positive	upwards

There is one inflection point: at $x = 2$. There is only one point where the tangent is horizontal: also at $x = 2$. The graph is sketched in Fig. 2.5.

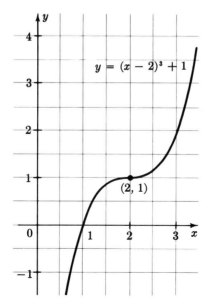

$$y = (x - 2)^3 + 1$$

(2, 1)

FIG. 2.5

EXERCISES

Find where $y = f(x)$ is concave up and concave down. Locate inflection points:

1. $f(x) = 4(x - 3)^2$

2. $f(x) = -3(x + 7)^2$

3. $f(x) = x^3 + 3x^2 + 3x + 1$

4. $f(x) = 2(x - 2)^3 + 1$

5. $f(x) = (x - 2)^3 + 2x$

6. $f(x) = x^3 + 3x^2 + 7x + 1$

7. $f(x) = -x^3 + 4x - 5$

8. $f(x) = x^3 - 6x^2 + 3x + 1.$

Sketch the curve:

9. $y - 2 = (x - 3)^3$

10. $y + 1 = -4(x + 1)^2$

11. $y = 4(x - 3)^3 + 2(x - 3)^2$

12. $y = (x + 1)^3 + 2$

13. $y = x^3 - x$

14. $y = 1 - 9x - x^3$

15. $y = x^3 - 2x^2 + x + 2$

16. $y = 2 + x - x^3.$

3. HINTS FOR SKETCHING CURVES

(1) Get as much "free" information as you can by inspection.

    (a) If easily done, find where $f(x)$ is positive, negative, or zero.

    (b) Look for symmetry. If $f(x)$ has the special property that $f(-x) = -f(x)$, then the graph $y = f(x)$ is symmetric through the origin as illustrated in Fig. 3.1a.

Examples.

$$y = x + \frac{1}{x}, \qquad y = x^3 + 5x,$$

$$y = \sin x, \qquad y = x^2 \sin 4x.$$

If $f(x) = f(-x)$, the curve is symmetric about the y-axis (Fig. 3.1b).

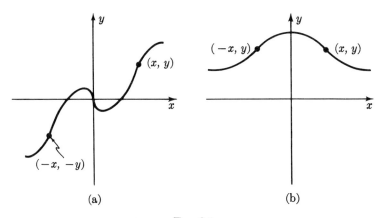

FIG. 3.1

Examples.

$$y = x^2 + \frac{1}{x^2}, \qquad y = 3x^4 + x^2 - 2,$$

$$y = \cos x, \qquad y = x \sin x.$$

(c) Find the behavior of the curve as $x \longrightarrow \infty$ and as $x \longrightarrow -\infty$.

(d) Find values of x, if any, for which the curve is not defined.

Examples.

$$y = x + \frac{1}{x} \qquad \text{is not defined for} \quad x = 0,$$

$$y = \sqrt{1 - x} \quad \text{is not defined for} \quad x > 1.$$

(2) Take the derivative. Its sign will tell you where the curve is rising, falling, or flat. Plot all points where the tangent is horizontal, i.e., where $y' = 0$. If you can, find the behavior of y' as $x \longrightarrow \infty$ and as $x \longrightarrow -\infty$.

(3) Take the second derivative. Its sign will indicate the proper concavity. Locate and plot all inflection points.

(4) For more accuracy, plot a few more points. Look for points that are easy to compute. Try $x = 0$, for example, or if not too hard, see where $y = 0$.

These hints are just suggestions; they are not sacred rules. Be flexible; there is no substitute for common sense.

EXAMPLE 3.1

Sketch $y = x + \dfrac{1}{x}$.

Solution: First notice that there is some important free information. Observe $f(-x) = -f(x)$; therefore, the graph is symmetric through the origin. So, once the curve is sketched for $x > 0$, it can be extended by symmetry to $x < 0$.

Here is some more quick information. If $x > 0$, then $y > 0$. The curve is undefined at $x = 0$, and $y \longrightarrow \infty$ as $x \longrightarrow 0$. If x is large, $y = x + (1/x)$ is slightly larger than x. So as $x \longrightarrow \infty$, the graph is slightly above the line $y = x$.

Combining this information, you expect the graph to be something like Fig. 3.2 for $x > 0$.

To confirm this sketch, take the derivative: $y' = 1 - \dfrac{1}{x^2}$.

Assuming x is positive,

$$y' < 0 \qquad \text{if} \quad x < 1,$$

$$y' = 0 \qquad \text{if} \quad x = 1,$$

$$y' > 0 \qquad \text{if} \quad x > 1.$$

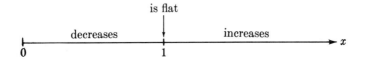

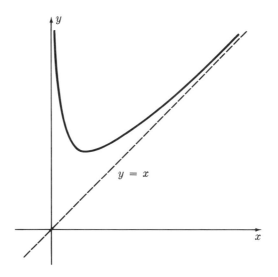

Fɪɢ. 3.2

The curve does rise and fall as in Fig. 3.2. It has a minimum point at $(1, 2)$. Now extend the graph by symmetry (Fig. 3.3) to negative values of x.

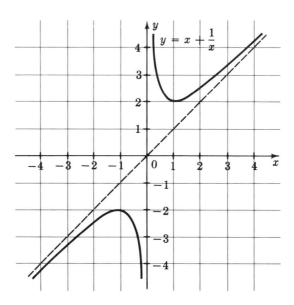

Fɪɢ. 3.3

EXERCISES

Sketch the curve $y = f(x)$ for $x \geq 0$, then by symmetry sketch the curve for $x \leq 0$:

1. $f(x) = x^2 + 1$
2. $f(x) = 4 - x^2$
3. $f(x) = x^3 - 3x$
4. $f(x) = 12x - x^3$
5. $f(x) = 3x^3 + x$
6. $f(x) = -12x^3 - 4x$
7. $f(x) = 4x + \dfrac{1}{x}$
8. $f(x) = -x - \dfrac{1}{x}.$

Sketch the curve:

9. $y = x^3 - x$
10. $y = 3x^3 - 2x$
11. $y = x^3 + 8$
12. $y = 3 - x^3$
13. $y = 8x + \dfrac{2}{x}$
14. $y = -x - \dfrac{16}{x}$
15. $y = 1 + \dfrac{1}{x}$
16. $y = 1 - \dfrac{1}{x}.$

Sketch the curve $y = f(x)$:

17. $f(x) = -x^3 + 3x - 4$
18. $f(x) = x^3 - 3x + 5$
19. $f(x) = 1 + 3x + x^3$
20. $f(x) = 4 - x - x^3$
21. $f(x) = x^3 - x^2 - 8x + 4$
22. $f(x) = 7 - 3x^2 - 2x^3$
23. $f(x) = 1 + \dfrac{1}{x + 1}$
24. $f(x) = 1 - \dfrac{1}{x - 1}.$

Graph the curve:

25. $y = 1 - 6x - 3x^2 - 2x^3$
26. $y = x^3 - 3x^2 + 4x + 1$
27. $y = \dfrac{x}{x + 1}$
28. $y = \dfrac{-x}{x + 1}$
29. $y = x + \dfrac{1}{x + 1}$
30. $y = x + \dfrac{1}{x - 1}$
31. $y = 1 + x + \dfrac{1}{x}$
32. $y = 1 - x - \dfrac{1}{x}.$

4. MAXIMA AND MINIMA

In many problems it is important to know the largest or the smallest value of a function in a certain range. In this and the next section we discuss some typical problems. We shall return to this subject in Chapter 10, Sections 2 and 3. A theoretical discussion is given in Chapter 20, Section 8 and Chapter 21, Sections 2 and 3.

EXAMPLE 4.1

A ball thrown straight up from the ground reaches a height of $80t - 16t^2$ ft in t sec. How high will it go?

Solution: We know the ball will go up, reach its maximum height, and then come down. So the graph of its height, $y(t) = 80t - 16t^2$, must look

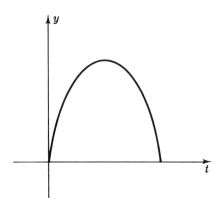

Fɪɢ. 4.1

something like Fig. 4.1. The maximum height occurs at the point on the curve where the tangent is horizontal, that is, where $y'(t) = 0$. Since

$$y(t) = 80t - 16t^2,$$

its derivative is

$$y'(t) = 80 - 32t.$$

Hence

$$y'(t) = 0 \qquad \text{when} \quad 80 - 32t = 0,$$

i.e., when

$$t = 2.5 \text{ sec.}$$

At that time the height is

$$y(2.5) = 80(2.5) - 16(2.5)^2 = 100 \text{ ft.}$$

> *Answer:* The ball will reach a maximum height of 100 ft.

EXAMPLE 4.2

What is the largest possible area of a rectangular rug whose perimeter is 60 ft?

Solution: Let x be the length and w the width of the rug (Fig. 4.2). Let $A(x) = x(30 - x)$. Since x is a length, $x > 0$; since x is less than half

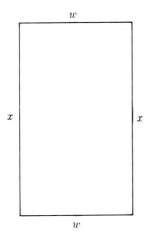

$$\text{F}_{\text{IG.}}\ 4.2$$

$$\text{perimeter} = 2x + 2w = 60,$$

$$w = 30 - x,$$

$$\text{area} = xw = x(30 - x).$$

the perimeter, $x < 30$. The problem then is to find the largest value of $A(x)$ in the range $0 < x < 30$. The derivative of $A(x)$ is

$$A'(x) = 30 - 2x.$$

Hence,

$$A'(x) > 0 \quad \text{where} \quad x < 15,$$

$$A'(x) = 0 \quad \text{where} \quad x = 15,$$

$$A'(x) < 0 \quad \text{where} \quad x > 15.$$

This information indicates that the graph (Fig. 4.3) has its highest point where $x = 15$, because its shape can be described as follows:

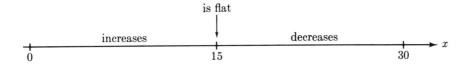

The corresponding area is

$$A(15) = 15(30 - 15) = 225.$$

Answer: 225 ft².

Note that $w = 15$ where $x = 15$; the optimal shape is a square. Actually it is unimportant that the perimeter be 60 ft. For any given perimeter, the square always has the largest area. See if you can modify the solution of this example to prove that.

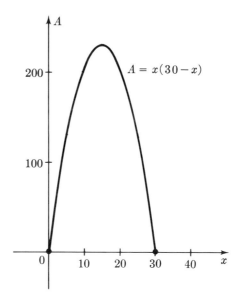

$A = x(30-x)$

FIG. 4.3   Note that the axes have different scales.

EXERCISES

Find the minimum value of the function:

1. $s(t) = t^2 - 4t + 6$

2. $f(x) = 2x^2 - 9x + 12$

3. $f(x) = 12x + \dfrac{1}{3x}, \quad x > 0.$

Find the maximum value of the function:

4. $s(t) = 4 + 6t - t^2$

5. $A(r) = -3r^2 + 3r + 1$

6. $f(x) = 12x + \dfrac{1}{3x}, \quad x < 0.$

7. A ball thrown straight up reaches a height of $3 + 40t - 16t^2$ ft in t sec. How high will it go?

8. Show that the rectangle of largest possible area, for a given perimeter, is a square.

9. Find the maximum slope of the curve $y = 6x^2 - x^3$.

10. The power output P of a battery is given by $P = EI - RI^2$, where E and R are constants and I is the current. Find the current for which the power output is a maximum.

11. During a typical 8-hr work day the quantity of gravel produced in a plant is $60t + 12t^2 - t^3$ tons, where t represents hours worked. When is the rate of production at a maximum?

12. Find the dimensions of the right circular cone having the greatest volume for a given slant height a.

13. A closed cylindrical can is to be made so that its volume is 52 in³. Find its dimensions if the total surface is to be a minimum.

14. Find the minimum vertical distance between the curves $y = 27x^3$ and $y = -1/x$ if $x \neq 0$.

15. Find the minimum vertical distance between the curves $y = (x - 3)^2$ and $y = -(x - 1)^2$.

A window of perimeter 16 ft has the form of a rectangle surmounted by a semicircle

16. For what radius of the semicircle is the window area greatest?

17. For what radius of the semicircle is the most light admitted, if the semicircle admits half as much light per unit area as the rectangle admits per unit area?

5. APPLICATIONS

EXAMPLE 5.1

An open box is constructed by removing a small square from each corner of a tin sheet and then folding up the sides. If the sheet is L in. on each side, what is the largest possible volume of the box?

Solution: Let each cutout square have side x. See Fig. 5.1.

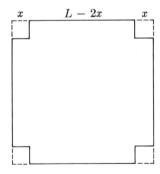 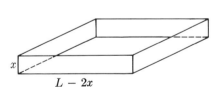

FIG. 5.1

Express the volume of the box as a function of x:

$$\text{Volume} = (\text{area of base}) \cdot (\text{height}).$$

The base is a square of side $L - 2x$, and the height is x. So the volume of the box is

$$V(x) = (L - 2x)^2 x = (L^2 - 4Lx + 4x^2)x$$
$$= L^2 x - 4Lx^2 + 4x^3.$$

By the nature of the problem, x must be positive but less than $L/2$, half the side of the sheet. The problem can now be stated in mathematical terms: Find the largest value of $V(x)$ in the range $0 < x < L/2$.

$$V(x) = L^2x - 4Lx^2 + 4x^3,$$

$$V'(x) = L^2 - 8Lx + 12x^2$$

$$= (L - 2x)(L - 6x).$$

The factor $L - 2x$ is positive because $x < L/2$. Therefore the sign of $V'(x)$ is the same as the sign of $(L - 6x)$:

$$V'(x) > 0 \qquad \text{for} \quad x < \frac{L}{6},$$

$$V'(x) = 0 \qquad \text{for} \quad x = \frac{L}{6},$$

$$V'(x) < 0 \qquad \text{for} \quad x > \frac{L}{6}.$$

The growth of $V = V(x)$ is determined:

Thus $V(x)$ has its maximum value for $x = L/6$:

$$V\left(\frac{L}{6}\right) = \left(L - \frac{2L}{6}\right)^2 \frac{L}{6} = \left(\frac{2L}{3}\right)^2 \frac{L}{6} = \frac{2L^3}{27}.$$

$$\textit{Answer:} \quad \frac{2L^3}{27} \text{ in}^3.$$

EXAMPLE 5.2

Ship A leaves a port at noon and sails due north at 10 mph. Ship B is 100 mi east of the port at noon and sailing due west at 6 mph. When will the ships be nearest each other?

Solution: Set up axes with the port at the origin and the y-axis pointing north. The relative position of the ships at t hr past noon is shown in Fig. 5.2. The distance between the ships is

$$f(t) = \sqrt{(100 - 6t)^2 + (10t)^2}.$$

There is a technical difficulty here. You do not yet have the tools to compute $f'(t)$ because of that annoying square root. Nevertheless, there is a simple way out. Just *square* $f(t)$. Let

$$g(t) = [f(t)]^2 = (100 - 6t)^2 + (10t)^2.$$

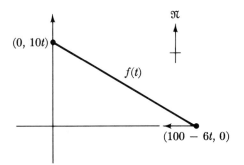

FIG. 5.2

The distance $f(t)$ is smallest precisely when its square $g(t)$ is smallest, and it is easier to minimize $g(t)$ than to minimize $f(t)$.

$$g(t) = (100 - 6t)^2 + (10t)^2$$

$$= 10{,}000 - 1200t + 36t^2 + 100t^2$$

$$= 10{,}000 - 1200t + 136t^2,$$

$$g'(t) = -1200 + 272t.$$

It follows that

$$g'(t) < 0 \quad \text{when} \quad t < \frac{1200}{272},$$

$$g'(t) = 0 \quad \text{when} \quad t = \frac{1200}{272},$$

$$g'(t) > 0 \quad \text{when} \quad t > \frac{1200}{272}.$$

```
                          is flat
                             |
                             ↓
   decreases                               increases
 +----------------------------+-------------------------------→ t
 0                          1200
                            ----
                            272
```

The minimum value of $g(t)$ occurs when

$$t = \frac{1200}{272} \approx 4.41 \text{ hr} \approx 4 \text{ hr, } 25 \text{ min.}^*$$

Answer: The ships are closest at approximately 4:25 P.M.

EXAMPLE 5.3

Suppose, in Example 5.2, ship A is already 70 mi north of the port at noon, but otherwise the problem is the same. Now when are the ships closest?

---

* For $x \approx y$, read, "x is approximately equal to y."

Solution: This time the correct diagram is Fig. 5.3.

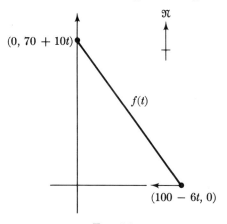

Let

$$g(t) = [f(t)]^2 = (100 - 6t)^2 + (70 + 10t)^2$$
$$= 136t^2 + 200t + 14{,}900,$$
$$g'(t) = 272t + 200.$$

But $g'(t)$ is positive when $t \geq 0$ (at noon and afterwards). That means the distance between the ships is increasing and will continue to increase.

> *Answer:* At noon the ships are as close as they ever will be.

EXAMPLE 5.4

A length of wire 28 in. long is cut into two pieces. One piece is bent into a 3:4:5 right triangle and the other piece is bent into a square. Show that the combined area is at least 18 in².

Solution: This is just a disguised minimum problem: Find the minimum possible combined area and check that it is at least 18 in².

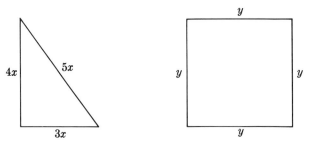

FIG. 5.4 For the triangle: perimeter $= 12x$; area $= \frac{1}{2}(3x)\,(4x) = 6x^2$. For the square: perimeter $= 4y$; area $= y^2$.

To avoid fractions, name the sides of the right triangle $3x$, $4x$, and $5x$. Let y denote the side of the square (Fig. 5.4). The combined perimeter is

$$12x + 4y = 28,$$

hence

$$y = 7 - 3x.$$

The combined area is

$$A(x) = 6x^2 + y^2$$
$$= 6x^2 + (7 - 3x)^2$$
$$= 15x^2 - 42x + 49.$$

By the nature of the problem, x must be positive. But since the perimeter of the triangle is less than 28 in.,

$$12x < 28 \quad \text{or} \quad x < \frac{28}{12} = \frac{7}{3}.$$

So the problem reduces to this: Find the least value of $A(x)$ in the range $0 < x < \frac{7}{3}$. Take the derivative:

$$A(x) = 15x^2 - 42x + 49,$$
$$A'(x) = 30x - 42.$$

Hence

$$A'(x) < 0 \quad \text{for} \quad 30x - 42 < 0, \quad \text{i.e., for} \quad x < \frac{7}{5},$$

$$A'(x) = 0 \quad \text{for} \quad x = \frac{7}{5},$$

$$A'(x) > 0 \quad \text{for} \quad 30x - 42 > 0, \quad \text{i.e., for} \quad x > \frac{7}{5}.$$

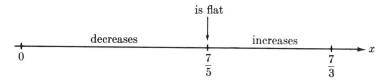

The minimum occurs for $x = \frac{7}{5}$. Since $A(x) = 6x^2 + (7 - 3x)^2$,

$$A\left(\frac{7}{5}\right) = 6\left(\frac{7}{5}\right)^2 + \left(7 - \frac{21}{5}\right)^2$$

$$= \frac{6 \cdot 49}{25} + \left(\frac{14}{5}\right)^2 = \frac{490}{25} = \frac{98}{5} = 19.6.$$

> *Answer:* The least possible combined area is 19.6 in². So the total area always exceeds 18 in².

EXAMPLE 5.5

Find the maximum combined area that can be achieved in Example 5.4.

Solution: Recall the diagram

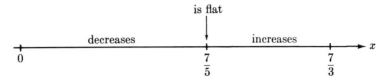

Thus the graph of $y = A(x)$ must have the shape of Fig. 5.5. The maximum

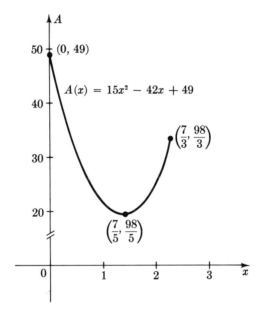

FIG. 5.5

of $A(x)$ in the range $0 \leq x \leq \frac{7}{3}$ occurs either at $x = 0$ or at $x = \frac{7}{3}$.

$$A(x) = 6x^2 + (7 - 3x)^2.$$

$$A(0) = 7^2 = 49, \qquad A\left(\frac{7}{3}\right) = 6\left(\frac{7}{3}\right)^2 + 0 = \frac{98}{3}.$$

The larger of these numbers is $A(0) = 49$. Therefore the combined area is greatest at $x = 0$. But if $x = 0$, there is no triangle at all, only a square!

Answer: 49 in².

An apology to the reader: The maximum area, 49 in², can be achieved only if there is no actual cut in the wire. As the example is worded, there is no maximum since the wire must be cut. With a cut, any area less than 49 in² is possible but not 49 in² itself. Technically speaking our solution is dishonest.

EXERCISES

1. A cylindrical tank (open top) is to hold V gal. How should it be made so as to use the least amount of material?

2. A page is to contain 27 in² of print. The margins at the top and bottom are 1.5 in., at the sides 1 in. Find the most economical dimensions of the page.

3. A triangular lot is bounded by two streets intersecting at right angles. The lengths of the street frontage for the lot are a and b ft. Find the dimensions of the largest rectangular building that can be placed on the lot, facing one of the streets.

4. Find the dimensions of the rectangle of maximum area that can be inscribed in the region bounded by the parabola $y = -8x^2 + 16$ and the x-axis.

5. An athletic field of $\frac{1}{4}$-mi perimeter consists of a rectangle with a semicircle at each end. Find the dimensions of the field so that the area of the rectangular portion is the largest possible.

6. As a man starts across a 200-ft bridge, a ship passes directly beneath the center of the bridge. If the ship is moving at the rate of 8 ft/sec and the man at the rate of 5 ft/sec, what is the shortest horizontal distance between them?

7. Find the point on the graph of the equation $y = \sqrt{x}$ nearest to the point $(1, 0)$.

8. Suppose in Ex. 6, the bridge is 50 ft high. Find the shortest *distance* between the man and the ship.

9. Two particles moving in the plane have coordinates $(2t, 8t^3 - 24t + 10)$ and $(2t + 1, 8t^3 + 6t + 1)$ at time t. How close do the particles come to each other?

10. The strength of a rectangular beam is given by $S = xy^2$, where x and y are its cross-sectional dimensions. Find the shape of the strongest beam that can be cut from a circular log of radius r.

Suppose the cost of producing x units is $f(x)$ dollars, and the price of x units is $h(x)$ dollars. Calculate the maximum net revenue possible for a manufacturer if:

11. $f(x) = 7.5x + 400, \qquad h(x) = 10x - 0.0005x^2$

12. $f(x) = 50x + 1200, \qquad h(x) = 55x - 0.001x^2$.

13. The cost per hour in dollars for fuel to operate a certain airliner is given by the equation $F = 0.005v^2$, where v is the speed in mph. If fixed charges amount to \$1200/hr, find the most economical speed for a 1500 mi trip.

6. ON PROBLEM SOLVING

A major part of your time in Calculus and other courses is devoted to solving problems. It is worth your while to develop sound techniques. Here are a few suggestions.

Think. Before plunging into a problem, take a moment to think. Read the problem again. Think about it. What are its essential features? Have you seen a problem like it before? What techniques are needed?

Try to make a rough estimate of the answer. It will help you understand the problem and will serve as a check against unreasonable answers. A car will *not* go 1000 mi in 3 hr; a weight dropped from 10,000 ft will *not* hit the earth at 5 mph; the volume of a tank is *not* -275 gal.

Examine the data. Be sure you understand what is given. Translate the data into mathematical language. Whenever possible, make a clear diagram and label it accurately. Place axes to simplify computations. If you get stuck, check that you are using *all* the data.

Avoid sloppiness.

(a) Avoid sloppiness in language. Mathematics is written in English sentences. A typical mathematical sentence is "$y = 4x + 1$." The equal sign is the verb in this sentence; it means "equals" or "is equal to." The equal sign is not to be used in place of "and," nor as a punctuation mark. *Quantities on opposite sides of an equal sign must be equal.*

Use short simple sentences. Avoid pronouns such as "it" and "which." Give names and use them. Consider the following example.

"To find the minimum of it, differentiate it and set it equal to zero, then solve it which if you substitute it, it is the minimum."

Better: "To find the minimum of $f(x)$, set its derivative $f'(x)$ equal to zero. Let x_0 be the solution of the resulting equation. Then $f(x_0)$ is the minimum value of $f(x)$."

(b) Avoid sloppiness in computation. Do calculations in a sequence of neat, orderly steps. Include all steps except utterly trivial ones. This will help eliminate errors, or at least make errors easier to find. Check any numbers used; be sure that you have not dropped a minus sign or transposed digits.

(c) Avoid sloppiness in units. If you start out measuring in feet, all lengths must be in feet, all areas in square feet, and all volumes in cubic feet. Do not mix feet and acres, seconds and years.

(d) Avoid sloppiness in the answer. Be sure to answer the question that is asked. If the problem asks for the *maximum value* of $f(x)$, the answer is not the *point* where the maximum occurs. If the problem asks for a *formula*, the answer is not a *number*.

EXAMPLE 6.1

Find the minimum of $f(x) = x^2 - 2x + 1$.

Solution 1:

$$2x - 2$$
$$x = 1$$
$$1^2 - 2 \cdot 1 + 1$$
$$0$$

Unbearable. This is just a collection of marks on the paper. There is absolutely no indication of what these marks mean or of what they have to do with the problem. When you write, it is your responsibility to inform the reader what you are doing. Assume he is intelligent, but not a mind reader.

Solution 2:

$$\frac{df}{dx} = 2x - 2 = 0 = 2x = 2 = x = 1$$

$$= f(x) = 1^2 - 2 \cdot 1 + 1 = 0.$$

Poor. The equal sign is badly mauled. This solution contains such enlightening statements as "$0 = 2 = 1$," and it does not explain what the writer is doing.

Solution 3:

$$\frac{df}{dx} = 2x - 2 = 0, \qquad 2x = 2, \qquad x = 1.$$

This is better than Solution 2, but contains two errors. Error 1: The first statement, "$df/dx = 2x - 2 = 0$," muddles two separate steps. First the derivative is computed, then the derivative is equated to zero. Error 2: The solution is incomplete because it does not give what the problem asks for, the minimum value of f. Instead, it gives the point x at which the minimum is assumed.

Solution 4:   The derivative of f is

$$f' = 2x - 2.$$

At a minimum, $f' = 0$. Hence

$$2x - 2 = 0, \qquad x = 1.$$

The corresponding value of f is

$$f(1) = 1^2 - 2 \cdot 1 + 1 = 0.$$

If $x > 1$, then $f'(x) = 2(x - 1) > 0$, so f is increasing. If $x < 1$, then $f'(x) = 2(x - 1) < 0$, so f is decreasing. Hence f is minimal at $x = 1$, and the minimum value of f is 0.

This solution is absolutely correct, but long. For homework assignments the following is satisfactory (check with your instructor):

Solution 5:

$$f'(x) = 2x - 2.$$

At min, $f' = 0$, $2x - 2 = 0$, $x = 1$. For $x > 1$, $f'(x) = 2(x - 1) > 0$, $f\uparrow$; for $x < 1$, $f'(x) = 2(x - 1) < 0$, $f\downarrow$.

Hence $x = 1$ yields min,

$$f_{\min} = f(1) = 1^2 - 2 \cdot 1 + 1 = 0.$$

The next solution was submitted by a student who took a moment to think.

Solution 6:
$$f(x) = x^2 - 2x + 1 = (x - 1)^2 \geq 0.$$
But
$$f(1) = (1 - 1)^2 = 0.$$
Hence the minimum value of $f(x)$ is 0.

6. Direction Fields and Motion

1. BASIC FACTS ABOUT DERIVATIVES

What can be said about a function $f(x)$ whose derivative $f'(x)$ is zero at each x ? Answer: $f(x)$ must be a constant function. To see this, imagine a short horizontal line segment through each point of the plane (Fig. 1.1).

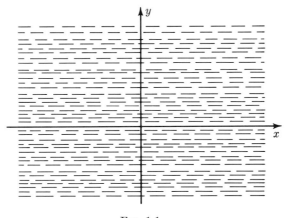

FIG. 1.1

If $f'(x) = 0$, the graph of $y = f(x)$ has slope zero at each point. Hence the direction of the graph at each point is indicated by the line segment at this point (Fig. 1.1). The graph must be a horizontal line.

> If $f'(x) = 0$ for each x, then $f(x) = c$, a constant function.

This is reasonable; if the rate of change of $f(x)$ is always zero, $f(x)$ never changes. So $f(x)$ is constant.

Now consider another question: How are two functions $f(x)$ and $g(x)$ related if $f'(x) = g'(x)$ for each x ? The answer is easy if you make one observation: The difference function $[f(x) - g(x)]$ has zero derivative. Indeed $f'(x) = g'(x)$, hence

$$[f(x) - g(x)]' = f'(x) - g'(x) = 0.$$

But a function with derivative zero is constant. Therefore $f(x) - g(x) = c$. See Fig. 1.2.

> Two functions with identical derivatives differ by a constant:
> If $f'(x) = g'(x)$ for each x, then $f(x) = g(x) + c$.

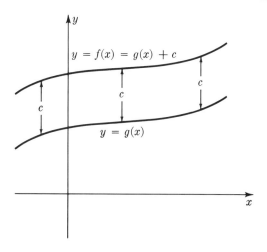

FIG. 1.2

For rigorous proofs of the facts above, see Chapter 21, Section 3.

EXERCISES

1. Use the relation $\dfrac{x}{x+1} + \dfrac{1}{x+1} = 1$ to find $\dfrac{d}{dx}\left(\dfrac{x}{x+1}\right)$.

2. Use the method of Ex. 1 to find $\dfrac{d}{dx}\left(\dfrac{x}{x+a}\right)$.

3. Use the relation $\dfrac{2x}{2x+5} + \dfrac{5}{2x+5} = 1$ to find $\dfrac{d}{dx}\left(\dfrac{2x}{2x+5}\right)$.

   $\left[\text{Hint: } \dfrac{5}{2x+5} = \dfrac{5}{2}\left(\dfrac{1}{x+\dfrac{5}{2}}\right)\cdot\right]$

4. Find: $\dfrac{d}{dx}\left(\dfrac{2x}{3x+4}\right)$.

5. Assume known $\dfrac{d}{dx}\sin^2 x = \sin 2x$. Find $\dfrac{d}{dx}\cos^2 x$.

2. DIRECTION FIELDS

Figure 1.1 is the simplest example of what is called a **direction. field**. Figures 2.1 and 2.2 show two familiar examples from nature.

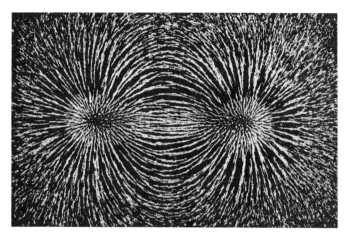

FIG. 2.1   Iron filings arrange themselves in the direction of lines of force around a magnet.

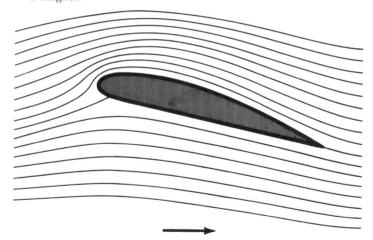

FIG. 2.2   Air flows in streamlines around an airfoil.

In calculus, the derivative of a function indicates the direction of its graph. Given a derivative $f'(x)$, there is a direction field associated with it.

> **EXAMPLE 2.1**
>
> Suppose the derivative of a function is $y' = 0.8$. Describe the function.

Solution: At each point of its graph, the slope is 0.8. Imagine a short line segment of a slope 0.8 at each point of the plane. The direction field in

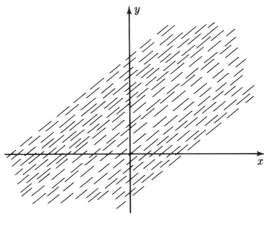

Fɪɢ. 2.3

Fig. 2.3 shows that the graph of $y = f(x)$ can only be a straight line of slope 0.8. Now

$$\frac{d}{dx}(0.8x) - 0.8.$$

Hence $y = 0.8x$ is a function whose graph is such a straight line. Any other

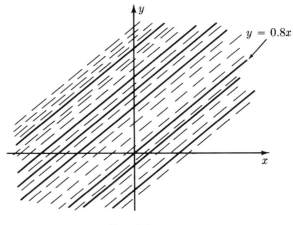

Fɪɢ. 2.4

function with the same derivative differs from $0.8x$ by a constant (Fig. 2.4).

Answer: $y = 0.8x + c.$

EXAMPLE 2.2

Describe all functions $y = f(x)$ for which $y' = x.$

Solution: Sketch the associated direction field. At each point (x, y) of the plane, imagine a short line segment whose slope is x. For example, at each point $(0, y)$ there is a segment of slope 0; at each point $(1, y)$ there

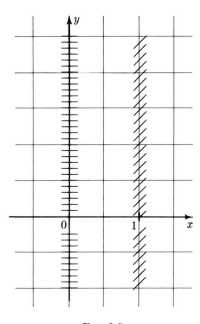

F IG. 2.5

is a segment of slope 1. See Fig. 2.5. Augment this figure by sketching more segments; soon a pattern emerges (Fig. 2.6). It is not hard to find the functions whose graphs are suggested by Fig. 2.6. They all satisfy $y' = x$. Since

$$\frac{d}{dx}\left(\frac{1}{2}x^2\right) = \frac{1}{2}\frac{d}{dx}(x^2) = \frac{1}{2}(2x) = x,$$

one such function is $y = x^2/2$. Any other function with the same derivative differs from this one by a constant (Fig. 2.7).

Answer: $y = \frac{1}{2}x^2 + c.$

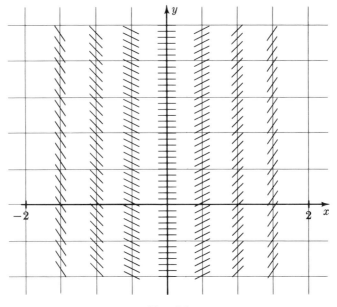

Fɪɢ. 2.6

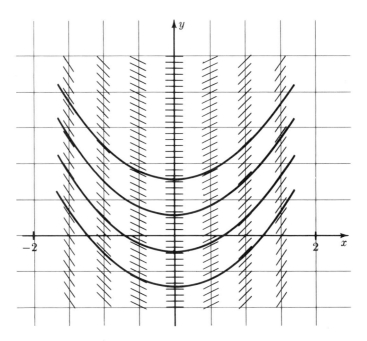

Fɪɢ. 2.7

EXAMPLE 2.3

Sketch the direction field associated with $y' = x - 2$. Find all functions $y = f(x)$ satisfying this equation.

Solution: Make a table.

x	$\frac{1}{2}$	1	$\frac{3}{2}$	2	$\frac{5}{2}$	3	$\frac{7}{2}$
$y' = x - 2$	$-\frac{3}{2}$	-1	$-\frac{1}{2}$	0	$\frac{1}{2}$	1	$\frac{3}{2}$

Now sketch the field. At each point $(\frac{1}{2}, y)$ draw a segment of slope $-\frac{3}{2}$; at each point $(1, y)$, a segment of slope -1; etc. Fig. 2.8 results. This figure

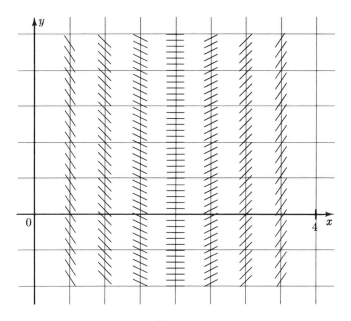

FIG. 2.8

suggests a family of parallel curves, each with a minimum at $x = 2$. See Fig. 2.9. Each curve in Fig. 2.9 is the graph of a function $y = f(x)$ for which $y' = x - 2$. Now

$$\frac{d}{dx}\left(\frac{1}{2}x^2 - 2x\right) = \frac{1}{2}\frac{d}{dx}(x^2) - 2\frac{d}{dx}(x) = x - 2.$$

Hence $y = (x^2/2) - 2x$ is a function with derivative $y' = x - 2$. Any other function with the same derivative differs from this one by a constant.

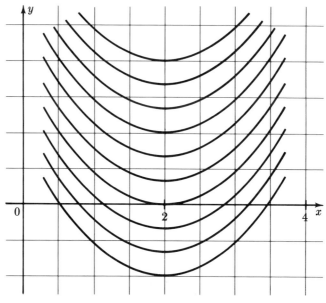

FIG. 2.9

Answer: $y = \frac{1}{2}x^2 - 2x + c.$

(These are the curves in Fig. 2.9.)

EXERCISES

Sketch the direction field and find all functions satisfying the equation:

1. $f'(x) = \frac{1}{2}$

2. $f'(x) = -0.8$

3. $y' = -x$

4. $y' = 2 - x$

5. $f'(x) = x^2$

6. $f'(x) = -x^2 + x$

7. $y' = -1/x^2$

8. $y' = 2/x^2.$

3. ANTIDIFFERENTIATION

Differentiation is the process that leads from a function $f(x)$ to its derivative $f'(x)$. The reverse is called **antidifferentiation**. It is the process of finding a function $f(x)$ whose derivative $f'(x)$ is known. Actually, there is not just one function whose derivative is $f'(x)$, but a family of functions which differ from each other by additive constants.

EXAMPLE 3.1

Find $f(x)$ if $f'(x) = x^2 + \dfrac{2}{x^2}$.

Solution: Since

$$\frac{d}{dx}(x^3) = 3x^2, \qquad \frac{d}{dx}\left(\frac{1}{3}x^3\right) = x^2.$$

Since

$$\frac{d}{dx}\left(\frac{1}{x}\right) = \frac{-1}{x^2}, \qquad \frac{d}{dx}\left(-\frac{2}{x}\right) = \frac{2}{x^2}.$$

Therefore,

$$f(x) = \frac{1}{3}x^3 - \frac{2}{x}$$

is a function whose derivative is

$$x^2 + \frac{2}{x^2}.$$

Any other function with the same derivative differs from

$$\frac{1}{3}x^3 - \frac{2}{x}$$

by a constant.

Answer: $f(x) = \dfrac{1}{3}x^3 - \dfrac{2}{x} + c.$

REMARK: The answer is a family of functions, not a single function.

EXAMPLE 3.2

Find the functions y for which

$$y' = (x + 5)^2 + 3x - 1.$$

Solution: In the last example we found that

$$\frac{d}{dx}\left(\frac{1}{3}x^3\right) = x^2.$$

By the Shifting Rule,

$$\frac{d}{dx}\left[\frac{1}{3}(x + 5)^3\right] = (x + 5)^2.$$

We know also that

$$\frac{d}{dx}\left(\frac{3}{2}x^2\right) = 3x \qquad \text{and} \qquad \frac{d}{dx}(-x) = -1.$$

Therefore,

$$y = \frac{1}{3}(x+5)^3 + \frac{3}{2}x^2 - x$$

is a function whose derivative is $(x+5)^2 + 3x - 1$.

> *Answer:* $y = \dfrac{1}{3}(x+5)^3 + \dfrac{3}{2}x^2 - x + c.$

Significance of Additive Constants

Adding a constant c to a function shifts its graph vertically c units. Therefore, antidifferentiation produces a family of parallel curves. For example, in the last section we saw that antidifferentiation of $x - 2$ produced the family of curves shown in Fig. 2.9. Each curve in Fig. 2.9 has an equation of the form

$$y = \frac{1}{2}x^2 - 2x + c.$$

A particular choice of the constant c singles out one curve of the family. In practice, c is usually chosen so that the curve will pass through a given point.

> **EXAMPLE 3.3**
>
> Find the curve $y = f(x)$ passing through the point $(0, 4)$ and such that $y' = x - 2$.

Solution: The curve must be one of the family of curves

$$y = \frac{1}{2}x^2 - 2x + c.$$

To find a suitable value of c, substitute $x = 0$, $y = 4$:

$$4 = \frac{1}{2}(0)^2 - 2(0) + c, \qquad c = 4.$$

> *Answer:* $y = \dfrac{1}{2}x^2 - 2x + 4.$

EXAMPLE 3.4

Find the curve $y = f(x)$ that satisfies

$$y' = 5x^2 - 3x - \frac{1}{x^2}$$

and passes through the point $(2, -1)$.

Solution: By antidifferentiation,

$$y = \frac{5}{3}x^3 - \frac{3}{2}x^2 + \frac{1}{x} + c.$$

Substitute $x = 2$, $y = -1$:

$$-1 = \frac{5}{3}(2)^3 - \frac{3}{2}(2)^2 + \frac{1}{2} + c$$

$$= \frac{40}{3} - 6 + \frac{1}{2} + c$$

$$c = -\frac{40}{3} + 6 - \frac{1}{2} - 1 = -\frac{53}{6}.$$

Answer: $y = \dfrac{5}{3}x^3 - \dfrac{3}{2}x^2 + \dfrac{1}{x} - \dfrac{53}{6}.$

EXERCISES

Use antidifferentiation to find $f(x)$ if:

1. $f'(x) = a$

2. $f'(x) = -9$

3. $f'(x) = -x$

4. $f'(x) = 4(x + 3)$

5. $f'(x) = 4x^2 + x$

6. $f'(x) = -3x^2$

7. $f'(x) = -4/x^2$

8. $f'(x) = 5/(x - 1)^2$

Find a function whose derivative is:

9. $x + 1$

10. $(3x - 5)(x + 1)$

11. $3x^2 + 2x + 1$

12. $7x^2 - 5x + 2$

13. $2x^2 - \dfrac{7}{x^2}$

14. $\left(x + \dfrac{1}{x}\right)^2$

15. $(x + 4)^2 + \dfrac{1}{x^2}$

16. $(x - 3)^2 + 2x + \dfrac{1}{x^2} - 1.$

Find the curve $y = f(x)$ such that:

17. $f'(x) = x - 5$ and $f(1) = 2$

18. $f'(x) = -(x + 3)$ and $f(0) = 4$

19. $\dfrac{dy}{dx} = 3x^2 - 4x + \dfrac{1}{x^2}$ and the point $(2, 9)$ is on the curve

20. $\dfrac{dy}{dx} = (3x - 4)^2 + 5x$ and the point $(1, 2)$ is on the curve

   [*Hint:* $(3x - 4)^2 = 9(x - \tfrac{4}{3})^2$].

4. VELOCITY

During the initial stage of flight, a rocket fired vertically reaches an elevation of $50t^2$ ft above the ground in t sec. How fast is the rocket rising 2 sec after it is fired?

This is a tricky question because it is not really clear what is meant by velocity at an instant. Usually we compute **average velocity** by the formula

$$\text{average velocity} = \frac{\text{displacement}}{\text{time}}$$

applied to a certain time interval. To be more precise, for the time interval between t_1 and t_2,

$$\text{average velocity} = \frac{(\text{position at time } t_2) - (\text{position at time } t_1)}{t_2 - t_1}.$$

This formula does not apply to "instantaneous velocity." Nevertheless, we can compute the average velocity between $t = 2$ and say, $t = 2.01$, or $t = 2.001$, or more generally, $t = 2 + h$.

The average velocity between $t = 2$ and $t = 2 + h$ is

$$\frac{50(2 + h)^2 - 50 \cdot 2^2}{(2 + h) - 2} = 50 \frac{(2 + h)^2 - 2^2}{h}$$

$$= 50 \frac{4h + h^2}{h} = 50(4 + h).$$

The smaller h is, the closer this average velocity is to 200 ft/sec.

The average velocity between $t = t_0$ and $t = t_0 + h$ is

$$\frac{50(t_0 + h)^2 - 50t_0^2}{(t_0 + h) - t_0} = 50 \frac{(t_0 + h)^2 - t_0^2}{h}$$

$$= 50 \frac{2t_0 h + h^2}{h} = 50(2t_0 + h).$$

The smaller h is, the stronger we get the message: At $t = t_0$ the instantaneous velocity is $100t_0$ ft/sec.

Here is an important observation. The preceding computation of velocity is exactly the same computation as that needed to find the slope of the curve $y = f(t) = 50t^2$. Thus the velocity of the rocket at time t_0 is numerically the same as the slope of $y = 50t^2$ at $t = t_0$.

This is no accident. The average velocity between $t = t_0$ and $t = t_0 + h$ is

$$\frac{\text{displacement}}{\text{time}} = \frac{f(t_0 + h) - f(t_0)}{h},$$

which is precisely the formula for the slope of the secant between two nearby points on $y = f(t)$. Thus the slope of the secant is like the "average speed" of $y = f(t)$ between t_0 and $t_0 + h$. As the interval gets smaller and smaller, the "average slope" approximates the "instantaneous slope" at t_0, that is, the derivative at t_0.

If $f(t)$ is the position of a moving body at time t, its **velocity** is defined to be $df(t)/dt$. Its **speed** is defined to be $|df(t)/dt|$.

Notice that df/dt may be negative. This happens, for instance, in the case of a falling body whose position is measured above ground level. Then displacement in any time interval is negative, leading to a negative velocity. Speed ignores the sign of the derivative. It measures only the *rate* of motion, while velocity also takes into account the *direction*.

Notation

The use of a dot to indicate derivative with respect to *time* is common practice. Instead of dy/dt, you often see $\dot{y}(t)$ or just $\dot{y}$.

EXAMPLE 4.1

A ball thrown straight up from the top of the Leaning Tower of Pisa is at a height $180 + 64t - 16t^2$ ft after t sec. Compute:
(a) its velocity after 1 sec,
(b) its maximum height,
(c) its velocity as it hits the ground.

Solution: Let $y(t) = 180 + 64t - 16t^2$. The velocity of the ball after t sec is

$$\dot{y}(t) = 64 - 32t = 32(2 - t).$$

(a) After 1 sec, the velocity is $\dot{y}(1) = 32(2 - 1) = 32$ ft/sec. (Since the velocity is positive, the ball is rising.)

(b) We need the maximum value of $y(t)$. Examine $\dot{y}(t)$:

$$\dot{y}(t) > 0 \quad \text{when} \quad t < 2, \qquad \dot{y}(2) = 0, \qquad \dot{y}(t) < 0 \quad \text{when} \quad t > 2.$$

Therefore the largest value of $y(t)$ is $y(2) = 244$. Since $\dot{y}$ is velocity, the highest point of the trajectory occurs when the velocity is zero. That is because the ball rises at first (positive velocity), then falls (negative velocity). In between is the highest point (zero velocity).

(c) The ball hits the ground when $y(t) = 0$. Solve for t:

$$y(t) = 180 + 64t - 16t^2 = 0,$$

$$4t^2 - 16t - 45 = 0,$$

$$t = \frac{16 \pm \sqrt{16^2 + 4 \cdot 4 \cdot 45}}{8} = 2 \pm \frac{\sqrt{16 + 45}}{2}.$$

There is only one *positive* time t for which $y(t) = 0$; it is

$$t = 2 + \frac{1}{2}\sqrt{61}.$$

At this instant the velocity is

$$\dot{y}\left(2 + \frac{1}{2}\sqrt{61}\right) = 32\left[2 - \left(2 + \frac{1}{2}\sqrt{61}\right)\right]$$

$$= -16\sqrt{61} \quad \text{ft/sec.}$$

Answer: (a) 32 ft/sec. (b) 244 ft. (c) $-16\sqrt{61}$ ft/sec. (The velocity is negative because the ball is falling.)

EXERCISES

1. A projectile shot straight up has height $s = -16t^2 + 980t$ ft after t sec. Compute its average velocity between $t = 2$ and $t = 3$, between $t = 2$ and $t = 2.1$. Compute its instantaneous velocity when $t = 2$.

2. During the initial stages of flight, a rocket reaches an elevation of $50t^2 + 500t$ ft in t sec. What is the average velocity between $t = 2$ and $t = 3$ sec? Find the instantaneous velocity when $t = 2$ and when $t = 3$. What is the average of the two instantaneous velocities?

3. A projectile launched from a plane has elevation $s = -16t^2 + 400t + 8000$ ft after t sec. What is its maximum elevation? Find its vertical velocity after 15 sec, and upon striking the ground.

4. An object projected upward has height $s = -16t^2 + 96t$ ft after t sec. Compute its velocity after 1.5 sec, its maximum height, and the speed with which it strikes the ground.

5. A penny is thrown straight up from the top of a 600-ft tower. After t sec, it is $s = -16t^2 + 24t + 600$ ft above ground. When does the penny begin to descend? What is its speed when 605 ft above ground, while going up, and while coming down?

6. A projectile fired at an angle of 45° with an initial velocity of 860 ft/sec has height $y = 430t \sqrt{2} - 16t^2$, and has a horizontal distance $x = 430t \sqrt{2}$ ft from its point of origin t sec after being fired. When does it strike the ground? How far will it go?

7. A body moves along a horizontal line according to the law $s = t^3 - 9t^2 + 24t$ ft. (a) When is s increasing and when decreasing? (b) When is the velocity increasing and when decreasing? (c) Find the total distance traveled between $t = 0$ and $t = 6$ sec.

8. Solve Ex. 7, assuming that the body moves according to $s = t^3 - 3t^2 - 9t$.

5. ACCELERATION

A falling weight moves faster and faster; its velocity increases; a car with brakes applied moves slower and slower; its velocity decreases. In many applications, it is important to know just how velocity is changing during motion.

> If $v(t)$ is the velocity of a moving object at time t, its **acceleration** is the derivative dv/dt or $\dot{v}(t)$.

Acceleration is the derivative of velocity. It measures the rate of change of velocity during motion. Positive acceleration indicates increasing velocity; negative acceleration, decreasing velocity; zero acceleration, constant velocity.

Remember that velocity itself is a derivative:

$$v(t) = \frac{ds}{dt} = \dot{f}(t),$$

where $s = f(t)$ is the position at time t. Therefore, acceleration is a second derivative, being the derivative of a derivative:

> acceleration $= \dfrac{d^2s}{dt^2} = \ddot{f}(t).$

EXAMPLE 5.1

A ball is $180 + 64t - 16t^2$ ft above the ground at time t sec. Find its acceleration at time t.

Solution: Let $s(t) = 180 + 64t - 16t^2$. The acceleration is

$$\frac{dv}{dt} \quad \text{or} \quad \frac{d^2s}{dt^2}.$$

Differentiate:

$$v(t) = \frac{ds}{dt} = 64 - 32t.$$

Differentiate again:

$$\frac{dv}{dt} = \frac{d^2s}{dt^2} = -32.$$

Answer: -32 ft/sec².

REMARK: The minus sign means that velocity is decreasing (from positive to negative to more negative).

EXAMPLE 5.2

A ball is thrown straight up from the top of a hill y_0 ft high with an initial velocity of v_0 ft/sec. Gravity causes a constant negative acceleration, $-g$ ft/sec². Find (a) its velocity, (b) its height t sec after release.

Solution: First find a formula for the velocity $v(t)$. Since acceleration is dv/dt, the data is

$$\frac{dv}{dt} = -g.$$

That means $v(t)$ is a function whose derivative is $-g$. In other words, $v(t)$ is an antiderivative of $-g$. One antiderivative is $-gt$; by the discussion in Section 1, all antiderivatives are of the form $-gt + c$, where c can be any constant. Hence,

$$v(t) = -gt + c.$$

To find the constant c that fits this problem, remember the value of $v(t)$ is given for $t = 0$. Set $t = 0$:

$$v_0 = v(0) = -g \cdot 0 + c.$$

$$c = v_0.$$

Hence

$$v(t) = -gt + v_0,$$

which is the required formula.

Use the same sort of argument to find a formula for $y(t)$, the elevation at time t. Since

$$\frac{dy}{dt} = v(t) = -gt + v_0,$$

$y(t)$ is an antiderivative of $-gt + v_0$. Therefore,

$$y(t) = -\frac{1}{2} gt^2 + v_0 t + k,$$

for some appropriate constant k. To find the right value of k, remember that the value of $y(t)$ is given for $t = 0$. Set $t = 0$:

$$y_0 = y(0) = 0 + 0 + k,$$

$$k = y_0.$$

Hence

$$y(t) = -\frac{1}{2} gt^2 + v_0 t + y_0.$$

Answer: (a) $v(t) = -gt + v_0$ ft/sec.

(b) $y(t) = -\frac{1}{2} gt^2 + v_0 t + y_0$ ft.

In Example 5.2 you solved a **differential equation.** That is an equation involving the derivatives of a function in which the function itself is the unknown. The data of Example 5.2 can be written:

$$\frac{d^2y}{dt^2} = -g, \qquad y(0) = y_0, \quad \dot{y}(0) = v_0.$$

The first equation is the differential equation; the other equations are **initial conditions.** To find $y(t)$, antidifferentiate twice. First you get dy/dt, then $y(t)$ itself. Each antidifferentiation involves a constant to be determined. The two constants are obtained from the two initial conditions, $y(0) = y_0$ and $\dot{y}(0) = v_0$.

EXAMPLE 5.3

An alpha particle enters a linear accelerator. It immediately undergoes a constant acceleration that changes its velocity from 1000 m/sec to 5000 m/sec in 10^{-3} sec. Compute its acceleration. How far does the particle move during this period of 10^{-3} sec?

Solution: For convenience, assume the accelerator lies along the positive x-axis starting at the origin. Also assume the particle enters when $t = 0$, and t sec later reaches position $x(t)$. Then

$$\ddot{x}(t) = a, \qquad \dot{x}(0) = 1000, \qquad x(0) = 0,$$

where a is the unknown constant acceleration. This is the same problem as Example 5.2 with different numbers: a instead of $-g$, $v_0 = 1000$, and $x_0 = 0$.

By exactly the reasoning of Example 5.2, obtain the following formulas:

$$v(t) = at + v_0 = at + 1000,$$

$$x(t) = \frac{1}{2} at^2 + 1000t.$$

Use the first formula to find a. Since $v(10^{-3}) = 5000$,

$$5000 = 10^{-3}a + 1000,$$

$$a = 4 \times 10^6 \quad \text{m/sec}^2.$$

From the second formula,

$$x(10^{-3}) = \frac{1}{2}\,(4)\,(10^6)\,(10^{-3})^2 + (1000)\,(10^{-3}) = 2 + 1.$$

> *Answer:* $a = 4 \times 10^6$ m/sec^2,
> the particle moves 3 m.

EXERCISES

Solve the differential equation:

1. $dy/dx = -16x$, $y(0) = 12$
2. $dy/dt = 3t^2 + 4$, $y(1) = -3$
3. $d^2y/dt^2 = -32$, $y(1) = 48$, $\dot{y}(0) = 64$
4. $d^2y/dx^2 = 8$, $y(0) = 2$, $y'(0) = 1$
5. $d^2y/dt^2 = 2t - 1$, $y(0) = 1.75$, $\dot{y}(0) = 0.25$
6. $d^2y/dx^2 = 3 - 4x$, $y(0) = 2$, $y'(1) = 6$.

7. A ball is thrown straight up with an initial velocity of 48 ft/sec. Gravity causes a constant negative acceleration, -32 ft/sec^2. How high will the ball go if it is released from a height of 4 ft?

8. An object slides down a 200-ft inclined plane with acceleration 8 ft/sec^2. If the object starts from rest with zero velocity, when does it reach the end of the plane? How fast is it going?

9. Starting from rest, with what constant acceleration must a car proceed to go 75 ft in 5 sec?

10. The makers of a certain automobile advertise that it will accelerate from 0 to 100 mph in 1 min. If the acceleration is constant, how far will the car go in this time?

11. During the initial stages of flight after blast-off, a rocket shot straight up has acceleration $24t$ ft/sec^2. The engine cuts out at $t = 10$ sec, after which only the force of gravity, -32 ft/sec^2, retards its motion. How high will the rocket go?

12. An airplane taking off from a landing field has a run of 3200 ft. If it starts with speed 20 ft/sec, moves with constant acceleration, and makes the run in 40 sec, with what speed does it take off?

13. A subway train starts from rest at a station and accelerates at a rate of 6 ft/sec^2 for 10 sec. It then runs at constant speed for 60 sec, after which it decelerates at 7 ft/sec^2 until it stops at the next station. Find the total distance covered.

14. Gravitation on the moon is 0.165 times that on the earth. If a bullet shot straight up from the earth will rise one mile, how far would it rise if shot on the moon?

7. Circular Functions

1. COSINE AND SINE

There is a most important technicality to understand from the start. In calculus, the unit of angle measurement is the **radian**. It is a very natural unit, taken so the central angle of an arc of length s on a circle of radius r has measure s/r radians. See Fig. 1.1. Since the radian is a ratio of lengths, it is a dimensionless quantity.

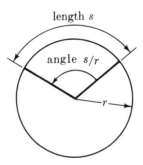

length s

angle s/r

r

FIG. 1.1

Every single formula in calculus involving angles and trigonometric functions has the angles measured in radians. However, the practical system of degrees, minutes, and seconds (inherited from the ancient Babylonians) dominates scientific measurement. This means that in solving a numerical problem by calculus, you must convert data given in degrees to radians before you start, and convert an answer obtained in radians back to degrees.

Normally one does not write "radian" after a number. The equality

$$\pi \text{ radians} = 180 \text{ degrees}$$

may be written

$$\pi = 180 \text{ degrees} = 180°.$$

The necessary conversion factors are

$$\pi = 180°, \qquad 1 \approx 57.2958° \qquad 0.0174533 \approx 1°.$$

The unit circle

$$x^2 + y^2 = 1$$

has circumference 2π. A particle moving on it with constant speed 1 unit/sec makes a complete circuit in 2π sec. Suppose that at time $t = 0$ the particle is at $(1, 0)$ and moving counterclockwise. Then its position is determined for all future time (and for all past time too). At time t, the particle will be at a point $(x(t), y(t))$, where

$$x^2(t) + y^2(t) = 1.$$

The radius from $(0, 0)$ to $(x(t), y(t))$ will make an angle t (radians) with the positive x-axis (Fig. 1.2).

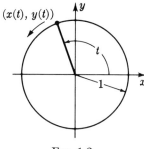

FIG. 1.2

The trigonometric functions **sine** and **cosine** can be defined in terms of this motion:

$$\begin{cases} \cos t = x(t) \\ \sin t = y(t). \end{cases}$$

They are related by

$$\cos^2 t + \sin^2 t = 1.$$

When $t = 0$, the particle is at $(1, 0)$. Hence

$$x(0) = 1, \qquad y(0) = 0,$$

or

$$\cos 0 = 1, \qquad \sin 0 = 0.$$

In any period of 2π sec, a complete circuit is made. Therefore

$$x(t + 2\pi) = x(t), \qquad y(t + 2\pi) = y(t),$$

or

$$\cos(t + 2\pi) = \cos t, \qquad \sin(t + 2\pi) = \sin t.$$

In words, $\cos t$ and $\sin t$ are **periodic functions** with **period** 2π.

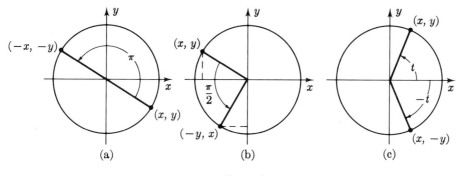

Fɪɢ. 1.3

Look at Fig. 1.3. The three drawings illustrate familiar formulas:

(a)
$$\begin{cases} \cos(t + \pi) = -\cos t \\ \sin(t + \pi) = -\sin t, \end{cases}$$

(b)
$$\begin{cases} \cos\left(t + \dfrac{\pi}{2}\right) = -\sin t \\ \sin\left(t + \dfrac{\pi}{2}\right) = \cos t, \end{cases}$$

(c)
$$\begin{cases} \cos(-t) = \cos t \\ \sin(-t) = -\sin t. \end{cases}$$

Each is a special case of the **addition laws**:

$$\begin{cases} \cos(s + t) = \cos s \cos t - \sin s \sin t \\ \sin(s + t) = \sin s \cos t + \cos s \sin t. \end{cases}$$

A rigorous treatment of the circular functions, including proofs of the addition laws, is given in Chapter 21, Section 7. (See also Exs. 4, 6, p. 105.)

EXERCISES

Convert to radian measure:

(Example: $30° = \pi/6$, $45° = \pi/4$)

1. $60°$, $150°$, $-240°$, $390°$, $-450°$, $900°$
2. $90°$, $-120°$, $210°$, $420°$, $-330°$, $480°$
3. $45°$, $-180°$, $270°$, $630°$, $-135°$, $495°$
4. $90°$, $135°$, $-315°$, $405°$, $-270°$, $765°$.

Convert to degrees:

5. $\dfrac{\pi}{2}$, $-\dfrac{2\pi}{3}$, $\dfrac{5\pi}{3}$, 3π, $-\dfrac{8\pi}{3}$, $\dfrac{50\pi}{3}$

6. π, $-\dfrac{3\pi}{2}$, $\dfrac{7\pi}{6}$, 5π, $-\dfrac{13\pi}{6}$, $\dfrac{17\pi}{3}$

7. $\dfrac{\pi}{4}$, $-\dfrac{7\pi}{4}$, $\dfrac{5\pi}{4}$, $-\dfrac{7\pi}{2}$, 13π, 4π

8. $\dfrac{3\pi}{2}$, $-\dfrac{3\pi}{4}$, $\dfrac{9\pi}{4}$, $-\dfrac{9\pi}{2}$, 7π, 6π.

Use the addition laws to derive a formula for:

9. $\cos 2t$

10. $\sin 2t$

11. $\sin(s - t)$

12. $\cos(s - t)$.

Compute the coordinates of the point on the unit circle determined by central angle t. See Fig. 1.2:

13. $t = \dfrac{\pi}{4}$, $-\dfrac{3\pi}{4}$, $\dfrac{11\pi}{4}$

14. $t = \dfrac{3\pi}{2}$, $-\dfrac{\pi}{4}$, $\dfrac{13\pi}{4}$

15. $t = \pi$, $-\dfrac{2\pi}{3}$, $\dfrac{13\pi}{6}$

16. $t = \dfrac{\pi}{6}$, $\dfrac{5\pi}{6}$, $-\dfrac{2\pi}{3}$.

Find all values of t (in radian measure) between 0 and 2π such that:

17. $\sin t = \sqrt{2}/2$

18. $\sin t = -\frac{1}{2}$

19. $\cos t = -\sqrt{3}/2$

20. $\cos t = \sqrt{2}/2$

21. $\sin(t + \pi) = 1$

22. $\cos(t + \pi) = 1$

23. $\sin t = \cos t$.

Show that:

24. $\cos 3t$ has period $2\pi/3$

25. $\sin 4t - \cos 4t$ has period $\pi/2$

26. $\cos 2\pi t$ has period 1

27. $\cos 2t + 2\cos t$ has period 2π

28. $3 \sin \frac{1}{2}t$ has period 4π.

2. GRAPHS

First we'll graph $x = \cos t$, paying special attention to the range from 0 to $\pi/2$. We take ten equally spaced points. From tables:

t	0	$\dfrac{\pi}{20}$	$\dfrac{2\pi}{20}$	$\dfrac{3\pi}{20}$	$\dfrac{4\pi}{20}$	$\dfrac{5\pi}{20}$	$\dfrac{6\pi}{20}$	$\dfrac{7\pi}{20}$	$\dfrac{8\pi}{20}$	$\dfrac{9\pi}{20}$	$\dfrac{\pi}{2}$
$\cos t$	1	0.99	0.95	0.89	0.81	0.71	0.59	0.45	0.31	0.16	0

In terms of degrees, this is a table of $\cos t$ at intervals of 9 degrees, from 0° to 90°.

As t increases from 0 to $\pi/2$, then $\cos t$ decreases from 1 to 0. It decreases very slowly at first: when t moves 10% of the way from 0 to $\pi/2$, then $\cos t$ decreases by only 1%; when t moves 20% of the way, $\cos t$ decreases by 5%. At the other end, $\cos t$ decreases rapidly: 31% of its total drop occurs in the last 20% of the way.

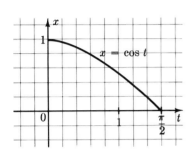

FIG. 2.1

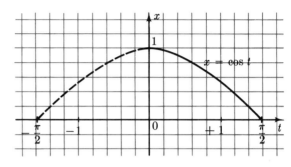

FIG. 2.2

Plotting the points given by the table we obtain Fig. 2.1. Because

$$\cos(-t) = \cos t,$$

we can fill in the graph from $-\pi/2 \le t < 0$ as indicated in Fig. 2.2. Because

$$\cos(t + \pi) = -\cos t,$$

we can fill in the graph for the values $\pi/2 < t \le 3\pi/2$, using what we already have (Fig. 2.3). Finally, because

$$\cos(t + 2\pi) = \cos t,$$

we can sketch the graph as far forwards and backwards as we wish (Fig. 2.4).

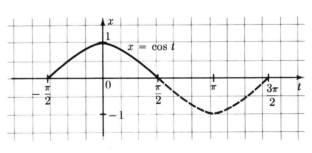

FIG. 2.3

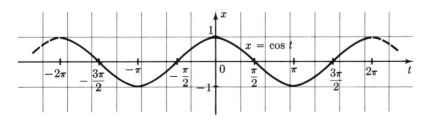

FIG. 2.4

Next, let's graph $x = \sin t$. We could treat this as a separate problem. But since $\sin t$ is related to $\cos t$, we can use the graph of $\cos t$ to find the graph of $\sin t$. Earlier we had

$$\sin\left(t + \frac{\pi}{2}\right) = \cos t,$$

for every value of t. Replace t by $t - \pi/2$:

$$\sin t = \cos\left(t - \frac{\pi}{2}\right).$$

Thus if t is time, the value now of $\sin t$ is the value $\pi/2$ sec ago of $\cos t$. Therefore the graph of $\sin t$ is the graph of $\cos t$ moved bodily $\pi/2$ units to the right (Figs. 2.5 and 2.6).

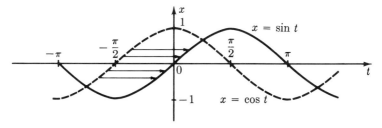

Fɪɢ. 2.5

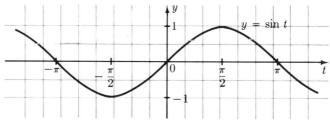

Fɪɢ. 2.6

Recall how $\cos t$ and $\sin t$ were defined by the motion of a particle on the unit circle moving with constant speed of 1 unit per second. If the particle

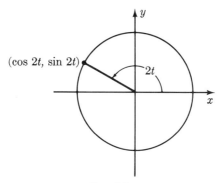

Fɪɢ. 2.7

were to move with twice that speed, its position at time t would be (cos $2t$, sin $2t$). See Fig. 2.7. Its x-coordinate cos $2t$ would run through the same values as before, only twice as fast. Therefore, the graph of cos $2t$ can be plotted by speeding up the graph of cos t by a factor of 2. See Fig. 2.8.

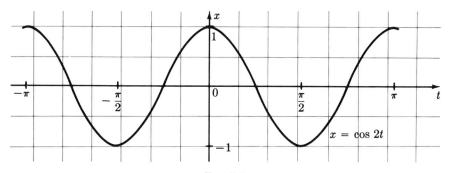

FIG. 2.8

In a similar way, the graph of cos $3t$ is the graph of cos t speeded up by a factor of 3. Analogous statements hold for sin $2t$, sin $3t$, etc. (Fig. 2.9).

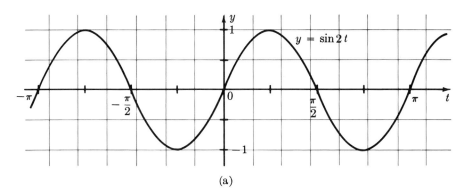

(a)

FIG. 2.9a

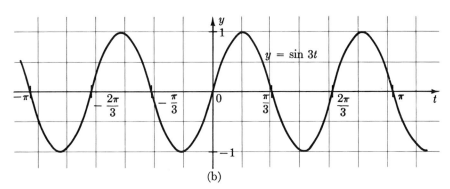

(b)

FIG. 2.9b

Sinusoidal Waves

The graph of $x = \cos t$ trails the graph of $x = \sin t$ by an amount $\pi/2$. See Fig. 2.5. We say that the graphs are **out of phase** by angle $\pi/2$.

More generally, if a point moves uniformly around a circle, its projection on a diameter, when graphed versus time, is a displaced sine curve. Such a graph is called a **sinusoidal wave**.

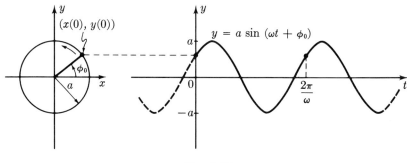

FIG. 2.10

A point rotates on a circle of radius a with uniform angular speed ω. Its y-projection as a function of time is the sinusoidal wave shown in Fig. 2.10. The initial angle ϕ_0 is called the **phase angle**. The equation of the graph is

$$y = a \sin(\omega t + \phi_0).$$

Many natural phenomena are described by sinusoidal waves: vibrations, alternating currents, electromagnetic radiation, sound waves, etc. The parameter ω in these phenomena is the **frequency** of the wave motion and the parameter a is the **amplitude**.

EXERCISES

Sketch the curve:

1. $x = \cos 3t$

2. $x = \sin 4t$

3. $y = \sin \frac{1}{2}t$

4. $y = \cos \frac{1}{2}t$

5. $y = \cos 2\pi t$

6. $y = \sin 2\pi t$

7. $f(t) = \sin(t + \pi)$

8. $f(t) = \cos(t + \pi)$

9. $x = \cos\left(t + \dfrac{\pi}{4}\right)$

10. $x = \sin\left(t + \dfrac{\pi}{4}\right)$

11. $x = 2 \sin t$

12. $x = 2 \cos t$

13. $y = 2 \cos 2t$

14. $y = 2 \sin 2t$

15. $x = 1 + \sin t$

16. $x = 1 + \cos t$

17. $f(t) = 1 - \cos t$

18. $f(t) = 1 - \sin t$

19. $x = \sin\left(2t - \dfrac{\pi}{3}\right)$

20. $x = 2 \cos\left(3t + \dfrac{\pi}{6}\right)$

21. $y = 3 \sin(\pi t + \pi)$

22. $y = 3 \sin\left(2\pi t - \dfrac{\pi}{8}\right)$.

3. DERIVATIVES

The two basic formulas are:

$$\frac{d}{dt}(\sin t) = \cos t$$

$$\frac{d}{dt}(\cos t) = -\sin t.$$

You will need them a million times.

Where do they come from? First let us analyze two special cases:

$$\text{(a)} \qquad \frac{d}{dt}(\sin t)\bigg|_{t=0} = 1,$$

$$\text{(b)} \qquad \frac{d}{dt}(\cos t)\bigg|_{t=0} = 0.$$

Statement (b) holds because $x = \cos t$ has its maximum at $t = 0$, so its

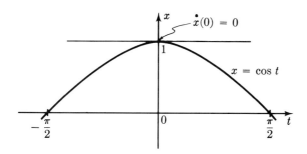

Fig. 3.1

tangent at $(0, 1)$ is horizontal (Fig. 3.1). Statement (a) is plausible because of strong numerical evidence from tables:

t	0.100	0.010	0.001
$\sin t$	0.09983	0.01000	0.00100

If t is small, $\sin t \approx t$. Hence the slope of $x = \sin t$ at the origin must equal the slope of $x = t$ at the origin, namely 1.

From (a) and (b) follow two important facts:

$$(a') \qquad \frac{\sin h}{h} \longrightarrow 1 \qquad \text{as} \quad h \longrightarrow 0;$$

$$(b') \qquad \frac{\cos h - 1}{h} \longrightarrow 0 \qquad \text{as} \quad h \longrightarrow 0.$$

The quotient in (a') is just the slope of the secant between $(0, 0)$ and a nearby point $(h, \sin h)$ on the curve $x = \sin t$. Statement (a') says that the slope of the secant approaches the slope of the tangent at $(0, 0)$. Statement (b') describes the corresponding situation for $x = \cos t$. (Important. Make sure you understand these points.)

From (a') and (b') follow the differentiation formulas for $\sin t$ and $\cos t$. The secant slope for two nearby points of the sine curve is

$$\frac{\sin(t + h) - \sin t}{h} .$$

But

$$\sin(t + h) = \sin t \cos h + \cos t \sin h,$$

therefore

$$\frac{\sin(t + h) - \sin t}{h} = \frac{(\sin t \cos h + \cos t \sin h) - \sin t}{h}$$

$$= \frac{\sin t \, (\cos h - 1) + \cos t \sin h}{h}$$

$$= \sin t \, \frac{\cos h - 1}{h} + \cos t \, \frac{\sin h}{h} .$$

This is excellent, because we know

$$\frac{\cos h - 1}{h} \longrightarrow 0 \qquad \text{and} \qquad \frac{\sin h}{h} \longrightarrow 1 \qquad \text{as} \quad h \longrightarrow 0.$$

Hence,

$$\frac{\sin(t + h) - \sin t}{h} \longrightarrow \cos t \qquad \text{as} \quad h \longrightarrow 0,$$

so

$$\frac{d}{dt} (\sin t) = \cos t.$$

Similarly, by using the addition law for cosines one establishes the other formula,

$$\frac{d}{dt} (\cos t) = -\sin t.$$

(See Chapter 21, Section 7 for rigorous proofs.)

From these formulas and the Scale Rule follow the formulas:

$$\frac{d}{dt}(\sin kt) = k \cos kt$$

$$\frac{d}{dt}(\cos kt) = -k \sin kt.$$

EXERCISES

Find:

1. $\dfrac{d}{dt}(\sin \pi t)$

2. $\dfrac{d}{dt}(\cos 3t)$

3. $\dfrac{d}{dx}(b \cos ax)$

4. $\dfrac{d}{dx}(b \sin ax)$

5. $\dfrac{d}{d\theta}\left(1 + \sin \dfrac{\pi\theta}{2}\right)$

6. $\dfrac{d}{dt}(3 - \cos 2t)$

7. $\dfrac{d}{dt}(t + \cos t)$

8. $\dfrac{d}{dt}(2t - \sin 2t).$

Differentiate:

9. $x = \sin(t + t_0)$

10. $x = 3 \cos\left(t - \dfrac{\pi}{4}\right)$

11. $f(t) = t^2 + \cos t$

12. $F(x) = x + \sin(x + 1)$

13. $y = 4x^2 + 3 \sin 4x$

14. $y = x^2 - \pi \cos(\pi x)$

15. $f(t) = \dfrac{1}{t} - \cos t$

16. $f(t) = 3 \sin 2t - 2 \cos 3t.$

Solve the differential equation:

17. $\dfrac{dy}{dt} = \cos t, \quad y(\pi/2) = 0$

18. $\dfrac{dy}{dt} = \sin t, \quad y(0) = 0$

19. $\dfrac{d^2y}{dx^2} = -\sin x, \quad y(0) = 1, \quad y'(\pi) = -1$

20. $\dfrac{d^2y}{dt^2} = \cos t + 1, \quad y(0) = -1, \quad \dot{y}(0) = 1.$

21. Prove: $\dfrac{d}{dt}(\cos t) = -\sin t.$ (*Hint:* $\cos(t + h) = ?$)

22. Use $\sin\left(t + \dfrac{\pi}{2}\right) = \cos t$ to derive the formula for the derivative of the cosine from that of the sine. (*Hint:* Shifting Rule.)

23. If $x(t) = \cos t$ and $y(t) = \sin t$, show that $\dot{x} = -y$, $\dot{y} = x$, $\ddot{x} + x = 0$, $\ddot{y} + y = 0$.

24. If $f(\theta) = a \cos k\theta + b \sin k\theta$, show $\dfrac{d^2}{d\theta^2}[f(\theta)] + k^2 f(\theta) = 0$.

25. Use the second derivative to find where $y = \cos t$ is concave upwards in the interval $0 \le t \le 2\pi$.

26. For what values of t between -2π and 2π does $y = \cos t$ have an inflection point?

27. Find all points on $y = \sin x$ where the slope is $\frac{1}{2}$.

28. The curves $y = \sin kx$ and $y = \cos kx$ intersect at right angles. Find k.

4. APPLICATIONS

EXAMPLE 4.1

A weight hangs 5 ft above the floor from a spring attached to the ceiling. If the weight is pulled down 6 in., then released at time 0, its height at time t will be $y(t) = 5 - \frac{1}{2} \cos \pi t$. Find its velocity and acceleration $\frac{1}{3}$ sec after release.

Solution: The velocity at time t is

$$\dot{y} = \frac{\pi}{2} \sin \pi t,$$

and the acceleration is

$$\ddot{y} = \frac{\pi^2}{2} \cos \pi t.$$

Substitute $t = \frac{1}{3}$ in these formulas.

> *Answer:* velocity $= \dfrac{\pi \sqrt{3}}{4}$ ft/sec.
>
> acceleration $= \dfrac{\pi^2}{4}$ ft/sec^2.

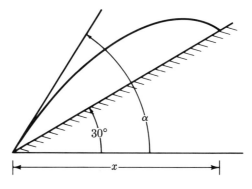

FIG. 4.1

EXAMPLE 4.2

A projectile is fired from the foot of a 30° slope (Fig. 4.1). It hits the hill at a horizontal distance

$$x = \frac{v_0^2}{g}\left[\sin 2\alpha - \frac{1}{\sqrt{3}}(1 + \cos 2\alpha)\right].$$

(Here v_0 is the initial velocity, α is the elevation of the gun, and g is the gravitational constant; air resistance is neglected.) For what angle α does the projectile reach farthest up the slope?

Solution: Find the angle α that maximizes x. This is equivalent to the given problem. Why?

By the nature of the problem, $\pi/6 \le \alpha \le \pi/2$. You must maximize

$$x = \frac{v_0^2}{g}\left[\sin 2\alpha - \frac{1}{\sqrt{3}}(1 + \cos 2\alpha)\right]$$

for $\pi/6 \le \alpha \le \pi/2$. It is ridiculous to fire at $\pi/6$ or $\pi/2$; the maximum value of x does not occur at either end of the range. Therefore, set the derivative equal to zero:

$$\frac{dx}{d\alpha} = \frac{v_0^2}{g}\left[2\cos 2\alpha + \frac{2}{\sqrt{3}}\sin 2\alpha\right].$$

Hence $dx/d\alpha = 0$ when

$$\cos 2\alpha = \frac{-1}{\sqrt{3}}\sin 2\alpha, \quad \text{that is,} \quad \tan 2\alpha = -\sqrt{3},$$

so $2\alpha = 2\pi/3$ or $2\alpha = 5\pi/3$. Since 2α is certainly not in the fourth quadrant,

$$2\alpha = \frac{2\pi}{3}, \quad \alpha = \frac{\pi}{3}.$$

Answer: 60°.

EXAMPLE 4.3

Sketch the curve $y = \cos 2x + 2\cos x$.

Solution: First draw $y = \cos 2x$ and $y = 2\cos x$ on the same graph (Fig. 4.2). It is possible to add these curves point by point. But the labor can be reduced by plotting

(1) a few points (x, y) easy to compute:

$$x = 0, \quad \frac{\pi}{2}, \quad \pi, \quad \frac{3\pi}{2}, \quad 2\pi;$$

(2) critical points (where the derivative vanishes).

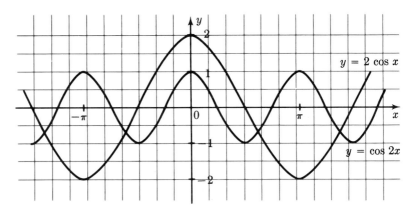

Fɪɢ. 4.2

Since the curve is periodic with period 2π, it is enough to sketch it only from 0 to 2π and then extend the sketch periodically. Plot the points in (1). See Fig. 4.3.

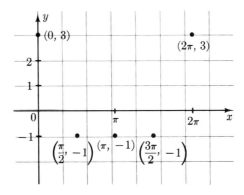

Fɪɢ. 4.3

Next, locate the critical points:

$$y = \cos 2x + 2 \cos x.$$

Hence

$$\frac{dy}{dx} = -2 \sin 2x - 2 \sin x$$

$$= -2(2 \sin x \cos x + \sin x)$$

$$= -2 \sin x \, (2 \cos x + 1).$$

Therefore $dy/dx = 0$ when either

$$\sin x = 0 \qquad \text{or} \qquad \cos x = -\frac{1}{2}.$$

The corresponding values of x are

$$x = 0, \quad \pi, \quad 2\pi; \qquad x = \frac{2\pi}{3}, \quad \frac{4\pi}{3}.$$

Augment Fig. 4.3 by plotting the critical points and indicating horizontal tangents (Fig. 4.4). These points suggest the sketch in Fig. 4.5.

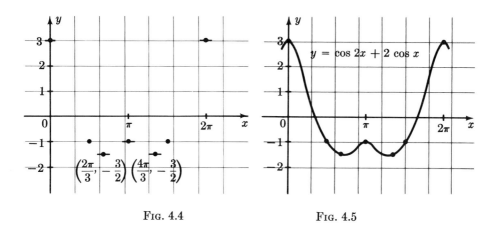

FIG. 4.4   FIG. 4.5

For greater accuracy plot more points, and using the derivative, get the correct slope at various points. Then extend the curve periodically (Fig. 4.6).

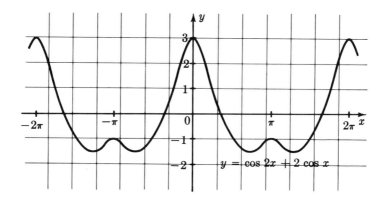

FIG. 4.6

EXERCISES

Sketch the graph of:

1. $y = x + \cos x$
2. $y = x^2 + 2 \cos x$
3. $h(t) = \sin t + \cos t$
4. $F(t) = 4 \sin t + \cos 4t$
5. $y = \sin 2x + 2 \sin x$
6. $y = \dfrac{1}{2} \sin 2t + \sin t.$

If the position of a point on a line as a function of time is given by $s(t) = A \sin Bt$ [or $s(t) = A \cos Bt$], then the motion is called **simple harmonic motion.** Describe the motion of the point and find its velocity and acceleration:

7. $s(t) = 2 \sin t$
8. $s(t) = 4 \cos 4t$
9. $s(t) = 3 \cos \pi t$
10. $s(t) = 2 \sin \dfrac{\pi t}{2}.$

11. A spring of length 1 ft is hung vertically. A weight attached to the free end stretches the spring 4 ft. If the weight is displaced 2 ft lower and released, then its distance (measured down from the ceiling) after t sec is $y = 5 + 2 \cos \omega t$, where $\omega^2 = g/4$ and $g = 32.2$ ft/sec². Describe the motion of the weight; give its velocity and acceleration.

12. A certain pendulum of length $2A$ swings out a circular arc when set into motion. If at time t the tip of the pendulum has horizontal position $x = A \sin 2\pi t$, describe this horizontal motion (shadow of the pendulum bob), giving velocity, acceleration, and position at critical values of t.

13. In Example 4.3 it would have sufficed to sketch the curve only for $0 \leq x \leq \pi$. How could we have known in advance?

14 Suppose in Example 4.2 the hill makes an angle ϕ with the horizontal. Then

$$x = \frac{v_0^2}{g} [\sin 2\alpha - \tan \phi \, (1 + \cos 2\alpha)].$$

Find the maximizing angle α in this case. Interpret geometrically.

15. (cont.) Solve Ex. 14 without calculus in the special case $\phi = 0$.

5. ROUND-OFF ERRORS

In this chapter we have used values of $\sin x$ and $\cos x$ taken from 5-place tables. These values are not exact; they are obtained by rounding-off numbers involving at least 6 decimal places. Even the values in 20-place tables involve small errors.

Whenever we are unable or unwilling to handle numbers with many digits, it is necessary to round them to fewer digits. There are three rules for rounding-off a number, applied regardless of the sign of the number:

(1) If the discarded portion is less than $5000 \cdots$, drop it.

(2) If the discarded portion is greater than $5000 \cdots$, drop it and add one to the last digit kept.

(3) If the discarded portion is exactly $5000 \cdots$, drop it and add zero or one to the last digit kept, making it even.

EXAMPLE 5.1

Round-off 6.14537 to 4, 3, 2, 1, and 0 decimal places.

Answer: 6.1454, 6.145, 6.15, 6.1, 6.

Note that it may be less accurate to round in two steps. For example, we round-off 6.14537 to 6.145, then we round-off 6.145 to 6.14. This is not as accurate as rounding-off 6.14537 directly to 6.15. Similarly, it is better to round-off 6.14537 directly to 6.1, rather than to 6.15 and 6.2 in two steps.

Rounding-off creates uncertainty and error. For example, a 4-place table gives sin 1 = 0.8415 and sin 1.8 = 0.9738. We can be sure only that sin 1 is between 0.84145 and 0.84155, and that sin 1.8 is between 0.97375 and 0.97385. In each case there may be an error as large as 0.00005. According to the tabulated values

$$\sin 1 + \sin 1.8 = 1.8153,$$

but all we really know is that this sum is between 1.81520 and 1.81540.

In computations involving many round-offs the situation may be more critical. Many small errors can accumulate and destroy the accuracy of a computation. For example, in Chapter 18 we shall compute such sums as

$$\sin 0.01 + \sin 0.02 + \sin 0.03 + \cdots + \sin 1.00.$$

If 4-place sine tables are used, each term may be in error by as much as 0.00005. If all errors accumulate, the sum may be in error by as much as 0.005, possibly unsatisfactory for the computation. Actually, it is unlikely that the error will be so large. Some of the values in the sine table are over-estimates and some are underestimates; therefore they tend to cancel each other. Nevertheless, the degree of precision in the computation is uncertain. In complicated problems, the question of round-off errors can be quite delicate.

EXERCISES

Round to 3 decimal places:

1. 0.4721

2. 0.9436

3. −9.5215

4. 14.0005

5. 0.12345

6. −1.34517

7. 3.442501

8. 4.71399

Round to 3 decimal places before and after performing the indicated calculation. Observe the difference in the results.

9. 0.4126 + 0.3215

10. 1.7925 + 2.3454

11. 1.3475 − 0.4934

12. 4.3244 − 3.1928

13. 0.3444 + 0.7174

14. 0.1435 + 0.3216 + 0.4075

15. 5.5042 − 10(0.2156 + 0.3347)

16. 0.3127/(0.4136 − 0.4135)

Calculate the answer to the nearest integer, rounding before and after the calculation. Compare the results.

17. (4.6) (3.5)

18. (4.4) (3.2)

19. (4.4) (3.5)

20. 3.5/2.4

21. 2.4/1.5

22. 2.6/0.6

8. The Exponential Function

1. INTRODUCTION

Let us review some properties of exponents. Begin with powers of 2:

$$2^0 = 1, \quad 2^1 = 2, \quad 2^2 = 2 \cdot 2 = 4, \quad 2^3 = 2 \cdot 2 \cdot 2 = 8,$$

$$2^4 = 2 \cdot 2 \cdot 2 \cdot 2 = 16, \quad 2^{10} = 1024, \quad 2^{12} = 4096.$$

Some negative powers:

$$2^{-1} = \frac{1}{2^1} = \frac{1}{2}, \quad 2^{-3} = \frac{1}{2^3} = \frac{1}{8}, \quad 2^{-6} = \frac{1}{2^6} = \frac{1}{64}.$$

There are also fractional powers. For example, $2^{1/2}$ is that number whose square is 2:

$$2^{1/2} = \sqrt{2} = 1.41421 \cdots.$$

$2^{5/3}$ is that number whose third power is 2^5:

$$(2^{5/3})^3 = 2^5 = 32,$$

$$2^{5/3} = (32)^{1/3} = \sqrt[3]{32} = 3.17480 \cdots.$$

One more, $2^{-1/2}$ is the reciprocal of $2^{1/2}$:

$$2^{-1/2} = \frac{1}{2^{1/2}} = \frac{1}{1.41421 \cdots} = 0.707106 \cdots.$$

These are all particular values of the function

$$f(x) = 2^x,$$

called the exponential function (with base 2). See Fig. 1.1. There is nothing special about the base 2. For each positive number a, there is an exponential function $f(x) = a^x$. See Fig. 1.2.

Numerical values of a^x are computed by logarithms, using the formula

$$\log(a^x) = x \log a.$$

In the examples that follow, 4-place tables of logs to the base 10 are used.

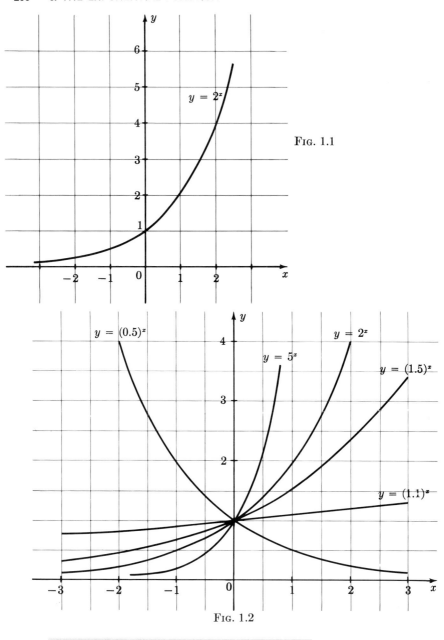

Fig. 1.1

Fig. 1.2

EXAMPLE 1.1

Find $(3.7)^{2.11}$ to four significant figures.*

Solution: Let $x = (3.7)^{2.11}$.

---

*In numerals involving a decimal point, the number of **significant digits** or **figures** is the number of digits from the left-most non-zero digit to the right-most digit. In numerals written without a decimal point, we shall follow the same rule, although this is not universally accepted practice.

$$\log x = (2.11)\,(\log 3.7)$$

$$\approx (2.11)\,(0.5682) \approx 1.1989.$$

Answer: $(3.7)^{2.11} \approx 15.81.$

EXAMPLE 1.2

Find $(0.782)^{-3.8}$ to four significant figures.

Solution: Let $x = (0.782)^{-3.8}$.

$$\log x = (-3.8)\,(\log 0.782)$$

$$\approx (-3.8)\,(0.8932 - 1) = (-3.8)\,(-0.1068) \approx 0.4058.$$

Answer: $(0.782)^{-3.8} \approx 2.546.$

REMARK: A crude approximation serves to check whether your answer is in the right ball park.

$$(0.782)^{-3.8} \approx (0.8)^{-4} = [(0.8)^2]^{-2} \approx (0.6)^{-2} = \frac{1}{0.36} \approx 2.8.$$

Laws of Exponents

The laws of exponents, taught in algebra, are three basic identities:

$$(1) \qquad a^x \cdot a^y = a^{x+y}.$$
$$(2) \qquad a^x \cdot b^x = (ab)^x.$$
$$(3) \qquad (a^x)^y = a^{xy}.$$

These important identities will be quite useful later. Indeed, the third one was already used in the computation of $2^{5/3}$ above.

EXERCISES

Evaluate a^x:

1. $a = \frac{1}{2};\quad x = 0, -1, 2, -3$

2. $a = 2;\quad x = -2, 0, 4, -1$

3. $a = 3;\quad x = 3, -2, 4, 1$

4. $a = \frac{2}{3};\quad x = -1, 0, 2, -3$

5. $a = 27;\quad x = \frac{1}{3}, -\frac{1}{3}, \frac{2}{3}, -\frac{4}{3}$

6. $a = \frac{1}{81};\quad x = -\frac{1}{4}, 0, \frac{3}{4}, -\frac{3}{2}.$

Use tables to evaluate to four significant figures:

7. $(2.4)^{4.15},\quad (0.614)^{-5.7}$

8. $(10)^{3.52},\quad (3.142)^{-2.7}$

9. $(2)^{1.91},\quad (15.5)^{-0.9}$

10. $(3.2)^{0.47},\quad (0.008)^{-4.7}.$

Simplify:

11. $9^{-3/2}(\frac{1}{3})^{-3},\quad 25^3(25)^{-3/2},\quad 4^3(\frac{1}{8})^3$

12. $8^{2/3}(4)^{-1/2},\quad 27^{1/3}(27)^{-2/3},\quad 2^{-7/2}(8^{9/2})$

13. $16^{-3/4}(\frac{1}{8})^{-5/3},\quad (343^2)^{-1/3},\quad [(4^2)\,(4^{-1/2})]^{2/3}$

14. $27^{4/3}(3)^{-1},\quad (0.0625^{-1/3})^{3/4},\quad (16^{-1/4})^2(16^{1/4})2^5.$

Use the laws of exponents to prove:

15. $\dfrac{a^x}{a^y} = a^{x-y}.$ 16. $\dfrac{a^x}{b^x} = \left(\dfrac{a}{b}\right)^x.$

Find all values of x for which the inequality is satisfied:

17. $3^x \geq 3$ 18. $(\tfrac{1}{2})^x < \tfrac{1}{2}$

19. $\dfrac{1}{2\sqrt{2}} < 2^x < 4096$ 20. $4^x > 2^{x+3}.$

2. DERIVATIVES

To find the slope of the curve $y = a^x$, choose a value x and a nearby value $x + h$. The slope of the corresponding secant is

$$\frac{a^{x+h} - a^x}{h} = \frac{a^x a^h - a^x}{h} = \frac{a^h - 1}{h} \cdot a^x.$$

Here is a curious observation. The quantity

$$\frac{a^h - 1}{h}$$

is the slope of the secant corresponding to 0 and h. See Fig. 2.1. Therefore,

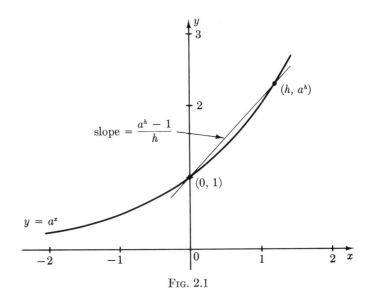

Fɪɢ. 2.1

for small values of h,

$$\frac{a^h - 1}{h} \approx \text{(slope of tangent at } x = 0\text{)}.$$

As $h \longrightarrow 0$, this quantity approaches the derivative of $y = a^x$ at $x = 0$:

$$\frac{a^h - 1}{h} \longrightarrow \frac{d}{dx}(a^x)\bigg|_{x=0}.$$

Return to the secant corresponding to x and $x + h$. Its slope is

$$\frac{a^h - 1}{h} \cdot a^x$$

Let h become smaller and smaller. This slope gets closer and closer to the derivative of $y = a^x$. Conclusion:

$$\frac{d}{dx}(a^x) = ka^x, \qquad \text{where} \quad k = \frac{d}{dx}(a^x)\bigg|_{x=0}.$$

EXAMPLE 2.1

Show that $\dfrac{d}{dx}(2^x)\bigg|_{x=0} \approx 0.7$.

Solution: Compute

$$\frac{2^h - 1}{h},$$

for $h = 0.01$ and $h = -0.01$.

$h = 0.01$:

$$\log 2^h = (0.01)(\log 2)$$

$$\approx (0.01)(0.30103) \approx 0.00301.$$

$$2^h \approx 1.007.$$

$$\frac{2^h - 1}{h} \approx \frac{0.007}{0.01} = 0.7.$$

$h = -0.01$:

$$\log 2^h = (-0.01)(\log 2)$$

$$\approx -0.00301 = 0.99699 - 1.$$

$$2^h \approx 0.9931.$$

$$\frac{2^h - 1}{h} \approx \frac{0.9931 - 1}{-0.01} = \frac{-0.0069}{-0.01} = 0.69 \approx 0.7.$$

EXAMPLE 2.2

Show that $\dfrac{d}{dx}\,(3^x)\,\Big|_{x=0} \approx 1.1.$

Solution: Compute

$$\frac{3^h - 1}{h}$$

for $h = 0.01$ and $h = -0.01$.

$h = 0.01$:

$$\log 3^h \approx (0.01)\,(0.47712) \approx 0.00477.$$

$$3^h \approx 1.011.$$

$$\frac{3^h - 1}{h} \approx \frac{0.011}{0.01} = 1.1.$$

$h = -0.01$:

$$\log 3^h \approx (-0.01)\,(0.47712) \approx -0.00477 = 0.99523 - 1.$$

$$3^h \approx 0.9891.$$

$$\frac{3^h - 1}{h} \approx \frac{-0.0109}{-0.01} = 1.09 \approx 1.1.$$

The Number e

In the two last examples we obtained

$$\frac{d}{dx}\,(2^x)\,\Big|_{x=0} \approx 0.7, \qquad \frac{d}{dx}\,(3^x)\,\Big|_{x=0} \approx 1.1.$$

These results imply

$$\frac{d}{dx}\,(2^x) \approx (0.7)2^x, \qquad \frac{d}{dx}\,(3^x) \approx (1.1)3^x.$$

Since 0.7 is less than 1 and 1.1 is greater than 1, they suggest that some-where between 2 and 3 there is a number a such that

$$\frac{d}{dx}\,(a^x)\,\Big|_{x=0} = 1 \qquad \text{or} \qquad \frac{d}{dx}\,(a^x) = a^x.$$

For that number a, the function a^x is its own derivative! More refined calculations show

$$\frac{d}{dx}\,(2.7)^x\,\Big|_{x=0} \approx 0.99325,$$

$$\frac{d}{dx}(2.8)^x\bigg|_{x=0} \approx 1.02962.$$

Narrowing the gap again,

$$\frac{d}{dx}(2.71)^x\bigg|_{x=0} \approx 0.99695,$$

$$\frac{d}{dx}(2.72)^x\bigg|_{x=0} \approx 1.00063.$$

Since 1.00000 is slightly more than $\frac{8}{10}$ of the way between 0.99695 and 1.00063, the desired number is probably slightly more than 2.718.

Conclusion: There is a number, called e, approximately 2.718, such that

$$\frac{d}{dx}(e^x)\bigg|_{x=0} = 1,$$

$$\frac{d}{dx}(e^x) = e^x.$$

The number e has been computed with great accuracy. To 15 places it is

$$e \approx 2.71828 \ 18284 \ 59045.$$

The number e, like the number π, is a fundamental constant of nature, independent of units of measurement. Its central role will become more and more clear as we proceed. Right now we have the striking property that the exponential function e^x reproduces itself under differentiation:

$$\frac{d}{dx}(e^x) = e^x.$$

The function e^x is of such importance it is called *the* exponential function. (For a rigorous treatment, see Chapter 21, Section 6.)

3. EXPONENTIAL FUNCTIONS

The exponential function $y = e^x$ is its own derivative; it satisfies the differential equation

$$\frac{dy}{dx} = y.$$

So does $y = ce^x$ where c is a constant:

$$\frac{dy}{dx} = \frac{d}{dx}(ce^x) = c\frac{d}{dx}(e^x) = ce^x = y.$$

Are there any other functions $y(x)$ satisfying the differential equation? To decide, plot the direction field associated with the differential equation.

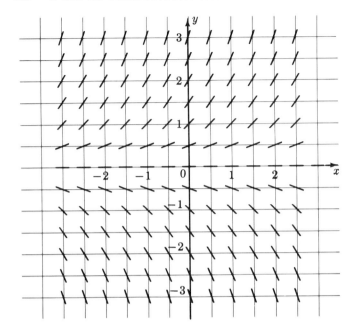

Fɪɢ. 3.1 Direction field $\dfrac{dy}{dx} = y$.

At each point (x, y) it has a short segment of slope y. See Fig. 3.1. A function $y(x)$ satisfies the differential equation

$$\frac{dy}{dx} = y$$

if the direction of its graph at each point coincides with this direction field. Such a function is called a **solution** of the differential equation.

Two facts are apparent from Fig. 3.1.

(1) The graph of each solution crosses the y-axis.
(2) Through each point of the y-axis passes the graph of exactly one solution.

The function ce^x is a solution, and its graph crosses the y-axis at $(0, c)$. By (2), it is the only solution whose graph passes through $(0, c)$.

Now consider any solution. By (1), its graph crosses the y-axis at a point $(0, c)$. Therefore it is the function ce^x.

Conclusion:

> Each solution of the differential equation
>
> $$\frac{dy}{dx} = y$$
>
> is a function of the form
>
> $$y = ce^x$$
>
> for some constant c.

The Function $y = e^{kx}$

Consider the function

$$y = e^{kx},$$

where k is a positive constant. It is obtained from $y = e^x$ by a change of scale (Fig. 3.2).

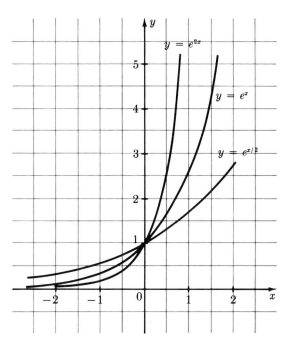

FIG. 3.2

Each function

$$y(x) = e^{kx}, \qquad k > 0,$$

possesses certain basic growth properties:

(1) $y(x) > 0$.
(2) $y(x) \longrightarrow \infty$ as $x \longrightarrow \infty$.
(3) $y(x) \longrightarrow 0$ as $x \longrightarrow -\infty$.
(4) The graph of $y = e^{kx}$ is always rising.

Now consider

$$y(x) = e^{-kx}.$$

Since

$$e^{-kx} = e^{k(-x)},$$

the graph (Fig. 3.3) of $y = e^{-kx}$ is the reflection in the y-axis of the graph of $y = e^{kx}$.

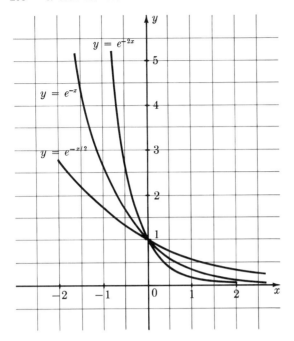

$y = e^{-2x}$

$y = e^{-x}$

$y = e^{-x/2}$

F\textsc{ig}. 3.3

Each function

$$y(x) = e^{-kx}, \qquad k > 0,$$

possesses these growth properties.

(1') $y(x) > 0$.
(2') $y(x) \longrightarrow 0$ as $x \longrightarrow \infty$.
(3') $y(x) \longrightarrow \infty$ as $x \longrightarrow -\infty$.
(4') The graph of $y = e^{-kx}$ is always falling.

Finally, consider $y = e^{kx}$ with $k = 0$:

$$y = e^{0 \cdot x} = e^0 = 1.$$

Derivative of e^{kx}

We find the derivative of $y(x) = e^{kx}$ (for k positive, negative, or zero) by use of the Scale Rule:

$$\frac{d}{dx}[f(kx)] = kf'(kx).$$

Applied to $f(x) = e^x$, this yields the important formula

$$\boxed{\frac{d}{dx}[e^{kx}] = ke^{kx}.}$$

Thus, the derivative of e^{kx} is k times the function itself. Stated differently, $y = e^{kx}$ satisfies the differential equation

$$\frac{dy}{dx} = ky.$$

By practically the same argument as above, we conclude:

> Each solution of the differential equation
>
> $$\frac{dy}{dx} = ky$$
>
> is a function of the form
>
> $$y = ce^{kx}$$
>
> for some constant c.

Values of e^x

The graph of $y = e^x$ is always rising (Fig. 3.4). What is more, it rises arbitrarily high for x large ($e^x \longrightarrow \infty$ as $x \longrightarrow \infty$) and becomes arbitrarily close to 0 for x large negative ($e^x \longrightarrow 0$ as $x \longrightarrow -\infty$). Consequently e^x takes on each positive value once.

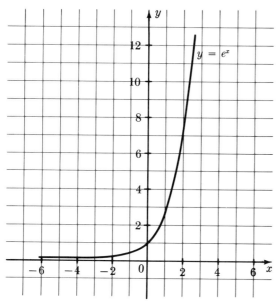

$y = e^x$

FIG. 3.4

> If $a > 0$, there is one number k for which
>
> $$e^k = a.$$

To find k, take logarithms:

$$k \log_{10} e = \log_{10} a,$$

$$k = \frac{\log_{10} a}{\log_{10} e}.$$

The denominator $\log_{10} e$ is used so often in computations it has a special name M. To ten places,

$$M = \log_{10} e \approx 0.43429\ 44819.$$

Other frequently used constants are

$$\frac{1}{M} \approx 2.30259, \qquad \log_{10} M \approx 0.63778 - 1.$$

Derivative of a^x

This chapter began with the exponential function $y = a^x$ to the base a. If $a > 0$, then

$$a = e^k, \qquad \text{where} \quad k = \frac{\log_{10} a}{M}.$$

By the laws of exponents,

$$a^x = (e^k)^x = e^{kx}.$$

In other words, each exponential function $y = a^x$ for $a > 0$ can be treated like $y = e^{kx}$ for an appropriate k. Thus

$$\frac{d}{dx}(a^x) = \frac{d}{dx}(e^{kx}) = ke^{kx} = ka^x.$$

Therefore

$$\frac{d}{dx}(a^x) = ka^x, \qquad \text{where} \quad k = \frac{\log_{10} a}{M}.$$

REMARK: Logarithms to any positive base b (different from 1) make sense. Recall

$$t = \log_b a \qquad \text{means} \qquad b^t = a.$$

In particular

$$k = \log_e a \qquad \text{means} \qquad e^k = a;$$

therefore the formula for the derivative reads

$$\boxed{\frac{d}{dx}(a^x) = (\log_e a)a^x.}$$

NOTE: If $a = e$, then $\log_e e = 1$ and the formula is particularly simple,

$$\frac{d}{dx}(e^x) = e^x.$$

Tables of **natural logarithms** ($\log_e$) are readily available.

1. Does $y = e^x + c$ satisfy the differential equation $dy/dx = y$?

Use graph paper to make a large accurate drawing of the direction field in Fig. 3.1 for $-3 \le x \le 3$ and $-4 \le y \le 4$. Sketch the curve that:

2. passes through $(2, 3)$ 3. passes through $(0, -\frac{1}{2})$.

4. Make another large graph for the range $-1 \le x \le 1$ and $0 \le y \le 3$. Obtain an approximation of the numerical value of e as follows: Approximate the curve through $(0, 1)$ by a "curve" consisting of line segments. When $x = 1$ the height of your curve should be about e. Why?

Differentiate:

5. $f(x) = e^{3x}$ 6. $f(x) = e^{-x}$

7. $y = e^{2x+1}$ 8. $y = e^{x-1} - e^{-3x}$

9. $y = \dfrac{e^x + e^{-x}}{2}$ 10. $y = \dfrac{e^x - e^{-x}}{2}$

11. $f(t) = e^{3t} - 4e^{2t}$ 12. $s(t) = \dfrac{e^{-2t}}{2} - e^t$

13. $y = 3e^{4x+1}$ 14. $y = (e^{3x})^2$

15. $f(x) = \dfrac{e^{2x} - e^{-x}}{e^x}$ 16. $f(x) = e^x(e^{-2x} + e^{-x})$.

Differentiate:

17. $f(x) = 10^x$ 18. $f(x) = 10^{-4x}$

19. $y = 5^{x-1}$ 20. $y = 5^{2x-1}$

21. $f(x) = 10^{4x-1}$ 22. $f(x) = 10^{2-3x}$

23. $y = (10^x + 10^{-x})^2$ 24. $y = 3(10^{-4x}) - 4(10^{3-x})$.

On the same graph sketch:

25. $e^x, \quad e^{2x}, \quad e^{x/2}, \quad e^{x/5}$ 26. $e^x, \quad e^{-x}, \quad e^{-2x}, \quad e^{-x/3}$.

27. Plot carefully the direction field $dy/dx = \frac{1}{2}y$ for $-2 \le x \le 2, 0 \le y \le 3$. Use it to sketch the curve $y = e^{x/2}$.

28. Plot carefully the direction field of $dy/dx = -y$ in the range $-1 \le x \le 1$, $0 \le y \le 3$. Use it to sketch the curve $y = e^{-x}$.

Sketch the curve:

29. $y = e^{x-1}$ 30. $y = e^{x+1}$

31. $y = 1 - e^{-x}$ 32. $y = 4e^x - 1$

33. $y = \dfrac{e^x + e^{-x}}{2}$ 34. $y = \dfrac{e^x - e^{-x}}{2}$.

Find a function y for which:

35. $y' = e^{2x}$ 36. $y' = e^{-2x} + 1$

37. $y' = e^x, \quad y(0) = 2$ 38. $y' = e^x - e^{-x}, \quad y(0) = 0$.

39. Verify that $y = 4e^x - 2e^{-x}$ satisfies the differential equation $y'' = y$.

40. Verify that $y = ae^{kx} - be^{-kx}$ satisfies the differential equation $y'' = k^2 y$.

41. Verify that $y = ae^{3x} + be^{2x}$ satisfies $y'' - 5y' + 6y = 0$.

42. Verify that $y = \dfrac{e^x + e^{-x}}{2}$ satisfies $y' + y = e^x$.

43. Find the 58-th derivative of the function in Ex. 42.

4. APPLICATIONS

The exponential function $y = e^{kx}$ satisfies the differential equation

$$\frac{dy}{dx} = ky.$$

Hence e^{kx} grows or decreases at a rate proportional to its own size, depending on whether k is positive or negative.

Bacteria Growth

A colony of bacteria with unlimited food and no enemies grows at a rate proportional to its size. If $N = N(t)$ is the number of bacteria at time t, then

$$\frac{dN}{dt} = kN, \qquad k > 0.$$

Therefore

$$N(t) - Ae^{kt},$$

where A is a constant. If at $t = 0$, the number is N_0, a known quantity, then

$$N_0 = N(0) = Ae^0 = A.$$

So $A = N_0$ is the appropriate constant for this problem. We conclude

$$N(t) = N_0 e^{kt}.$$

EXAMPLE 4.1

There are 10^5 bacteria at the start of an experiment and 3×10^7 after 24 hours. What is the growth law?

Solution: Denote by $N(t)$ the number of bacteria in t hours. Then

$$N'(t) = kN(t).$$

Therefore

$$N(t) = N_0 e^{kt} = 10^5 e^{kt}.$$

To find k, use the information that $N(24) = 3 \times 10^7$:

$$3 \times 10^7 = N(24) = 10^5 e^{24k}, \qquad e^{24k} = 3 \times 10^2 = 300.$$

Take logs:

$$(24k)\log_{10} e = \log_{10}(300), \qquad 24k = \frac{\log_{10}(300)}{\log_{10} e} \approx 5.7, \qquad k \approx 0.24.$$

Answer: $N(t) \approx 10^5 e^{0.24t}$, t measured in hours.
(Alternately, $N(t) = 10^5(300)^{t/24}$.)

REMARK: Although $N(t)$ jumps by 1 for each bacterium counted, it is treated like a smoothly growing function. Because $N(t)$ is very large, this simplification of the problem leads to highly accurate results.

Radioactive Decay

A radioactive element decays at a rate proportional to the amount present. Its **half-life** is the time in which a given quantity decays to one-half of its original mass.

> EXAMPLE 4.2
>
> Carbon-14, ^{14}C, has a half-life of 5668 years. Find its decay law.

Solution: Let $M(t)$ be the mass of ^{14}C at time t, measured in years. Then

$$\frac{dM}{dt} = -\lambda M,$$

where the **decay constant** λ is positive. The equation is written this way because dM/dt is negative. The solution is

$$M(t) = M_0 e^{-\lambda t},$$

where $M_0 = M(0)$, the initial mass. To evaluate λ, use the data:

$$\frac{M_0}{2} = M(5668) = M_0 e^{-5668\lambda}, \qquad e^{-5668\lambda} = \frac{1}{2}.$$

Take logs:

$$-5668\lambda \log_{10} e = -\log_{10} 2, \qquad \lambda = \frac{\log_{10} 2}{5668 \log_{10} e} \approx 0.000122.$$

> *Answer:* $M(t) \approx M_0 e^{-(0.000122)t}$.
> (Alternately, $M(t) = M_0 a^{-t}$ where $a = 2^{1/5668}$.)

Compound interest

> EXAMPLE 4.3
>
> \$1000 is deposited in a bank giving 5% annual interest compounded daily. Estimate its value in 10 years.

Solution: There is an exact expression for the value:

$$1000 \left(1 + \frac{0.05}{365}\right)^{10 \cdot 365}$$

Let us get a quick approximation. Suppose interest were compounded not daily, but continuously. Then the value would be growing at a rate proportional to itself. So if $A(t)$ is the amount at time t (in years),

$$\frac{dA}{dt} = 0.05A(t).$$

Solving,

$$A(t) = 1000e^{0.05t},$$

$$A(10) = 1000e^{(0.05)(10)}.$$

Answer: $1648.72.

Here is a table showing the actual and the approximated values after 10 years.

Compounded quarterly	Compounded monthly	Compounded daily	Compounded continuously
$1643.62	$1647.01	$1648.66	$1648.72

EXERCISES

1. Thorium X has a half-life of 3.64 days. Find its decay law. How long will it take for $\frac{2}{3}$ of a quantity to disintegrate?

2. Two pounds of a certain radioactive substance loses $\frac{1}{5}$ of its original mass in 3 days. At what rate is the substance decaying after 4 days?

3. Money compounded continuously will double in a year at what annual rate of interest?

4. How long will it take a sum of money compounded continuously at 7.5% per annum to show a 50% return?

5. A colony of bacteria has a population of 3×10^6 initially, and 9×10^6 two hours later. What is the growth law? How long does it take the colony to double?

6. Assume that population grows at a rate proportional to the population itself. In 1950 the US population was 151 million, in 1960 it was 178 million. Make a prediction for the year 2000.

7. Under ideal conditions the rate of change of pressure above sea level is proportional to the pressure. If the barometer reads 30 in. at sea level, and 25 in. at 4000 ft, find the barometric pressure at 20,000 ft.

8. In a certain calculus course, it was found that the number of students dropping out each day was proportional to the number still enrolled. If 2000 started out and 10% dropped after 28 days, estimate the number left after 12 weeks.

9. A 5-lb sample of radioactive material contains 2 lb of Radium F which has a half-life of 138.3 days and 3 lb of Thorium X which has a half-life of 3.64 days. When will the sample contain equal amounts of Radium F and Thorium X?

10. A salt in solution decomposes into other substances at a rate proportional to the amount still unchanged. If 10 lb of a salt reduces to 5 lb in $\frac{1}{2}$ hr, how much is left after 1 hr?

9. Techniques of Differentiation

1. INTRODUCTION

The derivative is a powerful tool of Calculus, useful in a wide variety of applications. As yet we are limited in its use because there are many functions we cannot differentiate. For example:

$$\frac{1}{x^3}, \qquad x^2 e^x, \qquad \tan x, \qquad \frac{x}{x^2 + 1}, \qquad e^{-x^2}, \qquad \frac{\sin x}{x}.$$

Soon we shall be able to differentiate virtually every function that arises in practice. In this chapter we shall develop three important rules for differentiation that enlarge enormously the class of functions we can handle.

First let us review the derivatives we know.

POWERS OF x:

$$\frac{d}{dx}(x) = 1, \qquad \frac{d}{dx}(x^2) = 2x, \qquad \frac{d}{dx}(x^3) = 3x^2;$$

$$\frac{d}{dx}(c) = 0, \qquad \frac{d}{dx}\left(\frac{1}{x}\right) = -\frac{1}{x^2}.$$

TRIGONOMETRIC FUNCTIONS:

$$\frac{d}{dx}(\sin x) = \cos x, \qquad \frac{d}{dx}(\cos x) = -\sin x.$$

EXPONENTIAL FUNCTION:

$$\frac{d}{dx}(e^x) = e^x.$$

SUM RULE:

$$\frac{d}{dx}[f(x) + g(x)] = \frac{d}{dx}[f(x)] + \frac{d}{dx}[g(x)].$$

CONSTANT MULTIPLE RULE:

$$\frac{d}{dx}[kf(x)] = kf'(x).$$

SHIFTING RULE:

If

$$g(x) = f(x + c),$$

then

$$\frac{d}{dx}g(x) = \frac{df}{dx}\bigg|_{x+c} = f'(x + c).$$

SCALE RULE:

If

$$g(x) = f(kx),$$

then

$$\frac{d}{dx}g(x) = k\frac{df}{dx}\bigg|_{kx} = kf'(kx).$$

EXAMPLE 1.1

Differentiate $y = (x - 6)^2 + 3e^{2x}$.

Solution:

$$\frac{d}{dx}(x^2) = 2x,$$

$$\frac{d}{dx}(x - 6)^2 = 2(x - 6). \qquad \text{(Shifting Rule)}$$

$$\frac{d}{dx}(e^x) = e^x,$$

$$\frac{d}{dx}(e^{2x}) = 2e^{2x}, \qquad \text{(Scale Rule)}$$

$$\frac{d}{dx}(3e^{2x}) = 3 \cdot 2e^{2x}. \qquad \text{(Constant Multiple Rule)}$$

The Sum Rule allows us to combine these derivatives.

Answer: $2(x - 6) + 6e^{2x}$.

EXAMPLE 1.2

Differentiate $y = 3 \sin 5x + \dfrac{2}{x}.$

Solution: Since

$$\frac{d}{dx}(\sin x) = \cos x,$$

$$\frac{d}{dx}(3\sin 5x) = 3(5\cos 5x).$$

Since

$$\frac{d}{dx}\left(\frac{1}{x}\right) = -\frac{1}{x^2},$$

$$\frac{d}{dx}\left(\frac{2}{x}\right) = -\frac{2}{x^2}.$$

The Sum Rule allows us to combine these derivatives.

$$Answer: \quad 15\cos 5x - \frac{2}{x^2}.$$

EXERCISES

Differentiate:

1. $f(x) = 2x^3 - x^2$
2. $f(x) = -x^3 + 4x$
3. $f(x) = 2e^{3x}$
4. $f(x) = \sin(-10x)$
5. $f(x) = \dfrac{3}{x+2}$
6. $f(x) = (x-1)^3 + \dfrac{3}{x+4}$
7. $f(x) = 5e^{-x} + \cos 4x$
8. $f(x) = \sin(x-1) + \cos(x-1)$
9. $f(x) = 7e^{x+4} + e^{5x}$
10. $f(x) = A\cos hx + B\cos kx$
11. $f(x) = \sin^2 x + \cos^2 x$
12. $f(x) = \frac{1}{2}(e^{3x} - e^{-3x}).$

2. DERIVATIVE OF A PRODUCT

We still cannot differentiate $x\sin x$ although we know the derivatives of the factors x and $\sin x$. We need a rule for differentiating products.

A natural first guess is that the derivative of $u(x) \cdot v(x)$ is $u'(x) \cdot v'(x)$. However, this is wrong. Try $u(x) = x$ and $v(x) = x^2$. Then $u(x) \cdot v(x) = x^3$, but $u'(x) \cdot v'(x) = 1 \cdot 2x = 2x$, which is not the derivative of x^3. Worse yet, try $u(x) = 1$, a constant function, $v(x)$ any function. Then $u(x) \cdot v(x) = v(x)$, but $u'(x) \cdot v'(x) = 0 \cdot v'(x) = 0$. This says the derivative of every function is zero—ridiculous. Here is the correct rule.

Product Rule If $u = u(x)$ and $v = v(x)$, then

$$\frac{d}{dx}(uv) = u\frac{dv}{dx} + v\frac{du}{dx}.$$

Expressed briefly,

$$(uv)' = uv' + vu'.$$

This rule will be justified in Section 6.

EXAMPLE 2.1

Differentiate $y = x \sin x$.

Solution: Use the Product Rule:

$$\frac{d}{dx}(x \sin x) = x\frac{d}{dx}(\sin x) + (\sin x)\frac{d}{dx}(x)$$

$$= x \cos x + \sin x.$$

Answer: $x \cos x + \sin x$.

EXAMPLE 2.2

Differentiate $y = (x + 1)^3 e^{5x}$.

Solution: By the Product Rule,

$$\frac{d}{dx}[(x + 1)^3 e^{5x}] = (x + 1)^3 \frac{d}{dx}(e^{5x}) + e^{5x}\frac{d}{dx}[(x + 1)^3]$$

$$= (x + 1)^3 \cdot 5e^{5x} + e^{5x} \cdot 3(x + 1)^2$$

$$= e^{5x}(x + 1)^2[5(x + 1) + 3].$$

Answer: $e^{5x}(x + 1)^2(5x + 8)$.

Differentiating Powers

Here is an important application of the Product Rule. Given $u(x)$ and its derivative $u'(x)$, what are the derivatives of $u^2(x)$, $u^3(x)$, etc? Apply the Product Rule to $u(x) \cdot u(x)$:

$$(u^2)' = (uu)' = uu' + uu'$$

$$= 2uu'.$$

Use this information to compute the derivative of u^3:

$$(u^3)' = (u^2 u)' = u^2 u' + u(u^2)'$$
$$= u^2 u' + u(2uu')$$
$$= 3u^2 u'.$$

Use this result to compute the derivative of u^4:

$$(u^4)' = (u^3 u)' = u^3 u' + u(u^3)'$$
$$= u^3 u' + u(3u^2 u')$$
$$= 4u^3 u'.$$

Summarizing:

$$\frac{d}{dx}(u^2) = 2u\frac{du}{dx},$$

$$\frac{d}{dx}(u^3) = 3u^2\frac{du}{dx},$$

$$\frac{d}{dx}(u^4) = 4u^3\frac{du}{dx}.$$

By now the pattern should be clear.

For each positive integer n,

$$\frac{d}{dx}(u^n) = nu^{n-1}\frac{du}{dx}.$$

In particular,

$$\frac{d}{dx}(x^n) = nx^{n-1}.$$

Thus the derivatives of x^3, x^8, x^{20}, x^{50} are respectively $3x^2$, $8x^7$, $20x^{19}$ and $50x^{49}$.

EXAMPLE 2.3

Differentiate $y = (x^2 + 1)^5$.

Solution:

$$\frac{d}{dx}(u^5) = 5u^4\frac{du}{dx}.$$

Take $u = x^2 + 1$. Then $du/dx = 2x$,

$$\frac{d}{dx}[(x^2 + 1)^5] = 5(x^2 + 1)^4 \cdot 2x.$$

Answer: $10x(x^2 + 1)^4.$

REMARK: This example can be done in a clumsy way by using the Binomial Theorem:

$$y = (x^2 + 1)^5 = x^{10} + 5x^8 + 10x^6 + 10x^4 + 5x^2 + 1,$$

$$\frac{dy}{dx} = 10x^9 + 40x^7 + 60x^5 + 40x^3 + 10x.$$

This method is tedious, and the answer is in a form less suitable for computation than the previous answer.

EXAMPLE 2.4

Differentiate $y = \left(e^{2x} + x^3 + \dfrac{1}{x}\right)^4.$

Solution:

$$\frac{d}{dx}(u^4) = 4u^3 \frac{du}{dx}.$$

Take $u = e^{2x} + x^3 + 1/x$. Then $du/dx = 2e^{2x} + 3x^2 - 1/x^2$,

$$\frac{d}{dx}\left[\left(e^{2x} + x^3 + \frac{1}{x}\right)^4\right] = 4\left(e^{2x} + x^3 + \frac{1}{x}\right)^3\left(2e^{2x} + 3x^2 - \frac{1}{x^2}\right).$$

Answer: $4\left(e^{2x} + x^3 + \dfrac{1}{x}\right)^3\left(2e^{2x} + 3x^2 - \dfrac{1}{x^2}\right).$

Square Roots

Suppose $u(x) > 0$. Then its positive square root $y = \sqrt{u(x)}$ makes sense. To compute dy/dx, first square y:

$$y^2 = u.$$

Then differentiate both sides:

$$2y\frac{dy}{dx} = \frac{du}{dx},$$

$$\frac{dy}{dx} = \frac{1}{2y}\frac{du}{dx} = \frac{1}{2\sqrt{u}}\frac{du}{dx}.$$

If $u(x) > 0$, then

$$\frac{d}{dx}(\sqrt{u}) = \frac{1}{2\sqrt{u}}\frac{du}{dx}.$$

EXAMPLE 2.5

Compute dy/dx:

(a) $y = \sqrt{x}$,

(b) $y = \sqrt{x^3 + 2}$,

(c) $y = \sqrt{x \cos x}$.

Solution: Use the formula

$$\frac{d}{dx}(\sqrt{u}) = \frac{1}{2\sqrt{u}}\frac{du}{dx}.$$

(a) Take $u = x$. Then

$$\frac{d}{dx}(\sqrt{x}) = \frac{1}{2\sqrt{x}}.$$

(b) Take $u = x^3 + 2$. Then $du/dx = 3x^2$,

$$\frac{d}{dx}(\sqrt{x^3 + 2}) = \frac{1}{2\sqrt{x^3 + 2}}(3x^2).$$

(c) Take $u = x \cos x$. Then

$$\frac{du}{dx} = x\frac{d}{dx}(\cos x) + \cos x\frac{d}{dx}(x) = -x \sin x + \cos x,$$

$$\frac{d}{dx}(\sqrt{x \cos x}) = \frac{1}{2\sqrt{x \cos x}}(-x \sin x + \cos x).$$

Answer: (a) $\dfrac{1}{2\sqrt{x}}$,

(b) $\dfrac{3x^2}{2\sqrt{x^3 + 2}}$,

(c) $\dfrac{\cos x - x \sin x}{2\sqrt{x \cos x}}$.

EXERCISES

Differentiate:

1. $y = x^2 e^x$

2. $y = x^2 \sin x$

3. $y = (x - 1)^4 e^{-3x}$

4. $y = (x^2 + 1)^2 \cos x$

5. $y = \sin x \cos x$

6. $y = e^{2x} \sin 3x$

7. $y = (\sin 2x + 1)^3$

8. $y = (x^5 e^x + 2x)^7$

9. $y = xe^x \sin x$

10. $y = x^2 e^{-x}(\sin 3x + \cos x)$

11. $y = (2x)^n, \quad n \geq 0$

12. $y = (\cos x)^k, \quad k \geq 0$

13. $y = x^2(\sin x)^3$

14. $y = \sqrt{x} \,(\sin x)$

15. $y = \sqrt{e^x}$

16. $y = (\sqrt{\sin x}) \,(\cos x)$

17. $y = \dfrac{1}{x} \sqrt{\dfrac{1}{x}}$

18. $y = x \sqrt{e^x + 1}$

19. $y = (5x - 1)^2(5x + 3)$

20. $y = (x + 1)^2(x - 1)^3$

21. $y = 3(3x - 2)^3(x - 2)^2$

22. $y = (-4x + 1)^3(-3x + 1)^4$.

23. Differentiate $y = \dfrac{\sin x}{x}$.

24. Differentiate $y = \dfrac{1}{x^3}$.

$\left[\textit{Hint:} \text{ Write } y = \dfrac{1}{x} \sin x.\right]$

$\left[\textit{Hint:} \text{ Write } y = \left(\dfrac{1}{x}\right)^3.\right]$

25. Verify the formula $\dfrac{d(x^5)}{dx} = 5x^4$ by differentiating the product x^4x; also by differentiating x^3x^2.

3. DERIVATIVE OF A QUOTIENT

We now discuss the rule for differentiating the quotient of two functions. The natural guess

$$\frac{d}{dx}\left[\frac{u(x)}{v(x)}\right] = \frac{du/dx}{dv/dx}$$

is again wrong. (Try to find examples showing this cannot be correct; almost any pair of functions will do.) Here is the correct formula:

Quotient Rule If $u = u(x)$ and $v = v(x) \neq 0$, then

$$\frac{d}{dx}\left(\frac{u}{v}\right) = \frac{v\,\dfrac{du}{dx} - u\,\dfrac{dv}{dx}}{v^2}.$$

Expressed briefly,

$$\left(\frac{u}{v}\right)' = \frac{vu' - uv'}{v^2}.$$

This rule will be justified in Section 6.

EXAMPLE 3.1

Differentiate $y = \dfrac{x}{x^2 + 1}$.

Solution: Use the Quotient Rule with $u(x) = x$ and $v(x) = x^2 + 1$:

$$\frac{d}{dx}\left(\frac{x}{x^2 + 1}\right) = \frac{(x^2 + 1)\dfrac{d}{dx}(x) - x\dfrac{d}{dx}(x^2 + 1)}{(x^2 + 1)^2}$$

$$= \frac{(x^2 + 1) - x(2x)}{(x^2 + 1)^2} = \frac{1 - x^2}{(x^2 + 1)^2}.$$

Answer: $\dfrac{1 - x^2}{(x^2 + 1)^2}.$

EXAMPLE 3.2

Differentiate $y = \tan x$.

Solution:

$$\tan x = \frac{\sin x}{\cos x}.$$

Use the Quotient Rule with $u(x) = \sin x$ and $v(x) = \cos x$:

$$\frac{d}{dx}\left(\frac{\sin x}{\cos x}\right) = \frac{\cos x\dfrac{d}{dx}(\sin x) - \sin x\dfrac{d}{dx}(\cos x)}{\cos^2 x}$$

$$= \frac{(\cos x)(\cos x) - (\sin x)(-\sin x)}{\cos^2 x}.$$

But $\cos^2 x + \sin^2 x = 1$.

Answer: $\dfrac{1}{\cos^2 x} = \sec^2 x.$

Derivatives of Powers

As a special case of the Quotient Rule, take $u(x) = 1$. The result is the formula for the derivative of a reciprocal:

$$\frac{d}{dx}\left(\frac{1}{v}\right) = \frac{-1}{v^2}\frac{dv}{dx}.$$

In particular, let $v(x) = u^n(x)$, where n is any positive integer. Since $d(u^n)/dx = nu^{n-1}\,du/dx$,

$$\frac{d}{dx}\left(\frac{1}{u^n}\right) = \frac{-1}{(u^n)^2}\left(nu^{n-1}\frac{du}{dx}\right)$$

$$= \frac{-nu^{n-1}}{u^{2n}}\frac{du}{dx}.$$

Hence

$$\frac{d}{dx}\left(\frac{1}{u^n}\right) = \frac{-n}{u^{n+1}}\frac{du}{dx}.$$

This formula may be written with negative exponents:

$$\frac{d}{dx}(u^{-n}) = -nu^{-n-1}\frac{du}{dx}.$$

Thus you differentiate a negative power of $u(x)$ the same way you differentiate a positive power: bring down the exponent, lower the power by one, then multiply by du/dx. The two formulas can be combined into one.

Power Rule   If p is any integer, positive, negative, or zero, then

$$\frac{d}{dx}(u^p) = pu^{p-1}\frac{du}{dx}.$$

In particular,

$$\frac{d}{dx}(x^p) = px^{p-1}.$$

Actually the case $p = 0$ has not been discussed. But in that case the formula holds for a very simple reason. What reason?

EXAMPLE 3.3

Differentiate $y = \dfrac{1}{(x^2 + 5x + 1)^3}$.

Solution: Use the Power Rule with $u = x^2 + 5x + 1$ and $p = -3$:

$$\frac{d}{dx}(u^{-3}) = -3u^{-4}\frac{du}{dx}$$

$$= -3(x^2 + 5x + 1)^{-4}\frac{d}{dx}(x^2 + 5x + 1).$$

Answer: $\dfrac{-3(2x + 5)}{(x^2 + 5x + 1)^4}.$

EXAMPLE 3.4

Differentiate $y = \dfrac{(\sin 2x)^3}{x^5}$.

Solution: By the Quotient Rule,

$$\frac{dy}{dx} = \frac{x^5\dfrac{d}{dx}[(\sin 2x)^3] - (\sin 2x)^3\dfrac{d}{dx}(x^5)}{(x^5)^2}.$$

Compute the derivatives of $(\sin 2x)^3$ and x^5:

$$\frac{d}{dx}[(\sin 2x)^3] = 3(\sin 2x)^2 \frac{d}{dx}(\sin 2x) = 3(\sin 2x)^2(\cos 2x) \cdot 2;$$

$$\frac{d}{dx}(x^5) = 5x^4.$$

Substitute these expressions:

$$\frac{dy}{dx} = \frac{x^5[6(\sin 2x)^2 \cos 2x] - 5x^4(\sin 2x)^3}{x^{10}}$$

$$= \frac{(\sin 2x)^2(6x \cos 2x - 5 \sin 2x)}{x^6}.$$

Alternate Solution: Write $y = x^{-5}(\sin 2x)^3$ and use the Product Rule:

$$\frac{dy}{dx} = x^{-5}\frac{d}{dx}[(\sin 2x)^3] + (\sin 2x)^3 \frac{d}{dx}(x^{-5})$$

$$= x^{-5}[6(\sin 2x)^2 \cos 2x] + (\sin 2x)^3(-5x^{-6})$$

$$= x^{-6}(\sin 2x)^2(6x \cos 2x - 5 \sin 2x).$$

$$\text{Answer:} \quad \frac{(\sin 2x)^2(6x \cos 2x - 5 \sin 2x)}{x^6}.$$

EXERCISES

Differentiate wherever the denominator is non-zero:

1. $y = \dfrac{x}{e^x}$

2. $y = \dfrac{\cos x}{\sin x}$ $(= \cot x)$

3. $y = \dfrac{x^2 - 1}{x^3 - 1}$

4. $y = \dfrac{x}{1 - x}$

5. $y = \dfrac{1}{(x^2 + 1)^6}$

6. $y = \dfrac{(x + 1)^2}{(x + 2)^n}$, $n \geq 0$

7. $y = \dfrac{\sin x + \cos x}{\sin x - \cos x}$

8. $y = \dfrac{2xe^x}{x^2 + 1}$

9. $y = \dfrac{(\cos 2x)^4}{x^3}$

10. $y = \dfrac{e^{2x} \sin 3x}{\cos 4x}$

11. $y = \sqrt{\dfrac{x + 1}{x - 1}}$

12. $y = \dfrac{\tan x}{\sqrt{x}}$

13. $y = \dfrac{(\sin x)^m}{(\cos x)^n}$

14. $y = \dfrac{e^x + e^{-x}}{e^x - e^{-x}}$

15. $y = \dfrac{1}{x \sin x}$

16. $y = \left(\dfrac{x}{e^x - 1}\right)^2.$

4. THE CHAIN RULE

Suppose y is a function of x, and x is a function of t. Then indirectly y is a function of t.

Here are three examples of such **composite functions.**

(1) If $y = \cos(t^2)$, then $y = \cos x$, where $x = t^2$.

(2) When a pebble is dropped into a smooth pond, a circular ripple begins to expand. Its area is πr^2, where r is a function of t. The area is indirectly a function $A(t)$ of time,

$$A(t) = \pi[r(t)]^2.$$

(3) If $y = (x^3 + x^2 + x + 1)^4$, then $y = u^4$, where $u = x^3 + x^2 + x + 1$. In this way, y is the composite of two simpler functions, $f(u) = u^4$ and $u(x) = x^3 + x^2 + x + 1$.

Here is the rule for differentiating composite functions:

> **Chain Rule**   If $y = y(x)$ and $x = x(t)$, then
> $$\frac{dy}{dt} = \frac{dy}{dx}\frac{dx}{dt}.$$

This rule will be justified in Section 6.

Basically, the Chain Rule says this: if y is changing p times as fast as x and x is changing q times as fast as t, then y is changing pq times as fast as t.

EXAMPLE 4.1

Differentiate $y = \cos(t^2)$.

Solution: Write $y = \cos x$, where $x = t^2$. By the Chain Rule,

$$\frac{dy}{dt} = \frac{dy}{dx}\frac{dx}{dt} = \frac{d}{dx}(\cos x)\frac{d}{dt}(t^2) = (-\sin x)(2t),$$

where $x = t^2$.

Answer: $-2t\sin(t^2)$.

EXAMPLE 4.2

Differentiate $y = e^{x^2-3x}$.

Solution: Write $y = e^u$, where $u = x^2 - 3x$. By the Chain Rule,

$$\frac{dy}{dx} = \frac{dy}{du}\frac{du}{dx} = e^u(2x - 3) = e^{x^2-3x}(2x - 3).$$

Answer: $e^{x^2-3x}(2x - 3)$.

EXAMPLE 4.3

Differentiate $y = (x^3 + x^2 + x + 1)^4$.

Solution: Write $y = u^4$, where $u = x^3 + x^2 + x + 1$. By the Chain Rule,

$$\frac{dy}{dx} = \frac{dy}{du}\frac{du}{dx} = 4u^3(3x^2 + 2x + 1).$$

Answer: $4(x^3 + x^2 + x + 1)^3(3x^2 + 2x + 1)$.

We have already met some special instances of the Chain Rule.

(1) The Shifting Rule:

$$\frac{d}{dx}[f(x + c)] = f'(x + c).$$

Write $y = f(u)$, where $u = x + c$. Then

$$\frac{dy}{dx} = \frac{dy}{du}\frac{du}{dx} = f'(u)\frac{d}{dx}(x + c) = f'(u) = f'(x + c).$$

(2) The Scale Rule:

$$\frac{d}{dx}[f(kx)] = kf'(kx).$$

Write $y = f(u)$, where $u = kx$. Then

$$\frac{dy}{dx} = \frac{dy}{du}\frac{du}{dx} = f'(u)\frac{d}{dx}(kx) = f'(u)k = f'(kx)k.$$

(3) The Power Rule:

$$\frac{d}{dx}[u^p(x)] = pu^{p-1}\frac{du}{dx}.$$

Write $y = u^p$, where $u = u(x)$. Then

$$\frac{dy}{dx} = \frac{dy}{du}\frac{du}{dx} = pu^{p-1}\frac{du}{dx}.$$

EXERCISES

Differentiate:

1. $y = \sin(x^3)$

2. $y = \cos(e^x)$

3. $y = e^{\sin 2x}$

4. $y = \sqrt{2 + \cos(x/5)}$

5. $y = (x^3 + x - 3)^5$

6. $y = \sqrt{x^2 + 7}$

7. $y = e^{ax^2 + bx + c}$

8. $y = (\sin \sqrt{x})^2$

9. $y = e^{e^x}$

10. $y = [\cos(3 - x^2)]^3$

11. $y = [(x^3 + 2x)^5 + x^2]^2$

12. $y = \{[(x + 1)^2 + 1]^2 + 1\}^2$

13. $y = e^{x^2} + e^{-x^2}$

14. $y = \sqrt{1 + \sqrt{2x}}.$

5. LIMITS

In order to justify the rules stated in the preceding sections, we must recall the meaning of a derivative.

Given a function $f(x)$, consider the value of

$$\frac{f(a + h) - f(a)}{h},$$

where h is near zero. If there is a number A such that

$$\frac{f(a + h) - f(a)}{h} \approx A,$$

and if this approximation can be made as close as desired by taking h close enough to zero, we say that A is the derivative of $f(x)$ at $x = a$, and write $f'(a) = A$. It is customary to summarize by the notation

$$\lim_{h \to 0} \frac{f(a + h) - f(a)}{h} = f'(a).$$

The left side of this equation is read "the limit of $[f(a + h) - f(a)]/h$ as h approaches zero." Alternative notation is:

$$\frac{f(a + h)\quad f(a)}{h} \longrightarrow f'(a) \qquad \text{as} \quad h \longrightarrow 0.$$

For example, suppose $f(x) = x^2$ and $a = 3$. Then

$$\frac{f(3 + h) - f(3)}{h} = \frac{(3 + h)^2 - 3^2}{h} = 6 + h.$$

Thus, the closer h is to zero, the more precise is the approximation

$$\frac{f(3 + h) - f(3)}{h} \approx 6.$$

Therefore, the derivative $f'(3)$ is

$$\lim_{h \to 0} \frac{f(3 + h) - f(3)}{h} = 6.$$

For more details, see Chapter 20, Section 6 and Chapter 21, Section 1.

EXERCISES

Find the limit:

1. $\lim_{h \to 0} \dfrac{(2 + h)^3 - 8}{h}$

2. $\lim_{h \to 1} \dfrac{h^2 - 1}{h - 1}$

3. $\lim\limits_{h\to 0} \dfrac{(x+h)^4 - x^4}{h}$

4. $\lim\limits_{x\to 2} (x^3 + 1)$

5. $\lim\limits_{x\to 0} \dfrac{(1+2x)^2 - 1}{x}$

6. $\lim\limits_{x\to 0} \dfrac{(1+\frac{1}{2}x)^2 - 1}{x}$

7. $\lim\limits_{h\to 0} \dfrac{h}{(h+1)^3 - 1}$

8. $\lim\limits_{x\to 0} \dfrac{1}{(x-1)^3}$

9. $\lim\limits_{x\to 0} \dfrac{(x+1)^2}{(x-1)^3}$

10. $\lim\limits_{k\to 0} \dfrac{(2-k)^5 - 32}{k}$.

11. Find $\lim\limits_{x\to 0} \dfrac{\sqrt{2+x} - \sqrt{2}}{x}$. (*Hint:* "Rationalize" the numerator, i.e., multiply and divide by $\sqrt{2+x} + \sqrt{2}$.)

12. Find $\lim\limits_{x\to 0} \dfrac{(2+x)^{1/3} - (2)^{1/3}}{x}$. (*Hint:* Proceed as in Ex. 11, using the identity $y^3 - z^3 = (y-z)(y^2 + yz + z^2)$.)

13. Now find $\lim\limits_{x\to 0} \dfrac{(2+x)^{1/4} - (2)^{1/4}}{x}$.

14. Let $h \to 0$ in the relation

$$\frac{d}{dx}\left[\frac{1}{(x+h)x} \right] = \frac{1}{h}\frac{d}{dx}\left[\frac{1}{x} - \frac{1}{x+h} \right] = \frac{1}{h}\left[-\frac{1}{x^2} + \frac{1}{(x+h)^2} \right]$$

to deduce again that $\dfrac{d}{dx}\left(\dfrac{1}{x^2}\right) = \dfrac{-2}{x^3}$.

6. JUSTIFICATION OF THE RULES

The basic tool needed in this section is an approximation formula,
$$f(a+h) \approx f(a) + f'(a)h \qquad \text{for} \quad h \approx 0.$$
To express this approximation more precisely, write
$$f(a+h) = f(a) + f'(a)h + e(h),$$
where $e(h)$ denotes the error. It is much smaller than h when h is small:
$$\frac{e(h)}{h} = \left[\frac{f(a+h) - f(a)}{h} - f'(a) \right] \longrightarrow 0.$$

This follows directly from the definition of the derivative. For the theory underlying the approximation and the justifications that follow, see Chapter 21, Section 1.

The rules for differentiation presented in this chapter can be justified by careful use of this estimate. In order to give the spirit of the justifications without being burdened with technical details, we shall use instead the simpler formula
$$f(a+h) \approx f(a) + f'(a)h.$$

THE PRODUCT RULE

Suppose $f(x) = u(x)v(x)$. The derivative $f'(a)$ is the limit as $h \longrightarrow 0$ of

$$\frac{f(a + h) - f(a)}{h} = \frac{u(a + h)v(a + h) - u(a)v(a)}{h}.$$

We shall use the abbreviations

$$u = u(a), \qquad v = v(a), \qquad u' = u'(a), \qquad v' = v'(a).$$

The numerator of the fraction on the right can be approximated by means of the formulas

$$u(a + h) \approx u + u'h, \qquad v(a + h) \approx v + v'h.$$

Thus

$$u(a + h)v(a + h) - u(a)v(a) \approx (u + u'h)(v + v'h) - uv$$
$$= (uv' + vu')h + u'v'h^2.$$

It follows that

$$\frac{f(a + h) - f(a)}{h} \approx (uv' + vu') + u'v'h.$$

The second term on the right has limit zero as $h \longrightarrow 0$. Therefore

$$f'(a) = \lim_{h \to 0} \frac{f(a + h) - f(a)}{h} = uv' + vu'.$$

In other words,

$$\frac{d}{dx}(uv) = uv' + vu'.$$

THE QUOTIENT RULE

Suppose $f(x) = u(x)/v(x)$ and $v(a) \neq 0$. The derivative $f'(a)$ is the limit as $h \longrightarrow 0$ of

$$\frac{f(a + h) - f(a)}{h} = \frac{1}{h}\left[\frac{u(a + h)}{v(a + h)} - \frac{u(a)}{v(a)}\right]$$
$$= \frac{1}{h}\left[\frac{u(a + h)v(a) - u(a)v(a + h)}{v(a + h)v(a)}\right].$$

By the approximations

$$u(a + h) \approx u + u'h, \qquad v(a + h) \approx v + v'h,$$

the numerator of the last fraction is approximately

$$(u + u'h)v - u(v + v'h) = (vu' - uv')h,$$

and the denominator is approximately

$$(v + v'h)v = v^2 + v'vh.$$

(If h is very small, then $v^2 + v'vh$ is very close to v^2, hence is non-zero.) Thus

$$\frac{f(a + h) - f(a)}{h} \approx \frac{1}{h}\left[\frac{(vu' - uv')h}{v^2 + v'vh}\right] = \frac{vu' - uv'}{v^2 + v'vh}.$$

The term $v'vh \longrightarrow 0$ as $h \longrightarrow 0$. Therefore

$$f'(a) = \lim_{h \to 0}\left[\frac{f(a + h) - f(a)}{h}\right]$$

$$= \lim_{h \to 0}\left[\frac{vu' - uv'}{v^2 + v'vh}\right] = \frac{vu' - uv'}{v^2}.$$

In other words,

$$\frac{d}{dx}\left(\frac{u}{v}\right) = \frac{vu' - uv'}{v^2}.$$

THE CHAIN RULE

Suppose $y = y(x)$ where $x = x(t)$. Then dy/dt at $t = a$ is the limit as $h \longrightarrow 0$ of

$$\frac{y[x(a + h)] - y[x(a)]}{h}.$$

We shall use the abbreviations

$$x_0 = x(a), \qquad y_0 = y[x(a)], \qquad \frac{dx}{dt} = \frac{dx}{dt}\bigg|_{t=a}, \qquad \frac{dy}{dx} = \frac{dy}{dx}\bigg|_{x=x(a)}.$$

We shall estimate $y[x(a + h)]$ by two linear approximations. First, since $x(a + h) \approx x_0 + (dx/dt)h$, we have

$$y[x(a + h)] \approx y[x_0 + \frac{dx}{dt}h].$$

Second, since $y(b + k) \approx y(b) + y'(b)k$, we substitute $b = x_0$ and $k = (dx/dt)h$ to obtain

$$y[x_0 + \frac{dx}{dt}h] \approx y_0 + \frac{dy}{dx}\frac{dx}{dt}h.$$

Hence

$$y[x(a + h)] \approx y_0 + \frac{dy}{dx}\frac{dx}{dt}h,$$

and consequently

$$\frac{y[x(a + h)] - y[x(a)]}{h} \approx \frac{y_0 + \dfrac{dy}{dx}\dfrac{dx}{dt}h - y_0}{h} = \frac{dy}{dx}\frac{dx}{dt}.$$

Therefore

$$\frac{dy}{dt} = \lim_{h \to 0} \frac{y[x(a+h)] - y[x(a)]}{h} = \frac{dy}{dx}\frac{dx}{dt}.$$

7. REVIEW

This is a good time to review the formulas introduced in this chapter. Memorize them; you will need them over and over again.

$$\frac{d}{dx}(uv) = u\frac{dv}{dx} + v\frac{du}{dx}. \qquad \text{(PRODUCT RULE)}$$

$$\frac{d}{dx}\left(\frac{u}{v}\right) = \frac{v\dfrac{du}{dx} - u\dfrac{dv}{dx}}{v^2}. \qquad \text{(QUOTIENT RULE)}$$

For each integer p,

$$\frac{d}{dx}(u^p) = pu^{p-1}\frac{du}{dx}. \qquad \text{(POWER RULE)}$$

$$\frac{d}{dx}(\sqrt{u}) = \frac{1}{2\sqrt{u}}\frac{du}{dx}.$$

If y is a function of x, and x is a function of t, then

$$\frac{dy}{dt} = \frac{dy}{dx}\frac{dx}{dt}. \qquad \text{(CHAIN RULE)}$$

Be especially careful with the Chain Rule. Approximately 86% of all mistakes in differentiation can be traced to misuse of the Chain Rule. For example:

Typical mistake	Correct answer
$\dfrac{d}{dx}[(5x)^3] = 3(5x)^2$	$3(5x)^2 \cdot 5$
$\dfrac{d}{dx}(x^2 + x)^5 = 5(x^2 + x)^4$	$5(x^2 + x)^4(2x + 1)$
$\dfrac{d}{dx}(\sin 4x)^2 = 2\sin 4x \cos 4x$	$8\sin 4x \cos 4x$
$\dfrac{d}{dx}(e^{3x}) = e^{3x}$	$3e^{3x}$
$\dfrac{d}{dx}(\sqrt{1-5x}) = \dfrac{1}{2\sqrt{1-5x}}$	$\dfrac{-5}{2\sqrt{1-5x}}.$

Also be careful with the Quotient Rule. Avoid using $uv' - vu'$ as the numerator in place of $vu' - uv'$. To remember which, it is helpful to recall that $u/v = u \cdot v^{-1}$. Thus

$$\frac{d}{dx}\left(\frac{u}{v}\right) = \frac{d}{dx}\,(uv^{-1}) = v^{-1}\frac{du}{dx} + u\frac{d}{dx}\,(v^{-1})$$

$$= v^{-1}\frac{du}{dx} - uv^{-2}\frac{dv}{dx} = \frac{vu' - uv'}{v^2}.$$

To test your skill, here is a collection of miscellaneous differentiation problems that can be done with the techniques we have developed.

EXERCISES

Differentiate:

1. $y = \dfrac{2x + 1}{2x - 1}$

2. $y = (1 + 2\sqrt{x})^3$

3. $y = e^{1/x}$

4. $y = \sqrt{\dfrac{x}{x + 1}}$

5. $y = e^{ax}\cos bx$

6. $y = \left(\dfrac{2}{x^2} + \dfrac{3}{x^5}\right)^{-2}$

7. $y = \dfrac{x}{\sqrt{1 - x^2}}$

8. $y = x^3 e^{-x}$

9. $y = \sin\sqrt{\dfrac{x}{6}}$

10. $y = \dfrac{1}{1 + 2x + 3x^2}$

11. $y = x^2\sqrt{x^2 - a^2}$

12. $y = e^{xe^x}$

13. $y = \sin^3 kx$

14. $y = \left(\dfrac{x + 1}{x + 3}\right)^2$

15. $y = x\sin\dfrac{1}{x}$

16. $y = \dfrac{e^{ax}}{\sqrt{bx}}$

17. $y = \dfrac{4 - x}{\sqrt{8x - x^2}}$

18. $y = 3x\cos(x^2)$

19. $y = \dfrac{\sin 2x}{x^3}$

20. $y = \dfrac{1}{(2\sin x)^5}$

21. $y = x^2 e^{-3/x}$

22. $y = \sqrt{x + \sqrt{x}}$

23. $y = \cos^4 x - \sin^4 x$

24. $y = \dfrac{1}{1 + e^{-x}}$

25. $y = \left(\dfrac{x}{e^{2x} + 1}\right)^3$

26. $y = \sqrt{x}/\cos(2\sqrt{x})$

27. $y = xe^{-ax}\sin bx$

28. $y = \dfrac{1 - \sqrt{3x}}{1 + \sqrt{3x}}$

29. $y = \left(1 + \cos^2 \dfrac{x}{2}\right)^3$

30. $y = \dfrac{x}{(x^3 + 1)^2}$

31. $y = \dfrac{e^x - e^{-x}}{e^x + e^{-x}}$

32. $y = \sqrt{x}\, e^{-\sqrt{x}}$.

33. Show that the derivative of $e^x p(x)$, where $p(x)$ is a polynomial, is a function of the same form.

34. Show that the derivative of $p(x)/q(x)$, where $p(x)$ and $q(x)$ are polynomials, is a function of the same form.

10. Applications

1. RATE PROBLEMS

If two physical quantities are related and both are changing, then their rates of change are also related. Quite a number of physical problems involve this idea.

EXAMPLE 1.1

A large spherical balloon is inflated by a pump that injects 10 ft³/sec of helium. At the instant when the balloon contains 972π ft³ of gas, how fast is its radius increasing?

Solution: Denote the radius and volume of the balloon at time t by $r(t)$ and $V(t)$. The derivative $dV/dt = 10$ ft³/sec is given. The derivative dr/dt is required at a specific time.

The formula for the volume V of a sphere of radius r is $V = \frac{4}{3}\pi r^3$. Hence

$$V(t) = \frac{4}{3}\pi[r(t)]^3.$$

To find a relation between dr/dt and dV/dt, differentiate using the Chain Rule:

$$\frac{dV}{dt} = \frac{dV}{dr}\frac{dr}{dt} = \frac{4}{3}\pi \cdot 3r^2 \cdot \frac{dr}{dt} = 4\pi r^2 \frac{dr}{dt}.$$

Solve for dr/dt:

$$\frac{dr}{dt} = \frac{1}{4\pi r^2}\frac{dV}{dt} = \frac{10}{4\pi r^2}.$$

This formula tells the rate of change of the radius at any instant, in terms of the radius. At the instant in question, the volume is 972π ft³, so the radius can be found by solving

$$\frac{4}{3}\pi r^3 = 972\pi.$$

Thus

$$r^3 = \frac{3}{4\pi} \cdot 972\pi = 729, \qquad r = 9.$$

But when $r = 9$,

$$\frac{dr}{dt} = \frac{10}{4\pi \cdot 9^2} = \frac{10}{324\pi}.$$

$$Answer: \quad \frac{10}{324\pi} \approx 0.00982 \text{ ft/sec.}$$

EXAMPLE 1.2

A point P moves with increasing speed around a circle of radius 10 ft, starting at Q when $t = 0$. See Fig. 1.1. When $\frac{1}{3}$ of the way around the circle, its speed is 9 ft/sec. At that instant, how fast is the length PQ increasing?

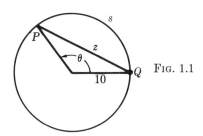

Fig. 1.1

Solution: At time t, let z be the length of PQ, let s be the arc length, and let θ be the central angle (Fig. 1.1). Given: $ds/dt = 9$ ft/sec when $\theta = 2\pi/3$, that is, when $s = 10 \cdot 2\pi/3$ ft. Find dz/dt at that instant.

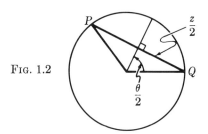

Fig. 1.2

To do so, obtain a relation between z and s. From Fig. 1.2,

$$\frac{z}{2} = 10 \sin \frac{\theta}{2},$$

But from the previous figure, $s = 10\theta$, hence

$$z = 20 \sin \frac{\theta}{2} = 20 \sin \frac{s}{20}.$$

This is the desired relation; now differentiate using the Chain Rule:

$$\frac{dz}{dt} = \left(20 \cos \frac{s}{20}\right) \frac{1}{20} \frac{ds}{dt}.$$

At the instant in question,

$$\cos\frac{s}{20} = \cos\frac{\theta}{2} = \cos\frac{\pi}{3} = \frac{1}{2} \quad \text{and} \quad \frac{ds}{dt} = 9.$$

Hence

$$\frac{dz}{dt} = 20 \cdot \frac{1}{2} \cdot \frac{1}{20} \cdot 9 = \frac{9}{2}.$$

Answer: 4.5 ft/sec.

EXAMPLE 1.3

A rectangular tank has a sliding panel S that divides it into two adjustable tanks of width 3 ft. See Fig. 1.3. Water is poured into the left compartment at the rate of 5 ft³/min. At the same time S is moved to the right at the rate of 3 ft/min. When the left compartment is 10 ft long it contains 70 ft³ of water. Is the water level rising or falling? How fast?

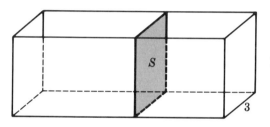

Fɪɢ. 1.3

Solution: Let x be the length of the left compartment; let y and V be the depth and the volume of the water in the left compartment. Then x, y, and V are all functions of time. Given:

$$\frac{dx}{dt} = 3 \text{ ft/min}, \qquad \frac{dV}{dt} = 5 \text{ ft}^3/\text{min}.$$

Compute: dy/dt when $x = 10$ and $V = 70$.

To do so, find a relation between x, y, and V. At any instant

$$V = 3xy.$$

Differentiate with respect to t:

$$\frac{dV}{dt} = 3x\frac{dy}{dt} + 3\frac{dx}{dt}y.$$

Substitute the data at the instant in question:

$$5 = 3 \cdot 10 \cdot \frac{dy}{dt} + 3 \cdot 3 \cdot y,$$

$$\frac{dy}{dt} = \frac{5 - 9y}{30}.$$

At the given instant, $V = 70$ and $x = 10$, hence $y = 7/3$. Therefore

$$\frac{dy}{dt} = \frac{5 - 9(7/3)}{30} = -\frac{16}{30}.$$

The water level is falling at the rate of 8/15 ft/min.

Alternate Solution: Instead of differentiating the equation $V = 3xy$, solve for y first, then differentiate:

$$y = \frac{1}{3}\frac{V}{x},$$

$$\frac{dy}{dt} = \frac{1}{3}\frac{x\dfrac{dV}{dt} - V\dfrac{dx}{dt}}{x^2}.$$

At the given instant,

$$\frac{dy}{dt} = \frac{1}{3}\frac{10 \cdot 5 - 70 \cdot 3}{10^2} = -\frac{16}{30}.$$

> *Answer:* Falling at the rate of 8/15 ft/min.

EXERCISES

1. A stone thrown into a pond produces a circular ripple which expands from the point of impact. If the radius of the ripple increases at the rate of 1.5 ft/sec, how fast is the area growing when the radius is 8 ft?

2. Water flows into an inverted conical tank at the rate of 27 ft³/min. When the depth of the water is 2 ft, how fast is the level rising? Assume the height of the tank is 4 ft and the radius at the top is 1 ft.

3. A 6-ft man walks away from a 12-ft lamp post at the rate of 4 ft/sec. How fast is his shadow lengthening when he is 21 ft from the post?

4. Two cars leave an intersection. One travels north at 30 mph, the other east at 40 mph. How fast is the distance between them increasing at the end of 1 min? 5 min?

5. A tetrahedron has vertices at $(0, 0, 0)$, $(x, 0, 0)$, $(0, y, 0)$ and $(0, 0, z)$. Suppose x, y, and z are increasing with time according to the formulas $x = 2t$, $y = t^3$, and $z = 3t^2$. When $t = 2$, how fast is the volume of the tetrahedron increasing? Measure lengths in cm and time in sec.

6. A point moves from the origin along the curve $y = x^3 - 3x^2$ so that its x-coordinate increases 3 ft/sec. Find the rate at which the distance from the point to the origin is increasing when the point is at $(1, -2)$.

7. If the volume of an expanding cube is increasing at the rate of 4 ft³/min, how fast is its surface area increasing when the surface area is 24 ft²?

8. If a chord sweeps (without turning) across a circle of radius 10 ft at the rate of 6 ft/sec, how fast is the length of the chord decreasing when it is $\frac{3}{4}$ of the way across?

9. An observer is standing $\frac{1}{4}$ mi from a railroad track as a train goes by at 80 mph. When the front of the train is 2 mi away from the nearest point on the track to the observer, at what speed is it moving away from him?

10. A lighthouse beacon 2 mi from a straight beach revolves once every 48 sec. How fast is the spot of light moving when it is 5 mi down the beach from the point nearest to the lighthouse? (*Hint:* $d(\tan \theta)/d\theta = \sec^2 \theta$.)

11. A 15-ft ladder leans against a vertical wall. If the top slides downward at the rate of 2 ft/sec, find the speed of the lower end when it is 12 ft from the wall.

12. An elevated train on a track 30 ft above the ground crosses a (perpendicular) street at the rate of 50 ft/sec at the instant that an automobile, approaching at the rate of 30 ft/sec, is 40 ft up the street. Find how fast the train and the automobile are separating 2 sec later.

13. A conical water tank is mounted with its vertex down. The angle of the vertex is 60°. Water is pumped into the tank at a rate of 5 ft³/min, and water evaporates from the tank at a rate (ft³/min) equal to 0.01 times the exposed surface area (ft²). At what depth, if any, will the water stop rising?

14. Thread of radius 10^{-3} m is being wound on a ball at the rate of 2 m/sec. Assume that the ball is a perfect sphere at each instant, and consists entirely of thread with no empty space. Find the rate of increase of the radius when the radius is 0.08 m.

15. Two concentric circles are expanding, the outer radius at the rate of 2 ft/sec and the inner one at 5 ft/sec. At a certain instant, the outer radius is 10 ft and the inner radius is 3 ft. At this instant, is the area of the ring between the two circles increasing or decreasing? How fast?

16. A point P moves to the right along the x-axis at the rate of 4 cm/sec. Let R_P denote the region under the curve $y = e^{-x^2}$ between $x = 0$ and $x = P$. Find the rate of change of the area of R_P when P is at $x = 3$.

17. A barber pole is a 3-ft cylinder of radius 4 in. The red spiral stripe on its surface makes exactly 1.5 turns from bottom to top. As the pole rotates at the rate of 40 rpm, how fast does the stripe appear to move vertically?

2. MAXIMA AND MINIMA REVISITED

Here is the basic problem: find the maximum value or the minimum value of $f(x)$ in an interval $a \le x \le b$.

In theory, it is easy to locate the maximum or the minimum:

> The maximum of a smooth function $f(x)$ in the interval $a \le x \le b$ occurs either at a value of x where $f'(x) = 0$, or at one of the end points, a or b. The same is true for the minimum of $f(x)$.

This statement is easy to see graphically (Fig. 2.1). At points where

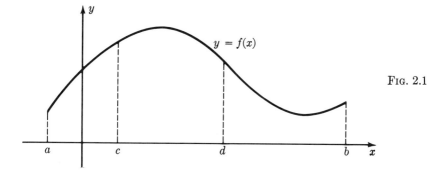

$y = f(x)$

Fig. 2.1

$f'(x) > 0$, the graph is rising ($x = c$ for example). Neither the maximum nor the minimum can occur at such a point because the graph is higher to the right and lower to the left. At points where $f'(x) < 0$, the graph is falling ($x = d$ for example), and for a similar reason neither the maximum nor the minimum can occur there. Hence if $a < x_0 < b$ and $f(x_0)$ is the maximum or the minimum value of $f(x)$, then $f'(x_0) = 0$.

This argument does not apply at the end points a and b, however. (Why not?) The maximum or the minimum may occur at one of the end points without the derivative vanishing there (Fig. 2.2).

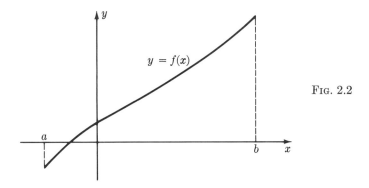

FIG. 2.2

This discussion suggests a procedure for solving the basic problem.

To find the maximum and minimum of $f(x)$ in the interval $a \leq x \leq b$, locate all points x where $f'(x) = 0$. Call these $x_1, x_2, \cdots, x_n$. The maximum is the largest of the numbers $f(a), f(x_1), f(x_2), \cdots, f(x_n), f(b)$. The minimum is the smallest of these.

In practice, this procedure may involve unnecessary work. The derivative of the function graphed in Fig. 2.3 is zero at x_1, x_2, x_3, x_4, x_5, and x_6.

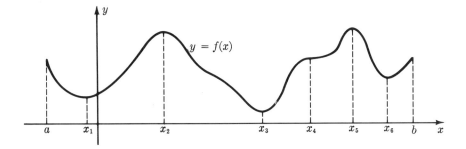

FIG. 2.3

Certainly the maximum does not occur at x_1, x_3, x_4, or x_6. We need a way to eliminate such points quickly.

What can the graph of $y = f(x)$ look like near a point $x = c$ where the derivative is zero? There are only four possible shapes (Fig. 2.4). The figures show a maximum in case (a) and a minimum in case (b). The remaining two cases are neither maxima nor minima.

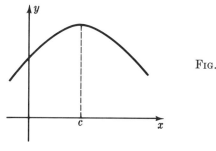

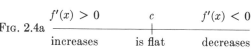

Fig. 2.4a

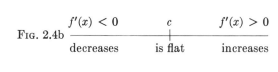

Fig. 2.4b

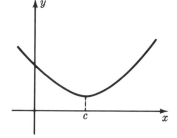

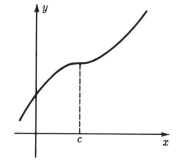

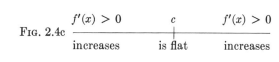

Fig. 2.4c

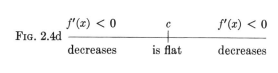

Fig. 2.4d

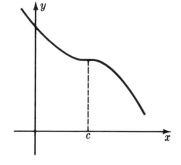

The maximum of $f(x)$ in the interval $a \le x \le b$ occurs either at $x = a$, or at $x = b$, or at an interior point $x = c$ where

(1) $f'(c) = 0$, and
(2) $f'(x)$ changes from positive to negative as x increases through c.
   In other words, $f'(x) > 0$ for $x < c$ and $f'(x) < 0$ for $x > c$.

The minimum occurs either at $x = a$, or at $x = b$, or at an interior point $x = c$ where

(1) $f'(c) = 0$, and
(2) $f'(x)$ changes from negative to positive as x increases through c.

(These statements presuppose that $f'(x) = 0$ only at a finite set of points in the interval $a \le x \le b$.)

Sometimes the second derivative can be used to determine how the sign of $f'(x)$ behaves near $x = c$. Suppose $f'(c) = 0$. If $f''(c) > 0$, the derivative $f'(x)$ is increasing at c, hence $f'(x)$ increases from negative to zero to positive. If $f''(c) < 0$, then $f'(x)$ decreases from positive to zero to negative.

Suppose $f'(c) = 0$.

(i) If $f''(c) < 0$, the maximum value of $f(x)$ may occur at $x = c$, but the minimum cannot.
(ii) If $f''(c) > 0$, the minimum value of $f(x)$ may occur at $x = c$, but the maximum cannot.

This makes good sense geometrically. Recall that if $f''(c) < 0$, the graph is concave downwards and so cannot have its minimum at c. If $f''(c) > 0$, the graph is concave upwards and so cannot have its maximum at c.

REMARK: The case $f'(c) = 0$ *and* $f''(c) = 0$ is inconclusive. For example, the functions $f_4(x) = x^4$, $f_5(x) = x^5$, and $f_6(x) = -x^6$ all satisfy these conditions at $c = 0$. Yet $f_4(x)$ has a minimum at $x = 0$, and $f_6(x)$ has a maximum at $x = 0$, whereas $f_5(x)$ has neither (Fig. 2.5). In general, see Chapter 21, Sections 2 and 3 for the theory behind maxima and minima.

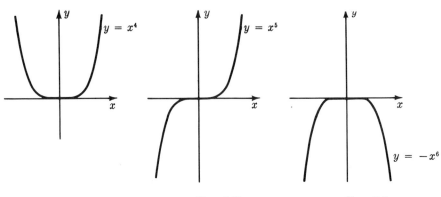

FIG. 2.5a   FIG. 2.5b   FIG. 2.5c

EXAMPLE 2.1

Find the maximum value of the function $f(x) = \dfrac{1}{2}x - \sin x$ in the range $0 \le x \le 4\pi$.

Solution: The maximum occurs either at 0 or 4π, or at a zero of the derivative,

$$f'(x) = \frac{1}{2} - \cos x.$$

Thus

$$f'(x) = 0 \qquad \text{if} \quad \cos x = \frac{1}{2}.$$

In the range $0 \le x \le 4\pi$, zeros of the derivative occur at

$$x = \frac{\pi}{3}, \quad \frac{5\pi}{3}, \quad \frac{7\pi}{3}, \quad \frac{11\pi}{3}.$$

Hence, there are six possible places where the maximum can occur. To eliminate some of them, consider the second derivative, $f''(x) = \sin x$:

$$f''\left(\frac{\pi}{3}\right) = f''\left(\frac{7\pi}{3}\right) = \sin\frac{\pi}{3} > 0,$$

$$f''\left(\frac{5\pi}{3}\right) = f''\left(\frac{11\pi}{3}\right) = \sin\frac{5\pi}{3} < 0.$$

The values $5\pi/3$ and $11\pi/3$, for which $f''(x)$ is negative, are candidates for the maximum. The others, $\pi/3$ and $7\pi/3$, are candidates for the minimum; eliminate them. Hence the maximum of $f(x)$ occurs at one of the points

$$0, \quad \frac{5\pi}{3}, \quad \frac{11\pi}{3}, \quad 4\pi.$$

Evaluate $f(x) = \frac{1}{2}x - \sin x$ at each of these points:

$$f(0) = 0,$$

$$f\left(\frac{5\pi}{3}\right) = \frac{5\pi}{6} - \sin\frac{5\pi}{3} = \frac{5\pi}{6} + \frac{\sqrt{3}}{2},$$

$$f\left(\frac{11\pi}{3}\right) = \frac{11\pi}{6} - \sin\frac{11\pi}{3} = \frac{11\pi}{6} + \frac{\sqrt{3}}{2},$$

$$f(4\pi) = 2\pi = \frac{11\pi}{6} + \frac{\pi}{6}.$$

The largest of these is $f(11\pi/3)$.

Alternate Solution: Sketch $y = \frac{1}{2}x - \sin x$ by graphically subtracting the curve $y = \sin x$ from the line $y = \frac{1}{2}x$. See Fig. 2.6. From the figure it is

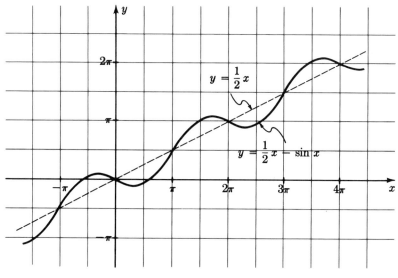

Fɪɢ. 2.6

evident that the maximum occurs in the interval $3\pi \leq x \leq 4\pi$. Hence only $11\pi/3$ and 4π are serious candidates.

$$Answer: \quad \frac{11\pi}{6} + \frac{\sqrt{3}}{2} \approx 6.6256.$$

Absence of End Points

Some problems may require the maximum value of $f(x)$ for all x or only for $x \geq 0$. In the first case there are no end points; in the second case, there is a left end point but no right end point. Generally, such problems are worked by the techniques of this section, except that it is not necessary to consider end points if there are none.

EXAMPLE 2.2

Find the smallest value of $f(x) = x^4 - 108x$.

Solution: In this problem x is unrestricted; there are no end points. Differentiate:

$$f'(x) = 4x^3 - 108 = 4(x^3 - 27).$$

Thus

$$f'(x) = 0 \quad \text{for} \quad x = 3.$$

It is easy to see that $f(x)$ has a minimum at $x = 3$. Either observe the sign of $f'(x)$ near $x = 3$, or compute the second derivative $f''(x) = 12x^2$, positive for $x = 3$.

Answer: $f(3) = -243$.

Note that there is no maximum value of $f(x)$ in this problem. In general, a function $f(x)$ need not have a maximum or a minimum unless x is restricted to an interval with two end points. For example, take $f(x) = 1/(1 + x^2)$, where x is unrestricted. This function has maximum value 1, but no minimum value (it takes all values between 0 and 1, excluding zero). As another example, take $f(x) = 1/x$. For $x > 0$, this function has neither a maximum nor a minimum.

Remarks on Finding Maxima and Minima

In most maximum and minimum problems there are only one or two zeros of the derivative to consider, and possibly two end points. Often you can rule out the end points by physical considerations. Then you have to decide which zero of the derivative gives the maximum or the minimum. If it is easy to compute the second derivative, do so. If not, or if the second derivative is zero, try observing the sign of the derivative near the point in question. Better yet, graph the function if that is easy. Be flexible.

EXERCISES

Find the maximum and minimum in the interval indicated:

1. $f(x) = \sin 4\pi x;\quad 0 < x < \frac{1}{2}$

2. $f(x) = 2x^3 - 3x^2 - 12x + 1;\quad -2 \le x \le 3$

3. $f(x) = e^{x^2 - 2x};\quad 0 \le x \le 2$

4. $f(x) = \sin 2x - \cos 2x;\quad 0 < x < \pi$

5. $f(x) = \dfrac{x}{x^2 - x + 1};\quad x$ unrestricted

6. $f(x) = \dfrac{1}{(x-1)(2-x)};\quad 1 < x < 2$

7. $f(x) = \dfrac{x}{3} + \dfrac{1}{x};\quad 1 \le x \le 2$

8. $f(x) = x^3 e^{-x};\quad 0 \le x$

9. $f(x) = \sin x \sin 2x;\quad 0 \le x \le \dfrac{\pi}{2}$

10. $f(x) = e^{-x} \sin x;\quad 0 \le x \le \pi$

11. $f(x) = \dfrac{1}{x} - \dfrac{1}{x^2} - \dfrac{1}{x^3};\quad 0 < x$

12. $f(x) = x - x^4;\quad 0 \le x \le 1$

13. $f(x) = x - \dfrac{3}{4}\sin x;\quad 0 \le x \le 4\pi.$

14. Approximate to 2 places the point x where $(\sin x)/x$ assumes its minimum value in the interval $\pi \le x \le 2\pi$.

15. Show that $e^x/x \ge e$ for all $x \ge 0$ and that $e^x/x = e$ only for $x = 1$. (*Hint:* Find the minimum of e^x/x.)

3. FURTHER EXAMPLES

EXAMPLE 3.1

Compute the volume of the largest right circular cone inscribed in a sphere of radius R.

Solution: The volume V of a cone is

$$V = \frac{1}{3}\pi r^2 h,$$

where r is the radius of its base and h is its height. If a cone is inscribed in a sphere of radius R, there ought to be a relation between r, h, and R. Make a careful drawing of a cross-section (Fig. 3.1).

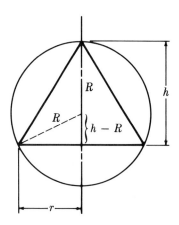

FIG. 3.1

From the drawing,

$$r^2 + (h - R)^2 = R^2,$$

$$r^2 = R^2 - (h - R)^2 = 2Rh - h^2.$$

Substitute:

$$V = \frac{1}{3}\pi r^2 h = \frac{1}{3}\pi(2Rh - h^2)h = \frac{\pi}{3}(2Rh^2 - h^3).$$

By the physical nature of the problem, $0 < h < 2R$. Thus you must maximize

$$V(h) = \frac{\pi}{3}(2Rh^2 - h^3)$$

in the interval $0 < h < 2R$.

There are no end points, hence the maximum occurs at a zero of the derivative:

$$\frac{dV}{dh} = \frac{\pi}{3}(4Rh - 3h^2) = \frac{\pi}{3}h(4R - 3h).$$

Therefore

$$\frac{dV}{dh} = 0 \qquad \text{for} \quad h = 0 \qquad \text{or} \qquad h = \frac{4}{3}R.$$

But $h = 0$ is excluded; the maximum must occur at $4R/3$. Since

$$V(h) = \frac{\pi}{3}h^2(2R - h),$$

$$V\left(\frac{4R}{3}\right) = \frac{\pi}{3}\left(\frac{4R}{3}\right)^2\left(\frac{2R}{3}\right) = \frac{32\pi R^3}{81}.$$

Answer: $\dfrac{32\pi R^3}{81}.$

REMARK: The answer has the correct form; a volume should be a cubic expression. Since the sphere has volume $\frac{4}{3}\pi R^3$, it follows easily that the volume of the largest cone that can be inscribed in a sphere is $\frac{8}{27}$ the volume of the sphere.

EXAMPLE 3.2

A 5-ft fence stands 4 ft from the wall of a house. How long is the shortest ladder that can reach from the ground outside the fence to the wall?

Solution: First, draw a diagram (Fig. 3.2). Now take a moment to

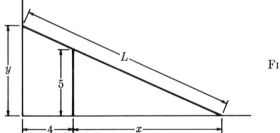

FIG. 3.2

think. If x is very small and positive, the ladder will be nearly vertical, certainly longer than is necessary. If x is large, the ladder will be nearly horizontal, again too long. The best choice of x seems to be somewhere around 5 or 6, surely between 2 and 10. In fact, as x increases starting near 0, it seems that L should decrease, reach a minimum, then increase thereafter.

To start the computation, note that

$$L^2 = (x + 4)^2 + y^2.$$

There is a relation between x and y: by similar triangles,

$$\frac{y}{x + 4} = \frac{5}{x},$$

$$y = \frac{5(x + 4)}{x}.$$

Hence,

$$L^2 = (x + 4)^2 + \frac{25(x + 4)^2}{x^2}$$

$$= (x + 4)^2 \left(1 + \frac{25}{x^2}\right).$$

Rather than take the square root, minimize L^2. The range of x is all positive values; there are no end points in this problem.

Differentiate L^2:

$$\frac{d}{dx}(L^2) = 2(x + 4)\left(1 + \frac{25}{x^2}\right) + (x + 4)^2\left(\frac{-50}{x^3}\right)$$

$$= 2(x + 4)\left[1 + \frac{25}{x^2} - \frac{25(x + 4)}{x^3}\right]$$

$$= 2(x + 4)\left[\frac{x^3 + 25x - 25(x + 4)}{x^3}\right].$$

Thus

$$\frac{d}{dx}(L^2) = \frac{2(x + 4)(x^3 - 100)}{x^3}.$$

There is only one positive value of x for which the derivative is zero: $x = \sqrt[3]{100}$. The derivative is negative for $x < \sqrt[3]{100}$, positive for $x > \sqrt[3]{100}$. Thus our physical intuition was correct: L^2 decreases, reaches a minimum near $x = 5$, then increases.

From the formula for L^2,

$$L = (x + 4)\sqrt{1 + \frac{25}{x^2}}$$

$$= \left(1 + \frac{4}{x}\right)\sqrt{x^2 + 25}.$$

The minimum value of L is

$$L(\sqrt[3]{100}) = \left(1 + \frac{4}{\sqrt[3]{100}}\right)\sqrt{100^{2/3} + 25}.$$

Answer: $\left(1 + \dfrac{4}{\sqrt[3]{100}}\right)\sqrt{100^{2/3} + 25} \approx 12.7$ ft.

EXAMPLE 3.3

The illumination of an object by a light source is directly proportional to the strength of the source and inversely proportional to the square of the distance between the source and the object. Two light bulbs, one 5 times as strong as the other, are 1 yd apart. At what point on the line between the bulbs should a screen be placed so that the illumination it receives is minimal?

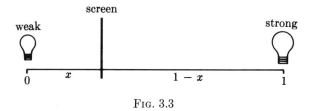

Fɪɢ. 3.3

Solution: First draw a diagram (Fig. 3.3). Apparently the screen should be closer to the weaker source; $x < \frac{1}{2}$. Even though one bulb is 5 times as strong as the other, the screen cannot be too close to the weaker bulb because of the inverse square rule. A reasonable guess: x is around 0.3 or 0.4. The illumination from the weaker bulb is

$$I_1 = \frac{k}{x^2},$$

where the constant k depends on the units of measurement. The illumination from the stronger bulb is

$$I_2 = \frac{5k}{(1-x)^2}.$$

The problem is to minimize

$$I = \frac{k}{x^2} + \frac{5k}{(1-x)^2},$$

for $0 < x < 1$. There are no end points in this problem since I is defined neither at $x = 0$ nor at $x = 1$. Differentiate:

$$\frac{dI}{dx} = -\frac{2k}{x^3} + \frac{10k}{(1-x)^3}.$$

This derivative is 0 for

$$\frac{2k}{x^3} = \frac{10k}{(1-x)^3}, \qquad \text{i.e.,} \quad 5x^3 = (1-x)^3.$$

Take cube roots:

$$(\sqrt[3]{5})x = 1 - x,$$

$$x = \frac{1}{1 + \sqrt[3]{5}} \approx 0.369.$$

The physics of the problem suggests this x gives a minimum. As a quick check, take the second derivative:

$$\frac{d^2I}{dx^2} = \frac{6k}{x^4} + \frac{30k}{(1 - x)^4},$$

which is always positive (the graph $y = I(x)$ is concave upwards). Hence x does give a minimum, so the guess was not bad. (Note that the minimum does *not* occur where $I_1 = I_2$.)

> *Answer:* $\dfrac{1}{1 + \sqrt[3]{5}} \approx 0.369$ yd from the weaker bulb.

EXAMPLE 3.4

Light travels between two points along the path that requires the least time. In different substances (water, air, glass, etc.) light travels at different speeds. Assume the upper half of the x, y-plane is a substance in which the speed of light is v_1 and the lower half is another substance in which the speed of light is v_2. Describe the path of a light ray traveling between two points in opposite halves of the plane.

Solution: Draw a diagram. Let the two points be $(0, a)$ and $(b, -c)$. See Fig. 3.4. A ray will travel from $(0, a)$ along a straight line to some point $(x, 0)$ and then along another straight line to $(b, -c)$. A value x must be found so that the time of travel is a minimum. Obviously $0 \le x \le b$.

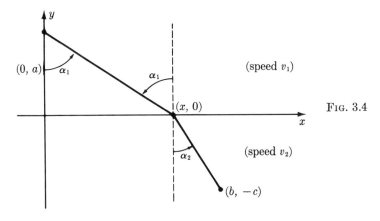

FIG. 3.4

The time required for a ray to travel from $(0, a)$ to $(x, 0)$ is

$$t_1 = \frac{\text{distance}}{\text{speed}} = \frac{\sqrt{x^2 + a^2}}{v_1}.$$

The time required from $(x, 0)$ to $(b, -c)$ is

$$t_2 = \frac{\sqrt{(b - x)^2 + c^2}}{v_2}.$$

Hence you must minimize

$$t = \frac{\sqrt{x^2 + a^2}}{v_1} + \frac{\sqrt{(b - x)^2 + c^2}}{v_2}$$

in the interval $0 \leq x \leq b$. It is plausible physically that the minimum will not occur at either end point.

Compute dt/dx:

$$\frac{dt}{dx} = \frac{x}{v_1 \sqrt{x^2 + a^2}} - \frac{b - x}{v_2 \sqrt{(b - x)^2 + c^2}}.$$

But from Fig. 3.4,

$$\frac{x}{\sqrt{x^2 + a^2}} = \sin \alpha_1, \qquad \frac{b - x}{\sqrt{(b - x)^2 + c^2}} = \sin \alpha_2.$$

Hence

$$\frac{dt}{dx} = \frac{\sin \alpha_1}{v_1} - \frac{\sin \alpha_2}{v_2}.$$

The derivative is zero if x is chosen to satisfy

$$\frac{\sin \alpha_1}{v_1} = \frac{\sin \alpha_2}{v_2}.$$

This equation is known as **Snell's Law of Refraction.** To see that it describes the path of least time, note that dt/dx is the difference of two terms. As x increases from 0 to b, the first term, $(\sin \alpha_1)/v_1$, increases steadily starting with 0. The second term, $(\sin \alpha_2)/v_2$, decreases steadily from some positive value to 0. Consequently, dt/dx starts negative at $x = 0$ and steadily increases to a positive value at $x = b$. Therefore, the minimum t occurs at the only x for which $dt/dx = 0$.

> *Answer:* The path is the broken line (Fig. 3.4)
> for which $\dfrac{\sin \alpha_1}{v_1} = \dfrac{\sin \alpha_2}{v_2}.$

EXAMPLE 3.5

A swampy region shares a long straight border with a region of farm land. A telephone cable is to be constructed connecting two locations, one in each region. Its cost is d_1 dollars per mile in the swampy region and d_2 dollars per mile in the farm land. What path should the cable take for its cost to be least?

Solution: Make a diagram with the x-axis as the border of the two regions and with the given points at $(0, a)$ and $(b, -c)$. See Fig. 3.5. The most economical path must be some broken line as shown. The cost of the cable from $(0, a)$ to $(x, 0)$ is

$$(\text{cost per mile})(\text{distance}) = d_1 \sqrt{x^2 + a^2} = \frac{\sqrt{x^2 + a^2}}{1/d_1},$$

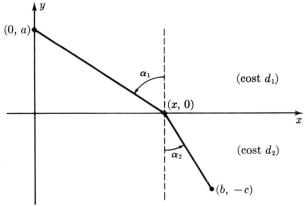

FIG. 3.5

and the cost from $(x, 0)$ to $(b, -c)$ is

$$\frac{\sqrt{(b-x)^2 + c^2}}{1/d_2}.$$

Therefore you must minimize the total cost,

$$\frac{\sqrt{x^2 + a^2}}{1/d_1} + \frac{\sqrt{(b-x)^2 + c^2}}{1/d_2}.$$

But this is precisely the same problem as in the last example!

Answer: The path is that shown in Fig. 3.5 with $\dfrac{\sin \alpha_1}{1/d_1} = \dfrac{\sin \alpha_2}{1/d_2}.$

EXERCISES

1. A man with 640 ft of fencing wishes to enclose a rectangular area and divide it into 5 pens with fences parallel to the short end of the rectangle. What dimensions of the enclosure make its area a maximum?

2. What points on the curve $xy^2 = 1$ are nearest the origin?

3. An open rectangular box has volume 15 ft^3. The length of its base is 3 times its width. Materials for the sides and base cost 60¢ and 40¢ per ft^2, respectively. Find the dimensions of the cheapest such box.

4. Find the dimensions of the rectangle of largest area that can be inscribed in an equilateral triangle of side s, if one side of the rectangle lies on the base of the triangle.

5. Find the dimensions of the rectangle of largest area that can be inscribed in a right triangle with legs of length a and b, if two sides of the rectangle lie along the legs of the triangle.

6. Given n numbers $a_1, a_2, \cdots, a_n$, show that

$$(x - a_1)^2 + (x - a_2)^2 + \cdots + (x - a_n)^2$$

is least when x is the average of the numbers.

7. Of all lines of negative slope through the point (a, b) in the first quadrant, find the one that cuts from the first quadrant a triangle of least area.

8. A wire 30 in. long is cut into two parts, one of which is bent into a circle, and the other into a square. How should the wire be cut so that the sum of the areas of the circle and the square is a minimum?

9. What is the maximum volume of the cylinder generated by rotating a rectangle of perimeter 48 in. about one of its sides?

10. If the equal legs of an isosceles triangle are L ft, how long should the base be to maximize the area of the triangle?

11. Find the line tangent to the curve $y = 4 - x^2$ at a point of the first quadrant that cuts from the first quadrant a triangle of minimum area.

12. The strength of a beam of fixed length and rectangular cross-section is proportional to the width and to the square of the depth of the cross-section. Find the proportions of the beam of greatest strength that can be cut from a circular log.

13. A railroad will run a special train if at least 200 people subscribe. The fare will be \$8 per person if 200 people go, but will decrease 1¢ for each additional person who goes. (For example, if 250 people go, the fare will be \$7.50.) What number of passengers will bring the railroad maximum revenue?

14. Find the two positive numbers x and y for which $x + y = 1$, such that $x^3 y^4$ is maximum.

15. Two posts, 8 ft and 12 ft high, stand 15 ft apart. They are to be stayed by wires attached to a single stake at ground level, and running to the tops of the posts. Where should the stake be placed to use the least amount of wire?

16. One corner of a page of width a is folded over and just reaches the opposite side. See Fig. 3.6. Find x such that the length L of the crease is a minimum.

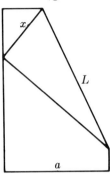

FIG. 3.6

17. A man in a rowboat 3 mi off a long straight shore wants to reach a point 5 mi up the shore. If he can row 2 mph and walk 4 mph, describe his fastest route.

18. Suppose in Ex. 17 the boat has a motor. How fast must the boat be able to go so that the fastest route is entirely by boat?

19. An isosceles triangle is circumscribed about a circle of radius r. Find its altitude if its perimeter is to be as small as possible.

20. Show that $e^x \geq x + 1$ for all values of x.

21. Archimedes proved that the area of the largest triangle inscribed in a given parabolic segment is $\frac{3}{4}$ of the area of the segment (Fig. 1.1, Chapter 8). Verify this for the parabola $y = x^2$.

22. The energy of a diatomic molecule is

$$U = \frac{a}{x^{12}} - \frac{b}{x^6},$$

where a and b are positive constants and x is the distance between the atoms. Find the **dissociation energy,** the maximum of $-U$.

The object of the next two examples is to prove an important inequality: if $a_1, a_2, \cdots, a_n$ are any positive numbers, then

$$\sqrt[n]{a_1 a_2 \cdots a_n} \leq \frac{a_1 + a_2 + \cdots + a_n}{n}.$$

In words, the **geometric mean** of a set of numbers does not exceed the **arithmetic mean** (average). We abbreviate the inequality by the notation

$$G_n \leq A_n.$$

23. Show that the maximum value of the ratio

$$\frac{\sqrt[n+1]{a_1 a_2 \cdots a_n x}}{\dfrac{1}{n+1}(a_1 + a_2 + \cdots + a_n + x)}$$

occurs for $x = A_n$, and compute the maximum. Conclude that

$$\frac{G_{n+1}}{A_{n+1}} \leq \left(\frac{G_n}{A_n}\right)^{n/(n+1)}.$$

24. By repeated application of Ex. 23, show that
$$\frac{G_n}{A_n} \le \left(\frac{G_1}{A_1}\right)^{1/(n+1)} = 1,$$
and therefore that
$$G_n \le A_n.$$
Explain why
$$G_n = A_n \qquad \text{if and only if} \quad a_1 = a_2 = \cdots = a_n.$$

11. Integration

1. INTRODUCTION

The great Greek mathematician Archimedes used ingenious methods to compute the area bounded by a parabola and a chord (Fig. 1.1).

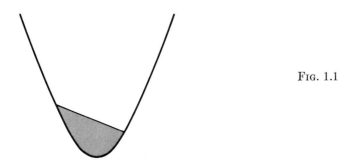

FIG. 1.1

In this chapter we shall develop tools of Calculus which make the solution of this and similar problems routine. These tools are used not only in such area problems, but also in a wide range of scientific and technical applications.

2. AREA UNDER A CURVE

The basic problem: Compute the area of the region in Fig. 2.1. The

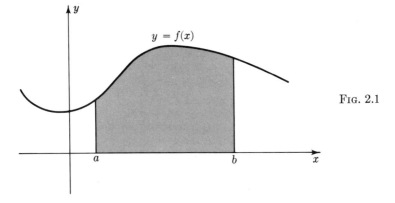

FIG. 2.1

region is bounded by the graph of a positive function $y = f(x)$, the x-axis, and the lines $x = a$ and $x = b$.

Archimedes solved this problem for a few special curves, each by an ingenious special method. In the next few pages you will learn a simple method of solving the problem *in general*, something beyond the reach of the most advanced mathematicians for about 2000 years after Archimedes.

The breakthrough came with the idea of changing the problem from a static one to a dynamic one. Instead of computing the area between two fixed lines, $x = a$ and $x = b$, compute it between a fixed line and a second *moving* line. See Fig. 2.2. Denote by $A(x)$ the area of the region shown in Fig. 2.2. When $x = a$, the area $A(a)$ is zero. As x moves to the right, $A(x)$

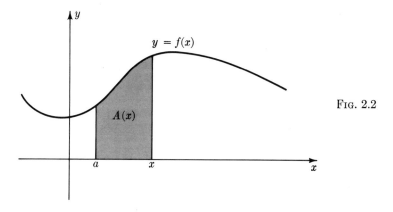

FIG. 2.2

increases. Furthermore, Fig. 2.2 suggests something about the rate of increase of $A(x)$. Where the curve is high $A(x)$ increases rapidly; where the curve is low $A(x)$ increases slowly. Apparently there is a relation between the rate of increase of $A(x)$ and the function $f(x)$.

Let us investigate the derivative of $A(x)$. For this we need to know the approximate value of

$$\frac{A(x + h) - A(x)}{h}$$

for small values of h. The numerator can be interpreted geometrically: It is the area under the curve between x and $x + h$. See Fig. 2.3. When h is small, the shaded region in Fig. 2.3 is approximately a rectangle of base h and height $f(x)$. See Fig. 2.4. Therefore,

$$A(x + h) - A(x) \approx h \cdot f(x).$$

Hence,

$$\frac{A(x + h) - A(x)}{h} \approx f(x),$$

and this approximation improves as $h \longrightarrow 0$. We conclude that $A'(x) = f(x)$,

or

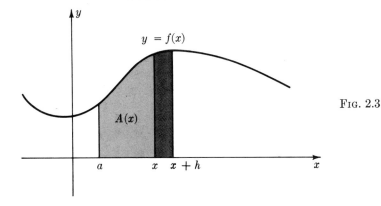

$$A(x) \text{ is an antiderivative of } f(x).$$

FIG. 2.3

FIG. 2.4

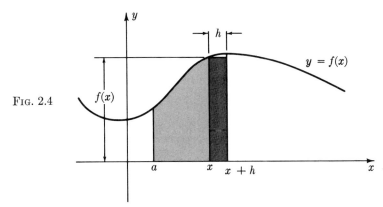

Thus the area under a curve $y = f(x)$ is described by an antiderivative of $f(x)$. In theory, the problem is nearly solved: the desired area $A(x)$ is an antiderivative of $f(x)$. But that does not give a formula for $A(x)$. In practice, you must beg, borrow, or steal an antiderivative. Suppose you are able to find one, $F(x)$. Since any two antiderivatives differ by a constant,

$$A(x) = F(x) + C$$

for some constant C. But you know $A(a) = 0$. Setting $x = a$, you find

$$0 = A(a) = F(a) + C,$$

$$C = -F(a).$$

Therefore,

$$A(x) = F(x) - F(a).$$

This is a formula for the area under $y = f(x)$ between a and x. In particular, the area between a and b is $A(b) = F(b) - F(a)$. This is the breakthrough, the area problem is solved by antidifferentiation!

Area Rule   If $y = f(x) \geq 0$ for $a \leq x \leq b$, then the area bounded by its graph, the x-axis, and the lines $x = a$ and $x = b$ is

$$F(b) - F(a),$$

where $F(x)$ is any antiderivative of $f(x)$.

The argument above shows that it makes no difference which antiderivative is used in applying the Area Rule; the value $F(b) - F(a)$ is the same for each antiderivative $F(x)$ of $f(x)$.

Here is a direct verification of that fact. If $F_1(x)$ and $F_2(x)$ are any antiderivatives of $f(x)$, then $F_2(x) = F_1(x) + C$ for some constant C. Hence

$$F_2(b) - F_2(a) = [F_1(b) + C] - [F_1(a) + C]$$
$$= F_1(b) - F_1(a).$$

Thus the constant drops out; the value $F(b) - F(a)$ is the same for each antiderivative.

Notation

$F(b) - F(a)$ is often denoted by $F(x) \Big|_a^b$.

Study this section carefully. It contains the basic idea of Integral Calculus.

3. APPLICATIONS OF THE AREA RULE

EXAMPLE 3.1

Compute the area under the graph of $y = x + 1$ between $x = 1$ and $x = 3$. See Fig. 3.1.

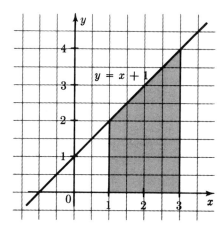

FIG. 3.1

Solution:

$$\text{Area} = F(3) - F(1),$$

where $F(x)$ is any antiderivative of $(x + 1)$. We know that

$$\frac{d}{dx}(x^2) = 2x,$$

hence

$$\frac{d}{dx}\left(\frac{1}{2}x^2\right) = x.$$

We also know that

$$\frac{d}{dx}(x) = 1.$$

Therefore, an antiderivative of $(x + 1)$ is $F(x) = \frac{1}{2}x^2 + x$, so

$$F(3) - F(1) = \left(\frac{1}{2} \cdot 3^2 + 3\right) - \left(\frac{1}{2} \cdot 1^2 + 1\right) = 6.$$

Answer: 6 square units.

CHECK: Since the region is a trapezoid, we can check our answer. The trapezoid has base 2 and legs 2 and 4.

$$\text{Area} = 2 \cdot \frac{2 + 4}{2} = 6 \text{ square units.}$$

EXAMPLE 3.2

Compute the area bounded by the parabola $y = 4 - x^2$ and x-axis (Fig. 3.2).

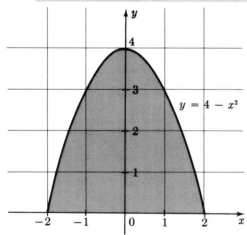

$y = 4 - x^2$

FIG. 3.2

Solution: The parabola intersects the x-axis at $x = 2$ and $x = -2$. Hence

$$\text{Area} = F(2) - F(-2),$$

where $F(x)$ is any antiderivative of $4 - x^2$. Take $F(x) = 4x - \frac{1}{3}x^3$. Then

$$F(2) - F(-2) = \left(4x - \frac{x^3}{3}\right)\Big|_{-2}^{2} = \left(8 - \frac{8}{3}\right) - \left(-8 + \frac{8}{3}\right) = \frac{32}{3}.$$

Answer: $\frac{32}{3}$ square units.

EXAMPLE 3.3

Compute the area under the curve $y = 1/x^2$ between $x = 3$ and $x = 5$. See Fig. 3.3.

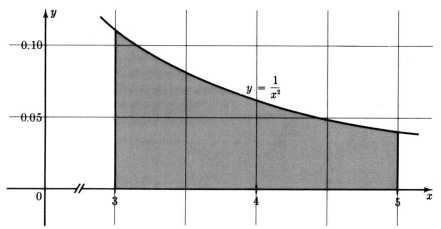

Fɪɢ. 3.3   (Note different scales on axes.)

Solution:

$$\text{Area} = F(5) - F(3),$$

where $F(x)$ is any antiderivative of $1/x^2$. One antiderivative is $F(x) = -1/x$, so

$$F(5) - F(3) = \left(-\frac{1}{5}\right) - \left(-\frac{1}{3}\right) = \frac{1}{3} - \frac{1}{5} = \frac{2}{15}.$$

Answer: $\dfrac{2}{15}$ square units.

EXAMPLE 3.4

Compute the area of a parabolic segment bounded by the curve $y = x^2$ and the line $y = 1$. See Fig. 3.4.

Solution: Compute the area under $y = x^2$ between -1 and 1, and subtract it from the area of the rectangle shown in Fig. 3.4.

$$(\text{Area under } y = x^2) = F(1) - F(-1)$$

$$= \frac{x^3}{3}\Big|_{-1}^{1} = \frac{(1)^3}{3} - \frac{(-1)^3}{3} = \frac{2}{3}.$$

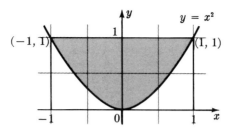

FIG. 3.4

The area of the rectangle is 2.

Answer: $2 - \dfrac{2}{3} = \dfrac{4}{3}$ square units.

EXAMPLE 3.5

Find the area enclosed by the ellipse

$$\frac{x^2}{a^2} + \frac{y^2}{b^2} = 1.$$

Solution: The equation may be solved for y if $y \geq 0$:

$$y = b\sqrt{1 - \frac{x^2}{a^2}} = \frac{b}{a}\sqrt{a^2 - x^2}.$$

Take into account the symmetry in the x-axis. Then the area is

$$A = 2\frac{b}{a}[F(a) - F(-a)],$$

where $F(x)$ is any antiderivative of

$$\sqrt{a^2 - x^2}.$$

It looks terribly difficult to find an antiderivative, however, note that $F(a) - F(-a)$ is the area under the curve $y = \sqrt{a^2 - x^2}$ between $x = -a$ and $x = a$. But this curve is a semicircle of radius a, hence its area is $\frac{1}{2}\pi a^2$. Therefore

$$A = \frac{2b}{a}\left(\frac{1}{2}\pi a^2\right) = \pi ab.$$

Answer: πab.

REMARK: If the ellipse is stretched in the y-direction by the factor a/b, it changes to a circle of radius a while its area changes by the factor a/b. See Fig. 3.5. This provides a geometric reason for the answer $\pi ab = (\pi a^2)/(a/b)$.

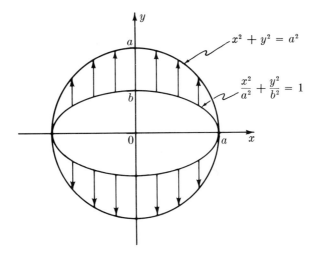

FIG. 3.5

EXERCISES

Compute the area under the graph $y = f(x)$ between $x = a$ and $x = b$:

1. $f(x) = \frac{1}{2}x$; $a = 1, b = 3$

2. $f(x) = 2 - x$; $a = 1, b = 2$

3. $f(x) = x + 7$; $a = -1, b = 2$

4. $f(x) = 3(x - 5)$; $a = 5, b = 7$

5. $y = (x - 1)^2$; $a = 1, b = 4$

6. $y = 4 - x^2$; $a = -2, b = 2$

7. $y = 4(x - 3)^2$; $a = 0, b = 6$

8. $y = 4x - x^2$; $a = 0, b = 4$

9. $y = \cos x$; $a = -\dfrac{\pi}{2}, b = \dfrac{\pi}{2}$

10. $y = \sin 2x$; $a = 0, b = \dfrac{\pi}{2}$

11. $y = \sin x + 4 \cos x$; $a = 0, b = \dfrac{\pi}{2}$

12. $y = \dfrac{1}{x^2} + \sin x$; $a = \dfrac{\pi}{2}, b = \pi$

13. $y = e^x$; $a = 0, b = 1$

14. $y = e^{-x/2}$; $a = -1, b = 0$

15. $y = e^x - 1$; $a = 0, b = 4$

16. $y = e^{3-3x}$; $a = 0, b = 1$.

Find the area bounded by:

17. $y = \frac{1}{2}x^2$, $y = x$

18. $y = x^2$, $y = 8 - x^2$

19. $y = e^x$,   the line $y = e$,   and the y-axis

20. $y = \dfrac{1}{x^2}$,   the line $x = 4$,   and the line $y = 4$.

4. THE DEFINITE INTEGRAL

For any function $f(x)$ defined for $a \leq x \leq b$, we write

$$\int_a^b f(x)\,dx = F(b) - F(a),$$

where $F(x)$ is an antiderivative of $f(x)$.

The expression

$$\int_a^b f(x)\,dx$$

is called the **definite integral** of $f(x)$ from a to b.

It is customary also to define

$$\int_b^a f(x)\,dx = F(a) - F(b).$$

It follows that

$$\int_b^a f(x)\,dx = -\int_a^b f(x)\,dx.$$

In terms of the definite integral, the Area Rule of the last section states:

If $f(x) \geq 0$ for $a \leq x \leq b$, then

$$\int_a^b f(x)\,dx$$

is the area of the region bounded by the curve $y = f(x)$, the x-axis, and the lines $x = a$ and $x = b$.

For negative functions this is not true, but the following is:

If $f(x) \leq 0$ for $a \leq x \leq b$, then

$$\int_a^b f(x)\,dx$$

is the negative of the area bounded by the curve $y = f(x)$, the x-axis, $x = a$, and $x = b$.

EXAMPLE 4.1

Show that for $b > 0$,

$$\int_0^b (-x^2)\,dx$$

is the negative of the area bounded by $y = -x^2$, the x-axis, $x = 0$, and $x = b$.

Solution:

$$\int_0^b (-x^2)\,dx = F(b) - F(0),$$

where $F(x)$ is any antiderivative of $-x^2$. Take $F(x) = -\frac{1}{3}x^3$; then

$$\int_0^b (-x^2)\, dx = -\frac{1}{3}b^3 - \left(-\frac{1}{3}\cdot 0^3\right) = -\frac{1}{3}b^3.$$

The region in question is R in Fig. 4.1. Its area is equal to that of region S under the curve $y = x^2$. But the area of S is

$$\int_0^b x^2\, dx = \frac{1}{3}x^3 \Big|_0^b = \frac{1}{3}b^3.$$

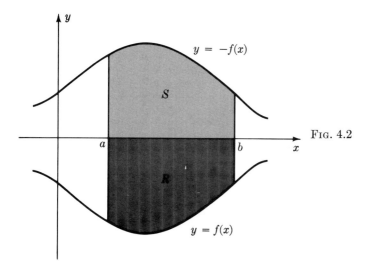

$y = x^2$

S

$b\ x$ FIG. 4.1

R

$y = -x^2$

$$Answer:\quad \int_0^b (-x^2)\, dx = -\frac{1}{3}b^3$$
$$= -(\text{area of } R).$$

The preceding example is typical for curves below the x-axis. If $f(x) \le 0$, then $y = -f(x)$ is a curve *above* the axis (Fig. 4.2). The regions R and S

$y = -f(x)$

S

a

b

FIG. 4.2

x

R

$y = f(x)$

have the same area. We want to show that

$$\int_a^b f(x)\,dx = -(\text{Area of } S).$$

Suppose $F(x)$ is an antiderivative of $f(x)$. Then $-F(x)$ is an antiderivative of $-f(x)$. Hence

$$\int_a^b f(x)\,dx = F(b) - F(a) = -\{[-F(b)] - [-F(a)]\}$$

$$= -\int_a^b [-f(x)]\,dx$$

$$= -(\text{Area of } S).$$

This establishes in general the statement preceding Example 4.1.

What can be said about

$$\int_a^c f(x)\,dx,$$

if $f(x)$ is positive for some values of x and negative for others?

To answer this question, we need a simple property of integrals:

> If $a < b < c$, then
>
> $$\int_a^c f(x)\,dx = \int_a^b f(x)\,dx + \int_b^c f(x)\,dx.$$

This property is easily verified:

$$\int_a^b f(x)\,dx + \int_b^c f(x)\,dx = [F(b) - F(a)] + [F(c) - F(b)]$$

$$= F(c) - F(a) = \int_a^c f(x)\,dx.$$

Returning to the question, suppose $f(x) \geq 0$ when $a \leq x \leq b$, but $f(x) \leq 0$ when $b \leq x \leq c$. See Fig. 4.3.

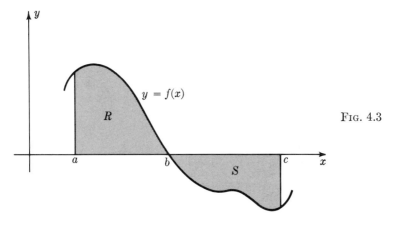

F<small>IG</small>. 4.3

$$\int_a^c f(x)\,dx = \int_a^b f(x)\,dx + \int_b^c f(x)\,dx.$$

The first integral on the right side is positive; it gives the area of R. The second is negative; it gives the negative of the area of S.

In general, if $y = f(x)$ lies partly above the x-axis and partly below, the integral

$$\int_a^c f(x)\,dx$$

adds up the areas, counting those above as positive and those below as negative.

> $$\int_a^c f(x)\,dx = [\text{area above the } x\text{-axis bounded by } y = f(x)]$$
> $$-[\text{area below the } x\text{-axis bounded by } y = f(x)],$$
> all areas taken between $x = a$ and $x = c$.

Alternate statement:

$$\int_a^c f(x)\,dx$$

is the **algebraic area** under $y = f(x)$ from a to c. ("Algebraic" means signed.)

EXAMPLE 4.2

Evaluate the definite integral $\displaystyle\int_0^{2\pi} \sin x\,dx$ and interpret the answer in terms of areas.

Solution:

$$\int_0^{2\pi} \sin x\,dx = F(2\pi) - F(0),$$

where $F(x)$ is any antiderivative of $\sin x$. One antiderivative is $-\cos x$, so

$$\int_0^{2\pi} \sin x\,dx = (-\cos 2\pi) - (-\cos 0) = -1 + 1 = 0.$$

It is certainly not true that there is zero area between $y = \sin x$ and the x-axis. But there is as much area above the axis as below it (Fig. 4.4).

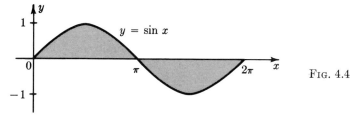

Fɪɢ. 4.4

Answer: 0. The areas determined by the curve $y = \sin x$ above and below the x-axis are equal and cancel each other.

EXAMPLE 4.3

One can of paint will cover 50 ft². How much paint is needed to cover the region bounded by $y = \sin x$ and the x-axis between $x = 0$ and $x = 2\pi$? Assume the unit on each axis is one yard.

Solution: If we treat the problem carelessly and integrate $\sin x$ between 0 and 2π, we reach a ridiculous conclusion: it takes no paint at all to cover the region! But remember, the integral

$$\int_a^b f(x)\, dx$$

gives the actual area under $y = f(x)$ only if $f(x) \geq 0$ between a and b.

Look at Fig. 4.4. The two humps of the curve have equal area; we can compute the area of the hump between 0 and π, then double the result.

$$\int_0^\pi \sin x\, dx = (-\cos \pi) - (-\cos 0) = 1 - (-1) = 2.$$

Thus the area of one hump is 2 yd² = 18 ft²; the total area is 36 ft². This will require $\frac{36}{50} = 0.72$ cans of paint.

Answer: **0.72 cans of paint.**

EXERCISES

Evaluate:

1. $\displaystyle\int_{-1}^2 x\, dx$

2. $\displaystyle\int_0^2 (1 - x)\, dx$

3. $\displaystyle\int_0^\pi \sin 2x\, dx$

4. $\displaystyle\int_{\pi/2}^{3\pi/2} \cos 3x\, dx$

5. $\displaystyle\int_{-2}^{-1} \frac{1}{x^2}\, dx$

6. $\displaystyle\int_{-4}^{-2} \left(\frac{1}{x^2} + x\right) dx$

7. $\displaystyle\int_0^{3\pi} (\cos x + \sin x)\, dx$

8. $\displaystyle\int_0^\pi (3 \sin 3x + 2 \cos 2x)\, dx$

9. $\displaystyle\int_{-2}^2 (3 + 2x - x^2)\, dx$

10. $\displaystyle\int_{-1}^2 (x - 1)(3x + 1)\, dx$

11. $\displaystyle\int_1^2 \left(\frac{5}{x^2} + e^{1-x}\right) dx$

12. $\displaystyle\int_0^1 (e^{3x} - x^2)\, dx$

13. $\displaystyle\int_a^b (b - x)(x - a)\, dx$

14. $\displaystyle\int_{-a}^a (x - a)^2\, dx.$

Compute the geometric area bounded by:

15. $f(x) = \cos 2x$ and the x-axis; $-\dfrac{\pi}{4} \leq x \leq \dfrac{\pi}{2}$

16. $f(x) = \sin 4x$ and the x-axis; $0 \leq x \leq \dfrac{\pi}{2}$

17. $y = x^2 - 5x + 6$ and the x-axis between $x = 0$ and $x = 3$

18. $y = x^2 - 7x + 12$, the x-axis, and the lines $x = 3$ and $x = 5$.

19. Show $\displaystyle\int_a^b + \int_b^c = \int_a^c$ holds even if $b < a$ or $b > c$.

20. Consider the "calculation" $\displaystyle\int_{-1}^1 \frac{dx}{x^2} = -\frac{1}{x}\Big|_{-1}^1 = -1 - 1 = -2$. Why is the answer ridiculous? Why is the calculation ridiculous?

5. AREAS AND AVERAGES

The problem of computing the area of a region under the graph of a positive function $y = f(x)$ can be solved by antidifferentiation. Here is another useful approach to the same problem.

Slice the region into a number of thin pieces, each approximately rectangular (Fig. 5.1). The area is approximately the total area of the rec-

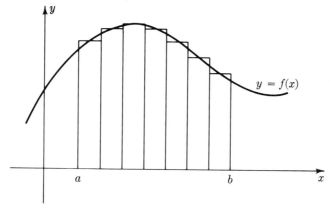

$y = f(x)$

Fɪɢ. 5.1

tangles shown in Fig. 5.1. Slicing the region into a larger number of nearly rectangular pieces produces a better estimate of the area (Fig. 5.2).

> The area under a curve can be approximated as
> closely as desired by the combined areas of rec-
> tangles, provided the rectangles are thin enough.

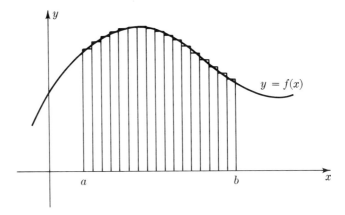

FIG. 5.2

We now translate into mathematical language this process of slicing and approximating by rectangles.

Start by dividing the interval from $x = a$ to $x = b$ into a number of equal parts (subintervals):

On the first subinterval, which runs from x_0 to x_1, construct a rectangle with that subinterval as its base. For its height choose the value of $f(x)$ at the midpoint $\bar{x}_1$. See Fig. 5.3. The area of this rectangle is $f(\bar{x}_1)\,(x_1 - x_0)$, a good approximation to the area under $y = f(x)$ between x_0 and x_1.

Now repeat the process in the second subinterval. Construct a rectangle whose base is the interval from x_1 to x_2 and whose height is $f(\bar{x}_2)$, where $\bar{x}_2$ is

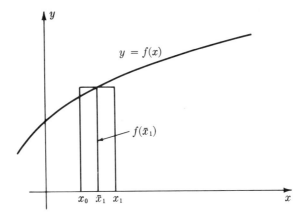

FIG. 5.3

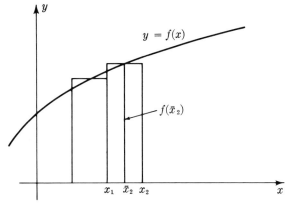

F<small>IG.</small> 5.4

the midpoint (Fig. 5.4). The area of the second rectangle is $f(\bar{x}_2) \, (x_2 - x_1)$. Continue in this way, constructing a collection of rectangles whose combined areas approximate the area under $y = f(x)$ between $x = a$ and $x = b$. Then

$$\text{Area} = \int_a^b f(x) \, dx \approx \text{(total area of rectangles)}$$

$$= f(\bar{x}_1) \, (x_1 - x_0) + f(\bar{x}_2) \, (x_2 - x_1)$$

$$+ \, \cdots \, + f(\bar{x}_n) \, (x_n - x_{n-1}).$$

The quantities $(x_1 - x_0)$, $(x_2 - x_1)$, $(x_3 - x_2)$, $\cdots$ are all equal, being the lengths of the subintervals. Denote their common value $(b - a)/n$ by Δx. With this notation,

$$\int_a^b f(x) \, dx \approx [f(\bar{x}_1) + f(\bar{x}_2) + \, \cdots \, + f(\bar{x}_n)] \, \Delta x.$$

We now have a mathematical translation of the statement following Fig. 5.2:

If $f(x) \geq 0$ for $a \leq x \leq b$, then the sum

$$[f(\bar{x}_1) + f(\bar{x}_2) + \, \cdots \, + f(\bar{x}_n)] \, \Delta x$$

is as close as desired to

$$\int_a^b f(x) \, dx,$$

provided $\Delta x = (b - a)/n$ is small enough.

The statement above has a useful interpretation. Divide the interval from a to b into n equal pieces. Then

$$\int_a^b f(x)\, dx \approx [f(\bar{x}_1) + f(\bar{x}_2) + \cdots + f(\bar{x}_n)]\, \Delta x$$

$$= [f(\bar{x}_1) + f(\bar{x}_2) + \cdots + f(\bar{x}_n)]\, \frac{b-a}{n}$$

$$= \left[\frac{f(\bar{x}_1) + f(\bar{x}_2) + \cdots + f(\bar{x}_n)}{n} \right] (b-a).$$

The quantity

$$\frac{f(\bar{x}_1) + f(\bar{x}_2) + \cdots + f(\bar{x}_n)}{n}$$

is the average of the numbers $f(\bar{x}_1)$, $f(\bar{x}_2)$, $\cdots$, $f(\bar{x}_n)$, where the points $\bar{x}_1, \bar{x}_2, \cdots , \bar{x}_n$ are evenly distributed through the interval from a to b.

Thus the integral is approximately $(b-a)$ times the average of a large number of values of the function $f(x)$. The integral is trying to tell us the "average value" of $f(x)$ between a and b.

$$\int_a^b f(x)\, dx = (b-a) \cdot (\text{average value of } f(x) \text{ for } a \leq x \leq b).$$

This should not be surprising. It says that the area of a region under a curve (Fig. 5.5a) equals the area of a rectangle (Fig. 5.5b) constructed on the same base with height equal to the "average height" of the curve.

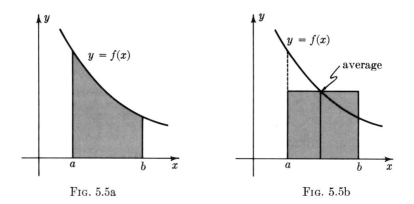

FIG. 5.5a   FIG. 5.5b

EXAMPLE 5.1

The hunger h of a shark of weight x tons is $h = x^2$. What is the average hunger of sharks weighing from 1 to 3 tons?

Solution: By the preceding formula,

$$\int_1^3 x^2\, dx = (3-1)\ (\text{average value of } x^2 \text{ for } 1 \leq x \leq 3).$$

$$\text{Average value} = \frac{1}{3-1} \int_1^3 x^2 \, dx$$

$$= \frac{1}{2} \cdot \frac{x^3}{3} \Big|_1^3 = \frac{1}{2} \frac{3^3 - 1^3}{3} = \frac{13}{3}.$$

Answer: $\dfrac{13}{3}$ units of hunger.

Functions Not Necessarily Positive

The sum

$$[f(\bar{x}_1) + f(\bar{x}_2) + \cdots + f(\bar{x}_n)] \, \Delta x$$

can be formed for any function $f(x)$, not only for one with positive values. Suppose for example $f(x) \leq 0$ when $a \leq x \leq b$. On the one hand,

$$\int_a^b f(x) \, dx = -(\text{area of } R),$$

where R is the region shown in Fig. 5.6. On the other hand, if R is approxi-

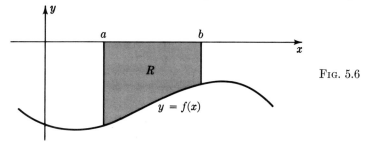

Fig. 5.6

mated by thin rectangles, the area of a typical rectangle is $-f(\bar{x}_i) \, \Delta x$, since $f(\bar{x}_i)$ is negative. Therefore

$$[f(\bar{x}_1) + f(\bar{x}_2) + \cdots + f(\bar{x}_n)] \, \Delta x \approx -(\text{area of } R)$$

$$= \int_a^b f(x) \, dx.$$

In general, the following assertion holds:

> The sum
>
> $$[f(\bar{x}_1) + f(\bar{x}_2) + \cdots + f(\bar{x}_n)] \, \Delta x$$
>
> is as close as desired to
>
> $$\int_a^b f(x) \, dx,$$
>
> provided $\Delta x = (b - a)/n$ is small enough.

We have seen that this statement is true if either $f(x) \geq 0$ or $f(x) \leq 0$ throughout the interval from a to b. If $f(x)$ has both positive and negative values, the interval can be divided into subintervals on which either $f(x) \geq 0$ or $f(x) \leq 0$. The statement applies to each subinterval and consequently to the full interval.

Even if $f(x)$ has both positive and negative values, it makes sense to speak of the average value of $f(x)$ between $x = a$ and $x = b$.

The **average value** of a function $f(x)$ for $a \leq x \leq b$ is

$$\frac{1}{b-a} \int_a^b f(x)\, dx.$$

EXAMPLE 5.2

Find the average value of $\cos x$ for $0 \leq x \leq \pi$.

Solution: The average value is

$$\frac{1}{\pi - 0} \int_0^\pi \cos x\, dx = \frac{1}{\pi}[F(\pi) - F(0)],$$

where $F(x)$ is any antiderivative of $\cos x$. One antiderivative is $F(x) = \sin x$, hence

$$\text{Average} = \frac{1}{\pi}[\sin \pi - \sin 0] = 0.$$

Answer: **0.**

REMARK: The answer seems reasonable from a graph of $y = \cos x$. See Fig. 5.7. The positive and negative values of $\cos x$ cancel each other, so the average value of $\cos x$ is zero.

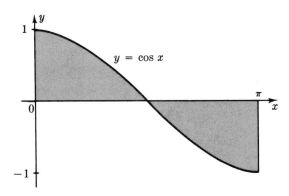

FIG. 5.7

REMARK: A rigorous development of the definite integral usually begins with rectangular approximations similar to those considered in this section. See Chapter 21, Sections 4 and 5 for one such development.

EXERCISES

Find the average value of $y = f(x)$ between $x = a$ and $x = b$:

1. $f(x) = x$; $a = 0, b = 2$

2. $f(x) = x + 1$; $a = 0, b = 2$

3. $f(x) = x^2$; $a = -1, b = 1$

4. $f(x) = 4 - x^2$; $a = -2, b = 2$

5. $f(x) = \sin \pi x$; $a = 0, b = 2$

6. $f(x) = \sin 3\pi x$; $a = 0, b = 2$

7. $f(x) = (x - 4)^2$; $a = 0, b = 4$

8. $f(x) = 1/x^2$; $a = 1, b = 3$.

Approximate the average value of $y = f(x)$ between $x = a$ and $x = b$ by taking the average of the n numbers $f(\bar{x}_1), f(\bar{x}_2), \cdots, f(\bar{x}_n)$. Compare your answer to the average value obtained by integration:

9. $f(x) = x^2$; $a = 0, b = 1, n = 4$

10. $f(x) = x^3$; $a = 0, b = 1, n = 4$

11. $f(x) = \sin x$; $a = 0, b = \dfrac{\pi}{2}, n = 3$

12. $f(x) = \cos x$; $a = 0, b = \dfrac{\pi}{2}, n = 3$.

13. If x shares of a certain stock are sold, the market value in dollars per share is $37 + [25 \times 10^5/(x + 500)^2]$. What is the average value per share on sales of 0 to 2000 shares?

14. What is the average area of circles with radius between 1 and 2 ft?

15. The rainfall per day, measured in inches, x days after the beginning of the year, is $0.00002(6511 + 366x - x^2)$. By integration, estimate the average daily rainfall for the first 60 days of the year.

16. A car starting from rest accelerates 11 ft/sec². Find its average speed during the first 10 sec.

Compare the average value of $f(x)$ for $a \le x \le b$ to the average of the two numbers $f(a)$ and $f(b)$:

17. $f(x) = \sin x$; $a = 0, b = \pi$

18. $f(x) = -x^2 + 3x - 2$; $a = 1, b = 2$

19. $f(x) = e^x$; $a = 0, b = 1$

20. $f(x) = 1/x^2$; $a = -3, b = -1$

21. $f(x) = 3x - 2$; $a = -5, b = 10$

22. $f(x) = \sin x + x$; $a = -2, b = 2$.

12. Applications of Integration

1. INTRODUCTION

The definite integral

$$\int_a^b f(x)\, dx$$

was introduced in Chapter 8 to compute areas. It turns out, however, to be a powerful tool not only in area problems, but in a surprisingly large number of other applications.

Basically the reason is this. The area of a region under the curve $y = f(x)$ can be sliced into a large number of thin pieces, each approximately a rectangle of area $f(\bar{x}_i)\, \Delta x$. The integral "adds up" these pieces. In many other situations, a complicated quantity can be divided into a large number of small parts, each given by $f(\bar{x}_i)\, \Delta x$. The integral "adds up" these parts just as it does for area.

Here are four examples.

(1) AREA. Slice the region from a to b under a curve $y = f(x)$ into thin pieces, each approximately a rectangle of area

$$\text{(height)} \cdot \text{(base)} = f(\bar{x}_i)\, \Delta x.$$

The integral

$$\int_a^b f(x)\, dx$$

"adds up" these areas.

Even the notation is suggestive: $f(x)\, dx$ represents $f(\bar{x}_i)\, \Delta x$, and the symbol

$$\int_a^b f(x)\, dx$$

means "sum" the quantities $f(x)\, dx$ between $x = a$ and $x = b$. The integral sign "$\int$" was originally an "S" for sum.

(2) DISTANCE. If a particle moves to the right along the x-axis with velocity $v(t)$ at time t, how far does it move between $t = a$ and $t = b$?

Divide the time interval into a large number of very short equal time intervals, each of duration Δt. In the i-th short time interval, the velocity is practically constant, so the distance traveled in this short period of time is approximately

$$\text{(velocity)} \cdot \text{(time)} = v(\bar{t}_i)\, \Delta t.$$

The integral

$$\int_a^b v(t)\,dt$$

"adds up" all these little distances and gives the overall distance traveled.

(3) WORK.   Suppose at each point of the x-axis there is a force of magnitude $f(x)$ pulling a particle. How much work is done by the force in moving the particle from $x = a$ to $x = b$?

Slice the interval from a to b into a large number of small pieces of length Δx. In the i-th piece the force is nearly constant, so the work it does there is approximately

$$(\text{force}) \cdot (\text{distance}) = f(\bar{x}_i)\,\Delta x.$$

The integral

$$\int_a^b f(x)\,dx$$

"adds up" these little bits of work and gives the total work done.

(4) VOLUME.   A base is being shaped on a potter's wheel (Fig. 1.1). For

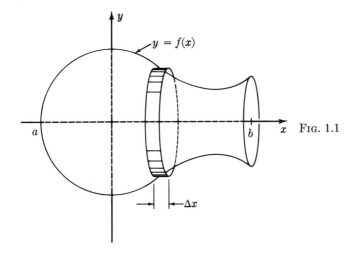

FIG. 1.1

each x between a and b, its cross-section is a circle of radius $f(x)$. What is the volume of the vase?

Slice the vase into thin slabs by cuts perpendicular to the x-axis. Each slab is nearly a cylindrical disk of volume

$$(\text{area of base}) \cdot (\text{thickness}) = [\pi f^2(\bar{x}_i)]\,\Delta x.$$

The integral

$$\int_a^b \pi f^2(x)\,dx$$

"adds up" these small volumes and gives the total volume of the vase.

Summary

The integral "adds up" many small quantities:

AREA = sum of thin rectangles of area $f(\bar{x}_i)\, \Delta x$,
DISTANCE = sum of short distances, $v(\bar{t}_i)\, \Delta t$,
WORK = sum of small amounts of work, $f(\bar{x}_i)\, \Delta x$,
VOLUME = sum of thin cylindrical disks of volume $\pi f^2(\bar{x}_i)\, \Delta x$.

2. AREA

EXAMPLE 2.1

Find the area of the region bounded by two curves $y = f(x)$ and $y = g(x)$, where $f(x) > g(x)$, and the lines $x = a$ and $x = b$. See Fig. 2.1.

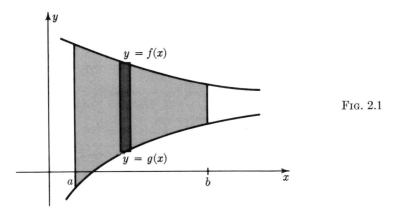

FIG. 2.1

Solution: Think of the region as approximately a large number of thin rectangles. A typical one, shown in Fig. 2.1, has height $[f(\bar{x}_i) - g(\bar{x}_i)]$, width Δx, and area $[f(\bar{x}_i) - g(\bar{x}_i)]\, \Delta x$, which we shall abbreviate as above by $[f(x) - g(x)]\, dx$. The integral

$$\int_a^b [f(x) - g(x)]\, dx$$

"adds up" these areas.

Answer: $\displaystyle\int_a^b [f(x) - g(x)]\, dx.$

REMARK: It is important to know which curve is the upper boundary and which is the lower boundary. If we had reversed them, then the answer would have been

$$\int_a^b [g(x) - f(x)]\, dx,$$

which is the negative of the area. If the curves cross, the upper and lower

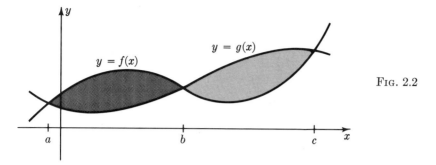

boundaries reverse (Fig. 2.2). The shaded area is computed by

$$\int_a^b [f(x) - g(x)]\, dx + \int_b^c [g(x) - f(x)]\, dx.$$

Under each integral sign, the upper curve is written first. If we compute just

$$\int_a^c [f(x) - g(x)]\, dx,$$

the two areas will be counted with opposite signs and may cancel each other.

EXAMPLE 2.2

Compute the area of the region bounded by the curves $y = e^{x/2}$ and $y = 1/x^2$, and the lines $x = 2$ and $x = 3$.

Solution: Sketch the region (Fig. 2.3). Think of the region between

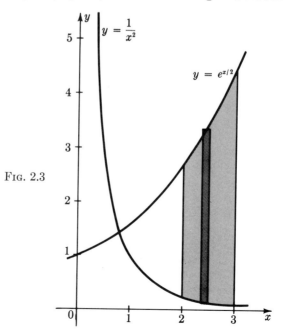

Fɪɢ. 2.3

$x = 2$ and $x = 3$ as being composed of rectangular slabs. The area of a typical slab is

$$\left(e^{x/2} - \frac{1}{x^2}\right) dx.$$

Hence

$$\text{Area} = \int_2^3 \left(e^{x/2} - \frac{1}{x^2}\right) dx = F(3) - F(2),$$

where $F(x)$ is an antiderivative of $e^{x/2} - 1/x^2$. Since

$$\frac{d}{dx}(e^{x/2}) = \frac{1}{2}e^{x/2},$$

an antiderivative of $e^{x/2}$ is $2e^{x/2}$. Since

$$\frac{d}{dx}\left(\frac{1}{x}\right) = -\frac{1}{x^2},$$

an antiderivative of $-1/x^2$ is $1/x$. Therefore an antiderivative of $e^{x/2} - 1/x^2$ is $F(x) = 2e^{x/2} + 1/x$. Consequently

$$\text{Area} = F(3) - F(2) = \left(2e^{3/2} + \frac{1}{3}\right) - \left(2e + \frac{1}{2}\right)$$

$$= 2(e^{3/2} - e) - \frac{1}{6}$$

$$= 2e(e^{1/2} - 1) - \frac{1}{6}.$$

Answer: $2e(e^{1/2} - 1) - \dfrac{1}{6}$

≈ 3.360 square units.

EXAMPLE 2.3

Compute the area of the region bounded by $y = x^2 - 4$ and $y = \frac{1}{2}x + 1$.

Solution: It is not clear from the statement of the problem what the region is; a graph is indispensable. Make a rough sketch (Fig. 2.4). The region is a parabolic segment. But the figure is not accurate enough; the crucial points P and Q must be known. They can be computed by solving simultaneously

$$\begin{cases} y = x^2 - 4 \\ y = \dfrac{1}{2}x + 1. \end{cases}$$

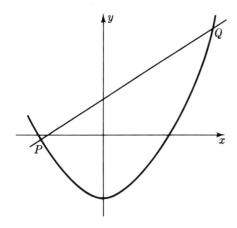

F<small>IG.</small> 2.4

Eliminate y:

$$x^2 - 4 = \frac{1}{2} x + 1,$$

$$2x^2 - x - 10 = 0.$$

Factor:

$$(2x - 5)(x + 2) = 0,$$

$$x = -2, \quad \frac{5}{2}.$$

The corresponding y values are 0 and 9/4. Therefore $P = (-2, 0)$ and $Q = (\frac{5}{2}, \frac{9}{4})$. Now Fig. 2.4 can be replaced by a more accurate sketch (Fig. 2.5).

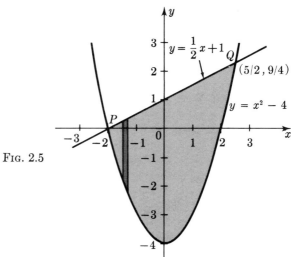

F<small>IG.</small> 2.5

Slice the region between $x = -2$ and $x = \frac{5}{2}$ into thin vertical rectangles. The area of a typical rectangle is

$$\left[\left(\frac{1}{2} x + 1 \right) - (x^2 - 4) \right] dx = \left(5 + \frac{1}{2} x - x^2 \right) dx.$$

Hence

$$\text{Area} = \int_{-2}^{5/2} \left(5 + \frac{1}{2} x - x^2 \right) dx$$

$$= \left(5x + \frac{1}{4} x^2 - \frac{1}{3} x^3 \right) \Big|_{-2}^{5/2}$$

$$= \left[5 \left(\frac{5}{2} \right) + \frac{1}{4} \left(\frac{5}{2} \right)^2 - \frac{1}{3} \left(\frac{5}{2} \right)^3 \right] - \left[5(-2) + \frac{1}{4} (-2)^2 - \frac{1}{3} (-2)^3 \right]$$

$$= \frac{729}{48}.$$

Answer: $\dfrac{243}{16}$ square units.

EXERCISES

Compute the area of the region bounded by:

1. $y = 8 - x^2$ and $y = -2x$
2. $y = x^2 + 5$ and $y = 6x$
3. $y = 3x^2$ and $y = -3x^2$, and the lines $x = -1$ and $x = 1$
4. $y = 1 - x^2$ and $y = x^2 - 1$
5. $y = x^3 - 5x^2 + 6x$ and $y = x^3$
6. $y = x^2 - 8x$ and $y = x$
7. $y = \cos x$ and $y = \sin x$, between $x = \dfrac{\pi}{4}$ and $x = \dfrac{5\pi}{4}$
8. $y = 2 \sin \dfrac{\pi}{4} x$ and $y = (x - 3)(x - 4)$, between $x = 2$ and $x = 4$
9. $y = e^x$, $y = e^{-x}$, and $y = e^2$
10. $y = \cos x - 1$ and $y = 1 - \cos 2x$, between $x = 0$ and $x = 2\pi$
11. $y = \dfrac{1}{x^2}$, $y = x$, and $y = 8x$ (*Hint:* sketch carefully)
12. $y = \dfrac{1}{x^2}$, $y = 0$, $y = x^2$, and $x = 3$.
13. Find a so that the area bounded by $y = x^2 - a^2$ and $y = a^2 - x^2$ is 9.
14. Find the fraction of the area of one hump of the curve $y = \sin x$ that lies above $y = \frac{1}{2}$.

3. DISTANCE

EXAMPLE 3.1

An α particle enters an accelerator at time $t = 0$. After t sec, its velocity is $10^7 t^2$ m/sec. How far does the particle move during the first 10^{-2} sec?

Solution: Think of the time interval $t = 0$ to $t = 10^{-2}$ sec divided into tiny subintervals. In a typical subinterval of duration Δt, the velocity is nearly constant, $10^7 t^2$. The distance moved during this short period is approximately $10^7 t^2 \, \Delta t$. The integral

$$\int_0^{10^{-2}} 10^7 t^2 \, dt$$

adds up these tiny distances.

$$(\text{total distance}) = \int_0^{10^{-2}} 10^7 t^2 \, dt = 10^7 \times \frac{1}{3} t^3 \Big|_0^{10^{-2}} = \frac{10}{3} \text{ m.}$$

$$\textit{Answer:} \quad \frac{10}{3} \text{ m.}$$

EXAMPLE 3.2

A particle moving along the x-axis is at the origin when $t = 0$. At time t its velocity is $\dfrac{1}{(t+1)^2}$, which is rapidly decreasing. Show that the particle will never pass the point $x = 1$.

Solution: The distance moved between $t = 0$ and $t = b$ is

$$\int_0^b v(t) \, dt = \int_0^b \frac{1}{(t+1)^2} \, dt = F(b) - F(0),$$

where $F(t)$ is an antiderivative of $1/(t+1)^2$. Since

$$\frac{d}{dt}\left(-\frac{1}{t}\right) = \frac{1}{t^2},$$

it follows from the Shifting Rule that

$$\frac{d}{dt}\left(\frac{-1}{t+1}\right) = \frac{1}{(t+1)^2}.$$

Therefore,

$$\int_0^b \frac{1}{(t+1)^2} \, dt = \frac{-1}{t+1}\Big|_0^b = \frac{-1}{b+1} - (-1) = 1 - \frac{1}{b+1}.$$

$$\text{Distance moved} = 1 - \frac{1}{b+1}.$$

Answer: At any time $t = b$, no matter how far in the future, the particle will have moved less than one unit. Hence it never passes the point $x = 1$.

Negative Velocity

The formula

$$\text{distance} = \int_a^b v(t)\, dt$$

is valid only when the velocity $v(t)$ is positive during motion. If $v(t) \leq 0$ between $t = a$ and $t = b$, then

$$\int_a^b v(t)\, dt$$

is the negative of the distance traveled. (We hope this reminds you of area bounded by a curve lying below the axis.)

The reason is simple: if $v(t)$ is negative, then the distance traveled during an interval of length Δt is not $v(t)\, \Delta t$, but $|v(t)|\, \Delta t = -v(t)\, \Delta t$. Therefore the integral adds up little quantities $v(t)\, \Delta t$, which are the negatives of little distances. Its value then is the negative of the distance traveled.

If $v(t) \geq 0$ when $a \leq t \leq b$, and $v(t) \leq 0$ when $b \leq t \leq c$, then

$$\int_a^c v(t)\, dt = \int_a^b v(t)\, dt + \int_b^c v(t)\, dt,$$

where the first integral on the right is the distance moved between $t = a$ and $t = b$, and the second is the negative of the distance moved between $t = b$ and $t = c$. For example, if a particle moves to the right between $t = a$ and $t = b$, then moves to the left returning to its original position when $t = c$,

$$\int_a^c v(t)\, dt = 0$$

because

$$\int_a^b v(t)\, dt \qquad \text{and} \qquad \int_b^c v(t)\, dt$$

cancel each other. So

$$\int_a^c v(t)\, dt$$

measures not necessarily distance traveled, but the **displacement,** the difference between the initial position and final position. If $v(t) \geq 0$ throughout the motion, then displacement and distance traveled are the same, but if $v(t)$ changes sign, they are different.

The integral of the velocity

$$\int_a^b v(t)\ dt$$

gives the displacement between time $t = a$ and time $t = b$.

If $v(t) \geq 0$ through the motion, this displacement is the same as the distance traveled. If $v(t) \leq 0$ throughout the motion, it is the negative of the distance traveled.

The preceding assertions are really nothing new. If $F(t)$ denotes the position of the particle at time t, then $F'(t) = v(t)$; in other words $F(t)$ is an antiderivative of $v(t)$. Therefore,

$$\int_a^b v(t)\ dt = F(b) - F(a)$$

$$= \text{(position at time } b) - \text{(position at time } a) = \text{displacement.}$$

EXAMPLE 3.3

A ball is thrown up from the ground at $t = 0$. At time t its velocity is $80 - 32t$ ft/sec. How far does it travel in the first 5 sec?

Solution:

$$80 - 32t > 0 \qquad \text{when} \qquad t < \frac{5}{2},$$

$$80 - 32t < 0 \qquad \text{when} \qquad t > \frac{5}{2}.$$

The distance traveled in the first $\frac{5}{2}$ sec is

$$\int_0^{5/2} (80 - 32t)\ dt = (80t - 16t^2)\ \Big|_0^{5/2} = 100 \text{ ft.}$$

After $t = \frac{5}{2}$, the velocity is negative. Therefore, the distance traveled in the next $\frac{5}{2}$ sec is

$$-\int_{5/2}^5 (80 - 32t)\ dt = (-80t + 16t^2)\ \Big|_{5/2}^5 = 100 \text{ ft.}$$

Answer: 200 ft.

REMARK: Note in the example that

$$\int_0^5 v(t)\ dt = \int_0^5 (80 - 32t)\ dt = 0.$$

That is because the ball ends up where it started; its net displacement is zero. Actually it moves 100 ft with positive velocity (upwards) and 100 ft with negative velocity (downwards). The integral, however, counts these distances with opposite signs, so they cancel out.

A body has velocity $v = f(t)$. Find the distance covered between $t = a$ and $t = b$:

1. $f(t) = 2t + 1$; $a = 0, b = 2$ 2. $f(t) = -32t$; $a = 0, b = 8$

3. $f(t) = 3 \sin \pi t$; $a = 0, b = 1$ 4. $f(t) = 4 \cos \pi t$; $a = 0, b = \dfrac{1}{2}$

5. $f(t) = t + \dfrac{4}{(t+1)^2}$; $a = 0, b = 2$

6. $f(t) = t^2 + \dfrac{2}{(3t+9)^2}$; $a = 1, b = 4$

7. $f(t) = 3t^2 + 4t + 1$; $a = 0, b = 3$
8. $f(t) = 4t - t^2$; $a = 0, b = 2$.

A body has velocity $v = v(t)$. Find the displacement of the body between $t = a$ and $t = b$:

9. $v(t) = 3t - 1$; $a = 0, t = 1$

10. $v(t) = t - \dfrac{8}{t^2}$; $a = 1, b = 4$

11. $v(t) = 4 \sin \dfrac{\pi}{2} t$; $a = 0, b = 3$

12. $v(t) = \cos \dfrac{\pi}{4} t$; $a = 0, b = 8$.

If a body has velocity $v = f(t)$, find the total distance covered and the displacement between $t = a$ and $t = b$:

13. $f(t) = e^{t-2} - 1$, $a = 1, b = 3$ 14. $f(t) = t^2 - 3t + 2$; $a = 0, b = 3$
15. $f(t) = \sin t + \cos t$; $a = 0, b = 2\pi$
16. $f(t) = 1 - 2 \cos t$; $a = 0, b = \pi$.

4. WORK

Suppose an object is moved along the x-axis from $x = a$ to $x = b$ by a force of magnitude $f(x)$. Divide the interval into a large number of short pieces, each of length Δx.

The work done moving the object from x_{i-1} to x_i is approximately $f(\bar{x}_i) \, \Delta x$, because in this very short interval the force is nearly constant. These little pieces of work are added up by an integral:

$$\text{Work} = \int_a^b f(x) \, dx.$$

REMARK CONCERNING UNITS: If force is measured in pounds and distance in feet, then work is measured in foot-pounds. If force is measured in dynes and distance in centimeters, then work is measured in dyne-centimeters.

EXAMPLE 4.1

At each point of the x-axis (marked off in feet) there is a force of $(5x^2 - x + 2)$ pounds pulling an object. Compute the work done in moving it from $x = 1$ to $x = 4$.

Solution:

$$\text{Work} = \int_1^4 (5x^2 - x + 2)\, dx = \left(\frac{5}{3}x^3 - \frac{1}{2}x^2 + 2x\right)\Big|_1^4$$

$$= \frac{320}{3} - \frac{19}{6}.$$

Answer: 103.5 ft-lb.

EXAMPLE 4.2

According to Newton's Law of Gravitation, two bodies attract each other with a force proportional to the product of their masses and inversely proportional to the square of the distance between them:

$$\text{force} = k\frac{Mm}{x^2},$$

where M and m are the masses, and x is the distance between them. If one of the bodies is fixed at the origin, how much work is done in moving the other from $x = a$ to $x = b$, where a and b are positive? (Assume k, M, and m are known.)

Solution:

$$\text{Work} = \int_a^b \frac{kMm}{x^2}\, dx = kMm\left(-\frac{1}{x}\right)\Big|_a^b.$$

Answer: $kMm\left(\dfrac{1}{a} - \dfrac{1}{b}\right)$ units of work.

REMARK: When $a < b$ the work is positive because you do work against the gravitational force. But when $a > b$ the free mass moves towards the fixed mass, opposite to your direction of pull. Hence you do negative work. Imagine moving the free mass from a to b and then back to a. The total work is zero. Why?

EXAMPLE 4.3

According to Hooke's Law, when a spring is stretched a short distance, there is a restoring force proportional to the amount of stretching. If 2 ft-lb of work are needed to stretch a certain spring 4 in., how much work is needed to stretch it 1 ft?

FIG. 4.1

Solution: Imagine the spring placed on the *x*-axis with its fixed end at the origin. Suppose it is stretched from the origin to *x*. See Fig. 4.1. By Hooke's Law there is a force of magnitude kx pulling the spring back to the origin. The work required to stretch it from $x = 0$ to $x = b$ is

$$\int_0^b kx \, dx = \frac{k}{2} x^2 \bigg|_0^b = \frac{kb^2}{2},$$

proportional to the square of the distance. Now 1 ft is 3 × 4 in., hence the work required to stretch the spring 1 ft is 3^2 times that required to stretch it 4 in.

Answer: $3^2 \times 2 = 18$ ft-lb.

EXERCISES

1. Find the work done by a force $f(x) = 3x + 2$ dynes in moving an object from $x = 1$ cm to $x = 7$ cm.

2. At each point of the *x*-axis (marked off in feet) there is a force of $(x^2 - 5x + 6)$ lb pushing to the right against an object. Compute the work done in moving it from $x = 1$ to $x = 5$.

3. A 50-ft chain weighing 2 lb/ft is attached to a drum hung from the ceiling. The ceiling is high enough so that the free end of the chain does not touch the floor. How much work is required to wind up the chain around the drum?
   [*Hint:* When *x* ft of chain have been wound up, the weight of the chain still unwound is $(100 - 2x)$ lb.]

4. In the previous exercise, suppose that a 200-lb weight is attached to the free end. How much work is required to wind up the chain?

5. The force in pounds required to stretch a certain spring *x* ft is $F = 8x$. How much work is required to stretch the spring 6 in., 1 ft, 2 ft?

6. A 3-lb force will stretch a spring 0.5 ft. How much work is required to stretch the spring 2 ft?

From Newton's Law of Gravitation, the force of attraction of the earth on an object of weight m lb at a distance x mi from the center of the earth, is $F = \dfrac{(4000)^2\, m}{x^2}$ lb.

7. How much work is required to lift a 1000-lb payload into a 300-mi-high orbit? a 600-mi-high orbit? Assume the radius of the earth is 4000 mi.

8. A 5-lb monkey is attached to the free end of a 20-ft hanging chain which weighs 0.25 lb/ft. The monkey climbs the chain to the top. How much work does he do?

13. Volumes

1. COORDINATES AND GRAPHS

A systematic study of figures in space requires the introduction of co-ordinates. We set up x-, y-, and z-axes as follows. The plane of this page is the y, z-plane as indicated in Fig. 1.1. The x-axis is conceived perpendicular

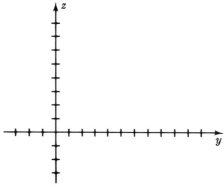

Fig. 1.1

to the page, straight out towards you. By taking an oblique projection from a direction where x, y, and z are all positive, one obtains Fig. 1.2a.

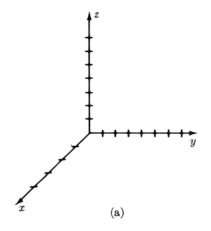

(a)

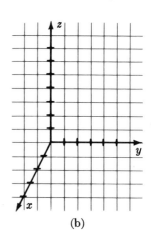

(b)

Fig. 1.2

Rectangular graph paper is useful for space graphs. After you fix scales on the perpendicular y- and z-axes, draw the x-axis from the origin towards the lower left with slope about 2 and use the horizontal rulings to fix its scale (Fig. 1.2b).

A point (x, y, z) is located by marking its projection $(x, y, 0)$ in the x, y-plane and going up or down the corresponding amount z. (From the habit of living in the x, y-plane for so long, we think of the z-direction as "up.")

EXAMPLE 1.1

Locate $(3, 2, 4)$ and $(1, 3, -2)$.

Solution: See Fig. 1.3.

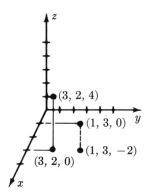

Fɪɢ. 1.3

The portion of space where x, y, and z are positive is called the **first octant.** (No one numbers the other seven octants.) Sometimes part of a figure which is not in the first octant is shown; dotted lines indicate it is behind the coordinate planes (Fig. 1.4). The angle at which the x-axis is

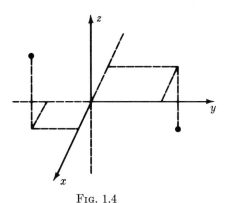

Fɪɢ. 1.4

drawn in the y, z-plane is up to you. Choose it so that your drawing is as uncluttered as possible. Actually it is perfectly alright to take a projection into other than the y, z-plane, so that the y- and z-axes are not drawn perpendicular (Fig. **1.5**).

drawn in the y, z-plane is up to you. Choose it so that your drawing is as uncluttered as possible. Actually it is perfectly alright to take a projection into other than the y, z-plane, so that the y- and z-axes are not drawn perpendicular (Fig. 1.5).

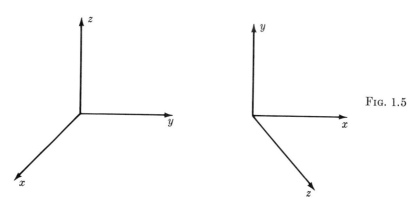

Fɪɢ. 1.5

Distance Formula

The distance D between two points whose coordinates are

$$(x_0, y_0, z_0) \qquad \text{and} \qquad (x_1, y_1, z_1)$$

is given by the Distance Formula:

$$D^2 = (x_1 - x_0)^2 + (y_1 - y_0)^2 + (z_1 - z_0)^2.$$

This formula follows from two applications of the Pythagorean Theorem (Fig. 1.6). First

$$E^2 = (y_1 - y_0)^2 + (z_1 - z_0)^2,$$

then

$$D^2 = (x_1 - x_0)^2 + E^2$$

$$= (x_1 - x_0)^2 + (y_1 - y_0)^2 + (z_1 - z_0)^2.$$

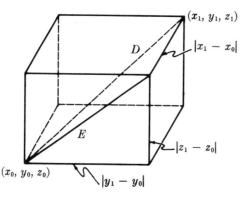

Fɪɢ. 1.6

Draw a graph, locating the points:

1. $(1, 2, 3)$, $(1, 3, 4)$
2. $(2, 4, 1)$, $(2, -4, 1)$
3. $(-1, 2, 1)$, $(2, 2, -1)$
4. $(1, -3, 3)$, $(3, 2, -2)$.

Locate the points and compute the distance between them:

5. $(0, 0, 0)$, $(4, 1, 3)$
6. $(4, 5, 3)$, $(1, 3, 2)$
7. $(1, 1, 1)$, $(-2, 0, 2)$
8. $(-3, -2, 4)$, $(-1, 3, -2)$.

9. Draw the perpendicular from the point $(2, 4, 3)$ to each coordinate axis and find the length of each perpendicular segment.

Draw the parallelepiped with edges parallel to the axes and locate the vertices. The ends of a diagonal are the points:

10. $(0, 0, 0)$, $(2, 3, 1)$
11. $(4, 2, 3)$, $(1, 1, 1)$.

Are the points vertices of a right triangle? If so, find its area:

12. $(0, 0, 0)$, $(2, 3, 0)$, $(5, 1, 1)$
13. $(3, 1, 0)$, $(4, 2, 4)$, $(3, 4, 1)$
14. $(-1, 2, -6)$, $(3, -2, 4)$, $(9, -5, 1)$
15. $(3, 2, 5)$, $(-1, 4, -7)$, $(-5, 8, -5)$.

Do the points lie on a straight line?

16. $(0, 0, 0)$, $(1, 3, 2)$, $(2, 6, 4)$
17. $(0, 0, 0)$, $(-1, 3, -4)$, $(2, -5, 8)$
18. $(1, 1, 1)$, $(0, 1, 2)$, $(-1, -3, -5)$
19. $(1, -1, -2)$, $(-1, 2, 3)$, $(3, -4, -7)$
20. $(1, 1, 0)$, $(1, 0, 1)$, $(0, 1, 1)$.

Mark the points A, B, C on a graph; they determine a plane Π. Then mark the points D, E; they determine a line λ. Construct with a straight edge the point where λ intersects Π:

21. $A = (0, 0, 0)$, $B = (1, 2, 0)$, $C = (0, 0, 1)$, $D = (1, 0, 0)$, $E = (0, 1, 0)$
22. A, B, C, D as in Ex. 21, $E = (0, 1, 1)$
23. A, B, C as in Ex. 21, $D = (2, 1, 0)$, $E = (0, 3, 1)$
24. $A = (1, 0, 0)$, $B = (0, 2, 0)$, $C = (0, 0, 3)$, $D = (0, 0, 2)$, $E = (2, 2, 0)$
25. A, B, C, E as in Ex. 24, $D = (0, 1, 1)$.

Mark the points A_1, B_1, C_1; A_2, B_2, C_2 on a graph. They determine planes Π_1 and Π_2. Construct with a straight edge their line of intersection:

26. $A_1 = (0, 0, 0)$, $B_1 = (0, 0, 1)$, $C_1 = (1, 2, 0)$; $A_2 = A_1$, $B_2 = (0, 2, 0)$, $C_2 = (1, 1, 2)$
27. A_1, B_1, C_1 as in Ex. 26; $A_2 = (1, 0, 0)$, $B_2 = B_1$, $C_2 = (0, 1, 2)$
28. $A_1 = (1, 0, 0)$, $B_1 = (0, 1, 0)$, $C_1 = (0, 0, 2)$; $A_2 = (2, 3, 0)$, $B_2 = (-1, 3, 2)$, $C_2 = (0, 0, 1)$.

2. PLANES

In the plane, the graph of a linear equation $ax + by = c$ is a straight line. In space, the graph of a linear equation

$$ax + by + cz = k \qquad (a, b, c \quad \text{not all } 0)$$

is a plane, not a line. The three simplest cases are shown in Fig. 2.1. In

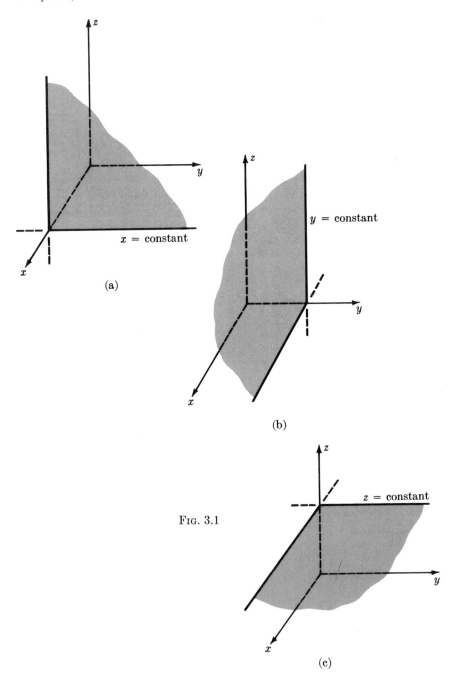

$x = \text{constant}$

(a)

$y = \text{constant}$

(b)

Fig. 3.1

$z = \text{constant}$

(c)

each of these cases two of the coefficients a, b, c are zero. If only one of the coefficients is zero, then the plane is parallel to the corresponding axis (Fig. 2.2).

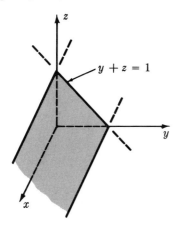

F ɪ ɢ. 2.2a   F ɪ ɢ. 2.2b

In the most general case, a, b, c are all different from zero. Often one can locate the plane by finding where it meets each of the three axes. For example, the point where

$$ax + by + cz = k$$

meets the x-axis is obtained by setting $y = z = 0$, and solving the resulting equation for x. The point is $(k/a, 0, 0)$.

EXAMPLE 2.1

Plot $x + y + z = 1$.

Solution: The points where the plane meets the three coordinate axes are

$$(1, 0, 0),   (0, 1, 0),   (0, 0, 1).$$

The portion in the first octant is shown in Fig. 2.3.

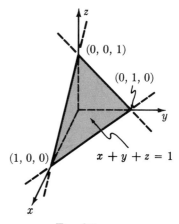

F ɪ ɢ. 2.3

This method fails if $k = 0$, that is, if $ax + by + cz = 0$, for then the plane passes through the origin. In this case however, you can locate the plane by finding its lines of intersection with two of the coordinate planes.

EXAMPLE 2.2

Plot $x - y - z = 0$.

Solution: This plane meets the coordinate plane $z = 0$ in the line $x - y = 0$, and meets the coordinate plane $y = 0$ in the line $x - z = 0$. The portion in the first octant is shown in Fig. 2.4.

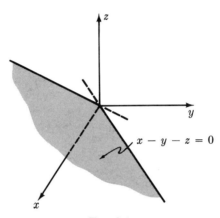

Fɪɢ. 2.4

EXERCISES

Sketch the plane:

1. $z = 3$
2. $y = -2$
3. $3y + 2x = 6$
4. $2x - z = 2$
5. $3y + 2x = 0$
6. $2x - z = 0$
7. $x + 2y + 3z = 6$
8. $4x - y + 2z = 4$
9. $y - x + 2z = 2$
10. $3x + 2y - z = 4$
11. $2x - y - z = 0$
12. $6z - 2x + y = 0$.

13. Find the equation of the plane perpendicular to the y-axis and passing through $(-1, -3, 8)$.

14. Find the equation of the plane which contains the whole x-axis and also passes through $(3, -1, 2)$.

15. Find the equation of the plane through $(0, 0, 0)$, $(2, 4, 3)$, and $(-1, -1, -1)$.

16. Find the equation of the plane through $(1, 0, 0)$, $(0, 2, 0)$, and $(0, 0, 3)$.

3. SURFACES

We shall graph some common curved surfaces. The first of these is the right circular cylinder.

EXAMPLE 3.1

Plot the set of points (x, y, z) satisfying $x^2 + y^2 = 1$.

Solution: This surface meets the x, y-plane in the unit circle (Fig. 3.1a). Given a point (x_0, y_0) on this circle, each of the points (x_0, y_0, z), for *any* value of z, is on the surface we seek.

Answer: The surface is the right circular cylinder whose base is the unit circle in the x, y-plane (Fig. 3.1b).

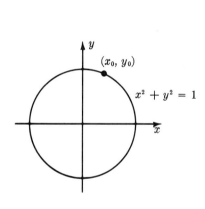

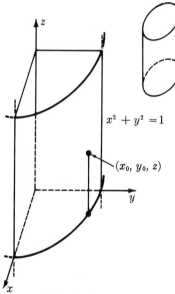

FIG. 3.1a   FIG. 3.1b

REMARK: Example 3.1 illustrates an important point. If an equation has one variable missing, then the graph in space is a cylinder (not necessarily right circular) parallel to the axis of the missing variable. For example, the graph in space of $z = y^2$ is obtained by drawing the parabola $z = y^2$ in the y, z-plane, then moving this parabola parallel to the x-axis. The result is a (right parabolic) cylinder whose generators are parallel to the x-axis, and whose cross section by each plane $x = a$ is a copy of the parabola.

EXAMPLE 3.2

Find an equation for a right circular cone.

Solution: Begin by choosing the coordinate system skillfully. Place the origin at the apex of the cone, and the y-axis along the axis of the cone (Fig. 3.2a). Each section by a plane $y = y_0$ is a circle. The radius of this circle is proportional to y. Let a denote the constant of proportionality

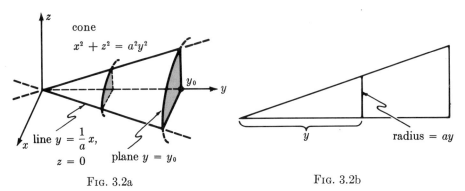

FIG. 3.2a   FIG. 3.2b

(Fig. 3.2b). Then

$$x^2 + z^2 = a^2y^2.$$

Note that the cone meets the plane $y = 1$ in the circle $x^2 + z^2 = a^2$ of radius a. This gives one interpretation of the constant a. The cone meets the x, y-plane in the pair of lines $x = \pm ay$ of slope $\pm 1/a$; this gives another interpretation of a.

Answer: $x^2 + z^2 = a^2y^2$.

EXAMPLE 3.3

Find the locus (graph) of $x^2 + y^2 + z^2 = 1$.

Solution: By the Distance Formula, this is the set of points (x, y, z) at distance 1 from $(0, 0, 0)$, i.e., a sphere of radius 1 with center at the origin. One-eighth of it is drawn in Fig. 3.3a and the whole sphere is sketched in Fig. 3.3b.

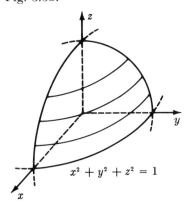

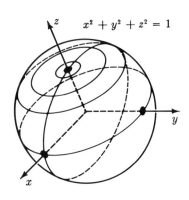

FIG. 3.3a   FIG. 3.3b

EXAMPLE 3.4

Plot the locus of $x^2 + y^2 + (z - 1)^2 = 1$.

Solution: By the Distance Formula, this is a sphere of radius 1 with center at $(0, 0, 1)$. It passes through the origin, just touching the x, y-plane at that point. Draw the portion in the first octant (Fig. 3.4).

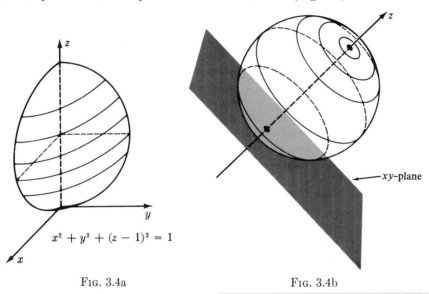

$$x^2 + y^2 + (z - 1)^2 = 1$$

xy-plane

FIG. 3.4a   FIG. 3.4b

EXERCISES

Sketch the surfaces:

1. $x^2 + (z - 1)^2 = 1$

2. $x^2 - 2x + y^2 - 6y + 9 = 0$
   [*Hint:* complete the square.]

3. $y = -(x - 4)^2$

4. $z + x^2 - 6x - 9 = 0$

5. $(x - 2)^2 + y^2 + z^2 = 4$

6. $(x + 2)^2 + (y - 1)^2 + z^2 = 1$

7. $x^2 - 6x + y^2 + z^2 + 5 = 0$

8. $x^2 - 2x + y^2 + z^2 = 3$

9. $(x - 1)^2 + z^2 = 9y^2$

10. $x^2 + y^2 - 4y + 4 - 4z^2 = 0$.

11. Find the equation of the sphere with center $(1, 2, 3)$ and radius 4.

12. Find the equation of the sphere with center $(1, -1, -1)$ and which passes through $(0, -5, 7)$.

13. Find the equation of the right circular cylinder which meets the plane $y = -1$ in a circle with center $(2, -1, 4)$ and radius 3.

14. Find the equation of the right circular cone with apex at $(3, 0, 0)$, apex angle $\pi/2$, and axis along the x-axis.

15. Find the equation of the right circular cone with apex $(1, 1, 1)$, with axis parallel to the y-axis, and which passes through the origin.

4. SOLIDS OF REVOLUTION

If a point, curve, or region is revolved about an axis in the same plane, it sweeps out a figure in space. We consider several examples.

(1) The point $(0, b, c)$ in the y, z-plane is revolved about the z-axis. It sweeps out a circle (Fig. 4.1a).

(2) The line $x = 0$, $y = b$ in the y, z-plane is revolved about the z-axis. It sweeps out a cylinder (Fig. 4.1b).

(3) A line $x = 0$, $ay + bz = c$ rotated about the z-axis generates a right circular cone (Fig. 4.1c).

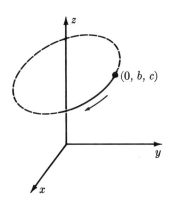

FIG. 4.1a

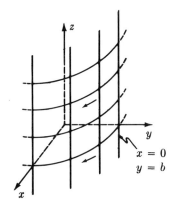

FIG. 4.1b

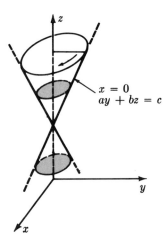

FIG. 4.1c

(4) A circle in the y, z-plane with center on the z-axis sweeps out a sphere when rotated about the z-axis (Fig. 4.2a).

(5) A circle in the y, z-plane, but which does not meet the z-axis, is rotated about the z-axis. It sweeps out a donut-shaped region called a right circular **torus** (Fig. 4.2b).

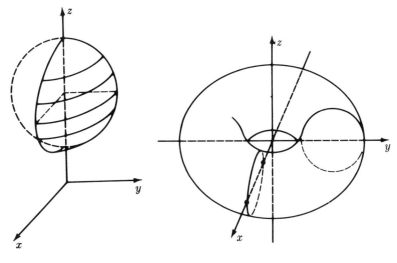

Fig. 4.2a   Fig. 4.2b

(6) Consider the region (Fig. 4.3a) in the y, z-plane bounded by the y-axis, the line $y = 1$, and the parabola $z = y^2$. When rotated about the z-axis, it generates the solid illustrated in Fig. 4.3b.

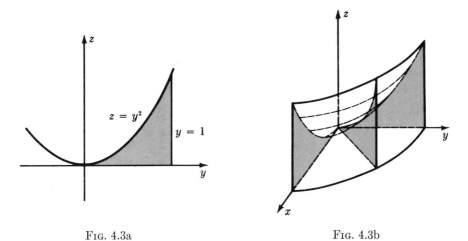

Fig. 4.3a   Fig. 4.3b

(7) The region bounded by a triangle in the first quadrant of the x, z-plane is rotated about the x-axis. The result is a ring-shaped solid

(Fig. 4.4). If you consider this solid carefully, you will see that it is bounded by three right circular cones centered on the *x*-axis.

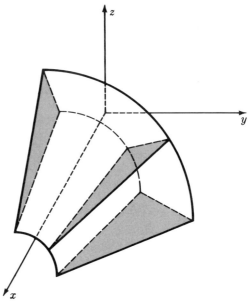

F<small>IG.</small> 4.4

In the next chapter we shall find the volumes of many of these solids.

EXERCISES

Sketch the locus:

1. the point $(a, 0, 0)$ rotated about the *x*-axis
2. the line $y = 0$, $x = 2$ rotated about the *x*-axis
3. the line $y = 0$, $z = c$ rotated about the *x*-axis
4. the line $y = 0$, $z = x$ revolved about the *x*-axis
5. the line $x = 0$, $z - 2y - 1 = 0$ revolved about the *z*-axis
6. the circle $x = 0$, $(y - 2)^2 + (z - 2)^2 = 1$ revolved about the *z*-axis
7. the circle $x = 0$, $(y - 1)^2 + (z - 1)^2 = 1$ rotated about the *y*-axis
8. the circle $y = 0$, $(x - 1)^2 + (z - 1)^2 = 2$ revolved about the *x*-axis
9. the parabola $x = 0$, $y = z^2$ rotated about the *y*-axis
10. the parabola $x = 0$, $y = z^2$ rotated about the *z*-axis
11. the curve $x = 0$, $yz = 1$ rotated about the *y*-axis.

12. The region in the y, z-plane bounded by the lines $y = z$ and $y = 2z - 2$ between $y = 2$ and $y = 4$ is rotated about the y-axis. Sketch the solid.

13. Do the same for the region of Ex. 12 rotated about the z-axis.

14. The region in the y, z-plane bounded by the curves $z = e^y$ and $z = 1$ between $y = 0$ and $y = 4$ is rotated about the y-axis. Sketch the solid.

5. SLICING

The volumes of many solids can be found by integration. The strategy in each case is the same. A solid is sliced into numerous thin pieces, each of which is approximately a familiar shape of known volume. The volume of the i-th piece is $f(\bar{x}_i)\,\Delta x$, the product of its base area $f(\bar{x}_i)$ by its thickness Δx. Addition of all these little pieces leads to the integral

$$\int_a^b f(x)\,dx$$

for the exact volume. [Recall that we abbreviate $f(\bar{x}_i)\,\Delta x$ by $f(x)\,dx$.]

The general plan of attack is executed on a particular solid in four steps: (1) choose a method of slicing the solid; (2) choose a variable x which locates the typical slice, and find the range $a \le x \le b$ that applies to the problem; (3) compute the volume $f(x)\,dx$ of the typical slice; (4) find an antiderivative of $f(x)$ and compute

$$\int_a^b f(x)\,dx.$$

Before actually computing volumes, we shall look at two area problems which are solved in the same spirit.

> **EXAMPLE 5.1**
>
> Find the area of a circle of radius r. (Assume the formula $c = 2\pi r$ for circumference.)

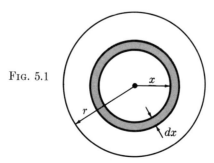

Fig. 5.1

Solution: Step 1.   Cut the circle into thin concentric rings (Fig. 5.1).

Step 2. Let x denote the radial distance of a ring from the center; $0 \le x \le r$.

Step 3. The typical ring has length $2\pi x$ and width dx, hence its area is $2\pi x\, dx$. The area of the circle is

$$\int_0^r 2\pi x\, dx.$$

Step 4. An antiderivative is πx^2, hence

$$\int_0^r 2\pi x\, dx = \pi x^2 \Big|_0^r = \pi r^2.$$

Answer: πr^2.

EXAMPLE 5.2

Find the area of a circular wedge of radius r and central angle α.

Solution: *Step 1.* Slice the wedge into many thin wedges (Fig. 5.2).

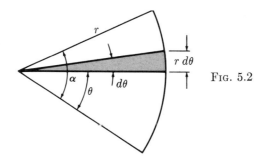

Fig. 5.2

Step 2. Let θ denote the central angle; $0 \le \theta \le \alpha$.

Step 3. The thin wedge is almost an isosceles triangle of base $r\, d\theta$, height r, and area

$$\frac{1}{2} r(r\, d\theta) = \frac{1}{2} r^2\, d\theta.$$

The area of the wedge is

$$\int_0^\alpha \frac{1}{2} r^2\, d\theta.$$

Step 4.

$$\int_0^\alpha \frac{1}{2} r^2\, d\theta = \frac{1}{2} r^2 \theta \Big|_0^\alpha = \frac{1}{2} r^2 \alpha.$$

Answer: $\dfrac{1}{2} r^2 \alpha$.

Note the special case $\alpha = 2\pi$. Then the wedge is the whole pie, of area πr^2, which agrees with the answer in the previous example.

6. VOLUME OF REVOLUTION

A region R in the y, z-plane is revolved about the y-axis (Fig. 6.1). Sup-

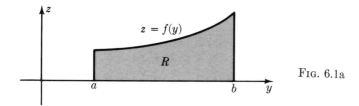

$z = f(y)$

R

a b y

FIG. 6.1a

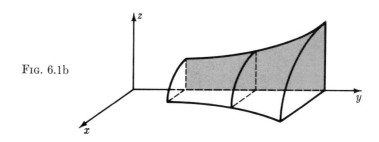

FIG. 6.1b

pose R is the region under a curve $z = f(y)$, where $a \leq y \leq b$. Divide the interval from a to b into many small pieces of width dy. Each of the resulting thin rectangles sweeps out a circular slab (Fig. 6.2). Each slab has radius

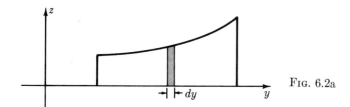

dy y

FIG. 6.2a

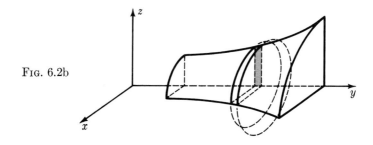

FIG. 6.2b

$f(y)$, base area $\pi f(y)^2$, thickness dy, and volume $\pi f(y)^2\, dy$. Consequently the volume of the solid of revolution is

$$\int_a^b \pi f(y)^2\, dy.$$

EXAMPLE 6.1

Find the volume of a sphere of radius a.

Solution: Step 1.   Slice the sphere into parallel slabs by planes.

Step 2.   Place the origin at the center of the sphere and choose the y-axis perpendicular to these planes. Thus $-a \le y \le a$. See Fig. 6.3a.

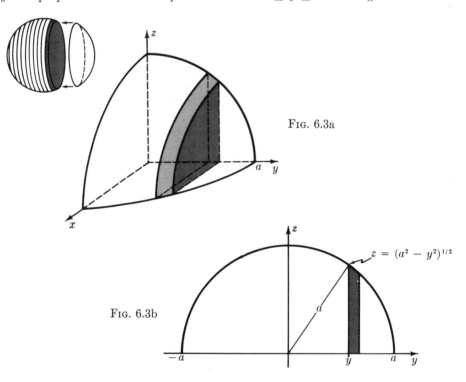

Fɪɢ. 6.3a

Fɪɢ. 6.3b

$$z = (a^2 - y^2)^{1/2}$$

Step 3.   Each slab has radius $z = \sqrt{a^2 - y^2}$. See Fig. 6.3b. Its thickness is dy, so its volume is $\pi z^2\, dy$. Consequently the volume of the sphere is

$$\int_{-a}^a \pi z^2\, dy = \int_{-a}^a \pi(a^2 - y^2)\, dy.$$

Step 4.   An antiderivative of $(a^2 - y^2)$ is $a^2 y - \frac{1}{3}y^3$. Hence

$$\int_{-a}^a \pi(a^2 - y^2)\, dy = \pi\left(a^2 y - \frac{1}{3}y^3\right)\Big|_{-a}^a$$

$$= \pi\left(a^3 - \frac{1}{3}a^3\right) - \pi\left(-a^3 + \frac{1}{3}a^3\right) = \frac{4}{3}\pi a^3.$$

$$Answer: \quad \frac{4}{3}\pi a^3.$$

EXAMPLE 6.2

A right circular cone of height h is constructed over a base of radius a. What is its volume?

Solution: The cone is a solid of revolution, obtained by revolving a right triangle about one leg. Choose the triangle indicated in Fig. 6.4a.

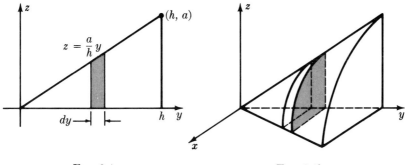

Fɪɢ. 6.4a   Fɪɢ. 6.4b

Rotate this triangle about the y-axis to generate the cone (Fig. 6.4b). Slice the cone into thin slabs, each of width dy. Note (Fig. 6.4a) that the triangle is the region under the curve $z = (a/h)y$, where $0 \le y \le h$. Since each slab has radius $(a/h)y$, its volume is

$$\pi\left(\frac{a}{h}y\right)^2 dy.$$

The volume of the cone is

$$\int_0^h \pi\frac{a^2}{h^2}y^2\, dy = \pi\frac{a^2}{h^2}\left(\frac{1}{3}y^3\right)\Big|_0^h$$

$$= \frac{\pi a^2}{3h^2}h^3.$$

Alternate Solution: Slice the cone into cylindrical shells rather than slabs (Fig. 6.5a), and choose z as the variable. Thus the triangle is sliced into thin strips parallel to the y-axis (Fig. 6.5b). Each thin-walled cylindrical shell has radius z, height $h - (h/a)z$, and thickness dz. Its volume is the product of its three dimensions:

$$(2\pi z)\left(h - \frac{h}{a}z\right)dz.$$

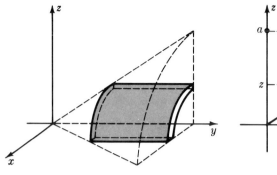

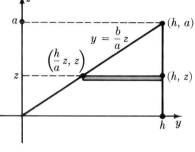

FIG. 6.5a   FIG. 6.5b

Hence the volume of the cone is

$$\int_0^a (2\pi z)\left(h - \frac{h}{a}z\right)dz = \int_0^a \left(2\pi hz - \frac{2\pi h}{a}z^2\right)dz$$

$$= \left(\pi hz^2 - \frac{2\pi h}{3a}z^3\right)\Bigg|_0^a = \left(\pi ha^2 - \frac{2\pi}{3}ha^2\right).$$

Answer: $\dfrac{1}{3}\pi a^2 h.$

EXAMPLE 6.3

The region in the y, z-plane bounded by the parabola $z = y^2$, the line $y = a$, and the y-axis is revolved about the z-axis. (Assume $a > 0$.) What is the resulting volume?

Solution: Slice the plane region by parallels to the y-axis (Fig. 6.6a).

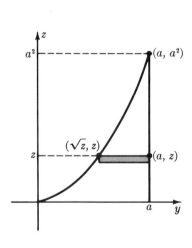

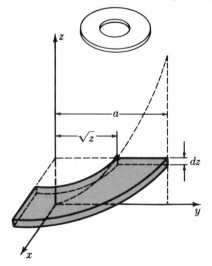

FIG. 6.6a   FIG. 6.6b

When the typical resulting strip is revolved about the z-axis, it sweeps out a thin circular washer (Fig. 6.6b). The base of the washer is the region between two concentric circles. Its area is

$$\pi a^2 - \pi (\sqrt{z})^2 = \pi (a^2 - z),$$

while its thickness is dz. Note that the variable in this solution is z, and $0 \leq z \leq a^2$.

The volume is

$$\int_0^{a^2} \pi(a^2 - z)\, dz = \pi \left(a^2 z - \frac{1}{2} z^2 \right) \Big|_0^{a^2}$$

$$= \pi \left(a^4 - \frac{1}{2} a^4 \right).$$

Alternate Solution: Proceed as indicated in Fig. 6.7. The region under

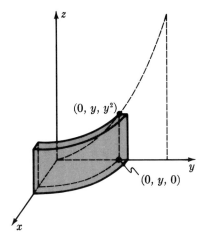

FIG. 6.7

the parabola is split into thin "rectangles" by parallels to the z-axis. Now y is the variable, and the solid of revolution is sliced into thin cylindrical shells. The typical shell has radius y, height y^2, and thickness dy, hence volume $(2\pi y)y^2\, dy$. The volume of the solid is

$$\int_0^a (2\pi y)y^2\, dy = \int_0^a 2\pi y^3\, dy.$$

While we do not yet "officially" know that

$$\frac{d}{dy} (y^4) = 4y^3,$$

it is no secret. Use it to integrate:

$$\int_0^a 2\pi y^3 \, dy = 2\pi \left(\frac{1}{4} y^4\right) \Big|_0^a = \frac{\pi}{2} a^4.$$

Answer: $\dfrac{\pi}{2} a^4.$

EXERCISES

The region of the y, z-plane whose boundary curves are given is revolved about the z-axis. Find the volume of the resulting solid of revolution:

1. z-axis, $y = 2z + 3$, $z = 0$, $z = 3$

2. z-axis, $y = \dfrac{3 - z}{2}$, $z = -1$, $z = 1$

3. z-axis, $y = \dfrac{1}{z + 1}$, $z = 0$, $z = 4$

4. z-axis, $y = \dfrac{-3}{z + 4}$, $z = -1$, $z = 1$

5. z-axis, $y = 3\sqrt{z}$, $z = 0$, $z = 4$.

6. The region of the x, y-plane bounded by $y = 16x^2$, $y = 2$, and $y = 4$ is revolved about the y-axis. Find the volume of the resulting solid.

7. The region of the x, y-plane bounded by the x-axis, $y = x + 1$, $x = 1$, and $x = 4$ is revolved about the line $y = -3$. Find the volume of the resulting solid.

8. The region of the x, y-plane bounded by the lines $x = 1$, $y = x$, and $x = -2y + 6$ is revolved about the line $y - -2$. Find the volume of the resulting solid.

9. The region of the x, z-plane bounded by $z = -1$, $z = e^{2x}$, $x = 0$, and $x = 2$ is revolved about the line $z = -1$. Find the volume of the resulting solid.

10. The region of the x, z-plane bounded by the z-axis, $y^2 = \sin z$, $z = 0$, and $z = \pi$ is revolved about the z-axis. Find the volume of the resulting solid.

11. Find the volume of a frustum of a right circular cone with lower radius R_0, upper radius R_1, and height h.

12. Find the volume of a sphere of radius a, with a hole of radius h drilled through its center.

13. A plane at distance h from the center of a sphere of radius a cuts off a spherical cap of height $a - h$. Find its volume.

14. Find the volume of the solid formed by revolving the triangle in the x, y-plane with vertices $(1, 1)$ $(0, 2)$, and $(2, 2)$ about the x-axis.

15. A circular hole is cut on center vertically through a sphere, leaving a ring of height h. Calculate the volume of the ring.

16. A circle of radius r_0 is revolved about a line in the same plane at distance R_0 from the center of the circle. Assume $R_0 > r_0$. Show that the resulting torus has volume $2\pi^2 R_0 r_0^2$. (*Hint:* Use washers; then identify the difficult integral which results as the area of a circle.)

17. The rectangle $-1 \le x \le 1$, $-2 \le y \le 2$, $z = 0$ moves upwards, its center always on the z-axis, and rotates counterclockwise at a uniform rate as it rises. Suppose it has turned $90°$ when it reaches $z = 1$. Find the volume swept out.

7. OTHER VOLUMES

The volumes of certain figures other than solids of revolution can also be found with the tools at our disposal.

EXAMPLE 7.1

A cone of height h has an irregular base of area A. Find the volume of the cone.

Solution: Let x denote distance measured from the apex toward the plane of the base (Fig. 7.1). The typical cross-section of the cone by a plane

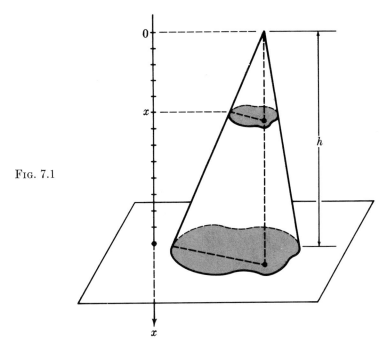

FIG. 7.1

parallel to the base, distance x from the apex, is a plane region similar to the base. The linear dimensions in this cross-section are proportional to x, so its area is proportional to x^2.

Let $f(x)$ denote this area. Then $f(x) = cx^2$. But $f(h) = A$, hence $ch^2 = A$. Therefore $c = A/h^2$ and

$$f(x) = \frac{A}{h^2} x^2.$$

Slice the cone into slabs by planes parallel to the base. A typical slab has base area $f(x)$, thickness dx, and volume

$$f(x)\, dx = \frac{A}{h^2} x^2\, dx.$$

Hence the volume of the cone is

$$\int_0^h \frac{A}{h^2}\, x^2\, dx = \frac{A}{h^2}\left(\frac{1}{3}x^3\right)\Bigg|_0^h = \frac{1}{3}\,Ah.$$

Answer: $\dfrac{1}{3}\,Ah.$

Prismoidal Formula

A **prismoid** is a region in space bounded by two parallel planes and one or more surfaces joining the planes (Fig. 7.2). There is a nice formula for

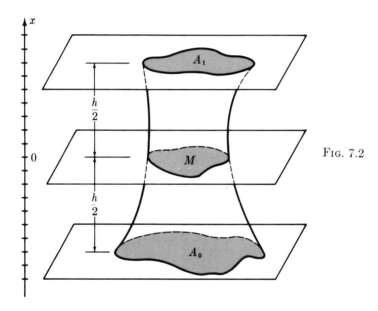

FIG. 7.2

the volume V of a prismoid whose cross-sectional area $f(x)$ is a *quadratic* function of the distance x, measured along an axis perpendicular to the base planes. The formula is

$$V = \frac{h}{6}\,(A_0 + 4M + A_1),$$

where h is the distance between base planes, A_0 and A_1 are the areas of the bases, and M is the cross-sectional area halfway between the bases.

To derive the formula, choose $x = 0$ at the midsection. Then x runs from $-h/2$ to $h/2$. The hypothesis is

$$f(x) = a + bx + cx^2.$$

Thus

$$A_0 = f\left(-\frac{h}{2}\right) = a - \frac{bh}{2} + \frac{ch^2}{4},$$

$$M = f(0) = a,$$

$$A_1 = f\left(\frac{h}{2}\right) = a + \frac{bh}{2} + \frac{ch^2}{4}.$$

Therefore

$$\frac{h}{6}(A_0 + 4M + A_1) = \frac{h}{6}\left(6a + \frac{ch^2}{2}\right).$$

But the volume, found by slicing, is

$$V = \int_{-h/2}^{h/2} f(x)\, dx$$

$$= \int_{-h/2}^{h/2} (a + bx + cx^2)\, dx$$

$$= \left(ax + \frac{1}{2}bx^2 + \frac{1}{3}cx^3\right)\Big|_{-h/2}^{h/2}$$

$$= \left(\frac{ah}{2} + \frac{bh^2}{8} + \frac{ch^3}{24}\right) - \left(\frac{-ah}{2} + \frac{bh^2}{8} - \frac{ch^3}{24}\right)$$

$$= ah + \frac{1}{12}ch^3$$

$$= \frac{h}{6}\left(6a + \frac{ch^2}{2}\right)$$

$$= \frac{h}{6}(A_0 + 4M + A_1).$$

EXAMPLE 7.2

Find the volume of the tent in Fig. 7.3a.

Solution: Measure x from the top down. The cross-section at position x is a rectangle (Fig. 7.3b). Its shorter dimension is proportional to x and

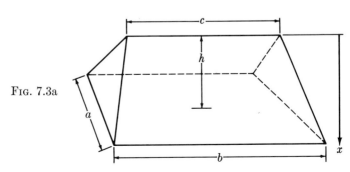

Fig. 7.3a

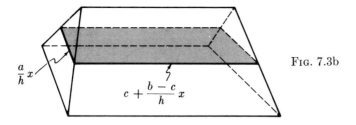

F<small>IG.</small> 7.3b

equal to a at $x = h$, hence it is $(a/h)x$. The longer dimension is a linear function of x, equal to c at $x = 0$ and to b at $x = h$, hence it is $c + [(b - c)/h]x$. The product of these dimensions,

$$\left(\frac{a}{h}x\right)\left(c + \frac{b - c}{h}x\right),$$

is the cross-sectional area. It is a quadratic function of x so the Prismoidal Formula applies:

$$A_0 = 0,$$

$$M = \left(\frac{a}{h} \cdot \frac{h}{2}\right)\left(c + \frac{b - c}{h} \cdot \frac{h}{2}\right) = \frac{a(b + c)}{4},$$

$$A_1 = ab.$$

Hence

$$V = \frac{h}{6}(A_0 + 4M + A_1)$$

$$= \frac{h}{6}\left(0 + 4\frac{a(b + c)}{4} + ab\right) = \frac{h}{6}(2ab + ac).$$

Answer: $\dfrac{ha}{6}(2b + c).$

C<small>HECK</small>:   When $c = 0$, the solid is a pyramid; when $c = b$, it is a right prism. In each case the formula above gives the correct volume.

EXAMPLE 7.3

Find the volume of a sphere of radius a by the Prismoidal Formula.

Solution: The cross-sectional area is a quadratic function, hence the formula applies with

$$h = 2a, \qquad A_0 = A_1 = 0, \qquad M = \pi a^2.$$

Conclusion:

$$V = \frac{2a}{6}(0 + 4\pi a^2 + 0).$$

Answer: $\dfrac{4}{3}\pi a^3.$

Area of a Sphere

We close this chapter with a surprise. We can use the (known) volume of a sphere to find its surface area.

EXAMPLE 7.4

Find the surface area A of a sphere of radius a.

Solution: Find the volume of the sphere by slicing it into concentric spherical shells (Fig. 7.4). Let $f(x)$ be the surface area of the typical shell

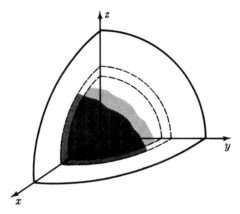

FIG. 7.4

at distance x from the center $(0 \leq x \leq a)$. Then $f(x)$ is proportional to x^2 and $f(a) = A$, hence

$$f(x) = \frac{A}{a^2} x^2.$$

The volume of the shell is

$$f(x) \, dx = \frac{A}{a^2} x^2 \, dx.$$

Hence

$$V = \int_0^a \frac{A}{a^2} x^2 \, dx = \frac{A}{a^2} \left(\frac{1}{3} x^3 \right) \Big|_0^a = \frac{A a}{3}.$$

But

$$V = \frac{4}{3} \pi a^3,$$

therefore

$$\frac{4}{3}\pi a^3 = \frac{Aa}{3}.$$

Answer: $A = 4\pi a^2.$

EXERCISES

Use the Prismoidal Formula to find the volume obtained by revolving the given region of the x, y-plane about the indicated line:

1. bounded by $x = 0$, $x + y = 2$, $y = 1$; about the y-axis
2. bounded by $y = 0$, $y = 3x + 1$, $x = 0$, $x = 3$; about the x-axis
3. bounded by $y = 2x^2$, $y = 2$, $y = 4$; about the y-axis
4. bounded by $y = x^2 - 2x + 2$, $y = 1$, $y = 5$; about $x = 1$
5. bounded by $x^2 + (y - 2)^2 = 16$, $y = 0$, $y = 4$; about the y-axis
6. bounded by $(x - 4)^2 + y^2 = 25$, $x = 2$, $x = 6$; about the x-axis.

In Ex. 7–10, the given region of the x, y-plane is revolved about the indicated line. Find the resulting volume provided the Prismoidal Formula applies:

7. bounded by the x-axis, $y = x^2$, $x = 1$, $x = 4$; about the x-axis
8. bounded by $y = \dfrac{1}{x}$, $y = 1$, $y = 3$, $x = 0$; about the y-axis
9. bounded by $y = 0$, $y = \sqrt{x}$, $x = 1$, $x = 4$; about the x-axis
10. bounded by $x = 0$, $y = \sqrt{x}$, $y = 1$, $y = 4$; about the y-axis.
11. Find the volume of the lower half (by height) of a cone of height 16 cm whose base is a semicircle of radius 4 cm surmounted by a square, one side of which is the diameter of the semicircle.
12. Find the volume of a pyramid of height 8 in., whose base is a 2×4 in. rectangle. What is the volume of the lower half (by height)?
13. An exponential horn is bounded by the 6 surfaces $x = e^{az}$, $x = -e^{az}$, $y = e^{az}$, $y = -e^{az}$, $z = 0$, $z = b$. Find its volume.

14. Inverse Functions and Logarithms

1. INVERSE FUNCTIONS

A function f assigns a number $y = f(x)$ to each number x. In this chapter we are concerned with the question: does the equation $y = f(x)$ determine a number x for each number y? This question can be tricky. For example, suppose $y = \cos x$. If $y = 3$, no value of x is determined since the equation $3 = \cos x$ is never satisfied. But if $y = 1$, infinitely many values of x are determined since the equation $1 = \cos x$ holds for $x = 0$, $\pm 2\pi$, $\pm 4\pi$, etc.

Life is most pleasant when $y = f(x)$ determines a unique x for each y. Let us consider some examples.

Suppose $f(x) = 2x - 5$. The equation $y = f(x) = 2x - 5$ can be solved for x in terms of y:

$$x = \frac{1}{2}(y + 5).$$

For each y, there is a unique x given by this formula.

Geometrically, the situation is simple. The graph of $y = 2x - 5$ is a straight line crossing each horizontal line once (Fig. 1.1). Given y, the graph

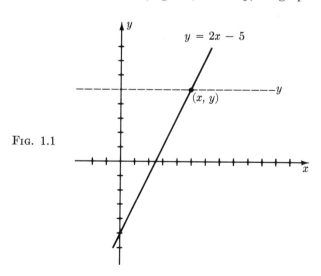

$y = 2x - 5$

(x, y)

FIG. 1.1

crosses the level y at a point (x, y) where $x = \frac{1}{2}(y + 5)$. Thus each y determines a unique x. In other words, x is a function of y. We write $x = f^{-1}(y)$ and read "f inverse of y," where

$$f^{-1}(y) = \frac{1}{2}(y + 5).$$

The line in Fig. 1.1 is the graph of both $y = f(x)$ and $x = f^{-1}(y)$. This is because the statements

$$y = f(x) \qquad \text{and} \qquad x = f^{-1}(y)$$

are equivalent.

Consider another example, $f(x) = x^3$. The curve $y = x^3$ is always rising; it crosses each horizontal line once (Fig. 1.2). Therefore the equation $y = f(x)$ determines one number x for each number y. We write

$$x = f^{-1}(y) = \sqrt[3]{y}.$$

Each point on the curve can be regarded as

$$(x, x^3) \qquad \text{or as} \qquad (\sqrt[3]{y}, y).$$

It is important to notice that

$$y = x^3 \qquad \text{and} \qquad x = \sqrt[3]{y}$$

are equivalent statements.

These examples illustrate an important situation: if the graph of $f(x)$ is always increasing or always decreasing, then the equation $y = f(x)$ defines a unique x for each y. Thus, associated with $f(x)$ is another function $x = f^{-1}(y)$, called the **inverse function of** $f(x)$.

If the equation $y = f(x)$ can be solved for x in terms of y, then $f^{-1}(y)$ is expressed by an explicit formula. Often, however, this is not possible. For example, $f(x) = x^5 + x$ is an increasing function and so has an inverse

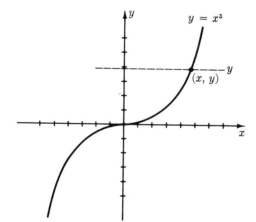

$$y = x^3$$

(x, y)

Fig. 1.2

function $f^{-1}(y)$. Yet we cannot solve $x^5 + x = y$ for x; the inverse function exists but there is no formula for it.

Recall that the statements

$$y = f(x) \quad \text{and} \quad x = f^{-1}(y)$$

are equivalent. It follows that

$$f^{-1}[f(x)] = f^{-1}[y] = x,$$

$$f[f^{-1}(y)] = f[x] = y.$$

Thus the actions of f and f^{-1} neutralize each other. For example, if $f(x) = 2x - 5$, then $f^{-1}(y) = \frac{1}{2}(y + 5)$, so

$$f^{-1}[f(x)] = f^{-1}[2x - 5] = \frac{1}{2}([2x - 5] + 5) = x.$$

Also,

$$f[f^{-1}(y)] = f\left[\frac{1}{2}(y + 5)\right] = 2\left[\frac{1}{2}(y + 5)\right] - 5 = y.$$

As another example, if $f(x) = x^3$, then $f^{-1}(y) = \sqrt[3]{y}$, so

$$f^{-1}[f(x)] = f^{-1}(x^3) = \sqrt[3]{x^3} = x.$$

Also,

$$f[f^{-1}(y)] = f(\sqrt[3]{y}) = (\sqrt[3]{y})^3 = y.$$

One more example. Imagine a group of men all with different names. For each name x, there is a man $X = f(x)$ with that name. For each man X, there is his name $x = f^{-1}(X)$. For instance,

$$f^{-1}[f(\text{john})] = \text{the name of the man } f(\text{john})$$

$$= \text{the name of the man whose name is john}$$

$$= \text{the name of John} = \text{john}.$$

Thus $f^{-1}[f(x)] = x$. Conversely,

$$f[f^{-1}(\text{George})] = \text{the man whose name is } f^{-1}(\text{George})$$

$$= \text{the man whose name is george}$$

$$= \text{George}.$$

Thus $f[f^{-1}(X)] = X$.

Warning: Do not confuse the inverse function $f^{-1}(x)$ with the reciprocal $1/f(x)$.

EXERCISES

Find the inverse function:

1. $y = 3x - 7$ 2. $y = -2x + 5$
3. $y = 4x - 1$ 4. $y = 10x + 10$

5. $y = \dfrac{2x - 7}{x + 4}$ $(x \neq -4)$ 6. $y = \dfrac{x + 1}{x - 1}$ $(x \neq 1)$

7. $y = \dfrac{x + 2}{x + 3}$ $(x \neq -3)$ 8. $y = \dfrac{3x + 4}{2x + 3}$ $\left(x \neq -\dfrac{3}{2} \right)$

9. $y = -\dfrac{1}{x}$ $(x \neq 0)$ 10. $y = \sqrt{x + 3}$ $(x > -3)$

11. $y = \sqrt{2x - 8}$ $(x > 4)$ 12. $y = \dfrac{\sqrt{x} + 1}{\sqrt{x} - 1}$ $(x > 1)$.

13. Let $f(x) = \dfrac{9}{x + 7} - 7$. Show $f^{-1}(x) = f(x)$.

14. Suppose $h(x) = h^{-1}(x)$ and $f(x) = g\{h[g^{-1}(x)]\}$.
    Show that $f^{-1}(x) = f(x)$.

15. Let $f(x) = 4x - 1$. Plot $y = f(x)$ and $y = f^{-1}(x)$ on the same graph. Verify that the two curves are mirror images in the line $y = x$.

16. Let $f(x) = ax + b$ where $a \neq 0$. Show that the graph of $y = f^{-1}(x)$ is a straight line of slope $1/a$.

17. Let $f(x) = x^3$. Sketch $y = f^{-1}(x)$.

18. Let $f(x) = x^3 + x$. Sketch $y = f^{-1}(x)$.

19. Let $f(x) = x^3 + x$ and let $g(x) = f^{-1}(x)$. Show that $g(x)^3 = -g(x) + x$.

20. Let f and g be the functions in Ex. 19. Compute $g(-2)$, $g(0)$, $g(2)$, $g(10)$, $g(30)$, $g(4^3 + 4)$.

21. Let $f(x) = \displaystyle\int_0^x t^2 \, dt$. Find $\displaystyle\int_0^{f^{-1}(x)} t^2 \, dt$. Explain.

2. GRAPHS AND DERIVATIVES

Suppose we wish to study an inverse function $x = f^{-1}(y)$. It seems more natural to consider x as the independent variable and y as the dependent variable, so let us study instead $y = f^{-1}(x)$. We have interchanged x and y; whenever the point (x, y) is on the graph of $x = f^{-1}(y)$, then the point (y, x) is on the graph of $y = f^{-1}(x)$, and conversely.

A simple relation exists between the points (x, y) and (y, x): they are mirror images of each other across the line $y = x$. See Fig. 2.1. Since the graph of $y = f^{-1}(x)$ is identical to that of $x = f(y)$, it is the reflection of the graph of $y = f(x)$.

> The graph of $y = f^{-1}(x)$ is the reflection of the graph of $y = f(x)$ across the line $y = x$.

As an example, take $f(x) = 2x - 5$. Then $f^{-1}(y) = \frac{1}{2}(y + 5)$, or $f^{-1}(x) = \frac{1}{2}(x + 5)$. See Fig. 2.2.

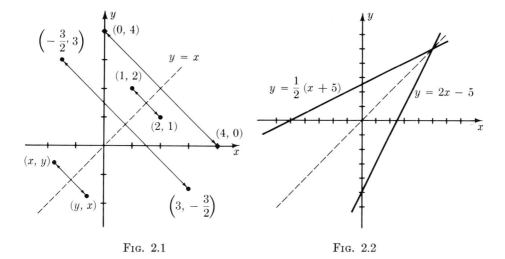

FIG. 2.1   FIG. 2.2

The lines in Fig. 2.2 are reflections of each other across the line $y = x$. Notice that their slopes, 2 and $\frac{1}{2}$, are reciprocals. The same is true of any pair of lines which are reflections of each other in $y = x$. If one line is $y = mx + b$, its reflection is $x = my + b$, that is, $y = (x/m) - (b/m)$. The slopes are m and $1/m$, respectively.

As another example of reflection, take $f(x) = x^3$. Then $f^{-1}(x) = \sqrt[3]{x}$. The graphs are shown in Fig. 2.3.

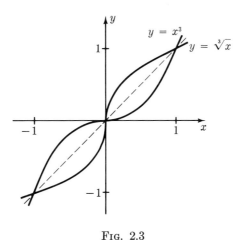

FIG. 2.3

Derivatives of Inverse Functions

The derivative of an inverse function can be expressed in terms of the derivative of the direct function by means of the following rule.

> If $g(x)$ is the inverse function of $f(x)$, then
>
> $$\frac{d}{dy}[g(y)]\bigg|_{y=f(x)} = \frac{1}{\dfrac{d}{dx}[f(x)]},$$
>
> provided $f'(x) \neq 0$. Briefly,
>
> $$\frac{dx}{dy} = \frac{1}{\dfrac{dy}{dx}}.$$

The rule makes good sense numerically. If y is changing 5 times as fast as x, then x is changing $\frac{1}{5}$ as fast as y.

The rule makes good sense geometrically, too. The graphs $y = f(x)$ and $y = g(x)$ are reflections of each other (Fig. 2.4). At corresponding points

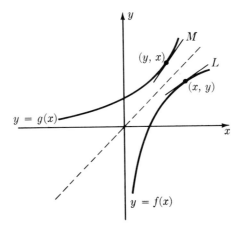

Fɪɢ. 2.4

(x, y) and (y, x), the tangent lines L and M also are reflections of each other. Hence their slopes are reciprocals:

$$\text{slope of } M = \frac{1}{\text{slope of } L}.$$

But the slopes of L and M are $f'(x)$ and $g'(y)$, respectively. Therefore

$$g'(y) = \frac{1}{f'(x)}.$$

If L is horizontal, then M is vertical, so the slope of M is not defined. In such a case $g(x)$ does not have a derivative at y.

Rᴇᴍᴀʀᴋ: For a theoretical discussion of inverse functions, see Chapter 20, Section 8 and Chapter 21, Section 1.

Applications

EXAMPLE 2.1

Compute the derivative of $x^{1/3}$.

Solution: The function $g(x) = x^{1/3}$ is the inverse of $f(x) = x^3$. Apply the rule with $y = f(x) = x^3$:

$$g'(y) = \frac{1}{f'(x)} = \frac{1}{3x^2}.$$

But $x = y^{1/3}$, therefore

$$g'(y) = \frac{1}{3y^{2/3}}, \qquad \text{that is,} \quad g'(x) = \frac{1}{3x^{2/3}}.$$

> *Answer:* For $x \neq 0$, $\dfrac{d}{dx}(x^{1/3}) = \dfrac{1}{3x^{2/3}}.$

REMARK: Since $y = x^3$ has a horizontal tangent at the origin, $y = x^{1/3}$ has a vertical tangent there. Consequently $x^{1/3}$ has no derivative at $x = 0$, but otherwise the derivative is $1/(3x^{2/3})$.

EXAMPLE 2.2

Compute the derivative of $x^{1/p}$, where p is an odd positive integer.

Solution: Use the same technique as in the last example. The curve $y = f(x) = x^p$, like the curve $y = x^3$, increases steadily. The inverse function, $g(x) = x^{1/p}$, is differentiated according to the formula

$$g'(y) = \frac{1}{f'(x)},$$

where $y = f(x) = x^p$, that is, $x = y^{1/p}$. Since $f'(x) = px^{p-1}$,

$$g'(y) = \frac{1}{px^{p-1}} = \frac{1}{p(y^{1/p})^{p-1}}$$

$$= \frac{1}{py^{1-1/p}}$$

$$= \frac{1}{p} y^{(1/p)-1}.$$

> *Answer:* If p is odd,
>
> $$\frac{d}{dx}(x^{1/p}) = \frac{1}{p} x^{(1/p)-1}, \quad x \neq 0.$$

EXAMPLE 2.3

Compute the derivative of $x^{1/p}$, where p is an even positive integer.

Solution: Compare the graphs of $y = x^p$ for p odd and for p even (Fig. 2.5). If p is even, the graph crosses no horizontal line below the x-axis,

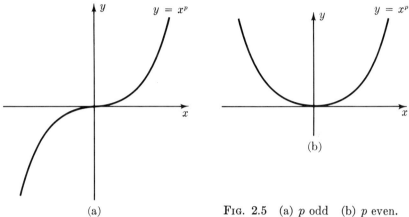

(a)   FIG. 2.5   (a) p odd   (b) p even.

but crosses each horizontal line above the x-axis twice. Therefore $f^{-1}(y)$ has no meaning if $y < 0$, and two possible meanings if $y > 0$. This ambiguity is avoided by agreeing to consider $y = x^p$ only for $x \geq 0$, and then defining the inverse function $x^{1/p}$. See Fig. 2.6. With this agreement, for p even,

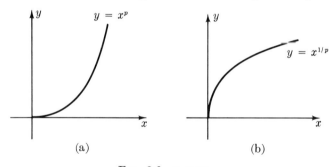

(a)   (b)

FIG. 2.6 p even.

$x^{1/p}$ is defined only for $x \geq 0$, and has non-negative values. For example, we agree that $x^{1/2}$ means the positive square root of x.

   Now that $x^{1/p}$ is defined, the computation of its derivative is precisely the same as in the last example.

> *Answer:*   If p is even,
>
> $$\frac{d}{dx}\left(x^{1/p}\right) = \frac{1}{p}\, x^{(1/p)-1}, \quad x > 0.$$

   A general rule for differentiating fractional powers follows from the last two examples.

Differentiation of Fractional Powers   Let $\dfrac{p}{q}$ be a fraction, $q > 0$. Then

$$\frac{d}{dx}\,(x^{p/q}) = \frac{p}{q}\,x^{(p/q)-1}.$$

If q is even, the rule holds for $x > 0$; if q is odd, it holds for all $x \neq 0$.

This rule says you differentiate fractional powers just as you do integral powers: bring down the power and lower the exponent by one.

The rule is easy to verify. Write

$$x^{p/q} = (x^{1/q})^p,$$

and use the Chain Rule:

$$\frac{d}{dx}\,(x^{p/q}) = p(x^{1/q})^{p-1} \cdot \frac{d}{dx}\,(x^{1/q})$$

$$= px^{(p-1)/q} \cdot \frac{1}{q}\,x^{(1/q)-1} = \frac{p}{q}\,x^{(p/q)-1}.$$

This derivation is valid provided $x^{1/q}$ can be differentiated. It can be if $x > 0$ for q even, or if $x \neq 0$ for q odd.

REMARKS: If $p/q \geq 1$, the formula is valid also at $x = 0$, although a special argument is needed to verify it. This will be done in Ex. 16.

Note that $x^{1/3}$ is not the same as $x^{2/6}$. The first function is defined for all x, the second only for $x \geq 0$.

EXAMPLE 2.4

Compute dy/dx if

$$\text{(a)}\quad y = \sqrt{x}, \quad x > 0;$$
$$\text{(b)}\quad y = \sqrt[3]{x^2 + 1};$$
$$\text{(c)}\quad y = (\sin x)^{-4/3}, \quad \sin x \neq 0.$$

Solution:

$$\frac{d}{dx}\,(x^{p/q}) = \frac{p}{q}\,x^{(p/q)-1}.$$

(a) $y = \sqrt{x} = x^{1/2}$;

$$\frac{dy}{dx} = \frac{1}{2}\,x^{(1/2)-1} = \frac{1}{2}\,x^{-1/2} = \frac{1}{2\sqrt{x}}, \quad x > 0.$$

(b) Use the Chain Rule. Set $y = u^{1/3}$, where $u = x^2 + 1$:

$$\frac{dy}{dx} = \frac{dy}{du}\frac{du}{dx} = \frac{1}{3}\,u^{-2/3}(2x) = \frac{1}{3(x^2 + 1)^{2/3}} \cdot 2x.$$

(c) Use the Chain Rule. Set $y = u^{-4/3}$, where $u = \sin x$:

$$\frac{dy}{dx} = \frac{dy}{du}\frac{du}{dx} = -\frac{4}{3}u^{-7/3}\cos x = -\frac{4}{3}(\sin x)^{-7/3}\cos x, \qquad \sin x \neq 0.$$

Answer:

(a) $\dfrac{1}{2\sqrt{x}}$, $x > 0$;

(b) $\dfrac{2x}{3(x^2+1)^{2/3}}$;

(c) $\dfrac{-4\cos x}{3(\sin x)^{7/3}}$, $\sin x \neq 0$.

EXERCISES

Differentiate:

1. $y = 3x^{1/5}$

2. $y = 2x^{1/2}$

3. $y = (10x)^{1/4}$

4. $y = (3x - 1)^{-5/3}$

5. $y = (x^2 - x + 4)^{7/6}$

6. $y = x + (3/\sqrt{x})$

7. $y = \dfrac{(e^x + 1)^{3/2}}{(e^x - 1)^{1/2}}$

8. $y = (3\cos x)^{3/4}$

9. $y = e^{2\sqrt{x}}$

10. $y = (\sin x + \cos x)^{-2/3}$

11. $y = (\sin x)^{p/8}$

12. $y = (x^2 + 1)^{-p/8}$.

13. Let $f(x) = ax^7$, $a > 0$. Find $\dfrac{d[f^{-1}(x)]}{dx}$.

14. Let $f^{-1}(x) = \dfrac{1}{2}\sqrt[3]{x}$. Find $\dfrac{d[f(x)]}{dx}$.

15. Let $f^{-1}(x) = x^{-5}$. Find $\dfrac{d[f(x)]}{dx}$.

16. Find $\dfrac{d}{dx}(x^{4/3})\Big|_{x=0}$ by use of the *definition*

$$\frac{d}{dx}f(x)\Big|_{x=0} = \lim_{x\to 0}\frac{f(x) - f(0)}{x - 0}.$$

Generalize to $x^{p/q}$ for $\dfrac{p}{q} > 1.$

3. NATURAL LOGARITHMS

In this section we study the inverse of the increasing function $y = e^x$. The inverse is denoted by

$$y = \ln x,$$

and is called the **natural logarithm** function. Figure 3.1 shows the graph of $y = \ln x$ as the reflection of the graph of $y = e^x$ across the line $y = x$.

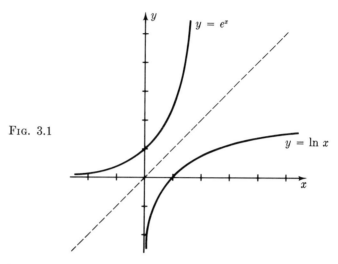

FIG. 3.1

Certain basic properties are immediate from Fig. 3.1.

$\ln x$ is defined only for $x > 0$,

$\ln x$ is an increasing function,

$\ln x < 0 \quad$ for $\quad 0 < x < 1$,

$\ln 1 = 0$,

$\ln x > 0 \quad$ for $\quad x > 1$.

Because $\ln x$ and e^x are inverse functions, two further statements are automatic:

$y = e^x$ is equivalent to $x = \ln y$,

$\ln(e^x) = x$ and $e^{\ln y} = y$.

Be sure that you can derive the second statement from the first.

Since $\ln e^x = x$, you can make $\ln x$ as large as desired by choosing large values of x. For example

$$\ln e^{10} = 10, \qquad \ln e^{100} = 100, \qquad \ln e^{1000} = 1000, \;\cdots\;.$$

Therefore the graph of $y = \ln x$ increases beyond all bounds as x increases (Fig. 3.1). Nevertheless the *rate* of increase is agonizingly slow. Not until $x = e^{10} \approx 22{,}000$ does the curve reach the level $y = 10$; not until $x = e^{100} \approx (2.7)10^{43}$ does it reach the level $y = 100$. Yet it does reach every level eventually:

$$\ln x \longrightarrow \infty \qquad \text{as} \quad x \longrightarrow \infty .$$

Algebraic Properties of ln x

Let us justify the name natural *logarithm* by showing that $\ln x$ behaves the way a logarithm should.

The exponential function e^x has some important algebraic properties:

$$(1) \qquad e^a e^b = e^{a+b},$$

$$(2) \qquad e^{-a} = \frac{1}{e^a},$$

$$(3) \qquad \frac{e^a}{e^b} = e^{a-b},$$

$$(4) \qquad (e^a)^b = e^{ab}.$$

Somehow, these properties ought to rub off onto the inverse function $\ln x$. They do. To see this, set $e^a = x$ and $e^b = y$; that means $a = \ln x$ and $b = \ln y$. Then each of the four statements above can be translated into a statement about $\ln x$ and $\ln y$. For example, property (1) can be translated as follows:

$$e^a e^b = e^{a+b},$$

$$xy = e^{(\ln x + \ln y)}.$$

Hence

$$\ln(xy) = \ln x + \ln y.$$

In a similar way, (2), (3), and (4) can be translated. Here are the results:

$$(1') \qquad \ln(xy) = \ln x + \ln y,$$

$$(2') \qquad \ln \left(\frac{1}{x} \right) = -\ln x,$$

$$(3') \qquad \ln \left(\frac{x}{y} \right) = \ln x - \ln y,$$

$$(4') \qquad \ln x^b = b \ln x.$$

You can make $\ln x$ as large negative as desired by choosing x small. Indeed, as $x \longrightarrow 0$ through positive values, $1/x \longrightarrow \infty$, hence $\ln (1/x) \longrightarrow \infty$.

By (2′),

$$\ln x = - \ln \left(\frac{1}{x}\right) \longrightarrow - \infty.$$

Thus

$$\boxed{\ln x \longrightarrow - \infty \qquad \text{as} \quad x \longrightarrow 0+.}$$

Relation of Natural Logs to Common Logs

Natural logarithms are logarithms to the base e. There is a simple relation between them and logarithms to the base 10. In Chapter 8 it was shown that if $e^k = a$, then

$$k = \frac{\log_{10} a}{\log_{10} e}.$$

But $k = \ln a$. Therefore

$$\ln a = \frac{1}{M} \log_{10} a, \qquad \text{where} \quad M = \log_{10} e \approx 0.43429.$$

Thus natural logs are proportional to common logs, and can be computed from a table of common logs by this formula. Of course tables of natural logs are available.

EXERCISES

Simplify:

1. $\ln e^{a+2}$

2. $e^{\ln x^2}$

3. $e^{-\ln x}$

4. $e^{2 \ln x + 5 \ln y}$

5. $\ln \sqrt{e}$

6. $\ln (1/e^{3/2})$

7. $(\log_2 3)(\log_3 2)$

8. $(\ln 10)(\log_{10} 3)(\log_3 e)$.

Use a common log table to compute to 5 places:

9. $\ln 20$

10. $\ln (0.5)$.

Use a natural log table to compute to 5 significant digits:

11. $\ln \dfrac{(4.71)(2.13)}{(5.09)}$

12. $(\sqrt{9.32})(\sqrt[3]{1.47})$.

13. Given $\ln 2 \approx 0.69$ and $\ln 3 \approx 1.10$. Compute $\ln 12$, $\ln \frac{2}{9}$, $\ln 256$, and $\ln \sqrt{.6}$ to 2 places.

14. Show that the estimate $2 < \ln 10 < 3$ follows from the estimate $2.5 < e < 3$.

15. Find the integer n for which $e^n < 1000 < e^{n+1}$.

16. Find the integer n for which $10^n < e^{100} < 10^{n+1}$.

4. DERIVATIVE OF ln x

The natural logarithm function inherits some useful algebraic properties from e^x. It also inherits a simple derivative:

$$\frac{d}{dx}(\ln x) = \frac{1}{x}, \qquad x > 0.$$

This follows easily from the rule for differentiating inverse functions. Let $f(x) = e^x$ and $g(x) = \ln x$, the inverse function. Then

$$g'(y) = \frac{1}{f'(x)}, \qquad \text{where} \quad y = f(x) = e^x.$$

Since $f'(x) = e^x$,

$$g'(y) = \frac{1}{e^x} = \frac{1}{y} \qquad \text{or} \qquad \frac{d}{dy}(\ln y) = \frac{1}{y}.$$

Thus

$$\frac{d}{dx}(\ln x) = \frac{1}{x}.$$

EXAMPLE 4.1

Find the largest value of $\dfrac{\ln x}{x}$.

Solution: Let $y = (\ln x)/x$. This function is defined for all $x > 0$. Differentiate:

$$\frac{dy}{dx} = \frac{x\dfrac{d}{dx}(\ln x) - (\ln x)\dfrac{d}{dx}(x)}{x^2}$$

$$= \frac{x \cdot \dfrac{1}{x} - \ln x}{x^2} = \frac{1 - \ln x}{x^2}.$$

It follows that

$$\frac{dy}{dx} > 0 \qquad \text{if} \quad \ln x < 1,$$

$$\frac{dy}{dx} = 0 \qquad \text{if} \quad \ln x = 1,$$

$$\frac{dy}{dx} < 0 \qquad \text{if} \quad \ln x > 1.$$

Consequently y is largest when $\ln x = 1$, or $x = e$.

Answer: $\dfrac{\ln e}{e} = \dfrac{1}{e}.$

EXAMPLE 4.2

Which is larger, e^π or π^e?

Solution: Take natural logarithms; the larger number has the larger logarithm:

$$\ln e^\pi = \pi, \qquad \ln \pi^e = e \ln \pi.$$

Now, is $\pi > e \ln \pi$ or is $\pi < e \ln \pi$; expressed differently, is

$$\frac{1}{e} > \frac{\ln \pi}{\pi} \qquad \text{or is} \qquad \frac{1}{e} < \frac{\ln \pi}{\pi}?$$

In the last example it was shown that

$$\frac{1}{e} > \frac{\ln x}{x}$$

for all $x > 0$ except $x = e$. In particular

$$\frac{1}{e} > \frac{\ln \pi}{\pi}.$$

Therefore $\pi > e \ln \pi$, which means

$$\ln e^\pi > \ln \pi^e.$$

Answer: $e^\pi > \pi^e$.

The Derivative of ln f(x)

If $f(x)$ has positive values, then $\ln f(x)$ is defined. The derivative of this function is computed by the Chain Rule. Write $y = \ln u$, where $u = f(x)$. Then

$$\frac{dy}{dx} = \frac{dy}{du}\frac{du}{dx} = \left(\frac{d}{du}\ln u\right)\left(\frac{d}{dx}f(x)\right)$$

$$= \frac{1}{u}f'(x) = \frac{1}{f(x)}f'(x).$$

Hence

$$\frac{d}{dx}[\ln f(x)] = \frac{f'(x)}{f(x)},$$

or

$$\boxed{\frac{d}{dx}(\ln u) = \frac{u'}{u}.}$$

EXAMPLE 4.3

Compute the derivative of $y = \ln(x^2 + 1)$.

Solution:

$$\frac{dy}{dx} = \frac{u'}{u} = \frac{(x^2 + 1)'}{(x^2 + 1)} = \frac{2x}{x^2 + 1}.$$

Answer: $\dfrac{2x}{x^2 + 1}$.

EXAMPLE 4.4

Compute the derivative of $y = \ln\left(\dfrac{1 + 2x}{1 - 2x}\right)$, where $-\dfrac{1}{2} < x < \dfrac{1}{2}$.

Solution:

$$\frac{dy}{dx} = \frac{\dfrac{d}{dx}\left(\dfrac{1 + 2x}{1 - 2x}\right)}{\left(\dfrac{1 + 2x}{1 - 2x}\right)}.$$

Differentiate the quotient in the numerator:

$$\frac{dy}{dx} = \frac{\left(\dfrac{(1 - 2x)2 - (1 + 2x)(-2)}{(1 - 2x)^2}\right)}{\left(\dfrac{1 + 2x}{1 - 2x}\right)}$$

$$= \frac{\left(\dfrac{4}{(1 - 2x)^2}\right)}{\left(\dfrac{1 + 2x}{1 - 2x}\right)} = \frac{4}{(1 - 2x)(1 + 2x)}.$$

Alternate Solution: Use the rules of logarithms before differentiating:

$$y = \ln\left(\frac{1 + 2x}{1 - 2x}\right)$$

$$= \ln(1 + 2x) - \ln(1 - 2x).$$

Now differentiate:

$$\frac{dy}{dx} = \frac{(1 + 2x)'}{(1 + 2x)} - \frac{(1 - 2x)'}{(1 - 2x)}$$

$$= \frac{2}{(1 + 2x)} - \frac{-2}{(1 - 2x)} = \frac{4}{(1 - 2x)(1 + 2x)}.$$

Answer: $\dfrac{4}{(1 - 2x)(1 + 2x)}$.

EXERCISES

Differentiate:

1. $y = \ln 5x$

2. $y = 3 \ln 4x$

3. $y = 2 \ln(x^2)$

4. $y = \ln(x^4)$

5. $y = \ln\left(\dfrac{1}{x}\right)$

6. $y = \ln(x^2 + x)$

7. $y = \ln(\sin x)$

8. $y = \ln(\cos x)$

9. $y = \ln(e^x)$

10. $y = \ln\left(\dfrac{x^2 + 1}{x^2 + 3}\right)$

11. $y = \ln(\ln x)$

12. $y = \sqrt{\ln x}$

13. $y = \dfrac{\ln(x^2 + 1)}{x}$

14. $y = x \ln x - x$

15. $y = (\ln x)^2$

16. $y = \ln(x^2 + x + 10)$

17. $y = \ln[\ln(\ln x)]$

18. $y = \ln\left(\dfrac{x^2}{1 + x^2}\right)$

19. $y = \dfrac{1}{\ln x}$

20. $y = \dfrac{\ln(x + 2)}{\ln(x + 1)}.$

21. Graph $y = \dfrac{\ln x}{x}.$

22. Show that $f(x) = \dfrac{\ln x}{x}$ steadily decreases for $x > e$. Find $\dfrac{d[f^{-1}(x)]}{dx}.$

23. (cont.) Let $e \leq a < b$. Show that $b^a < a^b$.

24. Graph $y = \dfrac{\ln x}{x^2}$ and find the maximum of y.

25. Compute the second derivative of $\ln x$. What information does it give about the shape of the curve $y = \ln x$?

5. LOGARITHMIC DIFFERENTIATION

Differentiation of products, quotients, and powers can often be simplified by taking natural logs before differentiating. Be careful, however, to take logs of positive functions only.

EXAMPLE 5.1

Compute the derivative of $y = \sqrt[3]{\dfrac{x^2 + 3}{x^4 + 1}}.$

Solution: Take the natural log of y and simplify, using rules of logarithms:

$$\ln y = \frac{1}{3} \ln \left(\frac{x^2 + 3}{x^4 + 1} \right)$$

$$= \frac{1}{3} [\ln(x^2 + 3) - \ln(x^4 + 1)].$$

This is legitimate since both $(x^2 + 3)$ and $(x^4 + 1)$ are positive functions. Now differentiate:

$$\frac{y'}{y} = \frac{1}{3} \left(\frac{2x}{x^2 + 3} - \frac{4x^3}{x^4 + 1} \right),$$

$$y' = \frac{y}{3} \left(\frac{2x}{x^2 + 3} - \frac{4x^3}{x^4 + 1} \right).$$

On the right side, replace y by its expression in x.

$$Answer: \quad \frac{1}{3} \left(\sqrt[3]{\frac{x^2 + 3}{x^4 + 1}} \right) \left(\frac{2x}{x^2 + 3} - \frac{4x^3}{x^4 + 1} \right).$$

EXAMPLE 5.2

Compute the derivative of $y = \dfrac{\sqrt{x}\, e^{2x}}{(5x + 1)^2}$ for $x > 0$.

Solution: Take logs and differentiate:

$$\ln y = \frac{1}{2} \ln x + 2x - 2 \ln(5x + 1),$$

$$\frac{y'}{y} = \frac{1}{2x} + 2 - 2 \left(\frac{5}{5x + 1} \right),$$

$$y' = y \left(\frac{1}{2x} + 2 - \frac{10}{5x + 1} \right).$$

$$Answer: \quad \frac{\sqrt{x}\, e^{2x}}{(5x + 1)^2} \left(\frac{1}{2x} + 2 - \frac{10}{5x + 1} \right).$$

The last two examples can be done without logs. Sometimes, however, it is essential to take logs before differentiating.

EXAMPLE 5.3

Compute the derivative of $y = x^x$, $x > 0$.

Solution: Take logs:

$$\ln y = x \ln x.$$

Now differentiate:

$$\frac{y'}{y} = x \frac{d}{dx} (\ln x) + \ln x \frac{d}{dx} (x)$$

$$= x \cdot \frac{1}{x} + \ln x = 1 + \ln x,$$

$$y' = y(1 + \ln x).$$

Answer: $x^x(1 + \ln x)$.

EXERCISES

Differentiate where valid by logarithmic differentiation:

1. $y = (x^3 + 2)^{1/2}$

2. $y = \left(\dfrac{x + 1}{(x + 2)^4} \right)^{1/3}$

3. $y = \left(\dfrac{x^2 + 4}{x + 7} \right)^6$

4. $y = \dfrac{(x + 1)(x + 2)}{(x + 4)(x + 5)}$

5. $y = (2x + 3)^{1/3} e^{-x^2}$

6. $y = \dfrac{x^2 e^{3x^3}}{(x + 3)^2}$

7. $y = x^{x-1}$

8. $y = (x + 2)^{x+3}$

9. $y = x^{1/x}$

10. $y = 2^{2x}$

11. $y = 3^{\ln x}$

12. $y = \left(1 + \dfrac{1}{x} \right)^x$

13. $y = 10^x$

14. $y = x^{x^x}$

15. $y = \dfrac{e^x(x^3 - 1)}{\sqrt{2x + 1}}$

16. $y = \sqrt{\dfrac{x^2 - 1}{x^2 + 1}}$.

6. ANTIDERIVATIVE OF 1/x

The basic formula

$$\frac{d}{dx} (\ln x) = \frac{1}{x}$$

supplies an antiderivative of $1/x$ for $x > 0$: the antiderivative is $\ln x$.

If $x < 0$, then $\ln x$ has no meaning but $\ln(-x)$ does, because $(-x)$ is positive. By the Chain Rule (or Scale Rule),

$$\frac{d}{dx} [\ln(-x)] = -\frac{1}{-x} = \frac{1}{x} \qquad \text{for} \quad x < 0.$$

> An antiderivative of $1/x$ is
>
> $$\ln x, \qquad \text{for} \quad x > 0,$$
>
> $$\ln(-x), \qquad \text{for} \quad x < 0.$$
>
> Stated briefly, an antiderivative of $1/x$ is
>
> $$\ln |x|, \qquad \text{if} \quad x \neq 0.$$

We now have an antiderivative of x^{-1}. Previously we had an antiderivative for any integral power x^n except x^{-1}:

$$x^n = \frac{d}{dx}\left(\frac{x^{n+1}}{n+1}\right), \qquad n \neq -1.$$

Now that gap is filled.

ln x as an Area

Using our new antiderivative, we see that for $x > 0$,

$$\int_1^x \frac{1}{t}\, dt = \ln t \bigg|_1^x = \ln x - \ln 1 = \ln x.$$

Thus $\ln x$ can be expressed as an integral:

$$\ln x = \int_1^x \frac{1}{t}\, dt, \qquad x > 0.$$

This suggests that $\ln x$ can be pictured either as an area (if $x > 1$) or as the negative of an area (if $x < 1$). See Fig. 6.1.

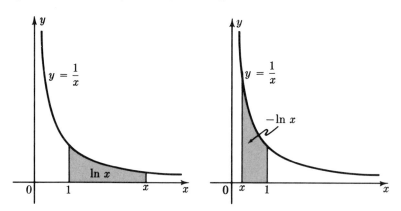

FIG. 6.1a   FIG. 6.1b

REMARK: See Chapter 21, Section 6 where $\ln x$ is introduced by means of the last formula and its properties are derived.

EXERCISES

Find:

1. $\displaystyle\int_{1/5}^{1} \frac{dt}{t}$

2. $\displaystyle\int_{1}^{e^x} \frac{dt}{t}$

3. $\displaystyle\int_{0}^{3} \frac{dt}{t+4}$

4. $\displaystyle\int_{1}^{2} \frac{dt}{t+1}$

5. $\displaystyle\int_3^6 \frac{dx}{2x-5}$

6. $\displaystyle\int_2^3 \frac{dx}{x-1}$

7. $\displaystyle\int_0^1 \frac{dt}{2-t}$

8. $\displaystyle\int_1^2 \frac{dt}{3-t}$

9. $\displaystyle\int_0^1 \frac{dt}{4-3t}$

10. $\displaystyle\int_1^3 \frac{dt}{7-2t}.$

11. Show that $\displaystyle\int_a^b \frac{dx}{x} = \int_{1/b}^{1/a} \frac{dx}{x}$ if $0 < a < b$. Interpret in terms of area.

12. Find the area under $y = \dfrac{1}{3x+4}$ from $x = 0$ to $x = 7$.

13. Find the area under $y = \dfrac{1}{4x-7}$ from $x = 2$ to $x = 5$.

14. Find $\displaystyle\int_2^3 \frac{du}{u^2-1}$. $\left[\text{\textit{Hint:}}\ \dfrac{1}{u^2-1} = \dfrac{1}{2}\left(\dfrac{1}{u-1} - \dfrac{1}{u+1}\right).\right]$

15. Find $\displaystyle\int_3^4 \frac{dx}{x^2-4}$. (See Ex. 14.)   16. Compute $\displaystyle\int_3^5 \frac{x\,dx}{x^2-4}.$

17. Compute $\displaystyle\int_1^5 \frac{x^3 - 2x^2 + 1}{x}\,dx.$

18. Express $\ln \frac{3}{2}$ as an integral and estimate it to 3 places using approximation by areas of rectangles (Ch. 11, Sect. 5) with $\Delta x = 0.1$.

19. Show that the area under the curve $y = 1/x$ between $x = 2$ and $x = 4$ is the same as the area between $x = 50$ and $x = 100$. Find a general principle.

20. Show that $\displaystyle\int_1^{t^2} \frac{1}{x}\,dx = 2\int_1^t \frac{1}{x}\,dx.$

21. Approximate $\displaystyle\int_1^N \frac{1}{x}\,dx$ by areas of rectangles (Ch. 11, Sect. 5) with $\Delta x = 1$. Deduce that

$$1 + \frac{1}{3} + \frac{1}{5} + \cdots \frac{1}{2N-1} \approx 1 + \frac{1}{2}\ln N.$$

Show that

$$1 + \frac{1}{2} + \frac{1}{3} + \cdots + \frac{1}{10,000} \approx 9.71.$$

22. (cont.) Deduce that

$$\frac{1}{2N+1} + \frac{1}{2N+3} + \frac{1}{2N+5} + \cdots + \frac{1}{4N-1} \approx \frac{1}{2}\ln 2.$$

7. RATE OF GROWTH OF ln *x*

The function $\ln x$ increases very slowly as $x \longrightarrow \infty$. To see just how slowly, we shall compare the rate of growth of $\ln x$ with that of other functions.

First of all, ln x grows much slower than x:

$$\frac{\ln x}{x} \longrightarrow 0 \qquad \text{as} \quad x \longrightarrow \infty.$$

To verify this, we study the function $y = (\ln x)/x$. Its derivative is

$$\frac{dy}{dx} = \frac{1 - \ln x}{x^2},$$

which is negative when $\ln x > 1$, that is, when $x > e$. So starting at $x = e$, the curve

$$y = \frac{\ln x}{x}$$

decreases. We must show it decreases toward *zero* as x increases.

Note that

$$\frac{\ln 10}{10} \approx \frac{2.303}{10} < 0.24.$$

Since the curve is decreasing,

$$\frac{\ln x}{x} < 0.24 \qquad \text{for all} \quad x > 10.$$

Similarly,

$$\frac{\ln 100}{100} = \frac{2 \ln 10}{100} < \frac{2(2.4)}{100} = 0.048.$$

Hence,

$$\frac{\ln x}{x} < 0.048 \qquad \text{for all} \quad x > 100.$$

Once more, this time with x *large:*

$$\frac{\ln 10^{100}}{10^{100}} = \frac{100 \ln 10}{10^{100}} < \frac{100(2.4)}{10^{100}} = 2.4 \times 10^{-98}.$$

Consequently,

$$\frac{\ln x}{x} < 2.4 \times 10^{-98} \qquad \text{for all} \quad x > 10^{100}.$$

Thus, x overwhelms $\ln x$ as x increases. Even though both functions become large, x becomes so much larger than $\ln x$ that the ratio $(\ln x)/x$ is as small as you please when x is large enough. Consequently,

$$\frac{\ln x}{x} \longrightarrow 0 \qquad \text{as} \quad x \longrightarrow \infty.$$

Perhaps we have been unrealistic in comparing $\ln x$ with x. Perhaps we should compare $\ln x$ with a smaller function, for example, with $\sqrt{x}$, which is much smaller than x. How does $\ln x$ compare with $\sqrt{x}$ or with $\sqrt[3]{x}$, which is smaller yet? The answer is that any positive power of x overwhelms $\ln x$.

If p is any positive number, then

$$\frac{\ln x}{x^p} \longrightarrow 0 \qquad \text{as} \quad x \longrightarrow \infty.$$

This follows from our study of $(\ln x)/x$. Let $x^p = y$. Then $x = y^{1/p}$ and

$$\frac{\ln x}{x^p} = \frac{\ln y^{1/p}}{y} = \frac{(1/p) \ln y}{y} = \frac{1}{p}\frac{\ln y}{y}.$$

As $x \longrightarrow \infty$, $y \longrightarrow \infty$. Hence $(\ln y)/y \longrightarrow 0$. Therefore

$$\frac{\ln x}{x^p} \longrightarrow 0 \qquad \text{as} \quad x \longrightarrow \infty.$$

As a rough check, let us estimate

$$\frac{\ln x}{\sqrt[3]{x}}$$

for some large values of x.

x	10^3	10^6	10^9	10^{30}	10^{300}
$\dfrac{\ln x}{\sqrt[3]{x}}$ (approx.)	0.69	0.14	0.021	6.9×10^{-9}	6.9×10^{-98}

Thus $\sqrt[3]{x}$ overwhelms $\ln x$ as $x \longrightarrow \infty$.

Not only is $\ln x$ small compared to x, but it is so small that any positive power $(\ln x)^p$ is small compared to x:

If p is any positive number, then

$$\frac{(\ln x)^p}{x} \longrightarrow 0 \qquad \text{as} \quad x \longrightarrow \infty.$$

This is just a variant of the statement that $(\ln x)/x^p \longrightarrow 0$ as $x \longrightarrow \infty$, with p replaced by $1/p$. In fact, since $1/p$ is positive,

$$\frac{\ln x}{x^{1/p}} \longrightarrow 0 \qquad \text{as} \quad x \longrightarrow \infty.$$

Therefore

$$\left(\frac{\ln x}{x^{1/p}}\right)^p \longrightarrow 0 \qquad \text{as} \quad x \longrightarrow \infty,$$

that is,

$$\frac{(\ln x)^p}{x} \longrightarrow 0 \qquad \text{as} \quad x \longrightarrow \infty.$$

Thus x overwhelms not only $\ln x$, but also any positive power of $\ln x$.
As a check, let us estimate

$$\frac{(\ln x)^5}{x}$$

for some large values of x.

x	10	10^2	10^3	10^4	10^5	10^6	10^{10}	10^{20}	10^{100}
$\dfrac{(\ln x)^5}{x}$ (approx.)	6.5	20.7	15.7	6.6	2.0	0.50	6.5×10^{-4}	2.1×10^{-12}	6.5×10^{-89}

Thus x eventually overwhelms $(\ln x)^5$.

REMARK: For rigorous proofs, see Chapter 21, Section 6.

EXERCISES

Find:

1. $\displaystyle \lim_{x \to \infty} \frac{x}{10^6 \ln x}$

2. $\displaystyle \lim_{x \to \infty} \frac{(x + 1) \ln x}{x^2}$

3. $\displaystyle \lim_{x \to \infty} \frac{(\ln x)^3}{x^{1/4}}$

4. $\displaystyle \lim_{x \to \infty} \frac{\log_{10} x}{x}$

5. $\displaystyle \lim_{x \to \infty} \frac{x^2 + 1}{x(\ln x)^2}$

6. $\displaystyle \lim_{x \to 0} [x \ln x]$ (*Hint:* Let $x = 1/y$.)

7. $\displaystyle \lim_{x \to 0} [x(\ln x)^{20}]$

8. $\displaystyle \lim_{x \to \infty} \frac{x \ln x}{x^p + 1}$ $(p > 1)$

9. $\displaystyle \lim_{x \to \infty} \frac{3(\ln x)^2 + 1}{x}$

10. $\displaystyle \lim_{x \to \infty} \frac{x^2(\ln x)^3}{x^3 \ln x + 1}.$

11. Let $p > 0$ and $q > 0$. Prove $\displaystyle \lim_{x \to \infty} \frac{(\ln x)^p}{x^q} = 0.$

12. For $p > 0$ and $q > 0$, find the maximum value of $f(x) = \dfrac{(\ln x)^p}{x^q}$, and the value
of x at which it occurs.

13. (cont.) Estimate the order of magnitude of this x for $p = 10^5$ and $q = 10^{-5}$.

14. For what values of x can you be sure that $\dfrac{\ln x}{x} < 10^{-10}$?

15. For what values of x can you be sure that $\dfrac{(\ln x)^2}{x} < 10^{-10}$?

16. Graph $y = x^x$ for $x > 0$. Find its minimum.

17. Graph $y = x^{1/x}$ for $x > 0$. Find its maximum.

8. RATE OF GROWTH OF e^x

The graphs of $\ln x$ and e^x are mirror images (Fig. 3.1). We know

$$\ln x \longrightarrow \infty \qquad \text{as} \quad x \longrightarrow \infty,$$

but the rate of growth is extremely slow. Since $\ln x$ increases very slowly, e^x ought to increase very rapidly. It does; we can show that as $x \longrightarrow \infty$, e^x eventually overwhelms x^p for any p.

If p is any positive number, then

$$\frac{e^x}{x^p} \longrightarrow \infty \qquad \text{as} \quad x \longrightarrow \infty.$$

A number is large if its natural logarithm is large. Observe

$$\ln\left(\frac{e^x}{x^p}\right) = \ln e^x - \ln x^p = x - p \ln x.$$

We know that $\ln x$ is much smaller than x. To emphasize this, we write

$$\ln\left(\frac{e^x}{x^p}\right) = x\left(1 - \frac{p \ln x}{x}\right).$$

Since

$$\frac{\ln x}{x} \longrightarrow 0 \qquad \text{as} \quad x \longrightarrow \infty,$$

the second term in the parentheses is less than $\frac{1}{2}$ once x is large enough. Hence,

$$\ln\left(\frac{e^x}{x^p}\right) > \frac{1}{2} x$$

for x large. Consequently,

$$\ln\left(\frac{e^x}{x^p}\right) \longrightarrow \infty \qquad \text{as} \quad x \longrightarrow \infty,$$

which implies

$$\frac{e^x}{x^p} \longrightarrow \infty \qquad \text{as} \quad x \longrightarrow \infty.$$

As an example, we compute

$$\frac{e^x}{x^{10}}$$

for some values of x.

x	5	10	20	30	40	50	100	1000
$\dfrac{e^x}{x^{10}} \approx$	1.5×10^{-5}	2×10^{-6}	5×10^{-5}	0.018	22.4	5.3×10^4	2.7×10^{23}	2.0×10^{404}

After a slow start, e^x overwhelms x^{10}.

We repeat the two basic facts concerning rate of growth of the logarithm and exponential functions.

$$
\begin{cases}
\text{If } p \text{ is any positive number, then} \\[1em]
\dfrac{\ln x}{x^p} \longrightarrow 0 \\[2em]
\hspace{3em} \text{as} \quad x \longrightarrow \infty. \\[1em]
\dfrac{e^x}{x^p} \longrightarrow \infty
\end{cases}
$$

See Chapter 21, Section 6 for further discussion.

EXERCISES

Find:

1. $\displaystyle\lim_{x \to \infty} \frac{x^4}{e^x}$

2. $\displaystyle\lim_{x \to \infty} \frac{x^7 e^x}{e^{2x} + 3}$

3. $\displaystyle\lim_{x \to \infty} \frac{e^{x+1} - e^x}{e^x - x}$

4. $\displaystyle\lim_{x \to \infty} \frac{1 + \ln x}{e^{2x}}$.

5. Show that $x^{-10} e^{\sqrt[3]{x}}$ increases towards ∞ as $x \longrightarrow \infty$.

6. Let $f(x) = e^x/x^p$, where $p > 0$. Show that $f'(x) \longrightarrow \infty$ as $x \longrightarrow \infty$.

7. Graph $y = e^x/x$.

8. Find the smallest value of e^x/x^{10}.

9. According to our results $e^x/x^{100} \longrightarrow \infty$ as $x \longrightarrow \infty$. Yet when $x = 100$, its value is $\approx 2.7 \times 10^{-157}$. Is that a contradiction?

10. Verify that $e^7 \approx 10^3$. This is useful in making rough approximations. Use it to get a quick estimate of e^{23}. Find a similar relation between a power of 2 and a power of 10.

11. Arrange these functions in order of their size as $x \longrightarrow \infty$: $e^x, e^{10x}, e^{x^2}, e^{e^x}, x^3, 10^x$.

12. Find some functions that increase to infinity as $x \longrightarrow \infty$, but much slower than $\ln x$.

15. Trigonometric Functions

1. BASIC PROPERTIES

In this chapter, it is assumed you are familiar with the functions $\sin x$ and $\cos x$. It will help to review Chapter 7.

Recall the definitions of the other trigonometric functions:

$$\tan x = \frac{\sin x}{\cos x}, \qquad \sec x = \frac{1}{\cos x},$$

$$\cot x = \frac{\cos x}{\sin x}, \qquad \csc x = \frac{1}{\sin x}.$$

(NOTE: The cotangent function is sometimes written ctn x.)

Here are some basic properties of these functions.

(1) *Periods.* The functions $\sin x$ and $\cos x$ are periodic with period 2π:

$$\sin(x + 2\pi) = \sin x, \qquad \cos(x + 2\pi) = \cos x.$$

The other four trigonometric functions are defined in terms of $\sin x$ and $\cos x$. They inherit the period 2π. For example,

$$\sec(x + 2\pi) = \frac{1}{\cos(x + 2\pi)} = \frac{1}{\cos x} = \sec x.$$

About $\tan x$ and $\cot x$, more can be said. Recall that

$$\sin(x + \pi) = -\sin x, \qquad \cos(x + \pi) = -\cos x.$$

Therefore,

$$\tan(x + \pi) = \frac{\sin(x + \pi)}{\cos(x + \pi)} = \frac{-\sin x}{-\cos x} = \tan x.$$

Thus $\tan x$ has period π and the same is true of $\cot x$.

> The functions $\sin x$, $\cos x$, $\sec x$, and $\csc x$ have period 2π. The functions $\tan x$ and $\cot x$ have period π.

(2) *Parity.* Recall that $\sin(-x) = -\sin x$ and $\cos(-x) = \cos x$. It follows that

$$\tan(-x) = -\tan x, \qquad \sec(-x) = \sec x,$$

$$\cot(-x) = -\cot x, \qquad \csc(-x) = -\csc x.$$

A function $f(x)$ is an **even function** if $f(-x) = f(x)$. A function $f(x)$ is an **odd function** if $f(-x) = -f(x)$.

> The functions cos x and sec x are even functions. The functions sin x, tan x, cot x, and csc x are odd functions.

Do not assume that every function is either odd or even. For example, $x^2 + 2x$ and sin x + cos x are neither odd nor even.

The graph of an even function is symmetric about the y-axis; examples are $y = x^2$ and $y = \cos x$. The graph of an odd function is symmetric through the origin; examples are $y = x^3$ and $y = \sin x$. See Fig. 1.1.

The evenness or oddness of a function is called its **parity.**

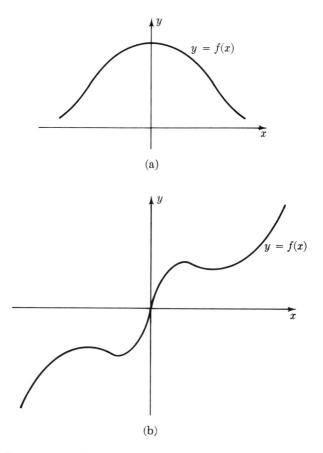

(a)

(b)

FIG. 1.1   (a) Graph of an even function: $f(x) = f(-x)$.
(b) Graph of an odd function: $f(x) = -f(-x)$.

(3) *Domain of definition.* The functions sin x and cos x are defined for all x. Because of zeros in the denominators, tan x and sec x are not defined where cos $x = 0$: at $\pm\pi/2$, $\pm3\pi/2$, $\pm5\pi/2$, etc. Similarly, cot x and csc x are not defined where sin $x = 0$: at 0, $\pm\pi$, $\pm2\pi$, etc.

Graphs of Trigonometric Functions

Let us graph $y = \tan x$. We know that tan x is an odd function and has period π. It suffices to sketch the curve from 0 to $\pi/2$; the graph can than be extended by oddness and periodicity.

Since

$$\tan x = \frac{\sin x}{\cos x},$$

tan $x \geq 0$ for $0 \leq x < \pi/2$. Furthermore, as x increases from 0 toward $\pi/2$, the numerator increases starting at 0, while the denominator decreases from 1 to 0. Therefore as x increases starting at 0, the function tan x increases starting at 0; as $x \longrightarrow \pi/2$, then tan $x \longrightarrow \infty$. Near $x = 0$ however, sin $x \approx x$ and cos $x \approx 1$. Therefore tan $x \approx x$; the graph has slope 1 at the

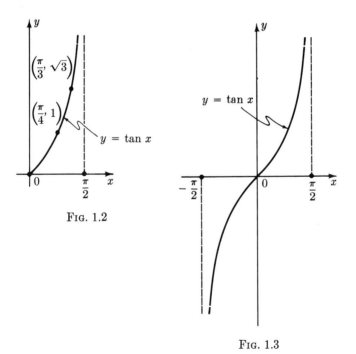

FIG. 1.2

FIG. 1.3

origin (Fig. 1.2). By the oddness of tan x, we extend the graph from 0 to $-\pi/2$. See Fig. 1.3. Since tan x has period π, the curve in Fig. 1.3 can be extended indefinitely (Fig. 1.4).

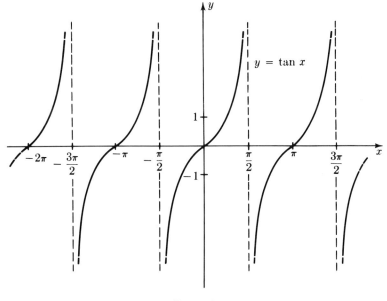

Fig. 1.4

By a similar argument, we obtain the graph of cot x. See Fig. 1.5. In each period of length π, both tan x and cot x take every value once.

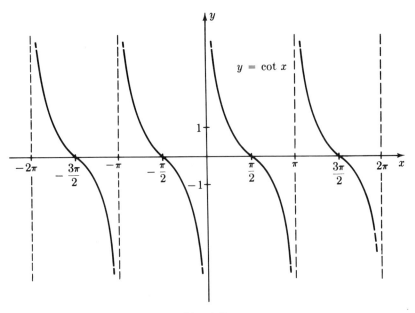

Fig. 1.5

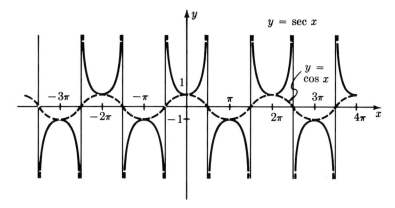

FIG. 1.6

The graphs of sec x and csc x are sketched by taking reciprocals of cos x and sin x. See Figs. 1.6 and 1.7. Both sec x and csc x take all values except those between -1 and $+1$; in other words $|\sec x| \geq 1$ and $|\csc x| \geq 1$.

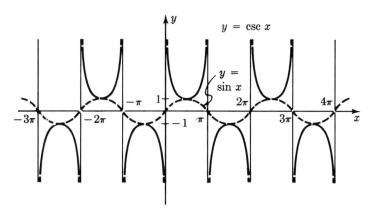

FIG. 1.7

EXERCISES

Find the least period:

1. $\sin 2x$

2. $\tan 3x$

3. $\sin 2\pi x$

4. $\cot x + \csc x$

5. $3 \sec \pi x + \cos \pi x$

6. $3 \cos 2\pi x - 5 \sin 2\pi x$

7. $(\sin x)^{-2}$

8. $\sqrt{1 + \cos \dfrac{x}{2}}$

9. $\sin x \sin 3x$

10. $\tan x + \tan\left(x - \dfrac{\pi}{6}\right)$

11. $\sin 3x + \cos 4x$

12. $\sin x + \cos \dfrac{x}{3}$.

Find the parity:

13. $\sin 2x$

14. $\cot 3x$

15. $\left(x + \dfrac{1}{x}\right) \sin x$

16. $x \sin^3 x + 2 \cos x$

17. $e^x - e^{-x}$

18. $\tan(x^2)$

19. $x^2 + x$

20. $\dfrac{\sin x}{x}$.

21. There are some simple rules of parity in the multiplication of integers:

$$\text{even} \cdot \text{even} = \text{even}, \quad \text{even} \cdot \text{odd} = \text{even}, \quad \text{odd} \cdot \text{odd} = \text{odd}.$$

Do the same rules hold in the multiplication of functions?

22. If $f(x)$ is an odd function, show that $f(0) = 0$.

Graph:

23. $y = \tan 3x$

24. $y = \cot 4x$

25. $y = 2 \sec 2\pi x$

26. $y = \csc\left(x - \dfrac{\pi}{4}\right)$

27. $y = \sec x - \csc x$

28. $y = \tan 2x + \cot 2x$

29. $y = \sec^2 x$

30. $y = \sec^3 x$.

2. IDENTITIES

The most common identity relating trigonometric functions is

$$\sin^2 x + \cos^2 x = 1.$$

Dividing both sides first by $\cos^2 x$ and then by $\sin^2 x$, we obtain two identities:

$$\tan^2 x + 1 = \sec^2 x,$$
$$\cot^2 x + 1 = \csc^2 x.$$

These formulas are helpful in expressing one trigonometric function in terms of another. For example,

$$\sin x = \pm \sqrt{1 - \cos^2 x},$$
$$\sec x = \pm \sqrt{\tan^2 x + 1},$$
$$\cot x = \pm \sqrt{\csc^2 x - 1} = \pm \frac{\sqrt{1 - \sin^2 x}}{\sin x}.$$

In each case, some additional information is needed in order to choose the correct sign.

> **EXAMPLE 2.1**
>
> Express $\sin \alpha$ and $\cos \alpha$ in terms of $\tan \alpha$ for $0 < \alpha < \dfrac{\pi}{2}$.

Solution:

$$\cos \alpha = \frac{1}{\sec \alpha} = \frac{1}{\pm \sqrt{\tan^2 \alpha + 1}},$$

$$\sin \alpha = \tan \alpha \cdot \cos \alpha = \frac{\tan \alpha}{\pm \sqrt{\tan^2 \alpha + 1}}.$$

Since $\sin \alpha$, $\cos \alpha$, and $\tan \alpha$ are positive for $0 < \alpha < \pi/2$, choose the positive square root.

> *Answer:* For $0 < \alpha < \dfrac{\pi}{2}$,
>
> $$\sin \alpha = \frac{\tan \alpha}{\sqrt{\tan^2 \alpha + 1}};$$
>
> $$\cos \alpha = \frac{1}{\sqrt{\tan^2 \alpha + 1}}.$$

Addition Formulas

The next most important identities are the **addition formulas**:

$$\sin(x + y) = \sin x \cos y + \cos x \sin y,$$

$$\cos(x + y) = \cos x \cos y - \sin x \sin y.$$

(These are probably familiar from Trigonometry; a derivation is given in Chapter 21, Section 7, p. 578.   See also Exs. 4, 6, p. 105.)

A number of related identities are derived from the addition formulas. If y is replaced by $-y$, there follow easily

$$\sin(x - y) = \sin x \cos y - \cos x \sin y,$$

$$\cos(x - y) = \cos x \cos y + \sin x \sin y.$$

If $y = x$, the addition formulas yield the **double angle formulas**:

$$\sin 2x = 2 \sin x \cos x,$$

$$\cos 2x = \cos^2 x - \sin^2 x.$$

The latter formula has alternate forms, obtained on replacing $\cos^2 x$ by $1 - \sin^2 x$, or $\sin^2 x$ by $1 - \cos^2 x$:

$$\cos 2x = 1 - 2 \sin^2 x,$$

$$\cos 2x = 2 \cos^2 x - 1.$$

From these follow the identities

$$\sin^2 x = \frac{1}{2} (1 - \cos 2x),$$

$$\cos^2 x = \frac{1}{2} (1 + \cos 2x).$$

EXAMPLE 2.2

Find an antiderivative of $\cos^2 x$.

Solution: According to the preceding identity,

$$\cos^2 x = \frac{1}{2} (1 + \cos 2x).$$

An antiderivative of $\frac{1}{2}$ is $\frac{1}{2}x$; an antiderivative of $\frac{1}{2} \cos 2x$ is $\frac{1}{4} \sin 2x$.

Answer: $\dfrac{1}{2} x + \dfrac{1}{4} \sin 2x.$

EXAMPLE 2.3

Compute the derivative of $y = \sin x \cos x$.

Solution: By the Product Rule,

$$\frac{dy}{dx} = \sin x \frac{d}{dx} (\cos x) + \cos x \frac{d}{dx} (\sin x)$$

$$= (\sin x) (- \sin x) + \cos x (\cos x)$$

$$= \cos^2 x - \sin^2 x.$$

Alternate Solution: By the double angle formula, $\sin x \cos x = \frac{1}{2} \sin 2x$. By the Chain Rule,

$$\frac{dy}{dx} = \frac{d}{dx} \left(\frac{1}{2} \sin 2x \right) = \frac{1}{2} (\cos 2x) \cdot 2 = \cos 2x.$$

Note that the two answers agree: $\cos 2x = \cos^2 x - \sin^2 x$.

Answer: $\cos 2x.$

EXERCISES

1. Suppose $0 < x < \pi/2$. Express $\sin x$ in terms of
   (a) $\cot x$ (b) $\sec x$.

2. Express $\cos(x - \pi/3)$ in terms of $\sin x$ and $\cos x$.

3. Express $\cot^2 x$ in terms of $\cos^2 x$.

4. Express $\sin 3x$ in terms of $\sin x$. [*Hint:* $\sin 3x = \sin(2x + x)$.]

5. Express $\cos^4 x$ in terms of $\cos 2x$.

6. Show that $\tan 2x = \dfrac{2 \tan x}{1 - \tan^2 x}$.

7. Using two different identities, show that

$$\sin 15° = \tfrac{1}{4}(\sqrt{6} - \sqrt{2}) = \tfrac{1}{2}\sqrt{2 - \sqrt{3}}.$$

8. Compute the derivative of $\cos^2 x - \sin^2 x$ in two different ways.

9. Show that $\tan x/2 = \pm\sqrt{\dfrac{1 - \cos x}{1 + \cos x}}$, where the sign is $+$ if $0 < x < \pi$ and $-$ if $-\pi < x < 0$.

10. Prove that $\cos x \cos y = \tfrac{1}{2}[\cos(x + y) + \cos(x - y)]$.

11. Find similar formulas for $\sin x \cos y$ and $\sin x \sin y$.

12. Prove that

$$\cos x \cos 2x \cos 4x \cos 8x$$
$$= \frac{1}{8}(\cos x + \cos 3x + \cos 5x + \cdots + \cos 13x + \cos 15x).$$

3. DERIVATIVES

The basic differentiation formulas are these:

$$\frac{d}{dx}(\sin x) = \cos x \qquad\qquad \frac{d}{dx}(\cot x) = -\csc^2 x$$

$$\frac{d}{dx}(\cos x) = -\sin x \qquad\qquad \frac{d}{dx}(\sec x) = \sec x \tan x$$

$$\frac{d}{dx}(\tan x) = \sec^2 x \qquad\qquad \frac{d}{dx}(\csc x) = -\csc x \cot x.$$

The first two formulas are known; the rest follow easily. For example,

$$\frac{d}{dx}(\cot x) = \frac{d}{dx}\left(\frac{\cos x}{\sin x}\right) = \frac{-\sin^2 x - \cos^2 x}{\sin^2 x} = \frac{-1}{\sin^2 x} = -\csc^2 x;$$

$$\frac{d}{dx}(\csc x) = \frac{d}{dx}\left(\frac{1}{\sin x}\right) = \frac{-\cos x}{\sin^2 x} = -\csc x \cot x.$$

We look next at some useful relations between the trigonometric functions and their derivatives. If $y = \sin x$, then

$$\frac{dy}{dx} = \cos x = \pm \sqrt{1 - \sin^2 x} = \pm \sqrt{1 - y^2}.$$

For $-\pi/2 \le x \le \pi/2$, we choose the positive square root since $\cos x \ge 0$. Thus $y = \sin x$ satisfies the differential equation

$$\frac{dy}{dx} = \sqrt{1 - y^2}, \qquad -\frac{\pi}{2} \le x \le \frac{\pi}{2}.$$

By similar reasoning, we see that $y = \tan x$ satisfies the differential equation

$$\frac{dy}{dx} = 1 + y^2.$$

Indeed,

$$\frac{d}{dx}(\tan x) = \sec^2 x = 1 + \tan^2 x.$$

Similarly, $y = \sec x$ satisfies

$$\frac{dy}{dx} = \begin{cases} y\sqrt{y^2 - 1}, & 0 \le x < \dfrac{\pi}{2}, \\[2mm] -y\sqrt{y^2 - 1}, & -\dfrac{\pi}{2} < x \le 0. \end{cases}$$

EXERCISES

Differentiate:

1. $\sin \dfrac{x}{3}$

2. $\tan 10x$

3. $\cos^3 x$

4. $\sec^2 x$

5. $x \cot 2x$

6. $\sec \dfrac{1}{x}$

7. $\sqrt{2 - \csc^2 x}$

8. $\sin 3x + \cos 4x$

9. $\left(1 + \cos^5 \dfrac{x}{3}\right)^2$

10. $e^{-x} \csc x$

11. $\dfrac{1 + \sin x}{1 - \sin x}$

12. $\dfrac{1}{3 + \cos^2 5x}$

13. $\sec^3(2x^2)$

14. $e^{\sin 3x}$.

15. Find the 42nd derivative of $\sin x$.

16. Verify the formulas given in the text for the derivatives of $\tan x$ and $\sec x$.

17. Express $d(\csc x)/dx$ in terms of $\csc x$ for $0 < x < \pi/2$; thus find a differential equation which $\csc x$ satisfies.

18. Find a differential equation satisfied by $f(x) = 5 \sin 2x - \cos 2x$. (*Hint:* Differentiate twice.)

Use trigonometric identities to verify the formula:

19. $\dfrac{d}{dx} (\sec^4 x - \tan^4 x) = 4 \sec^2 x \tan x$

20. $\dfrac{d}{dx} (x - \sin x) = 2 \sin^2 \dfrac{x}{2}$

21. $\dfrac{d}{dx} (x + \sec x - \tan x) = \dfrac{\sin x}{1 + \sin x}.$

22. Verify that $\sin^2 x$ and $-\cos^2 x$ have identical derivatives. Does that mean that $\sin^2 x = -\cos^2 x$; if not, what does it mean?

4. APPLICATIONS

EXAMPLE 4.1

A point P moves counterclockwise at a constant speed around a circle of radius 50 ft, making 1 rpm. The tangent at P crosses the line $\overline{OA}$ at a point T. See Fig. 4.1. Compute the speed of T when $\theta = \pi/4$.

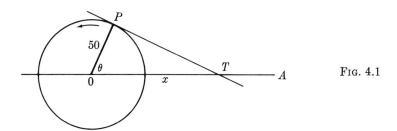

FIG. 4.1

Solution: We are given $d\theta/dt = 2\pi$ rad/min. We are asked to find dx/dt where $x = \overline{OT}$. A relation between θ and x is seen from the right triangle OPT, namely, $x = 50 \sec \theta$. Differentiating with respect to t:

$$\frac{dx}{dt} = 50 \sec \theta \tan \theta \frac{d\theta}{dt}.$$

When $\theta = \pi/4$, $\sec \theta = \sqrt{2}$ and $\tan \theta = 1$. Hence $dx/dt = 50 \sqrt{2} \cdot 2\pi$.

Answer: $100\pi \sqrt{2}$ ft/min.

EXAMPLE 4.2

A lighthouse stands 2 mi off a long straight shore, opposite a point *P*. Its light rotates counterclockwise at the constant rate of 1 rpm. How fast is the beam moving along the shore as it passes a point 3 mi to the right of *P*?

Solution: Set up axes with *P* at the origin and *x*-axis along the shore (Fig. 4.2a). The beam hits the shore at *x*. The rate of change of the angle θ is given:

$$\dot{\theta} = 2\pi \text{ rad/min.}$$

The problem: compute the derivative $\dot{x}$ at the instant when $x = 3$.

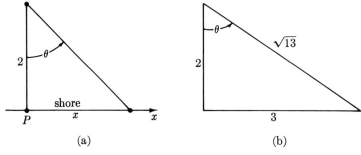

FIG. 4.2

There is a relation between *x* and θ suggested by the figure:

$$\frac{x}{2} = \tan \theta \qquad \text{or} \qquad x = 2 \tan \theta.$$

Now compute $\dot{x}$ by the Chain Rule:

$$\dot{x} = \frac{dx}{d\theta} \dot{\theta} = (2 \sec^2 \theta)(2\pi) = 4\pi \sec^2 \theta.$$

At the instant in question, $x = 3$. From Fig. 4.2b, $\sec \theta = \frac{1}{2}\sqrt{13}$. Hence

$$\dot{x} = 4\pi \left(\frac{13}{4}\right) = 13\pi.$$

Answer: 13π mi/min.

EXAMPLE 4.3

A 5-ft fence stands 4 ft from a house. What is the angle of inclination of the shortest ladder that can stand outside the fence and lean against the wall?

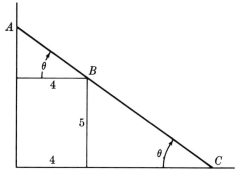

FIG. 4.3

Solution: Draw a diagram (Fig. 4.3). If θ is near 0 or near $\pi/2$, the ladder will be long. The best angle θ is probably near $\pi/4$.

Let L be the length of the ladder,

$$L = \overline{AB} + \overline{BC} = 4 \sec \theta + 5 \csc \theta.$$

The problem: find the angle θ in the range $0 < \theta < \pi/2$ that minimizes $L = L(\theta)$. Now

$$\frac{dL}{d\theta} = 4 \sec \theta \tan \theta - 5 \csc \theta \cot \theta$$

$$= 4 \frac{1}{\cos \theta} \frac{\sin \theta}{\cos \theta} - 5 \frac{1}{\sin \theta} \frac{\cos \theta}{\sin \theta}$$

$$= \frac{4 \sin^3 \theta - 5 \cos^3 \theta}{\sin^2 \theta \cos^2 \theta}.$$

As θ increases, the numerator changes from negative to zero to positive. Hence, L is minimized for just one value of θ:

$$\frac{dL}{d\theta} = 0 \quad \text{if} \quad 4 \sin^3 \theta = 5 \cos^3 \theta, \quad \text{that is,} \quad \tan^3 \theta = \tfrac{5}{4}.$$

Answer: The angle θ whose tangent is $\sqrt[3]{\tfrac{5}{4}} \approx 1.077$. From tables, $\theta \approx 47°8'$.

(A similar problem was discussed in Example 3.2, Chapter 10, p. 247.)

EXAMPLE 4.4

A man is in a rowboat 1 mi off shore. His home is 5 mi farther along the shore. If he can walk twice as fast as he can row, what is his quickest way home?

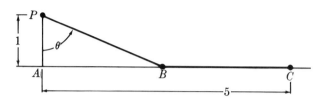

Fig. 4.4

Solution: Draw a diagram (Fig. 4.4). He should row to a point B, then walk to his home at C. Express everything in terms of the angle θ:

$$\overline{PB} = \sec \theta, \qquad \overline{BC} = 5 - \overline{AB} = 5 - \tan \theta.$$

Let s be his rowing speed and $2s$ his walking speed. The time required to reach home is

$$t = \frac{\overline{PB}}{s} + \frac{\overline{BC}}{2s} = \frac{\sec \theta}{s} + \frac{5 - \tan \theta}{2s}.$$

Since B must be between A and C, angle θ is at least 0 and at most the angle whose tangent is 5.

$$\frac{dt}{d\theta} = \frac{\sec \theta \tan \theta}{s} - \frac{\sec^2 \theta}{2s}$$

$$= \frac{\sin \theta}{s \cos^2 \theta} - \frac{1}{2s \cos^2 \theta} = \frac{2 \sin \theta - 1}{2s \cos^2 \theta}.$$

The derivative is 0 if $\sin \theta = \frac{1}{2}$, that is $\theta = \pi/6$. Its sign changes from minus to plus as θ increases through $\pi/6$. Hence t has its minimum at $\theta = \pi/6$. Notice that $\pi/6$ falls within the required range of θ because $\tan \pi/6 < 5$.

> *Answer:* The man should row to shore at an angle $\theta = \pi/6$ then walk the rest of the way (Fig. 4.4).

EXAMPLE 4.5

Describe the isosceles triangle of smallest area that circumscribes a circle of radius r.

Solution: Draw a few pictures (Fig. 4.5). If the triangle is too thin (Fig. 4.5a) or too wide (Fig. 4.5b), its area is unnecessarily large. The most efficient choice seems to be in between, perhaps equilateral (Fig. 4.5c).

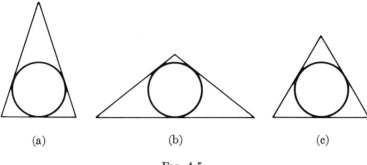

Fɪɢ. 4.5

Let 2θ be the apex angle, and express the area of the triangle in terms of θ. See Fig. 4.6.

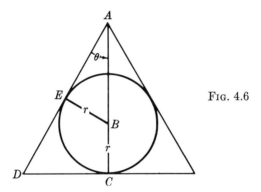

Fɪɢ. 4.6

$$\text{Area} = \frac{1}{2} \text{ base} \cdot \text{height} = \overline{CD} \cdot \overline{AC}.$$

Now $\overline{AC} = \overline{AB} + \overline{BC} = r \csc \theta + r$. From triangle ACD, observe that $\overline{CD} = \overline{AC} \tan \theta = (r \csc \theta + r) \tan \theta$. Therefore

$$\text{Area} = A(\theta) = (r \csc \theta + r)^2 \tan \theta$$
$$= r^2(\csc \theta + 1)^2 \tan \theta.$$

The function $A(\theta)$ is to be minimized. The range of θ is $0 < \theta < \pi/2$; there are no end points to consider.

$$\frac{dA}{d\theta} = r^2 \left[(\csc \theta + 1)^2 \frac{d}{d\theta} (\tan \theta) + \tan \theta \frac{d}{d\theta} (\csc \theta + 1)^2 \right]$$

$$= r^2[(\csc \theta + 1)^2 \sec^2 \theta + \tan \theta \cdot 2(\csc \theta + 1)(-\csc \theta \cot \theta)]$$

$$= r^2(\csc \theta + 1)[(\csc \theta + 1) \sec^2 \theta - 2 \csc \theta].$$

In the range $0 < \theta < \pi/2$, $\csc \theta + 1$ is positive. Hence, $dA/d\theta = 0$ if

$$(\csc \theta + 1) \sec^2 \theta - 2 \csc \theta = 0.$$

Multiply through by $\sin \theta \cos^2 \theta$:

$$1 + \sin \theta - 2 \cos^2 \theta = 0,$$

$$2 \sin^2 \theta + \sin \theta - 1 = 0,$$

$$(2 \sin \theta - 1)(\sin \theta + 1) = 0.$$

Therefore

$$\sin \theta = \frac{1}{2} \quad \text{or} \quad \sin \theta = -1.$$

Since $0 < \theta < \pi/2$, the case $\sin \theta = -1$ is irrelevant. Hence, the minimum occurs for $\sin \theta = \frac{1}{2}$, i.e., for $\theta = \pi/6$. It follows that the desired triangle is equilateral. Its side is

$$2\overline{CD} = 2r\left(\csc \frac{\pi}{6} + 1\right) \tan \frac{\pi}{6} = 2r(2 + 1)\frac{1}{\sqrt{3}} = 2r\sqrt{3}.$$

Answer: An equilateral triangle of side $2r\sqrt{3}$.

REMARK: For physical reasons we were so confident that $A(\theta)$ had a *minimum* at $\pi/6$ (not a maximum or neither) we did not check. Actually the check is easy. Rather than setting the derivative equal to zero immediately, we can express it in the form

$$\frac{dA}{d\theta} = r^2(\csc \theta + 1) \frac{(2 \sin \theta - 1)(\sin \theta + 1)}{\cos^2 \theta \sin \theta}.$$

All factors are positive throughout the interval $0 < \theta < \pi/2$ except $(2 \sin \theta - 1)$. Hence the sign of $dA/d\theta$ is the same as the sign of $(2 \sin \theta - 1)$, which changes from minus to plus as θ increases through $\pi/6$. Thus $A(\theta)$ definitely has a minimum at $\pi/6$.

EXERCISES

1. Sketch the curve $y = 2 \sin x + \cos 2x$ for $0 \le x \le \pi/2$. Indicate the maximum and minimum points.

2. A point P moves at the rate of 3 rpm counterclockwise around the circle of radius 50 ft centered at the origin. Determine how fast the distance between P and the point $(50\sqrt{2}, 0)$ is increasing when $\theta = 3\pi/4$. See Fig. 4.7.

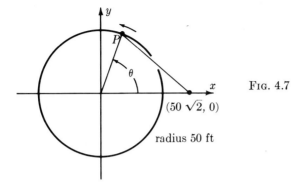

$(50 \sqrt{2}, 0)$

radius 50 ft

FIG. 4.7

3. The equal sides of an isosceles triangle are 10 in. If the vertex angle is increasing 1°/sec, how fast is the area of the triangle changing when the vertex angle is 45°? When is the area greatest?

4. A point P_1 moves around a circle of radius 3 ft at a steady rate of 2 rpm. A point P_2 moves in the same sense around a concentric circle of radius 5 ft at a steady rate of 1 rpm. If the points are 2 ft apart at $t = 0$, when is the first time their separation will be maximal?

5. A sector is cut from a circular piece of paper. The remaining paper is formed into a cone by joining together the edges of the sector without overlap. Find the sector angle that maximizes the volume of the cone.

6. An 8-ft ladder leans against a 4-ft fence. What is the largest horizontal distance the ladder can reach beyond the fence?
   (*Hint:* Use the angle between the ladder and the ground as the variable.)

7. A weight hangs at the end of an 8-ft rope rigged up by the pulley system shown in Fig. 4.8. The pulleys A and B are stationary and 2 ft apart on the same level. The pulley at C is moveable. The weight hangs as far below the level of A and B as possible. How far is that? (Ignore the small pulley diameters.)

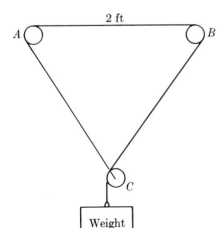

FIG. 4.8

8. A low-flying jet passes 450 ft directly over an observer on the ground. Shortly its angle of elevation is 30° and decreasing at the rate of 20°/sec. Compute the plane's speed.

9. Suppose Fig. 4.9 represents an electric clock of radius 3 in. and that Q is the tip of its second hand. How fast is the point P moving at 20 sec past 3:47 p.m.?

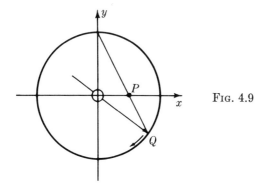

Fɪɢ. 4.9

10. Find the length of the longest pole that can be moved horizontally around the corner shown in Fig. 4.10.
    (*Hint:* For each angle θ between 0 and 90°, the ladder must be no longer than the diagonal line in Fig. 4.10.)

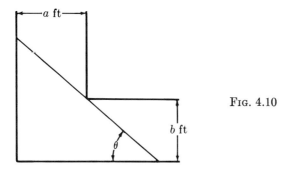

Fɪɢ. 4.10

11. Suppose in Ex. 10, the pole can be tilted so its ends touch the floor and the ceiling, which is c ft from the floor. Now how long can the pole be?

5. INVERSE TRIGONOMETRIC FUNCTIONS

Inverse of sin x

The sine of an angle does not completely determine the angle. For example, if $\sin x = \frac{1}{2}\sqrt{2}$, then x may be $\pi/4$, or $3\pi/4$, or $9\pi/4$, or $11\pi/4$, etc. This is clear from the graph of $\sin x$. See Fig. 5.1. The curve $y = \sin x$

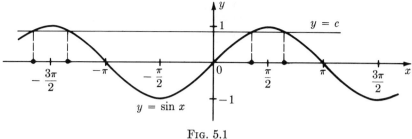

FIG. 5.1

intersects each horizontal line $y = c$, where $-1 \leq c \leq 1$, infinitely often; there are infinitely many values of x for which $\sin x = c$.

If, however, x is restricted to the interval $-\pi/2 \leq x \leq \pi/2$, then the equation $\sin x = c$ has a unique solution for each value of c in the interval $-1 \leq c \leq 1$. That is because the graph of the restricted function $y = \sin x$ is increasing (Fig. 5.2). There exists an inverse function, called arc sin:

$$y = \sin x \qquad \text{is equivalent to} \qquad x = \text{arc sin } y.$$

Thus arc sin y is the unique angle in the range from $-\pi/2$ to $\pi/2$ whose sine is y.

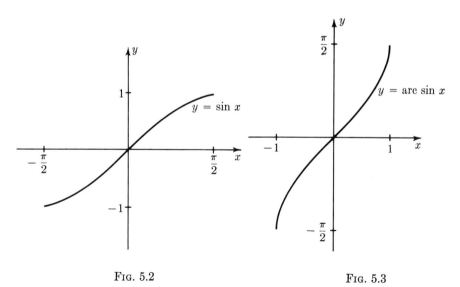

<table>
<tr><td style="text-align:center">FIG. 5.2</td><td style="text-align:center">FIG. 5.3</td></tr>
</table>

The graph of the function arc sin x is the reflection of the curve in Fig. 5.2 across the line $y = x$. See Fig. 5.3. The curve $y = $ arc sin x has vertical tangents at $(1, \pi/2)$ and $(-1, -\pi/2)$, reflecting the horizontal tangents of $y = \sin x$ at $(\pi/2, 1)$ and $(-\pi/2, -1)$.

> The function arc sin x is the inverse of sin x.
> It is defined for $-1 \le x \le 1$, and its values
> range from $-\pi/2$ to $\pi/2$.

Examples:

$$\text{arc sin } 1 = \frac{\pi}{2} \qquad\qquad \text{arc sin}(-1) = -\frac{\pi}{2}$$

$$\text{arc sin } \frac{1}{2} = \frac{\pi}{6} \qquad\qquad \text{arc sin}(\text{sin } x) = x, \qquad -\frac{\pi}{2} \le x \le \frac{\pi}{2}$$

$$\text{arc sin } 0 = 0 \qquad\qquad \text{sin}(\text{arc sin } x) = x$$

$$\text{arc sin} \left(-\frac{1}{\sqrt{2}} \right) = -\frac{\pi}{4} \qquad \text{arc sin}(-x) = -\text{ arc sin } x.$$

Inverse of cos x

Just as for sin x, the inverse of cos x can be defined only if x is suitably restricted. We agree to confine x to the interval $0 \le x \le \pi$. See Fig. 5.4.

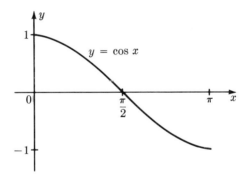

Fɪɢ. 5.4

In this interval the cosine function is decreasing; therefore the equation cos $x = c$ has a unique solution for each c in the interval $-1 \le c \le 1$. The inverse function is called arc cos:

$$y = \text{cos } x \qquad \text{is equivalent to} \qquad x = \text{arc cos } y.$$

Thus arc cos y is the unique angle in the range from 0 to π whose cosine is y.
The graph of the function arc cos x is the reflection of the curve in Fig. 5.4 across the line $y = x$. See Fig. 5.5.

> The function arc cos x is the inverse of cos x.
> It is defined for $-1 \le x \le 1$, and its values
> range from 0 to π.

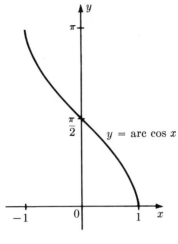

Fɪɢ. 5.5

Examples:

$$\text{arc cos } 1 = 0 \qquad\qquad \text{arc cos}(-1) = \pi$$

$$\text{arc cos } \frac{1}{2} = \frac{\pi}{3} \qquad\qquad \text{arc cos}(\cos x) = x, \qquad 0 \le x \le \pi$$

$$\text{arc cos } 0 = \frac{\pi}{2} \qquad\qquad \cos(\text{arc cos } x) = x$$

$$\text{arc cos }\left(-\frac{1}{\sqrt 2}\right) = \frac{3\pi}{4} \qquad \text{arc cos}(-x) = \pi - \text{arc cos } x.$$

To understand the last example, look at Fig. 5.5. The curve is symmetric with respect to the point $(0, \pi/2)$. Hence $\pi/2$ is the average of arc cos x and arc cos $(-x)$, i.e.,

$$\frac{\pi}{2} = \frac{1}{2}[\text{arc cos } x + \text{arc cos}(-x)],$$

from which arc cos$(-x) = \pi -$ arc cos x. For example,

$$\text{arc cos }\left(-\frac{1}{\sqrt 2}\right) = \pi - \text{arc cos }\left(\frac{1}{\sqrt 2}\right), \qquad \text{i.e.} \quad \frac{3\pi}{4} = \pi - \frac{\pi}{4}.$$

There is a relation between the functions arc sin x and arc cos x:

$$\boxed{\text{arc sin } x + \text{arc cos } x = \frac{\pi}{2}.}$$

To understand this relation, draw arc sin x and arc cos x on the same graph (Fig. 5.6). Then translate arc cos x downward $\pi/2$ units; the result is the graph of (arc cos x) $- \pi/2$. Clearly this curve is the reflection of the curve

$y = $ arc sin x in the x-axis. Therefore

$$\left(\text{arc cos } x - \frac{\pi}{2}\right) + \text{arc sin } x = 0.$$

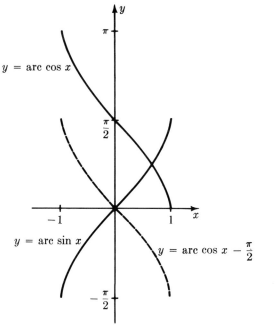

Fɪɢ. 5.6

Inverse of tan x

Recall the graph of tan x (Fig. 5.7). Consider only one branch of the graph, the one for which $-\pi/2 < x < \pi/2$. Then the equation tan $x = c$ has a unique solution for each number c. There exists an inverse function called arc tan:

$$y = \tan x \quad \text{is equivalent to} \quad x = \text{arc tan } y.$$

Thus arc tan y is the unique angle between $-\pi/2$ and $\pi/2$ whose tangent is y.

The graph of the function arc tan x is the reflection across the line $y = x$ of one branch of the curve $y = \tan x$. See Fig. 5.8.

> The function arc tan x is the inverse of tan x.
> It is defined for all x, and takes values between
> $-\pi/2$ and $\pi/2$.
>
> As $x \longrightarrow \infty$, arc tan $x \longrightarrow \dfrac{\pi}{2}$;
>
> as $x \longrightarrow -\infty$, arc tan $x \longrightarrow -\dfrac{\pi}{2}$.

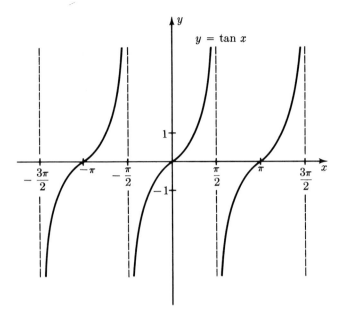

Fɪɢ. 5.7

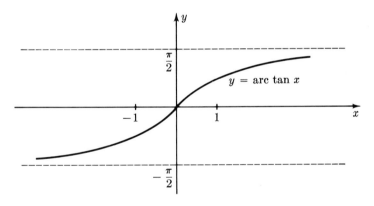

Fɪɢ. 5.8

Examples:

arc tan 0 = 0

arc tan 1 = $\dfrac{\pi}{4}$

arc tan$(-\sqrt{3}) = -\dfrac{\pi}{3}$

arc tan$(-x) = -$ arc tan x

arc tan(tan x) = x, $\qquad -\dfrac{\pi}{2} < x < \dfrac{\pi}{2}$

arc tan (100) $\approx$ 1.5608

arc tan (3437.7) $\approx$ 89° 59' $\approx$ 1.5705
  (*note:* $\pi/2 \approx$ 1.5708).

Inverses of the Other Trigonometric Functions

Inverses of the functions cot x, sec x, and csc x can be defined in a similar manner. Rather than discuss them in detail, we shall show their graphs (Figs. 5.9–5.11) and list a few basic relations.

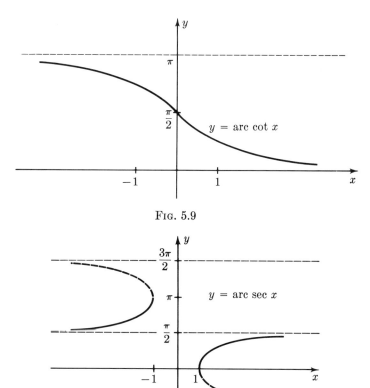

Fig. 5.9

Fig. 5.10 $0 \leq$ arc sec $x < \pi/2$ if $x \geq 1$; $\pi/2 <$ arc sec $x \leq \pi$ if $x \leq -1$.

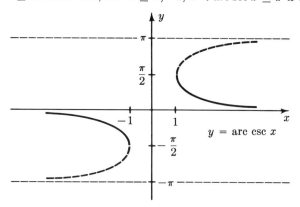

Fig. 5.11 $0 <$ arc csc $x \leq \pi/2$ if $x \geq 1$; $-\pi/2 \leq$ arc csc $x < 0$ if $x \leq -1$.

The following relations hold:

$$
\begin{array}{ll}
\text{arc tan } x + \text{arc cot } x = \dfrac{\pi}{2} & \text{arc sec } x = \text{arc cos}\left(\dfrac{1}{x}\right) \\[3mm]
\text{arc sec } x + \text{arc csc } x = \dfrac{\pi}{2} & \text{arc csc } x = \text{arc sin}\left(\dfrac{1}{x}\right).
\end{array}
$$

Notation

The following alternate notation is very common for inverse trigonometric functions:

$$
\text{arc sin } x = \sin^{-1} x, \qquad \text{arc tan } x = \tan^{-1} x, \qquad \text{etc.}
$$

Warning: Do not confuse

$$
\sin^{-1} x \qquad \text{with} \qquad \frac{1}{\sin x}.
$$

The notation $\sin^{-1} x$ is a bit awkward because we do write $\sin^n x$ for $(\sin x)^n$ when $n > 0$.

EXERCISES

Evaluate:

1. $\text{arc sin}\left(\dfrac{1}{\sqrt{2}}\right)$

2. $\text{arc cos}\left(-\dfrac{1}{\sqrt{2}}\right)$

3. $\text{arc tan } \sqrt{3}$

4. $\text{arc sec } 1$

5. $\text{arc sin } \dfrac{1}{2} - \text{arc sin}\left(-\dfrac{\sqrt{3}}{2}\right)$

6. $\cos[\text{arc cos}(0.35)]$

7. $\cos\left(\text{arc sin } \dfrac{3}{5}\right)$

8. $\text{arc tan}\left(\tan \dfrac{\pi}{4}\right)$

9. $\text{arc tan}(0.62) + \text{arc cot}(0.62)$

10. $\text{arc cos}\left(\dfrac{1}{2}\right) - \text{arc cos}\left(-\dfrac{1}{2}\right).$

11. Show that $2 \text{ arc cos } x = \text{arc cos }(2x^2 - 1)$ if $0 < x < 1$.
    (*Hint:* Use a double-angle formula.)

12. Show that $\text{arc tan } a + \text{arc tan } b = \text{arc tan } \dfrac{a+b}{1-ab}$ if $|a| < 1$ and $|b| < 1$.

13. Show that $\text{arc tan } \dfrac{1}{2} + \text{arc tan } \dfrac{1}{3} = \dfrac{\pi}{4}$.

14. Show that $\text{arc tan } x + \text{arc tan } \dfrac{1}{x} = \dfrac{\pi}{2}$ $\quad (x > 0)$.

15. Explain how the graphs in Figs. 5.9, 5.10, and 5.11 are obtained.

6. DERIVATIVES OF INVERSE FUNCTIONS

The derivatives of the inverse trigonometric functions are:

$$\frac{d}{dx}(\text{arc sin } x) = \frac{1}{\sqrt{1-x^2}} \qquad \frac{d}{dx}(\text{arc tan } x) = \frac{1}{1+x^2}$$

$$\frac{d}{dx}(\text{arc cos } x) = \frac{-1}{\sqrt{1-x^2}} \qquad \frac{d}{dx}(\text{arc cot } x) = \frac{-1}{1+x^2}$$

$$\frac{d}{dx}(\text{arc sec } x) = \begin{cases} \dfrac{1}{x\sqrt{x^2-1}}, & x > 1 \\[2ex] \dfrac{-1}{x\sqrt{x^2-1}}, & x < -1 \end{cases}$$

$$\frac{d}{dx}(\text{arc csc } x) = \begin{cases} \dfrac{-1}{x\sqrt{x^2-1}}, & x > 1 \\[2ex] \dfrac{1}{x\sqrt{x^2-1}}, & x < -1. \end{cases}$$

We shall justify the first three formulas; these are by far the most important.

First consider arc sin x. If $y = $ arc sin x, then $x = \sin y$. By the rule for differentiation of inverse functions,

$$\frac{dy}{dx} = \frac{1}{\dfrac{dx}{dy}} = \frac{1}{\dfrac{d}{dy}(\sin y)} = \frac{1}{\cos y}, \qquad \cos y \neq 0.$$

But

$$\cos y = \pm \sqrt{1 - \sin^2 y} = \pm \sqrt{1 - x^2}.$$

However, $\cos y > 0$ since y is between $-\pi/2$ and $\pi/2$ (by definition of arc sin x). Hence, the positive square root is the correct one. Therefore

$$\frac{d}{dx}(\text{arc sin } x) = \frac{1}{\cos y} = \frac{1}{\sqrt{1-x^2}}, \qquad -1 < x < 1.$$

This formula is not valid at ± 1 because there the denominator is zero. In fact, the function $y = $ arc sin x has no derivative at $x = +1$ and $x = -1$; its graph has vertical tangents at these values of x.

The formula for the derivative of arc cos x follows immediately. Since

$$\text{arc cos } x = \frac{\pi}{2} - \text{arc sin } x,$$

$$\frac{d}{dx}(\text{arc cos } x) = -\frac{d}{dx}(\text{arc sin } x) = \frac{-1}{\sqrt{1-x^2}}.$$

Next, consider arc tan x. If $y = $ arc tan x, then $x = \tan y$.

$$\frac{dy}{dx} = \frac{1}{\dfrac{dx}{dy}} = \frac{1}{\sec^2 y} = \frac{1}{1 + \tan^2 y} = \frac{1}{1 + x^2}.$$

Verification of the remaining differentiation formulas is left as an exercise.

REMARK: In Chapter 21, Section 7, a rigorous theory of the trigonometric functions is based on the formula above for (d/dx) (arc tan x).

EXERCISES

Differentiate:

1. arc sin $\dfrac{x}{3}$

2. arc cos $2x$

3. arc tan(x^2)

4. x arc sin$(2x + 1)$

5. (arc sin $3x)^2$

6. arc tan $\sqrt{x}$

7. arc cot $\dfrac{1}{x}$

8. arc sin $\dfrac{x}{x + 3}$

9. arc tan $\dfrac{x - 1}{x + 1}$

10. arc tan $\dfrac{1}{x}$ + arc cot x

11. $2x$ arc tan $2x - \ln \sqrt{1 + 4x^2}$

12. x arc cot $x + \ln \sqrt{1 + x^2}$.

13. Verify the formulas given in the text for the derivatives of arc cot x, arc sec x, and arc csc x.

7. APPLICATIONS

EXAMPLE 7.1

Find the area under the curves

$$\text{(a)} \qquad y = \frac{1}{\sqrt{1 - x^2}}, \qquad \text{from} \quad 0 \quad \text{to} \quad \frac{1}{2},$$

$$\text{(b)} \qquad y = \frac{1}{1 + x^2}, \qquad \text{from} \quad 0 \quad \text{to} \quad 1.$$

Solution: From the differentiation formulas for inverse trigonometric functions, we see that

$$\frac{d}{dx} \text{ (arc sin } x) = \frac{1}{\sqrt{1 - x^2}}, \qquad -1 < x < 1,$$

$$\frac{d}{dx} \text{ (arc tan } x) = \frac{1}{1 + x^2}.$$

Thus,

arc sin x is an antiderivative of $\dfrac{1}{\sqrt{1 - x^2}}$,

arc tan x is an antiderivative of $\dfrac{1}{1 + x^2}$.

Therefore

$$\int_0^{1/2} \frac{dx}{\sqrt{1 - x^2}} = \text{arc sin } x \ \Big|_0^{1/2} = \frac{\pi}{6} - 0,$$

and

$$\int_0^1 \frac{dx}{1 + x^2} = \text{arc tan } x \ \Big|_0^1 = \frac{\pi}{4} - 0.$$

Answer: (a) $\dfrac{\pi}{6}$; (b) $\dfrac{\pi}{4}$.

EXAMPLE 7.2

Show that $\displaystyle\int_0^z \frac{dx}{1 + x^2} < \frac{\pi}{2}$ no matter how large z is.

Solution:

$$\int_0^z \frac{dx}{1 + x^2} = \text{arc tan } x \ \Big|_0^z = \text{arc tan } z.$$

By definition, all values of arc tan z are between $-\pi/2$ and $\pi/2$, so the integral is less than $\pi/2$.

REMARK: As $z \longrightarrow \infty$, arc tan $z \longrightarrow \pi/2$. For this reason we write

$$\int_0^\infty \frac{dx}{1 + x^2} = \frac{\pi}{2}.$$

In geometric terms, the area under the curve $y = 1/(1 + x^2)$ between 0 and z is close to $\pi/2$ when z is large (Fig. 7.1). Furthermore, the larger

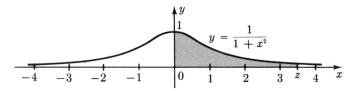

FIG. 7.1   Area of shaded region is nearly $\pi/2$.

z is, the closer the area is to $\pi/2$. Integrals of this type will be studied in "A Second Course in Calculus."

EXAMPLE 7.3

The circle shown in Fig. 7.2 has radius a ft. As the point P moves to the right at the rate of 7 ft/sec, how fast does the arc BQ increase?

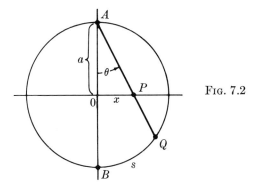

FIG. 7.2

Solution: Express the arc length s in terms of the angle θ. From plane geometry,

$$s = 2a\theta,$$

where θ is measured in radians. From the triangle AOP,

$$\theta = \text{arc} \tan \frac{x}{a}.$$

Hence,

$$s = 2a \ \text{arc} \tan \frac{x}{a}.$$

Differentiate with respect to time:

$$\dot{s} = 2a \frac{d}{dt}\left(\text{arc} \tan \frac{x}{a}\right)$$

$$= 2a \frac{1}{1 + \left(\dfrac{x}{a}\right)^2}\left(\frac{\dot{x}}{a}\right) = \frac{2a^2}{x^2 + a^2} \cdot 7.$$

Answer: $\dfrac{14a^2}{x^2 + a^2}$ ft/sec.

EXAMPLE 7.4

The Statue of Liberty is 150 ft tall and stands on a 150-ft pedestal. How far from the base should you stand so you can photograph the statue with largest possible angle? Assume camera level is 5 ft.

Solution: Draw a diagram, labelling the various distances and angles as indicated (Fig. 7.3). The problem is to choose x in such a way that the

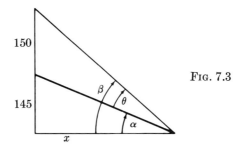

F<small>IG.</small> 7.3

angle θ is greatest. If x is very small or very large, θ will be small. A reasonable guess at the optimal value of x is 200–300 ft.

Express θ as a function of x. From Fig. 7.3,

$$\theta = \beta - \alpha,$$

$$\cot \alpha = \frac{x}{145}, \qquad \cot \beta = \frac{x}{295}.$$

Hence

$$\theta = \text{arc cot} \frac{x}{295} - \text{arc cot} \frac{x}{145}.$$

This is the function of x to be maximized. The range of x is $x > 0$; there are no end points.

Differentiate:

$$\frac{d\theta}{dx} = \frac{-\dfrac{1}{295}}{1 + \left(\dfrac{x}{295}\right)^2} + \frac{\dfrac{1}{145}}{1 + \left(\dfrac{x}{145}\right)^2} = \frac{145}{(145)^2 + x^2} - \frac{295}{(295)^2 + x^2}.$$

Therefore

$$\frac{d\theta}{dx} = 0 \quad \text{if} \quad \frac{145}{(145)^2 + x^2} = \frac{295}{(295)^2 + x^2}.$$

Solve for x:

$$(145)(295)^2 + 145x^2 = (295)(145)^2 + 295x^2,$$

$$x^2(295 - 145) = (145)(295)(295 - 145),$$

$$x^2 = (145)(295).$$

The only positive root of this equation is

$$x = \sqrt{(145)\,(295)} = 5\sqrt{1711} \approx 5(41.36) = 206.8.$$

Answer: Approximately 206.8 ft.

EXERCISES

1. A large picture hangs on the wall with its top T ft above eye level, and its bottom B ft above eye level. How far should you stand from the wall so that the angle at your eye subtended by the picture is as large as possible?

2. A balloon is released from eye level and rises 10 ft/sec. According to an observer 100 ft from the point of release, how fast is the balloon's elevation angle increasing 4 sec later?

3. Compute $\displaystyle\int_0^{\sqrt{3}/2} \frac{dx}{\sqrt{1 - x^2}}$.

4. Show that $\displaystyle\int_0^1 \frac{dx}{1 + x^2} = 3\int_1^{\sqrt{3}} \frac{dx}{1 + x^2}$.

5. Suppose the circle shown in Fig. 7.4 has radius 10 ft. Suppose also that x moves to the right in such a way that the length of the chord $\overline{AB}$ increases at the rate of 1 in./sec. How fast is the angle θ increasing when $\overline{AB}$ is 15 ft?

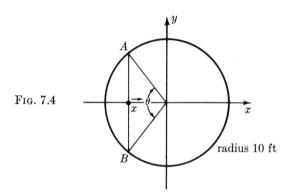

FIG. 7.4

radius 10 ft

8. HYPERBOLIC FUNCTIONS

The hyperbolic functions are certain combinations of exponential functions, with properties similar to those of the trigonometric functions. They are useful in solving differential equations and in evaluating integrals.

The three basic hyperbolic functions are the **hyperbolic sine,** the **hyperbolic cosine,** and the **hyperbolic tangent:**

$$\sinh x = \frac{e^x - e^{-x}}{2}, \qquad \cosh x = \frac{e^x + e^{-x}}{2},$$

$$\tanh x = \frac{\sinh x}{\cosh x} = \frac{e^x - e^{-x}}{e^x + e^{-x}}.$$

These functions are defined for all values of x. Their graphs are shown in

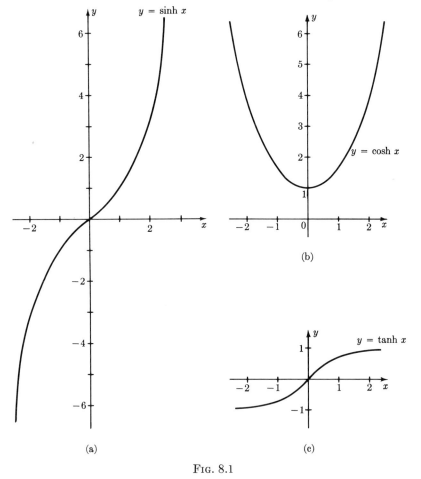

$$y = \sinh x$$

(a)

$$y = \cosh x$$

(b)

$$y = \tanh x$$

(c)

Fig. 8.1

Fig. 8.1. The less useful **hyperbolic cotangent, hyperbolic secant,** and **hyperbolic cosecant** are defined by

$$\coth x = \frac{1}{\tanh x}, \qquad \operatorname{sech} x = \frac{1}{\cosh x}, \qquad \operatorname{csch} x = \frac{1}{\sinh x}.$$

There are numerical tables for all of the hyperbolic functions.

From the definitions,

$$\sinh(-x) = -\sinh x, \qquad \cosh(-x) = \cosh x, \qquad \tanh(-x) = -\tanh x.$$

Thus $\sinh x$ and $\tanh x$ are odd functions, while $\cosh x$ is an even function.

Next,

$$\cosh^2 x = \left(\frac{e^x + e^{-x}}{2}\right)^2 = \frac{1}{4}(e^{2x} + 2 + e^{-2x}),$$

$$\sinh^2 x = \left(\frac{e^x - e^{-x}}{2}\right)^2 = \frac{1}{4}(e^{2x} - 2 + e^{-2x}).$$

Hence

$$\boxed{\cosh^2 x - \sinh^2 x = 1.}$$

It follows easily that

$$\tanh^2 x + \operatorname{sech}^2 x = 1, \qquad \coth^2 x - \operatorname{csch}^2 x = 1.$$

Note the similarity to trigonometric identities, except for sign. Virtually every identity involving trigonometric functions has an analogue involving hyperbolic functions. (But you must be careful with signs!) For example,

$$\cosh(u + v) = \cosh u \cosh v + \sinh u \sinh v,$$

$$\tanh 2x = \frac{2 \tanh x}{1 + \tanh^2 x}.$$

Each such identity can be proved by replacing the hyperbolic functions which occur with the corresponding combinations of exponential functions.

Inverse Hyperbolic Functions

The function $\sinh x$ increases steadily, and takes on each real value. Hence $\sinh x$ has an inverse function, written

$$\sinh^{-1} x \qquad \text{or} \qquad \text{arg sinh } x,$$

such that

$$\text{if} \quad x = \sinh y, \qquad \text{then} \quad y = \sinh^{-1} x.$$

Warning: Do not confuse

$$\sinh^{-1} x \qquad \text{with} \qquad \frac{1}{\sinh x}.$$

The graph of $y = \sinh^{-1} x$ is shown in Fig. 8.2. Since $\sinh x$ is given in terms of the exponential function, it stands to reason that $\sinh^{-1} x$ can be

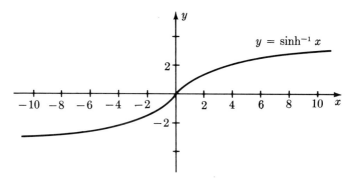

Fɪɢ. 8.2

expressed in terms of the logarithm. Indeed, if

$$y = \sinh^{-1} x,$$

then

$$x = \sinh y = \frac{e^y - e^{-y}}{2}.$$

Hence

$$e^y - 2x - e^{-y} = 0,$$

$$e^{2y} - 2xe^y - 1 = 0.$$

This is a quadratic for e^y; solve it:

$$e^y = x \pm \sqrt{x^2 + 1}.$$

Since $e^y > 0$, the plus sign must be chosen,

$$e^y = x + \sqrt{x^2 + 1},$$

$$y = \ln(x + \sqrt{x^2 + 1}).$$

The final result is

$$\boxed{\sinh^{-1} x = \ln(x + \sqrt{x^2 + 1}).}$$

The inverse hyperbolic cosine is defined only for $x \geq 1$. By a similar argument,

$$\boxed{\cosh^{-1} x = \ln(x + \sqrt{x^2 - 1}), \qquad x \geq 1.}$$

The inverse hyperbolic tangent is defined for $-1 < x < 1$ and can be expressed by the formula

$$\boxed{\tanh^{-1} x = \frac{1}{2} \ln\left(\frac{1 + x}{1 - x}\right), \qquad -1 < x < 1.}$$

Graphs of $\cosh^{-1} x$ and $\tanh^{-1} x$ are shown in Fig. 8.3.

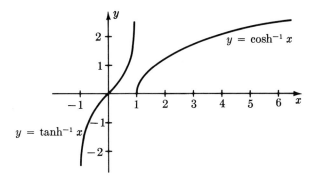

F<small>IG</small>. 8.3

Derivatives

Derivatives of the hyperbolic functions are easily obtained. For example,

$$\frac{d}{dx}(\sinh x) = \frac{d}{dx}\left(\frac{e^x - e^{-x}}{2}\right) = \frac{e^x + e^{-x}}{2} = \cosh x.$$

Similarly,

$\dfrac{d}{dx}(\sinh x) = \cosh x,$	$\dfrac{d}{dx}(\coth x) = -\operatorname{csch}^2 x,$
$\dfrac{d}{dx}(\cosh x) = \sinh x,$	$\dfrac{d}{dx}(\operatorname{sech} x) = -\operatorname{sech} x \tanh x,$
$\dfrac{d}{dx}(\tanh x) = \operatorname{sech}^2 x,$	$\dfrac{d}{dx}(\operatorname{csch} x) = -\operatorname{csch} x \coth x.$

Derivatives of the inverse functions are found in the usual way. For example, let $y = \sinh^{-1} x$. Then

$$x = \sinh y, \qquad \frac{dx}{dy} = \cosh y = \sqrt{1 + \sinh^2 y} = \sqrt{1 + x^2},$$

$$\frac{d}{dx}(\sinh^{-1} x) = \frac{1}{dx/dy} = \frac{1}{\sqrt{1 + x^2}}.$$

In this way one obtains

$$\frac{d}{dx}(\sinh^{-1} x) = \frac{1}{\sqrt{1 + x^2}},$$

$$\frac{d}{dx}(\cosh^{-1} x) = \frac{1}{\sqrt{x^2 - 1}},$$

$$\frac{d}{dx}(\tanh^{-1} x) = \frac{1}{1 - x^2}.$$

1. Express $7e^{2x} + 4e^{-2x}$ in terms of $\sinh 2x$ and $\cosh 2x$.

2. Prove $\sinh(x + y) = \sinh x \cosh y + \cosh x \sinh y$.

3. Express $\cosh 2x$ in terms of
   (a) $\cosh x$,   (b) $\sinh x$.

4. Verify that $(\cosh x + \sinh x)^n = \cosh nx + \sinh nx$.

5. Verify $\tanh^{-1} x = \dfrac{1}{2} \ln \left(\dfrac{1 + x}{1 - x} \right)$ for $-1 < x < 1$.

6. Find the 77-th derivative of $\sinh x$.

Differentiate:

7. $\sinh 5x$ 8. $\cosh \sqrt{x}$

9. $\cosh^2 3x - \sinh^2 3x$ 10. $(\tanh x)^3$

11. $\dfrac{1}{3} e^{2x} (2 \cosh x - \sinh x)$ 12. $1 + x \sinh^2 x$.

13. Show that $y = a \sinh cx + b \cosh cx$ satisfies the differential equation $d^2y/dx^2 = c^2 y$.

14. Describe the behavior as $x \to \infty$:

   (a) $\tanh x$ (b) $\dfrac{\sinh x}{e^x}$

   (c) $\operatorname{sech} x$ (d) $\dfrac{\cosh x}{\cosh 2x}$.

15. Prove

   (a) $\dfrac{d}{dx} (\cosh^{-1} x) = \dfrac{1}{\sqrt{x^2 - 1}}$ (b) $\dfrac{d}{dx} (\tanh^{-1} x) = \dfrac{1}{1 - x^2}$.

16. If the coordinates of a moving point are $x = a \cosh t$ and $y = b \sinh t$, where $a > 0$ and $b > 0$, describe its path.
   (*Hint:* Eliminate t.)

16. Techniques of Integration

1. INDEFINITE INTEGRALS

We have developed rules for differentiation of most functions that arise in practice. The reverse process, antidifferentiation, is much harder. There is no systematic procedure for antidifferentiation, rather, a few important techniques and a large bag of miscellaneous tricks. What is worse, there are functions which are not derivatives of any common function, for example

$$e^{-x^2}, \quad \frac{\sin x}{x}, \quad \frac{1}{\sqrt{(1 - x^2)(1 - k^2 x^2)}}.$$

In this chapter, we discuss some basic techniques of antidifferentiation, a few of the more common tricks, and the use of integral tables.

First, some notation. The symbol

$$\int f(x)\, dx,$$

called the **indefinite integral** of $f(x)$, denotes the most general antiderivative of $f(x)$. For example,

$$\int x^2\, dx = \frac{x^3}{3} + C,$$

$$\int \cos x\, dx = \sin x + C,$$

$$\int \frac{dx}{1 + x^2} = \arctan x + C.$$

To each differentiation formula, there corresponds an indefinite integral formula. For instance, to

$$\frac{d}{dx}(\tan x) = \sec^2 x$$

there corresponds

$$\int \sec^2 x\, dx = \tan x + C.$$

Let us list some integration formulas we know.

$$\int x^n \, dx = \frac{x^{n+1}}{n+1} + C \qquad\qquad \int \frac{dx}{x} = \ln |x| + C$$

$$(n \neq -1)$$

$$\int e^x \, dx = e^x + C \qquad\qquad \int \sec x \tan x \, dx = \sec x + C$$

$$\int \cos x \, dx = \sin x + C \qquad\qquad \int \csc x \cot x \, dx = -\csc x + C$$

$$\int \sin x \, dx = -\cos x + C \qquad\qquad \int \frac{dx}{\sqrt{1-x^2}} = \arcsin x + C$$

$$(|x| < 1)$$

$$\int \sec^2 x \, dx = \tan x + C \qquad\qquad \int \frac{dx}{1+x^2} = \arctan x + C$$

$$\int \csc^2 x \, dx = -\cot x + C \qquad\qquad \int \frac{dx}{x\sqrt{x^2-1}} = \text{arc sec } x + C$$

$$(x > 1)$$

2. DIFFERENTIALS AND SUBSTITUTIONS

We start with a technique that adapts known integration formulas to new situations.

Suppose we want an antiderivative for $\sin^2 x$. Since

$$\int x^2 \, dx = \frac{x^3}{3} + C,$$

it is natural to suspect that

$$\int \sin^2 x \, dx = \frac{\sin^3 x}{3} + C.$$

But this is wrong; indeed,

$$\frac{d}{dx}\left[\frac{\sin^3 x}{3}\right] = \sin^2 x \cos x.$$

Therefore a correct formula is

$$\int \sin^2 x \cos x \, dx = \frac{\sin^3 x}{3} + C,$$

which is fine, but it does not help us find an antiderivative of $\sin^2 x$. That problem must await a discussion of trigonometric identities in Section 6.

Similarly,

$$\int (x^2 + 1)^3 \, dx \neq \frac{(x^2 + 1)^4}{4} + C.$$

In fact,

$$\frac{d}{dx}\left[\frac{(x^2 + 1)^4}{4}\right] = (x^2 + 1)^3 \cdot 2x, \quad \text{not} \quad (x^2 + 1)^3.$$

Therefore a correct formula is

$$\int (x^2 + 1)^3 \cdot 2x \, dx = \frac{(x^2 + 1)^4}{4} + C.$$

But that does not solve the given problem. There is no short cut to finding

$$\int (x^2 + 1)^3 \, dx.$$

We must multiply out and integrate each term:

$$\int (x^2 + 1)^3 \, dx = \int (x^6 + 3x^4 + 3x^2 + 1) \, dx$$

$$= \frac{x^7}{7} + \frac{3x^5}{5} + x^3 + x + C.$$

These examples show that the plausible guess

$$\int [u(x)]^n \, dx = \frac{1}{n+1}[u(x)]^{n+1} + C$$

is wrong. The correct formula, a consequence of the Chain Rule, is

$$\int u^n \frac{du}{dx} \, dx = \frac{u^{n+1}}{n+1} + C, \quad n \neq -1.$$

Along with u^n, there must be the factor du/dx.

For a similar reason, the formula

$$\int e^x \, dx = e^x + C$$

does not imply

$$\int e^{u(x)} \, dx = e^{u(x)} + C.$$

The correct formula is

$$\int e^{u(x)} \frac{du}{dx} \, dx = e^{u(x)} + C.$$

Along with $e^{u(x)}$, there must be the factor du/dx. For example,

$$\int e^{x^2} \cdot 2x \, dx = e^{x^2} + C.$$

Here $u = x^2$ and $du/dx = 2x$. If the factor $2x$ were missing, we could not integrate.

Suppose $F(x)$ is an antiderivative of $f(x)$. Then

$$\int f[u(x)] \frac{du}{dx} \, dx = F[u(x)] + C.$$

The preceding assertion is just a restatement of the Chain Rule:

$$\frac{d}{dx} [F(u)] = \frac{dF}{du} \frac{du}{dx} = f(u) \frac{du}{dx}.$$

For example, if $f(x) = \sec^2 x$ and $F(x) = \tan x$, then

$$\int \sec^2 u \, \frac{du}{dx} \, dx = \tan u + C.$$

Each of the formulas listed in the last section gives rise to a more general formula in this way. For instance, from

$$\int \cos x \, dx = \sin x + C$$

follows

$$\int \cos u \, \frac{du}{dx} \, dx = \sin u + C;$$

from

$$\int \frac{dx}{1 + x^2} = \text{arc} \tan x + C$$

follows

$$\int \frac{1}{1 + u^2} \frac{du}{dx} \, dx = \text{arc} \tan u + C.$$

Typical applications of these two new formulas are:

$$\int \cos(3x + 1) \cdot 3 \, dx = \sin(3x + 1) + C,$$

$$\int \cos(\sqrt{x}) \, \frac{1}{2\sqrt{x}} \, dx = \sin(\sqrt{x}) + C,$$

and

$$\int \frac{1}{1 + e^{2x}} \, e^x \, dx = \text{arc} \tan(e^x) + C,$$

$$\int \frac{1}{1 + x^4} \cdot 2x \, dx = \text{arc} \tan(x^2) + C.$$

Differentials

The indefinite integral symbol

$$\int f(x) \, dx$$

denotes the general antiderivative of $f(x)$. Why write the "differential" dx ? Because we can introduce a notation that simplifies integration formulas.

For each function $u = u(x)$, we introduce the formal "differential"

$$du = u'(x) \, dx.$$

With this notation we replace

$$\int f[u(x)] \frac{du}{dx} \, dx$$

by

$$\int f(u) \, du.$$

Not only is the notation simpler, but also it reminds us of the important factor du/dx.

Properties of differentials which will be used repeatedly:

$$d(u + v) = du + dv;$$
$$d(cu) = c \, du, \qquad c \quad \text{a constant};$$
$$df(u) = f'(u) \, du.$$

The last property follows from the Chain Rule:

$$df(u) = \frac{d}{dx} [f(u)] \, dx = f'(u) \frac{du}{dx} \, dx = f'(u) \, du.$$

EXAMPLE 2.1

Evaluate $\displaystyle\int (e^x + x)^2(e^x + 1) \, dx.$

Solution: Let $u = e^x + x$. Then

$$du = \frac{du}{dx} \, dx = (e^x + 1) \, dx.$$

Hence,

$$\int (e^x + x)^2(e^x + 1) \, dx = \int u^2 \, du$$

$$= \frac{u^3}{3} + C = \frac{(e^x + x)^3}{3} + C.$$

$$\textit{Answer:} \quad \frac{(e^x + x)^3}{3} + C.$$

EXAMPLE 2.2

Evaluate $\displaystyle\int \frac{\text{arc tan } x}{1 + x^2}\, dx.$

Solution: Notice that

$$\frac{d}{dx}(\text{arc tan } x) = \frac{1}{1 + x^2}.$$

If $u = \text{arc tan } x$, then

$$du = \frac{du}{dx}\, dx = \frac{1}{1 + x^2}\, dx.$$

Hence

$$\int \frac{\text{arc tan } x}{1 + x^2}\, dx = \int u\, du = \frac{u^2}{2} + C = \frac{(\text{arc tan } x)^2}{2} + C.$$

Answer: $\displaystyle\frac{(\text{arc tan } x)^2}{2} + C.$

EXAMPLE 2.3

Find $\displaystyle\int \frac{\ln x}{x}\, dx.$

Solution: Set $u = \ln x$, then $du = dx/x$, so

$$\int \frac{\ln x}{x}\, dx = \int u\, du = \frac{u^2}{2} + C = \frac{(\ln x)^2}{2} + C.$$

Answer: $\displaystyle\frac{(\ln x)^2}{2} + C.$

EXERCISES

Find the indefinite integral:

1. $\displaystyle\int 2\cos 2x\, dx$

2. $\displaystyle\int \frac{2x}{1 + x^2}\, dx$

3. $\displaystyle\int 2xe^{x^2}\, dx$

4. $\displaystyle\int \frac{\ln^2 x}{x}\, dx$

5. $\displaystyle\int \frac{-2x}{\sqrt{1 - x^2}}\, dx$

6. $\displaystyle\int \sin x \cos x\, dx$

7. $\displaystyle\int \sin^3 x \cos x \, dx$

8. $\displaystyle\int (3x^2 + 1)(x^3 + x)^5 \, dx$

9. $\displaystyle\int \frac{2x}{(1 + x^2)^3} \, dx$

10. $\displaystyle\int \frac{3x^2}{4 + x^3} \, dx$

11. $\displaystyle\int \frac{-\sin x}{\cos^2 x} \, dx$

12. $\displaystyle\int (1 + \sin x)^3 \cos x \, dx$

13. $\displaystyle\int 5 \sec^2 5x \, dx$

14. $\displaystyle\int \sec^4 x \tan x \, dx$

15. $\displaystyle\int \frac{e^x + 2x}{e^x + x^2 + 1} \, dx$

16. $\displaystyle\int \sqrt{x - 2} \, dx$

17. $\displaystyle\int 8x \sqrt{4x^2 + 1} \, dx$

18. $\displaystyle\int \frac{e^x - e^{-x}}{e^x + e^{-x}} \, dx$

19. $\displaystyle\int \frac{e^{\sqrt{x}}}{2\sqrt{x}} \, dx$

20. $\displaystyle\int \frac{dx}{x \ln x}$.

3. SUMS AND CONSTANT FACTORS

Here are two simple integral formulas:

$$\int [f(x) + g(x)] \, dx = \int f(x) \, dx + \int g(x) \, dx,$$

$$\int cf(x) \, dx = c \int f(x) \, dx.$$

The first formula splits an integration problem into two parts. The second allows constant factors to slide across the integral sign. Both are derived from simple properties of differentiation. How?

Warning: Although constants can slide across the integral sign, variables cannot:

$$x \int x^2 \, dx \neq \int x^3 \, dx.$$

EXAMPLE 3.1

Evaluate $\displaystyle\int \left(e^x + \frac{1}{x^3}\right) dx$.

Solution:

$$\int \left(e^x + \frac{1}{x^3}\right) dx = \int e^x \, dx + \int x^{-3} \, dx.$$

Both integrals on the right are known:

$$\int e^x \, dx = e^x + C,$$

$$\int x^{-3} \, dx = \frac{x^{-2}}{-2} + C' = -\frac{1}{2x^2} + C'.$$

Answer: $e^x - \dfrac{1}{2x^2} + C + C'.$

REMARK: Since both C and C' are arbitrary constants, so is $C + C'$. Therefore, the answer can just as well be written as $e^x - 1/2x^2 + C$.

EXAMPLE 3.2

Evaluate $\displaystyle\int xe^{x^2} \, dx.$

Solution: Set $u = x^2$, then $du = 2x \, dx$. Hence $x \, dx = \frac{1}{2} \, du$, so

$$\int xe^{x^2} \, dx = \int e^{x^2} x \, dx = \int e^u \cdot \frac{1}{2} \, du$$

$$= \frac{1}{2} \int e^u \, du = \frac{1}{2} e^u + C = \frac{1}{2} e^{x^2} + C.$$

Here is a slightly different way to look at the problem. If $u = x^2$, then $du = 2x \, dx$. The integral contains $x \, dx$, which is not quite du; it lacks a factor of 2. Supply this factor by multiplying and dividing by 2:

$$\int xe^{x^2} \, dx = \frac{2}{2} \int xe^{x^2} \, dx$$

$$= \frac{1}{2} \int e^{x^2} \cdot 2x \, dx = \frac{1}{2} \int e^u \, du.$$

Answer: $\dfrac{1}{2} e^{x^2} + C.$

EXAMPLE 3.3

Evaluate $\displaystyle\int \frac{dx}{\sqrt{3x + 5}}.$

Solution: Set $u = 3x + 5$. Then $du = 3 \, dx$ and

$$\int \frac{dx}{\sqrt{3x + 5}} = \int \frac{\frac{1}{3} \, du}{\sqrt{u}} = \frac{1}{3} \int \frac{du}{\sqrt{u}}$$

$$= \frac{1}{3} \int u^{-1/2} \, du = \frac{1}{3} (2u^{1/2}) + C = \frac{2}{3} \sqrt{3x + 5} + C.$$

Alternate Solution: Set $u^2 = 3x + 5$. Then $2u \, du = 3 \, dx$ and

$$\int \frac{dx}{\sqrt{3x+5}} = \frac{2}{3} \int \frac{u \, du}{u} = \frac{2}{3} u + C$$

$$= \frac{2}{3} \sqrt{3x+5} + C.$$

Answer: $\dfrac{2}{3} \sqrt{3x+5} + C.$

EXAMPLE 3.4

Find $\displaystyle\int \frac{4x-5}{x^2+1} \, dx.$

Solution:

$$\int \frac{4x-5}{x^2+1} \, dx = 4 \int \frac{x \, dx}{x^2+1} - 5 \int \frac{dx}{x^2+1}.$$

In the first integral on the right, the numerator is nearly the differential of the denominator. Set $u = x^2 + 1$, so $du = 2x \, dx$, and throw in the needed factor 2:

$$4 \int \frac{x \, dx}{x^2+1} = 2 \int \frac{2x \, dx}{x^2+1} = 2 \int \frac{du}{u}$$

$$= 2 \ln |u| + C_1 = 2 \ln(x^2+1) + C_1 = \ln(x^2+1)^2 + C_1.$$

The second integral is arc tan $x + C_2$.

Answer: $\ln(x^2+1)^2 - 5 \text{ arc tan } x + C.$

EXAMPLE 3.5

Find $\displaystyle\int e^{-x^2} \, dx.$

DISCUSSION: The only formula that might apply is

$$\int e^u \, du = e^u + C,$$

with $u = -x^2$ and $du = -2x \, dx$. Unfortunately, a factor of x is lacking and there is nothing we can do about it. There is no simple function whose derivative is e^{-x^2}.

Find:

1. $\displaystyle\int (3x+1)^5\, dx$

2. $\displaystyle\int (x^3 + \sin x)\, dx$

3. $\displaystyle\int x(x^2+1)^3\, dx$

4. $\displaystyle\int (e^x + 3x)\,(e^x+3)\, dx$

5. $\displaystyle\int \cos 3x\, dx$

6. $\displaystyle\int \sin(x+2)\, dx$

7. $\displaystyle\int (\sin ax + \cos ax)\, dx$

8. $\displaystyle\int x \sin(x^2)\, dx$

9. $\displaystyle\int e^{3x}\, dx$

10. $\displaystyle\int \frac{1}{2}\,(e^{2x} + e^{-2x})\, dx$

11. $\displaystyle\int \frac{e^{2\sqrt{x}}}{\sqrt{x}}\, dx$

12. $\displaystyle\int x^2 e^{-x^3}\, dx$

13. $\displaystyle\int \frac{dx}{\sqrt{1+5x}}$

14. $\displaystyle\int \frac{\cos x}{(1-\sin x)^2}\, dx$

15. $\displaystyle\int \frac{x^3}{1+x^4}\, dx$

16. $\displaystyle\int \frac{3x-4}{1+x^2}\, dx$

17. $\displaystyle\int \frac{\ln(3x+1)}{3x+1}\, dx$

18. $\displaystyle\int (x+2)\,\sqrt[3]{x^2+4x+1}\, dx$

19. $\displaystyle\int \frac{dx}{(5-3x)^2}$

20. $\displaystyle\int \sin 5x \cos^2 5x\, dx$

21. $\displaystyle\int \tan^3 \frac{x}{2} \sec^2 \frac{x}{2}\, dx$

22. $\displaystyle\int \tan^2 3x\, dx.$

4. OTHER SUBSTITUTIONS

Frequently an integral can be simplified by an appropriate substitution.

EXAMPLE 4.1

Evaluate $\displaystyle\int x\sqrt{x+1}\, dx.$

Solution: Set $u^2 = x+1$. Then $x = u^2 - 1$, so $\sqrt{x+1} = u$, and $dx = 2u\, du$. Thus

$$\int x\sqrt{x+1}\, dx = \int (u^2-1)\cdot u \cdot 2u\, du = 2\int (u^4 - u^2)\, du$$

$$= 2\left(\frac{u^5}{5} - \frac{u^3}{3}\right) + C = \frac{2u^3}{15}\,(3u^2 - 5) + C,$$

where $u = \sqrt{x+1}$. Hence

$$\int x\sqrt{x+1}\,dx = \frac{2(x+1)^{3/2}}{15}[3(x+1)-5]+C.$$

Alternate Solution: Set $u = x + 1$. Then

$$\int x\sqrt{x+1}\,dx = \int (u-1)\sqrt{u}\,du = \int (u^{3/2}-u^{1/2})\,du$$

$$= 2\left(\frac{u^{5/2}}{5}-\frac{u^{3/2}}{3}\right)+C = \frac{2(x+1)^{3/2}}{15}(3x-2)+C$$

as before.

$$Answer: \quad \frac{2}{15}(x+1)^{3/2}(3x-2)+C.$$

EXAMPLE 4.2

Find $\displaystyle\int \frac{x\,dx}{(x-a)^3}$.

Solution: Set $u = x - a$. Then $x = u + a$ and $dx = du$:

$$\int \frac{x\,dx}{(x-a)^3} = \int \frac{(u+a)\,du}{u^3} = \int \left(\frac{1}{u^2}+\frac{a}{u^3}\right)du$$

$$= -\frac{1}{u}-\frac{a}{2u^2}+C = -\frac{1}{x-a}-\frac{a}{2(x-a)^2}+C.$$

$$Answer: \quad \frac{-2x+a}{2(x-a)^2}+C.$$

EXAMPLE 4.3

Evaluate $\displaystyle\int \frac{dx}{1+\sqrt[3]{x}}$.

Solution: Substitute $x = u^3$ and $dx = 3u^2\,du$:

$$\int \frac{dx}{1+\sqrt[3]{x}} = 3\int \frac{u^2\,du}{1+u}.$$

By long division,

$$\frac{u^2}{1+u} = u - 1 + \frac{1}{1+u}.$$

Hence

$$\int \frac{dx}{1 + \sqrt[3]{x}} = 3 \int \left(u - 1 + \frac{1}{1 + u} \right) du = 3 \left(\frac{u^2}{2} - u + \ln |1 + u| \right) + C$$

$$= 3 \left(\frac{1}{2} x^{2/3} - x^{1/3} + \ln |1 + x^{1/3}| \right) + C.$$

Answer:

$$\frac{3}{2} x^{2/3} - 3x^{1/3} + \ln |1 + x^{1/3}|^3 + C.$$

EXAMPLE 4.4

Find $\int \dfrac{dx}{a^2 + x^2}$.

Solution: We already have the formula

$$\int \frac{dx}{1 + x^2} = \arctan x + C.$$

The given integral is so like this one, we try to change it into this form. We set $x = ay$; then $dx = a\, dy$:

$$\int \frac{dx}{a^2 + x^2} = \int \frac{a\, dy}{a^2 + (ay)^2} = \frac{1}{a} \int \frac{dy}{1 + y^2} = \frac{1}{a} \arctan y + C.$$

Answer: $\dfrac{1}{a} \arctan \dfrac{x}{a} + C.$

EXERCISES

Find:

1. $\int x \sqrt{x + 3}\, dx$

2. $\int x^2 \sqrt{x + 3}\, dx$

3. $\int \dfrac{x}{\sqrt{2x + 5}}\, dx$

4. $\int (x^2 + x + 1) \sqrt{x + 1}\, dx$

5. $\int \dfrac{x^2\, dx}{(x - 1)^3}$

6. $\int \dfrac{x^3 - 5}{(x + 2)^2}\, dx$

7. $\int \dfrac{dx}{1 + \sqrt{x}}$

8. $\int \dfrac{x}{1 + \sqrt{x}}\, dx$

9. $\int \dfrac{dx}{x + \sqrt[4]{x}}$

10. $\int \dfrac{\sqrt{x} + 1}{x + 3}\, dx$

11. $\displaystyle\int \frac{e^{2x}}{1 + e^{4x}}\, dx$

12. $\displaystyle\int e^{2x} \sqrt{1 + e^x}\, dx$

13. $\displaystyle\int \frac{dx}{1 + (5x + 2)^2}$

14. $\displaystyle\int \frac{dx}{\sqrt{1 - 4x^2}}$

15. $\displaystyle\int \frac{dx}{\sqrt{a^2 - x^2}}, \quad a > 0$

16. $\displaystyle\int \frac{x + 1}{a^2 + b^2 x^2}\, dx$

17. $\displaystyle\int \frac{x^2\, dx}{1 + 3x^2}$ (long division)

18. $\displaystyle\int e^{\cos x} \sin x\, dx$

19. $\displaystyle\int \frac{x^4}{2 + x^2}\, dx$

20. $\displaystyle\int \frac{x^3\, dx}{\sqrt{a^2 - x^2}}$ $(u^2 = a^2 - x^2)$

21. $\displaystyle\int \frac{x^3}{x^2 + 1}\, dx$ $(u = x^2)$

22. $\displaystyle\int x^3 \sqrt{x^2 + 1}\, dx$ $(u^2 = x^2 + 1)$.

5. DEFINITE INTEGRALS

Indefinite integrals are studied mainly for the purpose of evaluating definite integrals. Recall that

$$\int_a^b f(x)\, dx = F(b) - F(a),$$

where $F(x)$ is an antiderivative of $f(x)$.

We have seen examples in which an indefinite integral

$$\int f(x)\, dx$$

is converted by a substitution $u = u(x)$ into an indefinite integral

$$\int g(u)\, du.$$

The latter integral is evaluated in terms of u, and then u is replaced by its expression in x. For computation of definite integrals, however, it is not necessary to convert back to x.

Suppose $\displaystyle\int f(x)\, dx$ is converted into $\displaystyle\int g(u)\, du$ by the substitution $u = u(x)$. Then

$$\int_a^b f(x)\, dx = \int_c^d g(u)\, du,$$

where $c = u(a)$ and $d = u(b)$.

Thus once the integral is changed into an integral in u, the computation can be done entirely in terms of u, *provided* the limits of the integral are changed correctly. This rule will be justified shortly.

EXAMPLE 5.1

Compute $\displaystyle\int_0^4 \sqrt{x^2 + 9} \cdot 2x \, dx$.

Solution: (Old way.) First evaluate the indefinite integral

$$\int \sqrt{x^2 + 9} \cdot 2x \, dx.$$

Make the substitution $u = x^2 + 9$, $du = 2x \, dx$:

$$\int \sqrt{x^2 + 9} \cdot 2x \, dx = \int u^{1/2} \, du = \frac{u^{3/2}}{3/2} + C.$$

Now change back to x:

$$\int \sqrt{x^2 + 9} \cdot 2x \, dx = \frac{2}{3} (x^2 + 9)^{3/2} + C.$$

Therefore,

$$\int_0^4 \sqrt{x^2 + 9} \cdot 2x \, dx = \frac{2}{3} (x^2 + 9)^{3/2} \Big|_0^4 = \frac{2}{3} (5^3 - 3^3) = \frac{196}{3}.$$

Solution: (New way.) Again substitute $u = x^2 + 9$. Note that

$$u = 25 \quad \text{for} \quad x = 4 \qquad \text{and} \qquad u = 9 \quad \text{for} \quad x = 0.$$

Therefore,

$$\int_0^4 \sqrt{x^2 + 9} \cdot 2x \, dx = \int_9^{25} u^{1/2} \, du = \frac{2}{3} u^{3/2} \Big|_9^{25} = \frac{2}{3} (5^3 - 3^3).$$

Alternate Solution: (Avoiding fractional exponents.) Set $u^2 = x^2 + 9$. Then $2u \, du = 2x \, dx$. Now

$$u = 5 \quad \text{for} \quad x = 4 \qquad \text{and} \qquad u = 3 \quad \text{for} \quad x = 0.$$

Therefore,

$$\int_0^4 \sqrt{x^2 + 9} \cdot 2x \, dx = \int_3^5 u \cdot 2u \, du = \frac{2}{3} u^3 \Big|_3^5 = \frac{2}{3} (5^3 - 3^3).$$

Answer: $\dfrac{196}{3}$.

EXAMPLE 5.2

Evaluate $\int_{1/2}^{1/\sqrt{2}} \dfrac{\text{arc sin } x}{\sqrt{1-x^2}}\, dx$.

Solution: Substitute

$$u = \text{arc sin } x, \qquad du = \frac{dx}{\sqrt{1-x^2}},$$

and note that

$$u\left(\frac{1}{2}\right) = \frac{\pi}{6}, \qquad u\left(\frac{1}{\sqrt{2}}\right) = \frac{\pi}{4}.$$

Therefore,

$$\int_{1/2}^{1/\sqrt{2}} \frac{\text{arc sin } x}{\sqrt{1-x^2}}\, dx = \int_{\pi/6}^{\pi/4} u\, du = \frac{u^2}{2}\bigg|_{\pi/6}^{\pi/4} = \frac{1}{2}\left(\frac{\pi^2}{16} - \frac{\pi^2}{36}\right).$$

Answer: $\dfrac{5\pi^2}{288}$.

Justification of Change of Limits

Suppose that a substitution $u = u(x)$ converts

$$f(x)\, dx \qquad \text{into} \qquad g(u)\, du.$$

That means

$$\int f(x)\, dx = \int g[u(x)]\frac{du}{dx}\, dx.$$

In other words

$$f(x) = g[u(x)]\frac{du}{dx}.$$

Let $G(u)$ be an antiderivative of $g(u)$. Then $F(x) = G[u(x)]$ is an antiderivative of $f(x)$:

$$\frac{dF}{dx} = \frac{dG}{du}\frac{du}{dx} = g(u)\frac{du}{dx} = f(x).$$

Therefore,

$$\int_a^b f(x)\, dx = F(b) - F(a);$$

$$\int_c^d g(u)\, du = G(d) - G(c).$$

But if $u(a) = c$ and $u(b) = d$, then

$$F(b) = G[u(b)] = G(d),$$
$$F(a) = G[u(a)] = G(c).$$

Consequently,

$$\int_a^b f(x)\, dx = \int_c^d g(u)\, du.$$

See Chapter 21, Section 5 for additional details.

EXERCISES

Compute the definite integral by making an appropriate substitution and changing the limits of integration:

1. $\displaystyle\int_0^2 x^3 \sqrt{x^4 + 9}\, dx$

2. $\displaystyle\int_0^5 x \sqrt{x + 4}\, dx$

3. $\displaystyle\int_{-1}^3 xe^{x^2}\, dx$

4. $\displaystyle\int_1^e \frac{\ln x}{x}\, dx$

5. $\displaystyle\int_4^5 \frac{x}{(x-2)^3}\, dx$

6. $\displaystyle\int_1^2 \frac{\sqrt{x^2 - 1}}{x}\, dx$

7. $\displaystyle\int_{\pi/6}^{\pi/2} \frac{\cos x}{\sqrt{\sin x}}\, dx$

8. $\displaystyle\int_0^{12} \frac{x^2}{\sqrt{2x + 1}}\, dx$

9. $\displaystyle\int_0^3 \frac{dx}{1 + \sqrt{1 + x}}$

10. $\displaystyle\int_{-\ln 2}^{-(1/2)\ln 2} \frac{e^x\, dx}{\sqrt{1 - e^{2x}}}$

11. $\displaystyle\int_0^1 \frac{x^3\, dx}{\sqrt{4 - x^2}}$

12. $\displaystyle\int_0^2 \frac{dx}{(x + 2)\sqrt{x + 1}}.$

6. USE OF IDENTITIES

The function under an integral sign is called the **integrand**. Keep in mind the possibility of simplifying the integrand by algebraic manipulation. Such tactics as factoring, combining fractions, and using trigonometric identities may convert a function into an equivalent form which is easier to integrate.

EXAMPLE 6.1

Evaluate $\displaystyle\int \sqrt{\frac{1 + x}{1 - x}}\, dx.$

Solution: Simplify the integrand by writing

$$\sqrt{\frac{1+x}{1-x}} = \sqrt{\frac{1+x}{1-x}} \cdot \frac{\sqrt{1+x}}{\sqrt{1+x}} = \frac{1+x}{\sqrt{1-x^2}}.$$

Then

$$\int \sqrt{\frac{1+x}{1-x}} \, dx = \int \frac{dx}{\sqrt{1-x^2}} + \int \frac{x \, dx}{\sqrt{1-x^2}}.$$

Both integrals on the right can be evaluated easily.

Answer: $\arcsin x - \sqrt{1-x^2} + C.$

Trigonometric Identities

EXAMPLE 6.2

Find $\displaystyle\int \cos^3 x \, dx.$

Solution: Convert the integrand into powers of $\sin x$, reserving a factor of $\cos x$ for the differential:

$$\cos^3 x = \cos^2 x \cos x = (1 - \sin^2 x) \cos x.$$

Hence

$$\int \cos^3 x \, dx = \int \cos x \, dx - \int \sin^2 x \cos x \, dx$$

$$= \sin x - \frac{\sin^3 x}{3} + C.$$

Answer: $\sin x - \dfrac{\sin^3 x}{3} + C.$

EXAMPLE 6.3

Find $\displaystyle\int \cos^3 x \sin^2 x \, dx.$

Solution:

$$\cos^3 x \sin^2 x = \cos^2 x \sin^2 x \cos x = (1 - \sin^2 x) \sin^2 x \cos x.$$

$$\int \cos^3 x \sin^2 x \, dx = \int \sin^2 x \cos x \, dx - \int \sin^4 x \cos x \, dx$$

$$= \frac{\sin^3 x}{3} - \frac{\sin^5 x}{5} + C.$$

Answer: $\dfrac{\sin^3 x}{3} - \dfrac{\sin^5 x}{5} + C.$

EXAMPLE 6.4

Find $\displaystyle\int \tan x \, dx.$

Solution:

$$\int \tan x \, dx = \int \frac{\sin x}{\cos x} \, dx = \int \frac{-du}{u},$$

where $u = \cos x$.

Answer: $-\ln|\cos x| + C = \ln|\sec x| + C.$

EXAMPLE 6.5

Find $\int \tan^2 x \, dx.$

Solution:

$$\int \tan^2 x \, dx = \int (\sec^2 x - 1) \, dx = \int \sec^2 x \, dx - \int dx.$$

Answer: $\tan x - x + C.$

EXAMPLE 6.6

Find $\int \tan^3 x \, dx.$

Solution:

$$\int \tan^3 x \, dx = \int \tan x \, (\sec^2 x - 1) \, dx$$

$$= \int \tan x \sec^2 x \, dx - \int \tan x \, dx.$$

The first integral is of the form

$$\int u \, du,$$

where $u = \tan x$; the second integral was done in Example 6.4.

Answer: $\dfrac{\tan^2 x}{2} + \ln|\cos x| + C.$

EXAMPLE 6.7

Find $\int \sin^2 x \, dx.$

Solution: Use the identity $\sin^2 x = \dfrac{1}{2}(1 - \cos 2x)$:

$$\int \sin^2 x \, dx = \frac{1}{2}\int dx - \frac{1}{2}\int \cos 2x \, dx.$$

Answer: $\dfrac{x}{2} - \dfrac{\sin 2x}{4} + C.$

Completing the Square

We have already seen the formulas

$$\int \frac{dx}{a^2 + x^2} = \frac{1}{a} \text{ arc tan } \frac{x}{a} + C,$$

$$\int \frac{dx}{\sqrt{a^2 - x^2}} = \text{arc sin } \frac{x}{a} + C, \qquad |x| \leq a.$$

Other integrals of this type are:

$$\int \frac{dx}{a^2 - x^2} = \frac{1}{2a} \ln \left| \frac{a + x}{a - x} \right| + C,$$

$$\int \frac{dx}{\sqrt{x^2 - a^2}} = \ln |x + \sqrt{x^2 - a^2}| + C, \qquad |x| \geq a,$$

$$\int \frac{dx}{\sqrt{x^2 + a^2}} = \ln |x + \sqrt{x^2 + a^2}| + C.$$

In the next chapter we shall show how these formulas are found. (Their correctness may be checked immediately by differentiating.)

The preceding formulas are useful when the integrand involves a quadratic polynomial or the square root of a quadratic polynomial. The basic trick is completing the square.

EXAMPLE 6.8

Evaluate $\displaystyle\int \frac{dx}{x^2 - 10x + 29}$.

Solution: Complete the square:

$$x^2 - 10x + 29 = x^2 - 10x + 25 + 4 = (x - 5)^2 + 2^2.$$

$$\int \frac{dx}{x^2 - 10x + 29} = \int \frac{dx}{2^2 + (x - 5)^2} = \int \frac{du}{a^2 + u^2}$$

$$= \frac{1}{a} \text{ arc tan } \frac{u}{a} + C,$$

where $u = x - 5$ and $a = 2$.

Answer: $\dfrac{1}{2} \text{ arc tan } \dfrac{x - 5}{2} + C.$

EXAMPLE 6.9

Evaluate $\int \dfrac{dx}{\sqrt{3 - x - x^2}}$.

Solution: First complete the square: $3 - x - x^2 = 3 - (x^2 + x)$ $= 3 - (x^2 + x + \frac{1}{4}) + \frac{1}{4} = \frac{13}{4} - (x + \frac{1}{2})^2$. Therefore

$$\int \frac{dx}{\sqrt{3 - x - x^2}} = \int \frac{dx}{\sqrt{\frac{13}{4} - \left(x + \frac{1}{2}\right)^2}} = \int \frac{du}{\sqrt{a^2 - u^2}} = \text{arc sin} \frac{u}{a} + C,$$

where $u = x + \frac{1}{2} = (2x + 1)/2$ and $a = \sqrt{\frac{13}{4}} = \sqrt{13}/2$

Answer: $\text{arc sin}\left(\dfrac{2x + 1}{\sqrt{13}}\right) + C.$

EXAMPLE 6.10

Evaluate $\int \dfrac{dx}{\sqrt{5x^2 - 2x}}$.

Solution: Complete the square:

$$5x^2 - 2x = 5\left(x^2 - \frac{2}{5}x + \frac{1}{25} - \frac{1}{25}\right) = 5\left[\left(x - \frac{1}{5}\right)^2 - \frac{1}{25}\right].$$

Therefore

$$\int \frac{dx}{\sqrt{5x^2 - 2x}} = \int \frac{dx}{\sqrt{5}\sqrt{\left(x - \frac{1}{5}\right)^2 - \frac{1}{25}}}$$

$$= \frac{1}{\sqrt{5}} \int \frac{du}{\sqrt{u^2 - a^2}} = \frac{1}{\sqrt{5}} \ln |u + \sqrt{u^2 - a^2}| + C,$$

where $u = x - \frac{1}{5}$ and $a = \frac{1}{5}$. But

$$u + \sqrt{u^2 - a^2} = \frac{1}{5}(5x - 1 + \sqrt{25x^2 - 10x}),$$

hence

$$\int \frac{dx}{\sqrt{5x^2 - 2x}} = \frac{1}{\sqrt{5}}\left(\ln |5x - 1 + \sqrt{25x^2 - 10x}| - \ln 5\right) + C.$$

Absorb $(\ln 5)/\sqrt{5}$ into C.

Answer: $\dfrac{1}{\sqrt{5}} \ln |5x - 1 + \sqrt{25x^2 - 10x}| + C.$

EXERCISES

Find:

1. $\displaystyle\int (\sin^2 3x + \cos^2 3x)\, dx$

2. $\displaystyle\int \cos x \csc x\, dx$

3. $\displaystyle\int \cos^3 x \sin^4 x\, dx$

4. $\displaystyle\int (\cos x - \sin x)^2\, dx$

5. $\displaystyle\int \sin^3 x \cos^2 x\, dx$

6. $\displaystyle\int \sin^3 ax\, dx$

7. $\displaystyle\int \cos^5 3x\, dx$

8. $\displaystyle\int \tan^2 x\, dx$

9. $\displaystyle\int \cos^4 x\, dx$

10. $\displaystyle\int \sin^2 \frac{x}{3} \cos^2 \frac{x}{3}\, dx$

11. $\displaystyle\int \tan^4 x\, dx$

12. $\displaystyle\int \tan^5 x\, dx$

13. $\displaystyle\int \sec^n kx \tan kx\, dx$

14. $\displaystyle\int \tan^2 x \sec^4 x\, dx$

15. $\displaystyle\int \frac{dx}{1 - \sin x}$

16. $\displaystyle\int \sin x \sqrt{\frac{\sec x + 1}{\sec x - 1}}\, dx.$

Evaluate the definite integrals:

17. $\displaystyle\int_0^{\pi/2} \sin 2x\, dx$

18. $\displaystyle\int_0^1 \cos^2 \pi x\, dx$

19. $\displaystyle\int_0^{2\pi} \cos 3x \cos 4x\, dx$ $\quad [(\cos A)(\cos B) = \tfrac{1}{2}(\cos\,? + \cos\,?).]$

20. $\displaystyle\int_0^{2\pi} \sin x \cos 3x\, dx.$

Find:

21. $\displaystyle\int \frac{dx}{x^2 + 2x + 5}$

22. $\displaystyle\int \frac{dx}{2x^2 + x + 6}$

23. $\displaystyle\int \frac{dx}{\sqrt{6x - x^2}}$

24. $\displaystyle\int \frac{3x + 10}{\sqrt{x^2 + 2x + 5}}\, dx$

25. $\displaystyle\int \frac{x\, dx}{\sqrt{4x - x^2}}$

26. $\displaystyle\int \frac{x^2\, dx}{x^2 - 4x + 9}$ $\quad$ (long division)

27. $\displaystyle\int \frac{x\, dx}{\sqrt{3x^4 - 4x^2 + 1}}$

28. $\displaystyle\int \frac{2x\, dx}{1 - x^2 - x^4}$

29. $\displaystyle\int \frac{dx}{bx - ax^2}$ $\quad a > 0, b > 0$

30. $\displaystyle\int \frac{dx}{a^2 x^2 + x}.$

17. Other Techniques

1. PARTIAL FRACTIONS

Any fraction of the form

$$\frac{cx + d}{(x - a)\,(x - b)}$$

can be split into the sum of two simpler fractions

$$\frac{A}{x - a} + \frac{B}{x - b}.$$

This decomposition into **partial fractions** simplifies integration since each term is easy to integrate.

> **EXAMPLE 1.1**
>
> Decompose $\dfrac{2x + 1}{(x - 3)\,(x - 4)}$ into partial fractions.

Solution: Write

$$\frac{2x + 1}{(x - 3)\,(x - 4)} = \frac{A}{x - 3} + \frac{B}{x - 4},$$

where A and B are constants to be determined. Multiply through by $(x - 3)\,(x - 4)$:

$$2x + 1 = A\,(x - 4) + B(x - 3)$$

$$= (A + B)x - (4A + 3B).$$

The coefficients of x on both sides of this identity must be equal. Hence

$$A + B = 2.$$

Also, the constants on both sides must be equal. Hence,

$$-4A - 3B = 1.$$

The unknowns A and B must satisfy these two equations simultaneously.

Solve: $A = -7$, $B = 9$. Therefore,

$$\frac{2x + 1}{(x - 3)(x - 4)} = \frac{-7}{x - 3} + \frac{9}{x - 4}.$$

Alternate Solution: There is a different way to compute A and B. Return to the equation

$$2x + 1 = A(x - 4) + B(x - 3).$$

This must hold for every value of x, in particular for $x = 3$ and $x = 4$:

$$x = 3: \quad 6 + 1 = A(3 - 4) + 0,$$
$$A = -7;$$
$$x = 4: \quad 8 + 1 = 0 + B(4 - 3),$$
$$B = 9.$$

Answer: $\quad \dfrac{2x + 1}{(x - 3)(x - 4)} = \dfrac{-7}{x - 3} + \dfrac{9}{x - 4}.$

EXAMPLE 1.2

Evaluate $\displaystyle\int \frac{dx}{a^2 - x^2}.$

Solution: Write

$$\frac{1}{a^2 - x^2} = \frac{1}{(a - x)(a + x)}$$
$$= \frac{A}{a - x} + \frac{B}{a + x}.$$

Multiply through by $(a - x)(a + x)$:

$$1 = A(a + x) + B(a - x).$$

Set $x = a$ to obtain $A = 1/2a$; then set $x = -a$ to obtain $B = 1/2a$. Hence

$$\frac{1}{a^2 - x^2} = \frac{1}{2a}\left(\frac{1}{a - x} + \frac{1}{a + x}\right).$$

Therefore,

$$\int \frac{dx}{a^2 - x^2} = \frac{1}{2a}\left(\int \frac{dx}{a - x} + \int \frac{dx}{a + x}\right)$$
$$= \frac{1}{2a}(-\ln|a - x| + \ln|a + x|) + C.$$

Answer: $\quad \dfrac{1}{2a}\ln\left|\dfrac{a + x}{a - x}\right| + C.$

Rational Functions

A **rational function** is the quotient of two polynomials. To integrate a rational function $p(x)/q(x)$, use partial fractions.

If degree $[p(x)] \geq$ degree $[q(x)]$, first divide $p(x)$ by $q(x)$:

$$\frac{p(x)}{q(x)} = r(x) + \frac{s(x)}{q(x)}.$$

Here $r(x)$ is a polynomial and $s(x)$ is a polynomial whose degree is less than that of $q(x)$.

EXAMPLE 1.3

Evaluate $\displaystyle\int \frac{x^3 + 4}{x^2 + x}\, dx.$

Solution: Divide $x^3 + 4$ by $x^2 + x$:

$$\frac{x^3 + 4}{x^2 + x} = x - 1 + \frac{x + 4}{x^2 + x}.$$

Hence

$$\int \frac{x^3 + 4}{x^2 + x}\, dx = \int (x - 1)\, dx + \int \frac{x + 4}{x^2 + x}\, dx$$

$$= \frac{x^2}{2} - x + \int \frac{x + 4}{x^2 + x}\, dx.$$

The problem is now reduced to evaluating the last integral. Write

$$\frac{x + 4}{x^2 + x} = \frac{x + 4}{x(x + 1)} = \frac{A}{x} + \frac{B}{x + 1}.$$

Multiply by $x(x + 1)$:

$$x + 4 = A(x + 1) + Bx.$$

Set $x = 0$ and $x = -1$ to obtain $A = 4$ and $B = -3$. Thus

$$\frac{x + 4}{x^2 + x} = \frac{4}{x} - \frac{3}{x + 1},$$

$$\int \frac{x + 4}{x^2 + x}\, dx = 4 \int \frac{dx}{x} - 3 \int \frac{dx}{x + 1}$$

$$= 4 \ln |x| - 3 \ln |x + 1| + C.$$

Answer: $\displaystyle \frac{x^2}{2} - x + \ln \left| \frac{x^4}{(x + 1)^3} \right| + C.$

Partial fractions are useful in the integration of rational functions $p(x)/q(x)$ provided the denominator can be completely factored into linear and quadratic factors. In practice, this is hard to do for polynomials of degree 3 or more, except in special cases.

Assume the degree of $q(x)$ exceeds that of $p(x)$, and that $q(x)$ is factored into linear and quadratic factors. Then for each factor $(x - a)$ there is a term:

$$\frac{A}{x - a}.$$

If $(x - a)^2$ occurs, there are two terms:

$$\frac{A_1}{x - a} + \frac{A_2}{(x - a)^2}.$$

If $(x - a)^3$ occurs, there are three terms:

$$\frac{A_1}{x - a} + \frac{A_2}{(x - a)^2} + \frac{A_3}{(x - a)^3}.$$

For each quadratic factor $x^2 + ax + b$ there is a term:

$$\frac{Ax + B}{x^2 + ax + b}.$$

If $(x^2 + ax + b)^2$ occurs, there are two terms:

$$\frac{Ax + B}{x^2 + ax + b} + \frac{Cx + D}{(x^2 + ax + b)^2},$$

and so on. For instance:

$$\frac{1}{(x - a)(x - b)(x - c)} = \frac{A}{x - a} + \frac{B}{x - b} + \frac{C}{x - c},$$

$$\frac{1}{(x - a)^2(x - b)} = \frac{A}{x - a} + \frac{B}{(x - a)^2} + \frac{C}{(x - b)},$$

$$\frac{1}{(x - a)(x^2 + bx + c)} = \frac{A}{x - a} + \frac{Bx + C}{x^2 + bx + c},$$

$$\frac{1}{(x - a)(x^2 + b^2)^2} = \frac{A}{x - a} + \frac{Bx + C}{x^2 + b^2} + \frac{Dx + E}{(x^2 + b^2)^2},$$

$$\frac{1}{x^4 - 1} = \frac{1}{(x - 1)(x + 1)(x^2 + 1)} = \frac{A}{x - 1} + \frac{B}{x + 1} + \frac{Cx + D}{x^2 + 1}.$$

EXAMPLE 1.4

Evaluate $\displaystyle\int \frac{dx}{x^4 - 1}.$

Solution: Write

$$\frac{1}{x^4 - 1} = \frac{A}{x - 1} + \frac{B}{x + 1} + \frac{Cx + D}{x^2 + 1}.$$

Multiply through by $(x - 1)(x + 1)(x^2 + 1)$:

$$1 = A(x + 1)(x^2 + 1) + B(x - 1)(x^2 + 1) + Cx(x - 1)(x + 1)$$
$$+ D(x - 1)(x + 1).$$

Set $x = 1$ and $x = -1$ to obtain $A = -B = \frac{1}{4}$. Set $x = 0$ to obtain $1 = A - B - D = \frac{1}{4} + \frac{1}{4} - D$. Hence $D = -\frac{1}{2}$. Choose any other value of x to find C. Try $x = 2$, for example:

$$1 = 15A + 5B + 6C + 3D = \frac{15}{4} - \frac{5}{4} + 6C - \frac{3}{2},$$

hence $C = 0$. Therefore

$$\frac{1}{x^4 - 1} = \frac{1}{4}\left(\frac{1}{x - 1}\right) - \frac{1}{4}\left(\frac{1}{x + 1}\right) - \frac{1}{2}\left(\frac{1}{x^2 + 1}\right),$$

$$\int \frac{dx}{x^4 - 1} = \frac{1}{4}\int \frac{dx}{x - 1} - \frac{1}{4}\int \frac{dx}{x + 1} - \frac{1}{2}\int \frac{dx}{x^2 + 1}$$

$$= \frac{1}{4}\ln|x - 1| - \frac{1}{4}\ln|x + 1| - \frac{1}{2}\text{arc tan } x + C.$$

$$\textit{Answer:}\quad \ln\left|\frac{x - 1}{x + 1}\right|^{1/4} - \frac{1}{2}\text{arc tan } x + C.$$

EXAMPLE 1.5

Evaluate $\displaystyle\int \frac{2x + 5}{(x - 1)(x + 3)^2}\, dx.$

Solution: Write

$$\frac{2x + 5}{(x - 1)(x + 3)^2} = \frac{A}{x - 1} + \frac{B}{x + 3} + \frac{C}{(x + 3)^2}.$$

Multiply through by $(x - 1)(x + 3)^2$:

$$2x + 5 = A(x + 3)^2 + B(x - 1)(x + 3) + C(x - 1).$$

Set $x = 1$ to obtain $A = \frac{7}{16}$; set $x = -3$ to obtain $C = \frac{1}{4}$. Choose any other value of x to find B, for example, $x = 0$:

$$5 = 9A - 3B - C = \frac{63}{16} - 3B - \frac{1}{4},$$

from which $B = -\frac{7}{16}$. Therefore,

$$\frac{2x + 5}{(x - 1)(x + 3)^2} = \frac{7}{16}\left(\frac{1}{x - 1}\right) - \frac{7}{16}\left(\frac{1}{x + 3}\right) + \frac{1}{4}\left(\frac{1}{(x + 3)^2}\right),$$

$$\int \frac{2x + 5}{(x - 1)(x + 3)^2}\, dx = \frac{7}{16}\int \frac{dx}{x - 1} - \frac{7}{16}\int \frac{dx}{x + 3} + \frac{1}{4}\int \frac{dx}{(x + 3)^2}.$$

Answer: $\dfrac{7}{16}\ln\left|\dfrac{x - 1}{x + 3}\right| - \dfrac{1}{4(x + 3)} + C.$

EXERCISES

Decompose into partial fractions:

1. $\dfrac{1}{(x + 1)(x - 1)}$

2. $\dfrac{x}{(x + 2)(x + 3)}$

3. $\dfrac{x^2}{(x + 1)(x - 2)}$

4. $\dfrac{1}{(x + 1)(x + 2)(x + 3)}$

5. $\dfrac{x}{(x + 1)(x + 2)(x + 3)}$

6. $\dfrac{1}{(x + 1)(x^2 + 4)}$

7. $\dfrac{x^4}{(x^2 + 1)^2}$

8. $\dfrac{x^3 - 1}{x(x^2 + 1)}$

9. $\dfrac{x + 1}{(x - 1)(x^2 + 4)}$

10. $\dfrac{1}{x(x + 1)^2}$.

Find:

11. $\displaystyle\int \frac{dx}{x^2 - 3x + 2}$

12. $\displaystyle\int \frac{dx}{(x - 2)(x + 4)}$

13. $\displaystyle\int \frac{x + 3}{x^2 + x}\, dx$

14. $\displaystyle\int \frac{x^2 + 1}{x^2 - 5x + 6}\, dx$

15. $\displaystyle\int \frac{2x + 3}{x^3 + x}\, dx$

16. $\displaystyle\int \frac{x\, dx}{(x + 1)^2(x - 3)}$

17. $\displaystyle\int \frac{dx}{(x - 2)^2(x^2 + 9)}$

18. $\displaystyle\int \frac{dx}{3x^2 - 13x + 4}$

19. $\displaystyle\int \frac{x^4\, dx}{x^3 - 1}$

20. $\displaystyle\int \frac{x\, dx}{x^4 - 1}$

21. $\displaystyle\int \frac{x^3\, dx}{x^2 + 3x + 2}$

22. $\displaystyle\int \frac{dx}{(x - 1)(x - 2)(x - 3)}$

23. $\displaystyle\int \frac{x^2 + x + 1}{(x - 3)(x^2 + 2x + 2)}\, dx$

24. $\displaystyle\int \frac{dx}{x(x - 3)^2}$

25. $\displaystyle\int \frac{\cos\theta\, d\theta}{\sin^2\theta + 7\sin\theta + 10}$

26. $\displaystyle\int \frac{dx}{\sqrt{x}\,(1 + \sqrt{x})(2 + \sqrt{x})}$.

2. TRIGONOMETRIC SUBSTITUTIONS

We have not yet integrated $\sec x$ and $\csc x$. The integral of $\sec x$ is done by a trick:

$$\sec x = \frac{\sec x \,(\sec x + \tan x)}{(\sec x + \tan x)}$$

$$= \frac{\sec x \tan x + \sec^2 x}{\sec x + \tan x}$$

$$= \frac{1}{\sec x + \tan x} \frac{d}{dx} (\sec x + \tan x).$$

Hence

$$\int \sec x \, dx = \int \frac{d \,(\sec x + \tan x)}{\sec x + \tan x} = \ln |\sec x + \tan x| + C.$$

In a similar manner, we may derive the formula

$$\int \csc x \, dx = - \ln |\csc x + \cot x| + C.$$

Integrals involving $a^2 - x^2$ or $a^2 + x^2$ are often simplified by trigonometric substitutions. The substitution $x = a \sin \theta$ changes $a^2 - x^2$ into $a^2 \cos^2 \theta$; the substitution $x = a \tan \theta$ changes $a^2 + x^2$ into $a^2 \sec^2 \theta$.

EXAMPLE 2.1

Evaluate $\displaystyle\int \frac{dx}{x^2 \sqrt{4 - x^2}}$.

Solution: Set $x = 2 \sin \theta$. Then

$$\int \frac{dx}{x^2 \sqrt{4 - x^2}} = \int \frac{2 \cos \theta \, d\theta}{(2 \sin \theta)^2 \sqrt{4 - 4 \sin^2 \theta}}$$

$$= \int \frac{2 \cos \theta \, d\theta}{4 \sin^2 \theta \cdot 2 \cos \theta} = \frac{1}{4} \int \frac{d\theta}{\sin^2 \theta}.$$

Hence

$$\int \frac{dx}{x^2 \sqrt{4 - x^2}} = \frac{1}{4} \int \csc^2 \theta \, d\theta = - \frac{1}{4} \cot \theta + C.$$

As a final step, express $\cot \theta$ in terms of x. This can be done quickly by drawing a right triangle (Fig. 2.1) that shows $x = 2 \sin \theta$. It follows that

$$\cot \theta = \frac{\sqrt{4 - x^2}}{x}.$$

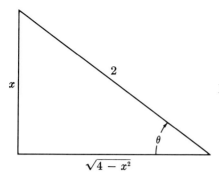

FIG. 2.1

$$\text{Answer:} \quad -\frac{\sqrt{4-x^2}}{4x} + C.$$

EXAMPLE 2.2

Evaluate $\displaystyle\int \frac{dx}{\sqrt{a^2 + x^2}}$.

Solution: Set $x = a \tan \theta$. Then

$$\int \frac{dx}{\sqrt{a^2 + x^2}} = \int \frac{a \sec^2 \theta \, d\theta}{\sqrt{a^2(1 + \tan^2 \theta)}} = \int \frac{a \sec^2 \theta \, d\theta}{a \sec \theta}$$

$$= \int \sec \theta \, d\theta = \ln |\sec \theta + \tan \theta| + C.$$

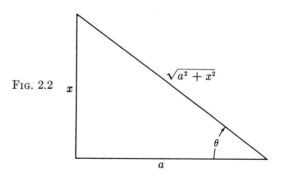

FIG. 2.2

Draw a right triangle (Fig. 2.2) showing $x = a \tan \theta$, and read off $\sec \theta$. Thus

$$\int \frac{dx}{\sqrt{a^2 + x^2}} = \ln \left| \frac{\sqrt{a^2 + x^2}}{a} + \frac{x}{a} \right| + C$$

$$= \ln |\sqrt{a^2 + x^2} + x| - \ln |a| + C.$$

Absorb $- \ln |a|$ into C.

$$\text{Answer: } \ln |\sqrt{x^2 + a^2} + x| + C.$$

EXAMPLE 2.3

Compute the definite integral $\displaystyle\int_0^1 \frac{dx}{(1 + x^2)^2}$.

Solution: Substitute $x = \tan \theta$. Then $\theta = 0$ for $x = 0$, and $\theta = \pi/4$ for $x = 1$. Hence

$$\int_0^1 \frac{dx}{(1 + x^2)^2} = \int_0^{\pi/4} \frac{\sec^2 \theta \, d\theta}{(1 + \tan^2 \theta)^2}$$

$$= \int_0^{\pi/4} \frac{d\theta}{\sec^2 \theta} = \int_0^{\pi/4} \cos^2 \theta \, d\theta.$$

Use the identity

$$\cos^2 \theta = \frac{1}{2} (1 + \cos 2\theta):$$

$$\int_0^1 \frac{dx}{(1 + x^2)^2} = \int_0^{\pi/4} \left(\frac{1}{2} + \frac{1}{2} \cos 2\theta \right) d\theta = \left(\frac{1}{2} \theta + \frac{1}{4} \sin 2\theta \right) \Big|_0^{\pi/4}$$

$$= \left(\frac{1}{2} \cdot \frac{\pi}{4} + \frac{1}{4} \sin \frac{\pi}{2} \right) - \left(\frac{1}{2} \cdot 0 + \frac{1}{4} \sin 0 \right)$$

$$= \left(\frac{\pi}{8} + \frac{1}{4} \right) - 0.$$

$$\text{Answer: } \frac{\pi}{8} + \frac{1}{4}.$$

EXAMPLE 2.4

Evaluate the indefinite integral $\displaystyle\int \frac{dx}{(1 + x^2)^2}$.

Solution: From the solution of the last example,

$$\int \frac{dx}{(1 + x^2)^2} = \frac{\theta}{2} + \frac{\sin 2\theta}{4} + C, \qquad x = \tan \theta.$$

It remains to express this function of θ in terms of x. Draw a right triangle showing $x = \tan \theta$. See Fig. 2.3. Thus

$$\theta = \text{arc tan } x,$$

$$\sin 2\theta = 2 \sin \theta \cos \theta = 2 \left(\frac{x}{\sqrt{1 + x^2}} \right) \left(\frac{1}{\sqrt{1 + x^2}} \right).$$

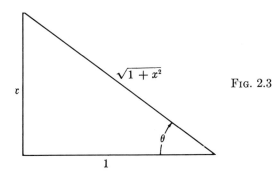

F<small>IG</small>. 2.3

$$Answer: \quad \frac{1}{2} \text{ arc tan } x + \frac{x}{2(1 + x^2)} + C.$$

EXERCISES

Use a trigonometric substitution:

1. $\displaystyle\int \frac{dx}{\sqrt{1 + x^2}}$

2. $\displaystyle\int x^3 \sqrt{1 + x^2}\, dx$

3. $\displaystyle\int \frac{x^3\, dx}{\sqrt{4 - x^2}}$

4. $\displaystyle\int \frac{x^2\, dx}{\sqrt{a^2 - x^2}}$.

5. $\displaystyle\int \frac{dx}{x^2 \sqrt{16 - x^2}}$

6. $\displaystyle\int \frac{dx}{x \sqrt{x^2 + 1}}$

7. $\displaystyle\int \frac{\sqrt{x^2 + a^2}}{x^2}\, dx$

8. $\displaystyle\int \frac{1 + x^2}{1 - x^2}\, dx$

9. $\displaystyle\int \frac{x^2\, dx}{(1 + x^2)^2}$

10. $\displaystyle\int \frac{\sqrt{x^2 - 9}}{x}\, dx$

In integrals involving the expression $x^2 + a^2$, the substitution $x = a \sinh \theta$ is often useful. Recall that $\cosh^2 x - \sinh^2 x = 1$ and $\sinh^{-1} x = \ln(x + \sqrt{x^2 + 1})$. Use this substitution:

11. $\displaystyle\int \frac{dx}{\sqrt{x^2 + a^2}}$

12. $\displaystyle\int \sqrt{x^2 + a^2}\, dx$

13. $\displaystyle\int \frac{x^2\, dx}{\sqrt{x^2 + a^2}}$

14. $\displaystyle\int \frac{\sqrt{x^2 + a^2}}{x^2}\, dx.$

3. INTEGRATION BY PARTS

In this section, we discuss a technique that converts an integration problem into a different integration problem, hopefully an easier one. The technique depends on the Product Rule:

$$\frac{d}{dx}(uv) = u\frac{dv}{dx} + v\frac{du}{dx},$$

where u and v are functions of x.

This rule can be expressed in terms of differentials. Multiply through formally by the symbol dx:

$$\frac{d}{dx}(uv)\,dx = u\frac{dv}{dx}\,dx + v\frac{du}{dx}\,dx.$$

The term on the left is $d(uv)$. On the right we have

$$\frac{dv}{dx}\,dx = dv, \qquad \frac{du}{dx}\,dx = du.$$

Product Rule in Differential Form

$$d(uv) = u\,dv + v\,du.$$

Rearranging terms in this rule, we have

$$u\,dv = d(uv) - v\,du,$$

and consequently

$$\int u\,dv = \int d(uv) - \int v\,du.$$

But

$$\int d(uv) = uv + C.$$

(Why?) Thus we obtain the formula for integration by parts:

Integration by Parts

$$\int u\,dv = uv - \int v\,du.$$

The constant is absorbed into the second integral. (See Chapter 21, Section 5 for more details.)

This formula converts the problem of integrating $u\,dv$ into that of integrating $v\,du$. With luck, the second integration is easier. There is no guarantee, however, that it need be.

EXAMPLE 3.1

Evaluate $\displaystyle\int x\cos x\,dx$.

Solution: Interpret the integral as

$$\int x\,d(\sin x).$$

Apply the formula for integration by parts with

$$u = x, \qquad du = dx; \qquad dv = \cos x \, dx, \qquad v = \sin x,$$

to obtain

$$\int x \cos x \, dx = uv - \int v \, du$$

$$= x \sin x - \int \sin x \, dx.$$

This is a bit of luck; the integral on the right is easy. Conclusion:

$$\int x \cos x \, dx = x \sin x + \cos x + C.$$

Answer: $\; x \sin x + \cos x + C.$

EXAMPLE 3.2

Evaluate $\displaystyle\int xe^x \, dx$.

Solution: Use integration by parts with

$$u = x, \qquad du = dx; \qquad dv = e^x \, dx, \qquad v = e^x.$$

Therefore

$$\int xe^x \, dx = xe^x - \int e^x \, dx$$

$$= xe^x - e^x + C.$$

Answer: $\; e^x(x - 1) + C.$

REMARK: It is possible to choose u and v differently:

$$\int xe^x \, dx = \int u \, dv,$$

where

$$u = e^x, \qquad du = e^x \, dx; \qquad dv = x \, dx, \qquad v = \frac{x^2}{2}.$$

Then integration by parts yields

$$\int xe^x \, dx = e^x \cdot \frac{x^2}{2} - \int \frac{x^2}{2} e^x \, dx,$$

which is true but does not help; the integral on the right is harder than the given one. Thus, it may be crucial how you factor the integrand into u and dv. It is also possible that no choice of u and dv helps.

Here are some further examples of integration by parts.

EXAMPLE 3.3

Evaluate $\int$ arc sin $x\ dx$.

Solution: Use integration by parts with

$$u = \text{arc sin } x, \quad du = \frac{dx}{\sqrt{1 - x^2}}; \quad dv = dx, \quad v = x.$$

Therefore

$$\int \text{arc sin } x\ dx = uv - \int v\ du = x \text{ arc sin } x - \int \frac{x\ dx}{\sqrt{1 - x^2}}.$$

In the integral on the right, substitute $y^2 = 1 - x^2$, $y\ dy = -x\ dx$:

$$-\int \frac{x\ dx}{\sqrt{1 - x^2}} = \int \frac{y\ dy}{y} = \int dy = y + C = \sqrt{1 - x^2} + C.$$

Answer: x arc sin $x + \sqrt{1 - x^2} + C.$

NOTE: "y" was used in the substitution step because "u" was used in the first step. Always take care not to confuse variables.

EXAMPLE 3.4

Compute $\int_1^2 \ln x\ dx$.

Solution: Use integration by parts with

$$u = \ln x, \quad du = \frac{dx}{x}; \quad dv = dx, \quad v = x.$$

Therefore

$$\int_1^2 \ln x\ dx = uv \Big|_1^2 - \int_1^2 v\ du = x \ln x \Big|_1^2 - \int_1^2 x \cdot \frac{dx}{x}$$

$$= (2 \ln 2 - 1 \ln 1) - x \Big|_1^2.$$

Answer: $2 \ln 2 - 1.$

Repeated Integration by Parts

Some problems require two or more integrations by parts.

EXAMPLE 3.5

Evaluate $\int x\ (\ln x)^2\ dx$.

Solution: Integrate by parts with

$$u = (\ln x)^2, \qquad du = \frac{2 \ln x \, dx}{x}; \qquad dv = x \, dx, \qquad v = \frac{x^2}{2}.$$

Therefore

$$\int x \, (\ln x)^2 \, dx = \frac{x^2 \, (\ln x)^2}{2} - \int \frac{x^2}{2} \cdot \frac{2 \ln x}{x} \, dx$$

$$= \frac{x^2 \, (\ln x)^2}{2} - \int x \ln x \, dx.$$

The problem now is to evaluate

$$\int x \ln x \, dx,$$

which is similar to the original integral except that $\ln x$ appears only to the first power. Therefore another integration by parts should reduce the integral to

$$\int x \, dx.$$

Try it. Integrate by parts again with

$$u = \ln x, \qquad du = \frac{dx}{x}; \qquad dv = x \, dx, \qquad v = \frac{x^2}{2}.$$

Therefore

$$\int x \ln x \, dx = \frac{x^2 \ln x}{2} - \int \frac{x^2}{2} \cdot \frac{dx}{x}$$

$$= \frac{x^2 \ln x}{2} - \frac{1}{2} \int x \, dx$$

$$= \frac{x^2 \ln x}{2} - \frac{x^2}{4} + C.$$

Combine the results:

$$\int x(\ln x)^2 \, dx = \frac{x^2(\ln x)^2}{2} - \left(\frac{x^2 \ln x}{2} - \frac{x^2}{4} + C \right).$$

Answer: $\dfrac{x^2}{4} [2(\ln x)^2 - 2 \ln x + 1] - C.$

EXAMPLE 3.6

Evaluate $\displaystyle\int x^3 e^x \, dx.$

Solution: Integrate by parts three times:

$$\int x^3 e^x \, dx = x^3 e^x - 3 \int x^2 e^x \, dx,$$

$$\int x^2 e^x \, dx = x^2 e^x - 2 \int x e^x \, dx,$$

$$\int x e^x \, dx = x e^x - \int e^x \, dx = x e^x - e^x + C.$$

Combine the results:

$$\int x^3 e^x \, dx = x^3 e^x - 3x^2 e^x + 6x e^x - 6e^x + C.$$

Answer: $e^x(x^3 - 3x^2 + 6x - 6) + C.$

EXAMPLE 3.7

Evaluate $\int e^x \cos x \, dx.$

Solution: Denote the integral by J. Integrate by parts with

$$u = e^x, \quad du = e^x \, dx; \quad dv = \cos x \, dx, \quad v = \sin x.$$

Therefore

$$J = e^x \sin x - \int e^x \sin x \, dx.$$

Integrate by parts again with

$$u = e^x, \quad du = e^x \, dx; \quad dv = \sin x \, dx, \quad v = -\cos x.$$

Therefore

$$\int e^x \sin x \, dx = -e^x \cos x + \int e^x \cos x \, dx.$$

The integral on the right is J again! Hence

$$\int e^x \sin x \, dx = -e^x \cos x + J.$$

Have we gone in a circle? No, because substitution of this expression in the first equation for J yields

$$J = e^x \sin x + e^x \cos x - J.$$

The minus sign on the right saves us from disaster. Solve for J:

$$J = \frac{1}{2}(e^x \sin x + e^x \cos x).$$

Don't forget the constant of integration.

$$Answer: \quad \frac{1}{2} e^x (\sin x + \cos x) + C.$$

EXERCISES

Find:

1. $\int x \sin x \, dx$

2. $\int x^2 \cos 3x \, dx$

3. $\int x e^{2x} \, dx$

4. $\int x \sec^2 x \, dx$

5. $\int \sqrt{x} \ln x \, dx$

6. $\int \text{arc} \cos x \, dx$

7. $\int \text{arc} \tan x \, dx$

8. $\int \ln(x^2 + 1) \, dx$

9. $\int x \, \text{arc} \tan x \, dx$

10. $\int x^3 e^{x^2} \, dx$

11. $\int e^{2x} \sin 3x \, dx$

12. $\int x^2 e^{-x} \, dx$

13. $\int x \cosh x \, dx$

14. $\int x^2 \sinh 3x \, dx$

15. $\int x^2 \cos ax \, dx$

16. $\int \sec^3 x \, dx.$

Compute:

17. $\int_{\pi}^{2\pi} x \cos x \, dx$

18. $\int_{1}^{e} (\ln x)^2 \, dx$

19. $\int_{1}^{2} x^2 \ln x \, dx$

20. $\int_{0}^{1/2} \text{arc} \sin x \, dx$

21. $\int_{0}^{1} e^x (x + 3)^2 \, dx$

22. $\int_{0}^{\pi/2} e^{2x} \sin x \, dx.$

4. REDUCTION FORMULAS

The integral

$$\int x^2 e^x \, dx$$

requires two integrations by parts. Each integration lowers the power of x by one until x disappears. In the same way

$$\int x^3 e^x \, dx$$

requires three integrations by parts, and

$$\int x^4 e^x \, dx$$

four integrations by parts. It is convenient to have a **reduction formula,** a formula that reduces

$$\int x^n e^x \, dx \qquad \text{to} \qquad \int x^{n-1} e^x \, dx.$$

Repeated use of such a formula reduces

$$\int x^n e^x \, dx \qquad \text{to} \qquad \int e^x \, dx.$$

EXAMPLE 4.1

Derive a reduction formula for $\int x^n e^x \, dx$.

Solution: Integrate by parts with

$$u = x^n, \qquad du = nx^{n-1} \, dx; \qquad dv = e^x \, dx, \qquad v = e^x :$$

$$\int x^n e^x \, dx = x^n e^x - \int e^x \cdot nx^{n-1} \, dx.$$

Answer: $\int x^n e^x \, dx = x^n e^x - n \int x^{n-1} e^x \, dx.$

REMARK: For abbreviation, write

$$J_n = \int x^n e^x \, dx.$$

Then the reduction formula is

$$J_n = x^n e^x - nJ_{n-1}.$$

EXAMPLE 4.2

Evaluate $\int x^5 e^x \, dx$.

Solution: Use the reduction formula just derived to compute J_5. By the reduction formula with $n = 5$,

$$J_5 = x^5 e^x - 5J_4.$$

By the reduction formula with $n = 4$,

$$J_4 = x^4 e^x - 4J_3.$$

Thus

$$J_5 = x^5 e^x - 5(x^4 e^x - 4J_3)$$
$$= x^5 e^x - 5x^4 e^x + 20J_3.$$

But by repeated use of the reduction formula,

$$J_3 = x^3 e^x - 3J_2$$
$$= x^3 e^x - 3(x^2 e^x - 2J_1)$$
$$= x^3 e^x - 3x^2 e^x + 6J_1$$
$$= x^3 e^x - 3x^2 e^x + 6(xe^x - J_0).$$

The integral J_0 is easy:

$$J_0 = \int x^0 e^x \, dx = e^x + C.$$

Hence

$$J_3 = e^x(x^3 - 3x^2 + 6x - 6) + C,$$

and consequently

$$J_5 = x^5 e^x - 5x^4 e^x + 20 e^x(x^3 - 3x^2 + 6x - 6) + C.$$

Answer:
$$e^x(x^5 - 5x^4 + 20x^3 - 60x^2 + 120x - 120) + C.$$

Question: Study the polynomial in the answer. How does each term follow from the preceding term? Can you write down the value of

$$\int x^6 e^x \, dx$$

by inspection?

EXAMPLE 4.3

Derive a reduction formula for $\displaystyle \int (\cos x)^n \, dx$.

Solution: Write

$$J_n = \int (\cos x)^n \, dx = \int (\cos x)^{n-1} \cos x \, dx,$$

and integrate by parts with

$$u = (\cos x)^{n-1}, \quad du = -(n-1)(\cos x)^{n-2} \sin x \, dx;$$
$$dv = \cos x \, dx, \quad v = \sin x:$$

$$\int (\cos x)^n \, dx = (\cos x)^{n-1} \sin x + \int (n-1)(\cos x)^{n-2} \sin^2 x \, dx$$

$$= (\cos x)^{n-1} \sin x + (n-1) \int (\cos x)^{n-2}(1 - \cos^2 x) \, dx.$$

Therefore,

$$J_n = (\cos x)^{n-1} \sin x + (n-1)J_{n-2} - (n-1)J_n.$$

Combine the terms in J_n:

$$nJ_n = (\cos x)^{n-1} \sin x + (n-1)J_{n-2}.$$

Now divide by n.

Answer: If $J_n = \displaystyle\int (\cos x)^n \, dx$, then

$$J_n = \frac{(\cos x)^{n-1} \sin x}{n} + \frac{n-1}{n} J_{n-2}.$$

REMARK: This reduction formula lowers the power of $\cos x$ by two. Therefore, repeated application will ultimately reduce J_n to J_0 or J_1, according as n is even or odd. But both of these are easy:

$$J_0 = \int (\cos x)^0 \, dx = \int dx = x + C,$$

$$J_1 = \int \cos x \, dx = \sin x + C.$$

EXAMPLE 4.4

Compute $\displaystyle\int_0^{\pi/2} (\cos x)^6 \, dx$.

Solution: Set

$$I_n = \int_0^{\pi/2} (\cos x)^n \, dx.$$

Then by the reduction formula of the last example,

$$I_n = \frac{(\cos x)^{n-1} \sin x}{n} \bigg|_0^{\pi/2} + \frac{n-1}{n} \int_0^{\pi/2} (\cos x)^{n-2} \, dx.$$

Hence,

$$I_n = 0 + \frac{n-1}{n} I_{n-2}.$$

Apply this formula with $n = 6$, then repeat with $n = 4$ and $n = 2$:

$$I_6 = \frac{5}{6} I_4 = \frac{5}{6} \left(\frac{3}{4} I_2 \right) = \frac{5}{6} \cdot \frac{3}{4} \left(\frac{1}{2} I_0 \right).$$

Therefore,

$$\int_0^{\pi/2} (\cos x)^6 \, dx = \frac{5 \cdot 3 \cdot 1}{6 \cdot 4 \cdot 2} \int_0^{\pi/2} dx = \frac{5 \cdot 3 \cdot 1}{6 \cdot 4 \cdot 2} \cdot \frac{\pi}{2}.$$

Answer: $\dfrac{5\pi}{32}$.

EXERCISES

Derive the reduction formula:

1. $\displaystyle\int (\ln x)^n\, dx = x\,(\ln x)^n - n \int (\ln x)^{n-1}\, dx, \quad n \neq -1$

2. $\displaystyle\int (\sin x)^n\, dx = -\frac{1}{n} (\sin x)^{n-1} \cos x + \frac{n-1}{n} \int (\sin x)^{n-2}\, dx$

3. $\displaystyle\int x^n \sin x\, dx = -x^n \cos x + n \int x^{n-1} \cos x\, dx$

4. $\displaystyle\int (\tan x)^n\, dx = \frac{(\tan x)^{n-1}}{n-1} - \int (\tan x)^{n-2}\, dx, \quad n \neq -1$

5. $\displaystyle\int \frac{dx}{(1+x^2)^n} = \frac{1}{2n-2} \frac{x}{(1+x^2)^{n-1}} + \frac{2n-3}{2n-2} \int \frac{dx}{(1+x^2)^{n-1}}, \quad n \neq 1.$

Using an appropriate reduction formula, compute the definite integral:

6. $\displaystyle\int_1^2 (\ln x)^2\, dx$

7. $\displaystyle\int_0^{\pi/2} \sin^7 x\, dx$

8. $\displaystyle\int_0^{\pi/2} \sin^8 x\, dx$

9. $\displaystyle\int_0^{\pi/4} \tan^{10} x\, dx$

10. $\displaystyle\int_0^1 \frac{dx}{(1+x^2)^3}$

11. $\displaystyle\int_{\pi/2}^{\pi} x^4 \sin x\, dx.$

12. Prove $\displaystyle\int_a^b (x-a)^m (b-x)^n\, dx = \frac{m!\,n!}{(m+n+1)!} (b-a)^{m+n+1}.$

5. TRICKS WITH DIFFERENTIALS [optional]

Integrals which involve $\sqrt{x^2 \pm a^2}$ can be handled by certain formal tricks. Examples are

$$\int \frac{dx}{\sqrt{x^2 \pm a^2}} \quad \text{and} \quad \int \sqrt{x^2 \pm a^2}\, dx.$$

Set

$$y^2 = x^2 \pm a^2.$$

Then

$$y\, dy = x\, dx, \qquad \frac{dx}{y} = \frac{dy}{x}.$$

In elementary ratio and proportion it is shown that if

$$\frac{a}{b} = \frac{c}{d}, \qquad \text{then} \qquad \frac{a}{b} = \frac{a+c}{b+d}.$$

Hence

$$\frac{dx}{y} = \frac{dx + dy}{x + y} = \frac{d(x + y)}{(x + y)}.$$

Conclusion:

$$\int \frac{dx}{y} = \int \frac{d(x + y)}{(x + y)} = \ln |x + y| + C,$$

$$\int \frac{dx}{\sqrt{x^2 \pm a^2}} = \ln |x + \sqrt{x^2 \pm a^2}| + C.$$

(This was previously obtained by trigonometric substitutions.)
   Next,

$$y \, dx = \frac{y^2 \, dx}{y} = \frac{x^2 \pm a^2}{y} \, dx$$

$$= \frac{x^2 \, dx}{y} \pm a^2 \frac{dx}{y} = x \, dy \pm a^2 \frac{dx}{y}.$$

But also $y \, dx = d(xy) - x \, dy$. Add:

$$2y \, dx = d(xy) \pm a^2 \frac{dx}{y}.$$

Integrate, using the first integral:

$$\int y \, dx = \frac{1}{2} xy \pm \frac{a^2}{2} \ln |x + y| + C,$$

$$\int \sqrt{x^2 \pm a^2} \, dx = \frac{1}{2} x \sqrt{x^2 \pm a^2} + \frac{a^2}{2} \ln |x + \sqrt{x^2 \pm a^2}| + C.$$

Similarly one can evaluate

$$\int \frac{\sqrt{x^2 \pm a^2}}{x} \, dx, \qquad \int \sqrt{a^2 - x^2} \, dx, \qquad \text{etc.}$$

EXERCISES

Find in the order given:

1. $\displaystyle \int \frac{\sqrt{x^2 \pm a^2}}{x} \, dx$

2. $\displaystyle \int \frac{\sqrt{x^2 \pm a^2} \, dx}{x^2}$

3. $\displaystyle \int \frac{\sqrt{x^2 \pm a^2} \, dx}{x^3}$

4. $\displaystyle \int \frac{dx}{x \sqrt{x^2 \pm a^2}}$

5. $\displaystyle\int \frac{dx}{x^2 \sqrt{x^2 \pm a^2}}$

6. $\displaystyle\int \frac{\sqrt{x^2 \pm a^2}\, dx}{x^4}$

7. $\displaystyle\int x^2 \sqrt{x^2 \pm a^2}\, dx.$

Find in the order given:

8. $\displaystyle\int \sqrt{a^2 - x^2}\, dx$

9. $\displaystyle\int \frac{dx}{x \sqrt{a^2 - x^2}}$

10. $\displaystyle\int \frac{\sqrt{a^2 - x^2}}{x}\, dx$

11. $\displaystyle\int \frac{x^2\, dx}{\sqrt{a^2 - x^2}}$

12. $\displaystyle\int \frac{\sqrt{a^2 - x^2}}{x^2}\, dx$

13. $\displaystyle\int \frac{dx}{x^2 \sqrt{a^2 - x^2}}.$

6. INTEGRAL TABLES

Inside the two covers of this book there is a short table of indefinite integrals. Much longer tables are available, for example those in the C.R.C. Standard Mathematical Tables and in Pierce's Table of Integrals.

A busy scientist does not want to bother with various tricks each time he encounters an integral; he uses integral tables. Not only do they save time, but they help eliminate errors.

We suggest that you get one of the more complete integral tables and spend some time browsing through it. Become familiar with the type of integral you can expect to find there.

Not every integral is listed in a table, but many can be transformed into integrals which are listed.

EXAMPLE 6.1

Use integral tables to evaluate $\displaystyle\int x^3 \sqrt{3 - 4x^2}\, dx.$

Solution: Most tables include a section on integrals involving $\sqrt{a^2 - x^2}$. Formula 177 of the C.R.C. tables states

$$\int x^3 \sqrt{a^2 - x^2}\, dx = -\left(\frac{1}{5} x^2 + \frac{2}{15} a^2\right)(a^2 - x^2)^{3/2}.$$

This is very close to what is wanted, except that $\sqrt{3 - 4x^2}$ appears instead of $\sqrt{a^2 - x^2}$. There are two simple ways of modifying the integrand: write either

$$\sqrt{3 - 4x^2} = \sqrt{4\left(\frac{3}{4} - x^2\right)} = 2\sqrt{\frac{3}{4} - x^2},$$

or

$$\sqrt{3 - 4x^2} = \sqrt{3 - (2x)^2} = \sqrt{3 - u^2}, \qquad \text{where} \quad u = 2x.$$

Use the first method with $a^2 = \frac{3}{4}$:

$$\int x^3 \sqrt{3 - 4x^2} \, dx = 2 \int x^3 \sqrt{\frac{3}{4} - x^2} \, dx$$

$$= -2 \left(\frac{1}{5} x^2 + \frac{2}{15} \cdot \frac{3}{4} \right) \left(\frac{3}{4} - x^2 \right)^{3/2}$$

Use the second method with $u = 2x$ and $a^2 = 3$:

$$\int x^3 \sqrt{3 - 4x^2} \, dx = \int \left(\frac{u}{2} \right)^3 \sqrt{3 - u^2} \cdot \frac{1}{2} \, du$$

$$= \frac{1}{16} \int u^3 \sqrt{3 - u^2} \, du$$

$$= -\frac{1}{16} \left(\frac{1}{5} u^2 + \frac{2}{15} \cdot 3 \right) (3 - u^2)^{3/2}$$

$$= -\frac{1}{16} \left(\frac{1}{5} \cdot 4x^2 + \frac{2}{5} \right) (3 - 4x^2)^{3/2}.$$

A little algebra shows that both answers agree.

$$\textit{Answer:} \quad -\frac{1}{40} (2x^2 + 1) (3 - 4x^2)^{3/2} + C.$$

EXAMPLE 6.2

Use integral tables to evaluate $\int e^{2x}(\sin x)^3 \, dx$.

Solution: In the C.R.C. integral tables under EXPONENTIAL FORMS is Formula 416:

$$\int e^{ax}(\sin bx)^n \, dx$$

$$= \frac{1}{a^2 + n^2 b^2} \Bigg[(a \sin bx - nb \cos bx)e^{ax} (\sin bx)^{n-1}$$

$$+ n(n - 1)b^2 \int e^{ax} (\sin bx)^{n-2} \, dx \Bigg].$$

This is a reduction formula which lowers the power of $\sin bx$ by two. Apply it with $a = 2$, $b = 1$, $n = 3$:

$$\int e^{2x}(\sin x)^3 \, dx$$

$$= \frac{1}{4 + 9} \Bigg[(2 \sin x - 3 \cos x)e^{2x} (\sin x)^2 + 6 \int e^{2x} (\sin x) \, dx \Bigg].$$

The integral on the right is given by Formula 407 with $a = 2$, $b = 1$. Its value is

$$\frac{e^{2x}(2 \sin x - \cos x)}{5}.$$

Substitute this into the preceding equation to obtain the answer.

$$Answer: \quad \frac{e^{2x}}{13}\left[(2 \sin x - 3 \cos x) \sin^2 x \right.$$
$$\left. + \frac{6}{5}(2 \sin x - \cos x)\right] + C.$$

Integral tables use abbreviations for common expressions. For instance, one section of the C.R.C. tables contains formulas involving X and $\sqrt{X}$, where $X = a + bx + cx^2$.

EXAMPLE 6.3

Use integral tables to evaluate

$$\int \frac{\sqrt{5x^2 + 2x + 3}}{x}\, dx.$$

Solution: Apply Formula 218 of the C.R.C. tables:

$$\int \frac{\sqrt{X}}{x}\, dx = \sqrt{X} + \frac{b}{2}\int \frac{dx}{\sqrt{X}} + a\int \frac{dx}{x\sqrt{X}}.$$

The integrals on the right are given by Formulas 193 and 214:

$$\int \frac{dx}{\sqrt{X}} = \frac{1}{\sqrt{c}} \ln\left(\sqrt{X} + x\sqrt{c} + \frac{b}{2\sqrt{c}} \right), \qquad c > 0,$$

$$\int \frac{dx}{x\sqrt{X}} = -\frac{1}{\sqrt{a}} \ln\left(\frac{\sqrt{X} + \sqrt{a}}{x} + \frac{b}{2\sqrt{a}} \right), \qquad a > 0.$$

In this case $X = 3 + 2x + 5x^2$; set $a = 3$, $b = 2$, $c = 5$, to obtain

$$\int \frac{\sqrt{5x^2 + 2x + 3}}{x}\, dx = \sqrt{5x^2 + 2x + 3}$$

$$+ \frac{1}{\sqrt{5}} \ln\left(\sqrt{5x^2 + 2x + 3} + x\sqrt{5} + \frac{1}{\sqrt{5}} \right)$$

$$- \sqrt{3} \ln\left(\frac{\sqrt{5x^2 + 2x + 3} + \sqrt{3}}{x} + \frac{1}{\sqrt{3}} \right) + C.$$

The C.R.C. tables use $\ln(\cdots)$; absolute values are understood.

$$\text{Answer:} \quad \sqrt{X} + \frac{1}{\sqrt{5}} \ln \left| \sqrt{X} + x \sqrt{5} + \frac{1}{\sqrt{5}} \right|$$

$$- \sqrt{3} \ln \left| \frac{\sqrt{X} + \sqrt{3}}{x} + \frac{1}{\sqrt{3}} \right| + C,$$

$$\text{where } X = 5x^2 + 2x + 3.$$

EXERCISES

Find, using tables:

1. $\displaystyle\int e^{-2x} \sin 5x \, dx$

2. $\displaystyle\int \sqrt{4 - x^2} \, dx$

3. $\displaystyle\int x^2 \sqrt{1 - 4x^2} \, dx$

4. $\displaystyle\int \frac{x^2 \, dx}{\sqrt{4 - 3x^2}}$

5. $\displaystyle\int \frac{x^2 \, dx}{2 + 5x^2}$

6. $\displaystyle\int (4 - x^2)^{5/2} \, dx$
   (trigonometric substitution)

7. $\displaystyle\int x^3 \sin \frac{x}{2} \, dx$

8. $\displaystyle\int (\ln x)^4 \, dx$

9. $\displaystyle\int \frac{x^2 - 6x - 2}{x \sqrt{10x^2 + 7}} \, dx$

10. $\displaystyle\int (x + 3)^2 \sqrt{x^2 + 2x + 5} \, dx.$

Compute:

11. $\displaystyle\int_0^1 \frac{x^4 + 2x^2 - 3}{x^4 + 2x^2 + 1} \, dx$

12. $\displaystyle\int_0^1 \frac{x^2 \, dx}{1 + 3x^2}$

13. $\displaystyle\int_0^\pi e^{3x} \cos^6 x \, dx$

14. $\displaystyle\int_0^{2\pi} \cos^2 x \sin^8 x \, dx$

15. $\displaystyle\int_0^1 \frac{dx}{(1 + 3x)^2(2 + 5x)}$

16. $\displaystyle\int_1^2 (x \ln x)^3 \, dx.$

18. Approximation Methods

1. NUMERICAL INTEGRATION

In many practical problems, the solution is expressed by a definite integral

$$\int_a^b f(x) \, dx.$$

The value of the integral is $F(b) - F(a)$, where $F(x)$ is an antiderivative of $f(x)$. But suppose you cannot find an antiderivative. The problem is still there, and your boss wants an answer. What do you do? Or suppose $f(x)$ is some physical quantity for which you have only a table of values, for instance velocities measured at intervals of 0.1 sec. Then what?

A practical procedure in problems of this type is to estimate

$$\int_a^b f(x) \, dx$$

if you cannot evaluate it exactly.

Recall that an integral is nearly a sum:

$$\int_a^b f(x) \, dx \approx [f(\bar{x}_1) + f(\bar{x}_2) + \cdots + f(\bar{x}_n)] \, \Delta x.$$

This approximate formula provides a method for estimating the integral. Divide the interval from a to b into n equal pieces of length Δx. Let $\bar{x}_1$, $\bar{x}_2$, $\cdots$ denote their midpoints:

Compute $f(\bar{x}_1)$, $f(\bar{x}_2)$, $\cdots$, $f(\bar{x}_n)$. Add these values and multiply by Δx. The result is an approximation to the value of the integral.

Rectangular Rule

$$\int_a^b f(x) \, dx \approx [f(\bar{x}_1) + f(\bar{x}_2) + \cdots + f(\bar{x}_n)] \, \Delta x.$$

The interval from a to b is divided into n equal parts, each of length $\Delta x = (b - a)/n$. The points $\bar{x}_1, \bar{x}_2, \cdots$ are the midpoints of these parts.

Great accuracy can be achieved by choosing Δx very small, i.e., n very large. Of course the amount of computation increases with n, so a computer may be needed. Often the procedure becomes too laborious for hand computation when n exceeds 15 or 20, but a computer can handle values of n in the thousands.

EXAMPLE 1.1

Estimate $\int_0^4 (x - 1)^2 \, dx$ and compare to the exact value.

Solution: Divide the interval from 0 to 4 into n equal parts. A reasonable choice of n for hand computation is 16, which means $\Delta x = 0.25$.

Tabulate $f(x) = (x - 1)^2$ at $\bar{x}_1 = 0.125$, $\bar{x}_2 = 0.375$, $\bar{x}_3 = 0.625$, etc. (Table 1.1).

TABLE 1.1

x	$f(x)$	x	$f(x)$	x	$f(x)$
0.125	0.765625	1.375	0.140625	2.625	2.640625
0.375	0.390625	1.625	0.390625	2.875	3.515625
0.625	0.140625	1.875	0.765625	3.125	4.515625
0.875	0.015625	2.125	1.265625	3.375	5.640625
1.125	0.015625	2.375	1.890625	3.625	6.890625
				3.875	8.265625

$$\int_0^4 (x - 1)^2 \, dx \approx [f(\bar{x}_1) + f(\bar{x}_2) + \cdots + f(\bar{x}_{16})] \, \Delta x = 9.31250.$$

The exact value of the integral is

$$\int_0^4 (x - 1)^2 \, dx = \frac{(x - 1)^3}{3} \Big|_0^4 = \frac{28}{3} = 9.33333 \cdots .$$

Notice that carrying 6 decimals in your work does *not* automatically guarantee 6-place accuracy. The answer, however, accurate to 1 decimal, is not bad considering the crude choice $\Delta x = 0.25$. A better estimate is obtained if $\Delta x = 0.1$. That requires more work since then $n = 40$, but still the computation can be done by hand. Here is the result:

$$\int_0^4 (x - 1)^2 \, dx \approx [f(0.05) + f(0.15) + \cdots + f(3.95)](0.1) = 9.33000,$$

which is closer.

For greater accuracy, use a computer, taking $n = 400$. Result:

$$\int_0^4 (x - 1)^2 \, dx \approx [f(0.005) + f(0.015) + \cdots + f(3.995)](0.01) \approx 9.33328,$$

correct to within 0.00006.

Answer: $\Delta x = 0.25: 9.31250$; $\Delta x = 0.1: 9.33000$;
$\Delta x = 0.01: 9.33328$; exact: $9\frac{1}{3} = 9.33333 \cdots$.

REMARK: Beware of false accuracy! The computer may give a 10-digit answer, regardless of the inaccuracy of the input data.

EXAMPLE 1.2

Estimate the area under the curve $y = \dfrac{1}{x}$ between $x = 1$ and $x = 3$.

Carry 4 significant digits in your work.

Solution: The area is given by the integral

$$\int_1^3 \frac{1}{x} \, dx.$$

To estimate it, divide the interval $1 \leq x \leq 3$ into 20 subintervals, each of length 0.1. Tabulate $f(x) = 1/x$ at the midpoints of these subintervals (Table 1.2).

TABLE 1.2

x	$f(x)$	x	$f(x)$	x	$f(x)$
1.05	0.9524	1.75	0.5714	2.45	0.4082
1.15	0.8696	1.85	0.5405	2.55	0.3922
1.25	0.8000	1.95	0.5128	2.65	0.3774
1.35	0.7407	2.05	0.4878	2.75	0.3636
1.45	0.6897	2.15	0.4651	2.85	0.3509
1.55	0.6452	2.25	0.4444	2.95	0.3390
1.65	0.6061	2.35	0.4255		

$$\int_1^3 \frac{1}{x} \, dx \approx [f(1.05) + f(1.15) + \cdots + f(2.95)](0.1) \approx 1.098.$$

For greater accuracy, use a computer, taking $n = 200$. Result:

$$\int_1^3 \frac{1}{x} \, dx \approx [f(1.005) + f(1.015) + \cdots + f(2.995)](0.01) \approx 1.098608.$$

Answer: $n = 20: 1.098$; $n = 200: 1.098608$.

More refined calculations show that to 6 significant digits the value is 1.09861.

EXERCISES

Estimate the integral by rectangular approximation, taking the suggested values of n. In each case compute the exact value of the integral and compare it to your estimate.

By hand carrying 4 places, $n = 4$ and $n = 10$:

1. $\displaystyle\int_1^2 (x^2 + x)\, dx$
2. $\displaystyle\int_0^4 (x + 1)^2\, dx$

3. $\displaystyle\int_0^2 e^x\, dx$
4. $\displaystyle\int_0^2 e^{-x}\, dx;$

by computer, $n = 10$ and $n = 100$:

5. $\displaystyle\int_1^2 \frac{1}{x^2}\, dx$
6. $\displaystyle\int_2^3 \left(x + \frac{1}{x^2}\right) dx;$

by computer, $n = 20$ and $n = 200$:

7. $\displaystyle\int_0^2 (1 + \sin x)\, dx$
8. $\displaystyle\int_0^2 3 \cos x\, dx.$

Estimate the integral by rectangular approximation, taking the suggested values of Δx, and carrying 4 places in your work:

9. $\displaystyle\int_{10}^{12} \log_{10} x\, dx;$ $\Delta x = 0.5, \Delta x = 0.2$

10. $\displaystyle\int_{10}^{12} x \log_{10} x\, dx;$ $\Delta x = 0.5, \Delta x = 0.2$

11. $\displaystyle\int_0^2 \frac{1}{x+1}\, dx;$ $\Delta x = 0.2, \Delta x = 0.01$

12. $\displaystyle\int_0^2 \frac{1}{x^2+1}\, dx;$ $\Delta x = 0.2, \Delta x = 0.01$

13. $\displaystyle\int_0^2 x \sin x\, dx;$ $\Delta x = 0.2, \Delta x = 0.01$

14. $\displaystyle\int_0^2 x \cos x\, dx;$ $\Delta x = 0.2, \Delta x = 0.01$

15. $\displaystyle\int_2^4 \left(x + \frac{1}{x}\right) dx;$ $\Delta x = 0.2, \Delta x = 0.01$

16. $\displaystyle\int_1^5 \sqrt{x}\, dx;$ $\Delta x = 0.25, \Delta x = 0.01.$

2. TRAPEZOIDAL APPROXIMATION

The numerical integration technique of the last section was based on the approximation of areas by rectangles (Fig. 2.1a). Another useful way to approximate areas is by trapezoids (Fig. 2.1b).

Examine a typical trapezoid (Fig. 2.2). It has base Δx and sides $f(x_{i-1})$ and $f(x_i)$. Hence its area is

$$\frac{\Delta x}{2} [f(x_{i-1}) + f(x_i)].$$

Estimate the integral

$$\int_a^b f(x)\, dx$$

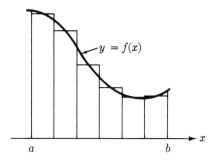

$y = f(x)$

FIG. 2.1a

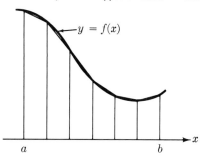

$y = f(x)$

FIG. 2.1b

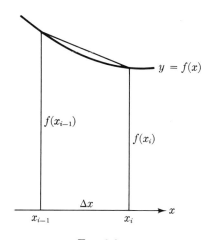

$y = f(x)$

$f(x_{i-1})$

$f(x_i)$

Δx

x_{i-1} x_i

FIG. 2.2

by the combined areas of the trapezoids in Fig. 2.1b:

(total area of trapezoids)

$$= \frac{\Delta x}{2}[f(x_0) + f(x_1)] + \frac{\Delta x}{2}[f(x_1) + f(x_2)] + \cdots + \frac{\Delta x}{2}[f(x_{n-1}) + f(x_n)]$$

$$= \frac{\Delta x}{2}\{[f(x_0) + f(x_1)] + [f(x_1) + f(x_2)] + \cdots + [f(x_{n-1}) + f(x_n)]\}$$

$$= \frac{\Delta x}{2}\{f(x_0) + 2f(x_1) + 2f(x_2) + \cdots + 2f(x_{n-1}) + f(x_n)\}.$$

Trapezoidal Rule

$$\int_a^b f(x)\,dx \approx \frac{\Delta x}{2}\{f(x_0) + 2f(x_1) + 2f(x_2) + \cdots + 2f(x_{n-1}) + f(x_n)\},$$

where $x_0, x_1, \cdots, x_n$ are equally spaced points dividing the interval from $a = x_0$ to $b = x_n$ into n equal parts, each of length $\Delta x = (b - a)/n$.

Each quantity $f(x_i)$, except the first and the last, occurs with coefficient 2. That is because each vertical line in Fig. 2.1b, except the first and the last, is a side of two trapezoids.

Like rectangular approximation, trapezoidal approximation is a simple procedure well-adapted to hand and computer use. It can be made as accurate as desired by choosing Δx very small, i.e., n very large. It has two advantages over the rectangular method, however.

First, the arithmetic is usually easier in hand computation. For example, suppose you estimate

$$\int_0^1 f(x)\, dx$$

with $\Delta x = 0.1$. You must compute $f(0)$, $f(0.1)$, $f(0.2)$, $\cdot\ \cdot\ \cdot$ when using trapezoids; you must compute $f(0.05)$, $f(0.15)$, $f(0.25)$, $\cdot\ \cdot\ \cdot$ when using rectangles. The latter computations generally involve more arithmetic.

Second, and more important, the trapezoid method is superior when the function is given by a table. For example, if $f(0)$, $f(0.1)$, $f(0.2)$, $\cdot\ \cdot\ \cdot$, $f(1.0)$ are given, this data is adequate for trapezoidal approximation to

$$\int_0^1 f(x)\, dx$$

with $\Delta x = 0.1$. For rectangular approximation with this data, you must take $\Delta x = 0.2$ and use only $f(0.1)$, $f(0.3)$, $f(0.5)$, $f(0.7)$, $f(0.9)$. This approximation is inferior since it uses a cruder Δx and only part of the data.

We illustrate use of the Trapezoidal Rule by some examples.

EXAMPLE 2.1

Use the Trapezoidal Rule to estimate $\displaystyle\int_0^1 (x + 1)\,(x - 1)^2\, dx.$

Solution: For hand computation take $\Delta x = 0.1$, $n = 10$. Tabulate $f(x) = (x + 1)\,(x - 1)^2$ at $x = 0, 0.1, 0.2, \cdot\ \cdot\ \cdot, 1.0$. See Table 2.1.

TABLE 2.1

x	$f(x)$	x	$f(x)$
0.0	1.000	0.6	0.256
0.1	0.891	0.7	0.153
0.2	0.768	0.8	0.072
0.3	0.637	0.9	0.019
0.4	0.504	1.0	0.000
0.5	0.375		

$$\int_0^1 f(x)\, dx \approx \frac{(0.1)}{2}\,[f(0) + 2f(0.1) + 2f(0.2) + \cdot\ \cdot\ \cdot + 2f(0.9) + f(1.0)]$$

$$= 0.4175.$$

For greater accuracy, use a computer, taking $n = 100$:

$$\int_0^1 f(x)\, dx$$

$$\approx \frac{(0.01)}{2}\,[f(0) + 2f(0.01) + 2f(0.02) + \cdots + 2f(0.99) + f(1.00)]$$

$$\approx 0.416675.$$

Answer: $\Delta x = 0.1\colon 0.4175;\ \Delta x = 0.01\colon 0.416675;$
exact: $\frac{5}{12} = 0.416666\cdots.$

EXAMPLE 2.2

Use the Trapezoidal Rule to estimate

$$\int_{0.5}^{1.0} \tan x\, dx.$$

Solution: For hand computation choose $\Delta x = 0.1$, $n = 5$, and use a table of tangents of angles in radians:

$$\int_{0.5}^{1.0} \tan x\, dx$$

$$\approx \frac{(0.1)}{2}\,[\tan(0.5) + 2\tan(0.6) + \cdots + 2\tan(0.9) + \tan(1.0)]$$

$$\approx 0.48681.$$

For greater accuracy, use a computer, taking $n = 50$:

$$\int_{0.5}^{1.0} \tan x\, dx$$

$$\approx \frac{(0.01)}{2}\,[\tan(0.50) + 2\tan(0.51) + \cdots + 2\tan(0.99) + \tan(1.00)]$$

$$\approx 0.48506.$$

(To 5 places, the actual value is 0.48504.)

Answer: $n = 5\colon 0.48681;$
$n = 50\colon 0.48506.$

EXERCISES

Carry 4 significant digits in hand computations.

Estimate the integral by trapezoidal approximation, taking the suggested values of n. In each case compare the values with the exact value obtained by integrating:

1. $\int_0^4 (x-1)^2\, dx;\quad n = 4,\, n = 10$ 2. $\int_1^2 (x^2 + x)\, dx;\quad n = 4,\, n = 10$

3. $\int_0^1 \sin x\, dx; \quad n = 10,\ n = 50$

4. $\int_0^1 (\sin x + \cos x)\, dx; \quad n = 10,\ n = 100.$

Estimate the integral by trapezoidal approximation, taking the suggested values of Δx:

5. $\int_0^{\pi/2} \sin^2 x\, dx; \quad \Delta x = \dfrac{\pi}{12},\ \Delta x = \dfrac{\pi}{180}$

6. $\int_0^{\pi/2} \cos^2 x\, dx; \quad \Delta x = \dfrac{\pi}{12},\ \Delta x = \dfrac{\pi}{180}$

7. $\int_0^1 (x-1)^2 (x+1)^2\, dx; \quad \Delta x = 0.1,\ \Delta x = 0.01$

8. $\int_1^{1.5} (x^3 + x)\, dx; \quad \Delta x = 0.1,\ \Delta x = 0.005$

9. $\int_1^2 x \sqrt{x}\, dx; \quad \Delta x = 0.1,\ \Delta x = 0.01$

10. $\int_{10}^{12} x \log_{10} x\, dx; \quad \Delta x = 0.2,\ \Delta x = 0.01$

11. $\int_1^{1.5} (1 + \tan x)\, dx; \quad \Delta x = 0.1,\ \Delta x = 0.005$

12. $\int_0^{\pi/2} \sin \dfrac{x}{2}\, dx; \quad \Delta x = \dfrac{\pi}{12},\ \Delta x = \dfrac{\pi}{180}.$

Estimate the integral by rectangular and trapezoidal approximation. Compare the estimates to the exact value obtained by integrating. Use $n = 10$:

13. $\int_1^2 x^2\, dx$

14. $\int_{0.5}^{1.0} \dfrac{dx}{x^2}$

15. $\int_0^1 \sin(x+1)\, dx$

16. $\int_0^1 \cos x\, dx.$

17. An automobile starting from rest accelerates for 15 sec. Velocity readings (in feet per second) taken at 1-sec intervals are: 0, 0.5, 2.1, 4.7, 8.3, 13.0, 18.7, 25.5, 33.3, 43.1, 53.0, 63.9, 75.9, 88.9, 102.9, 118.0. Estimate, using trapezoidal approximation, the distance the car traveled during this time.

18. Approximate $\int_N^{2N} \dfrac{1}{x}\, dx$ by the Trapezoidal Rule using $\Delta x = 1$. Deduce that

$$\frac{1}{N+1} + \frac{1}{N+2} + \frac{1}{N+3} + \cdots + \frac{1}{2N} \approx \ln 2.$$

(See Exs. 21, 22, p. 337.)

3. FLOWCHARTS [optional]

The computations involved in numerical integration are repetitive and boring. In doing them by hand, people become careless and error-prone.

A computer, however, is not subject to boredom and carelessness, and is especially suited for repetitive computations. It can provide speed and accuracy far beyond the capabilities of humans.

Standard programming languages such as Fortran, Algol, and PL/1 simplify the writing of programs for numerical integration and other tasks. Subroutines for common functions, $\sin x$, $\cos x$, e^x, $\sqrt{x}$, and others, are available in these languages and further simplify the work of the applied mathematician, engineer, or scientist.

Rather than use one of these languages, we shall describe computer routines by **flowcharts**. A flowchart is a diagram showing a step-by-step procedure for solving a problem; it can easily be translated into one of the programming languages.

Since flowcharting conventions vary, it is important to understand those we shall use (Fig. 3.1). Boxes represent the steps in a computation, and

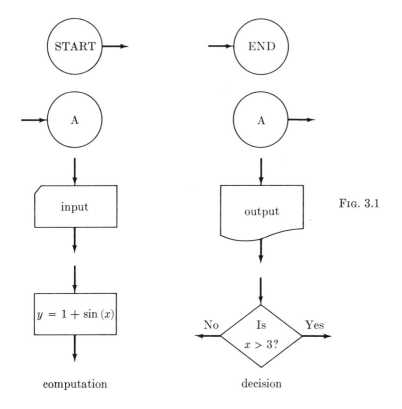

FIG. 3.1

arrows show the sequence of steps. The shape of each box indicates the nature of the step it represents. Circles label the beginning and end, and connections between parts of a long program. Rectangles represent computations. Boxes shaped like punched cards show the input data; boxes shaped like torn-off pieces of paper show the output. Diamonds indicate decision points, where the direction depends on the answer to some question.

The use of these conventions is illustrated in a flowchart (Fig. 3.2) for the trapezoidal approximation of Example 2.1. The statements "$f = 2f$,"

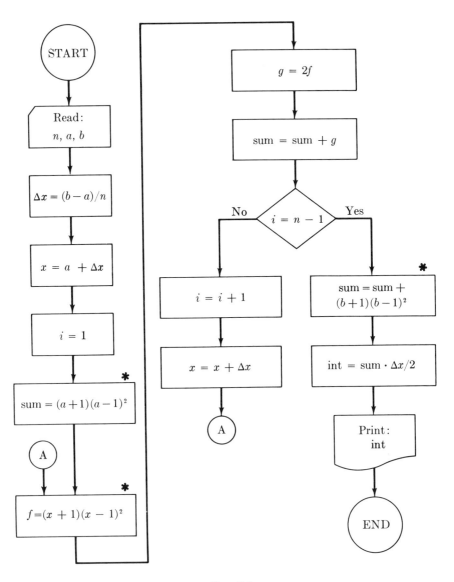

Fɪɢ. 3.2

"sum = sum + f," "$i = i + 1$," and "$x = x + \Delta x$" may appear foolish. But the equal sign in boxes is *not* the ordinary mathematical equal sign; instead, it is an abbreviated instruction. For instance, "$f = 2f$" means "calculate a new value for f, namely twice the current value"; and "$i = i + 1$"

means "increase the value of i by 1." (Sometimes a replacement arrow is used to avoid confusion: $f \leftarrow 2f$, $i \leftarrow i + 1$, and so forth.)

In Fig. 3.2, the boxes marked $*$ are the heart of the program. They contain the computation of the values $f(x_0)$, $f(x_1)$, $\cdots$, $f(x_n)$; the rest of the program puts these values together according to the Trapezoidal Rule. Consequently, the flowchart describes the trapezoidal approximation to

$$\int_a^b f(x)\, dx$$

for whichever function $f(x)$ appears in the starred boxes.

Study the flowchart in Fig. 3.2. Be sure you understand each step.

EXERCISES

Construct a flowchart for

1. $y = ax + b$; input a, b, and x
2. x, if $y = ax + b$; input a, b, and y
3. the roots of $ax^2 + bx + c = 0$; input a, b, and c.
4. Construct a flowchart for the Rectangular Rule.
5. Construct a flowchart for this variant of the Rectangular Rule: instead of $f(\bar{x}_i)$, use the value $f(x_i)$ of $f(x)$ at the right-hand endpoint of the subinterval.

4. APPROXIMATING A CURVE BY ITS TANGENT

One of the fundamental uses of Differential Calculus is the approximation of a curve by its tangent. In this and the next two sections we shall study such straight line approximations, their applications, and their generalizations: approximations by quadratic and cubic curves.

Under a microscope a smooth curve appears nearly straight (Fig. 4.1). Its tangent at $(a, f(a))$ is quite close to the curve, at least in a small neighborhood of that point (Fig. 4.2). The slope of the tangent line is $f'(a)$. By the point-slope formula, the equation of the tangent line is:

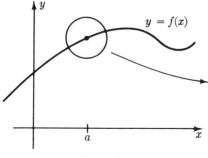

Fig. 4.1

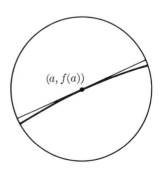

Fig. 4.2

$$y - f(a) = f'(a)\,(x - a) \qquad \text{or} \qquad y = f(a) + f'(a)\,(x - a).$$

Since the tangent is close to the curve, it is reasonable to expect that the linear function $f(a) + f'(a)\,(x - a)$ is a good approximation to the value of $f(x)$, at least for x near a. A good linear approximation is often useful, especially if $f(x)$ is hard to compute.

EXAMPLE 4.1

Find the equation of the line tangent to $y = 4 - (x - 2)^2$ at $(1, 3)$. How closely does it approximate the curve?

Solution: First check the consistency of the data. Is the point $(1, 3)$ really on the curve? Yes, because $3 = 4 - (1 - 2)^2$. Next,

$$y = 4 - (x - 2)^2,$$

$$y' = -2(x - 2).$$

The tangent at $(1, 3)$ has slope $y'(1) = 2$. Its equation is

$$y - 3 = 2(x - 1) \qquad \text{or} \qquad y = 2x + 1.$$

Sketch the curve and its tangent (Fig. 4.3). To see how closely the line

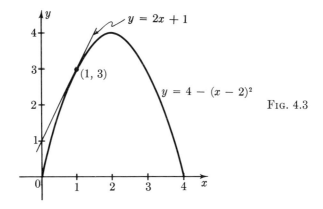

Fig. 4.3

approximates the curve, compute the difference

$$y(\text{curve}) - y(\text{line}) = [4 - (x - 2)^2] - [2x + 1]$$

$$= -x^2 + 2x - 1$$

$$= -(x - 1)^2.$$

Call this difference $e(x)$, the error in approximating the curve by its tangent. Because of the exponent 2, the error is very small when x is near 1. For example, when $x = 1.1$, the curve and the line are 0.01 units apart; when $x = 1.01$, they are 0.0001 units apart.

Answer: $y = 2x + 1$, very close to the curve near $(1, 3)$ since the error $e(x) = -(x - 1)^2$.

The result of this example can be interpreted numerically: $2x + 1$ is a good approximation to $4 - (x - 2)^2$ for values of x near 1. For example, if $0.99 \leq x \leq 1.01$, the approximation is correct to within 0.0001. When x is within 2 decimal places of 1, then $2x + 1$ is within 4 decimal places of $4 - (x - 2)^2$. This suggests that the error $e(x)$ not only approaches zero as $x \longrightarrow 1$, but also $e(x) \longrightarrow 0$ faster than $x \longrightarrow 1$. To see why, look at the ratio of $e(x)$ to $x - 1$:

$$\frac{e(x)}{x - 1} = \frac{-(x - 1)^2}{x - 1} = -(x - 1) \longrightarrow 0 \qquad \text{as} \qquad x \longrightarrow 1.$$

Both quantities are small when x is near 1, but $e(x)$ is much smaller.

EXAMPLE 4.2

Find the equation of the line tangent to $y = (x + 1)(x - 2)^2$ at $(-1, 0)$. How closely does it approximate the curve?

Solution: The data is consistent since

$$0 = (-1 + 1)(-1 - 2)^2.$$

Multiply out:

$$y = (x + 1)(x - 2)^2 = x^3 - 3x^2 + 4.$$

Hence

$$y' = 3x^2 - 6x,$$

$$y'(-1) = 9.$$

The equation of the tangent is

$$y - 0 = 9(x + 1).$$

Sketch the curve and its tangent (Fig. 4.4). The error is

$$e(x) = y(\text{curve}) - y(\text{line})$$

$$= (x+1)(x - 2)^2 - 9(x + 1)$$

$$= (x+1)[(x-2)^2 - 9]$$

$$= (x+1)(x^2 - 4x - 5)$$

$$= (x+1)^2(x - 5).$$

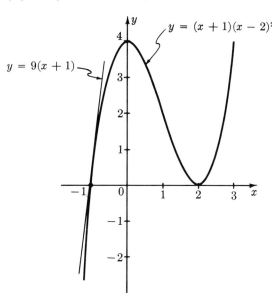

FIG. 4.4

The error is very small when x is near -1 because of the factor $(x + 1)^2$.

The other factor, $(x - 5)$, does no harm; it is approximately -6 when x is near -1.

> *Answer:* $y = 9(x + 1)$. The tangent is very close to the curve near $(-1, 0)$ since $e(x) \approx -6(x + 1)^2$.

REMARK: This example shows

$$(x + 1) (x - 2)^2 \approx 9(x + 1) \qquad \text{for} \quad x \approx -1.$$

More precisely,

$$(x + 1) (x - 2)^2 = 9(x + 1) + e(x),$$

where

$$e(x) = (x + 1)^2(x - 5).$$

Just as $e(x)/(x - 1) \longrightarrow 0$ in the last example, here

$$\frac{e(x)}{x + 1} = (x + 1) (x - 5) \longrightarrow 0 \qquad \text{as} \quad x \longrightarrow -1.$$

These examples illustrate a general principle:

> The equation of the tangent line to $y = f(x)$ at $(a, f(a))$ is
> $$y = f(a) + f'(a) (x - a).$$
> Let
> $$e(x) = f(x) - [f(a) + f'(a) (x - a)]$$
> denote the error in approximating the graph by the tangent. Then
> $$\frac{e(x)}{x - a} \longrightarrow 0 \qquad \text{as} \quad x \longrightarrow a.$$

The reason is simple:

$$e(x) = f(x) - [f(a) + f'(a) (x - a)]$$
$$= [f(x) - f(a)] - f'(a) (x - a),$$
$$\frac{e(x)}{x - a} = \frac{f(x) - f(a)}{x - a} - f'(a).$$

But as $x \longrightarrow a$,

$$\frac{f(x) - f(a)}{x - a} \longrightarrow f'(a).$$

Therefore,

$$\frac{e(x)}{x - a} \longrightarrow f'(a) - f'(a) = 0 \qquad \text{as} \quad x \longrightarrow a.$$

(See Chapter 21, Section 1 for a more precise treatment.)

Find the equation of the line tangent to the curve at the specified point; also find the error made in approximating the curve by its tangent:

1. $y = 1 - x^2$ at $(0, 1)$ 　　　　　　2. $y = 2x^2 + 3$ at $(1, 5)$

3. $y = x^3$ at $(3, 27)$ 　　　　　　　4. $y = x^2 + x + 1$ at $(-1, 1)$

5. $y = \dfrac{1}{3x + 4}$ at $(-1, 1)$ 　　　6. $y = x^2 - x^3$ at $(1, 0)$

7. $y = \sin x$ at $(\tfrac{1}{2}\pi, 1)$ 　　　　8. $y = e^{3x}$ at $(0, 1)$.

9. In Ex. 3, let $e(x)$ be the error made in approximating the curve by its tangent.
Find the ratio $\dfrac{e(x)}{x - 3}$.

10. Suppose that the population of a country is given by $P = 10^7 e^{t/10}$, where t is the time in years, initially 0. If the growth is assumed linear, how large is the error after 10 years?

Justify the approximation near $x = 0$:

11. $\sin x \approx x$ 　　　　　　　　　12. $e^x \approx 1 + x$

13. $\dfrac{1}{1 - x} \approx 1 + x$ 　　　　　　14. $\cos x \approx 1$.

5. ROOT FINDING

One of the most common problems in all branches of mathematics is that of solving difficult equations, for example:

$$x^5 - x - 3 = 0, \qquad \cos x = x, \qquad e^x = 4x^2.$$

There are no formulas for exact solutions of these equations. The best we can hope for are close numerical approximations to solutions.

It is customary to write equations so that the right side is zero, for example:

$$x^5 - x - 3 = 0, \qquad \cos x - x = 0, \qquad e^x - 4x^2 = 0.$$

Each equation is then of the form

$$f(x) = 0.$$

A value a for which $f(a) = 0$ is called a **root** or **solution** of the equation $f(x) = 0$. It is also called a **zero** of the function $f(x)$.

Bisection Method

The roots of $f(x) = 0$ are precisely those values of x for which the graph $y = f(x)$ intersects the x-axis. This point of view suggests a "brute force" method of approximating a root if the graph crosses the x-axis. Find two numbers x_0 and x_1 such that $f(x_0) < 0$ and $f(x_1) > 0$. The graph $y = f(x)$ must cross the x-axis between x_0 and x_1 (Fig. 5.1). Let x_2 be the midpoint

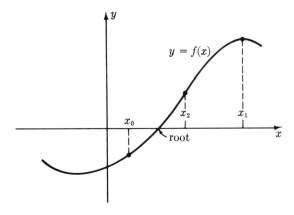

$$\text{Fig. 5.1}$$

of the segment from x_0 to x_1. Compute $f(x_2)$. If $f(x_2) > 0$, there is a root between x_0 and x_2 (as in Fig. 5.1); if $f(x_2) < 0$, there is a root between x_1 and x_2. In either case, let x_3 be the midpoint of the segment in which the root lies, and repeat the process.

This procedure is called **bisection.** At each step the root is "trapped" in an interval one half the length of the preceding interval. Therefore, after a sufficient number of repetitions, the root is trapped in as small an interval as desired. Thus, any degree of accuracy can be attained by a sufficient amount of work.

Newton–Raphson Method

Another scheme for finding roots is the **Newton–Raphson Method** (also known simply as **Newton's Method**). It is generally more efficient than the Bisection Method because it uses more information about the function.

The idea of the Newton–Raphson Method is simple. You want to know where the graph $y = f(x)$ crosses the x-axis. From a sketch of the graph, or by trial and error, make a guess, x_0. At the point $(x_0, f(x_0))$ of the graph draw the tangent line (Fig. 5.2). The tangent line crosses the x-axis at a point $(x_1, 0)$. If the guess x_0 is close to a root, Fig. 5.2 suggests that x_1 is even closer.

To compute x_1, write the equation of the tangent line:

$$y - f(x_0) = f'(x_0) \, (x - x_0).$$

Since $(x_1, 0)$ is on this line,

$$0 - f(x_0) = f'(x_0) \, (x_1 - x_0).$$

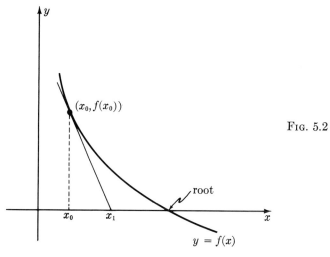

Fig. 5.2

Solve for x_1:

$$x_1 = x_0 - \frac{f(x_0)}{f'(x_0)}.$$

Now repeat the process with x_1 as your new guess (Fig. 5.3). Construct

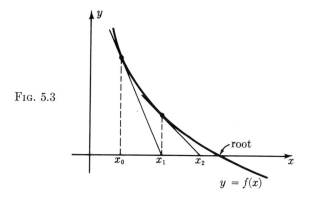

Fig. 5.3

the tangent at $(x_1, f(x_1))$. It crosses the x-axis at x_2, where

$$x_2 = x_1 - \frac{f(x_1)}{f'(x_1)}.$$

Repeat the procedure, obtaining a sequence of approximations $x_0, x_1,$ $x_2, \cdots$, where

$$x_{i+1} = x_i - \frac{f(x_i)}{f'(x_i)}.$$

A typical sequence is sketched in Fig. 5.4. (See Chapter 21, Section 3 for a discussion of the rate of approximation.)

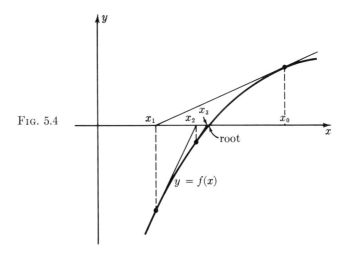

Fig. 5.4

EXAMPLE 5.1

Calculate $\sqrt{2}$. More precisely, use the Newton–Raphson Method to estimate the positive zero of $f(x) = x^2 - 2$. Choose $x_0 = 1$, and obtain the approximations x_1, x_2, and x_3.

Solution:

$$x_{i+1} = x_i - \frac{f(x_i)}{f'(x_i)}.$$

Since $f(x) = x^2 - 2$,

$$x_{i+1} = x_i - \frac{x_i^2 - 2}{2x_i} = \frac{x_i^2 + 2}{2x_i},$$

$$x_{i+1} = \frac{x_i}{2} + \frac{1}{x_i}.$$

Starting with $x_0 = 1$,

$$x_1 = \frac{x_0}{2} + \frac{1}{x_0} = \frac{1}{2} + 1 = \frac{3}{2},$$

$$x_2 = \frac{x_1}{2} + \frac{1}{x_1} = \frac{3}{4} + \frac{2}{3} = \frac{17}{12},$$

$$x_3 = \frac{x_2}{2} + \frac{1}{x_2} = \frac{17}{24} + \frac{12}{17} = \frac{577}{408}.$$

Answer: $x_1 = \frac{3}{2}$, $x_2 = \frac{17}{12}$, $x_3 = \frac{577}{408}$.

Note that

$$x_1 = 1.5, \qquad x_2 = 1.41666 \cdots, \qquad x_3 = 1.4142156 \cdots.$$

From a 6-place table,

$$\sqrt{2} = 1.414214 \cdots.$$

Thus x_3 is correct to within 0.000002.

REMARK: The formula for x_{i+1} in this example may be rewritten

$$x_{i+1} = \frac{1}{2}\left(x_i + \frac{2}{x_i}\right),$$

showing that x_{i+1} is the average of x_i and $2/x_i$. Likewise, approximating $\sqrt{n}$ for any $n > 0$ by the Newton–Raphson Method leads to a similar sequence of estimates:

$$x_{i+1} = \frac{1}{2}\left(x_i + \frac{n}{x_i}\right).$$

Each x_{i+1} is the average of x_i and n/x_i.

EXAMPLE 5.2

Estimate the smallest solution of the equation

$$x^3 - 6x^2 + 9x - 1 = 0.$$

Solution: Let $f(x) = x^3 - 6x^2 + 9x - 1$. Sketch $y = f(x)$ to get a rough idea of where zeros occur.

$$f(x) = x^3 - 6x^2 + 9x - 1,$$

$$f'(x) = 3x^2 - 12x + 9 = 3(x^2 - 4x + 3)$$

$$= 3(x - 1)(x - 3).$$

The curve is flat at $x = 1$ and $x = 3$. Use this information also to plot a few points, then sketch the graph (Fig. 5.5). The figure shows three zeros,

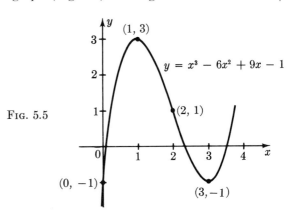

FIG. 5.5

the smallest of which is barely positive. As a first guess try $x_0 = 0.1$. Then use the formula:

$$x_{i+1} = x_i - \frac{f(x_i)}{f'(x_i)}$$

$$= x_i - \frac{x_i{}^3 - 6x_i{}^2 + 9x_i - 1}{3(x_i - 1)(x_i - 3)}.$$

Thus

$$x_1 = x_0 - \frac{x_0{}^3 - 6x_0{}^2 + 9x_0 - 1}{3(x_0 - 1)(x_0 - 3)}$$

$$= 0.1 - \frac{(0.1)^3 - 6(0.1)^2 + 9(0.1) - 1}{3(-0.9)(-2.9)}$$

$$= 0.1 + \frac{0.159}{7.83} \approx 0.120.$$

Repetition of the process yields:

$$x_2 \approx 0.1206,$$

$$x_3 \approx 0.12061.$$

Since x_2 and x_3 agree to 4 decimal places, it appears that 0.12061 is accurate to at least 4 places.

As a check, compute $f(x_3)$. If x_3 is close to a zero of $f(x)$, then $f(x_3)$ should be close to 0. In fact

$$f(x_3) \approx -0.000036.$$

Answer: 0.12061.

(Starting with the estimates 0 and $\frac{1}{2}$ and using the Bisection Method, it takes 10 iterations to achieve 4-place accuracy.)

REMARK: The notation can be simplified to avoid writing the subscript i repeatedly. This has two advantages: (1) you reduce the possibility of error by writing less and (2) you may wish to manipulate the expression

$$x_i - \frac{f(x_i)}{f'(x_i)}$$

into a form requiring fewer computational steps. Simplify the notation by setting

$$g(x) = x - \frac{f(x)}{f'(x)}.$$

Then

$$x_{i+1} = g(x_i).$$

In the example above, $f(x) = x^3 - 6x^2 + 9x - 1$,

$$g(x) = x - \frac{f(x)}{f'(x)}$$

$$= x - \frac{x^3 - 6x^2 + 9x - 1}{3x^2 - 12x + 9}$$

$$= x - \frac{x(x - 3)^2 - 1}{3(x - 1)(x - 3)}.$$

This form is economical for computation because each computed value of $(x - 3)$ is used twice.

EXAMPLE 5.3

Estimate the solutions of $\cos x = x$.

Solution: On the same graph plot $y = \cos x$ and $y = x$. See Fig. 5.6.

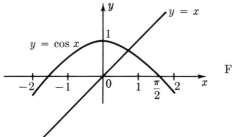

Fɪɢ. 5.6

The figure shows that $\cos x = x$ for only one value of x, roughly midway between 0 and $\pi/2 \approx 1.58$. A reasonable first guess is $x_0 = 0.8$. Apply the Newton–Raphson Method to $f(x) = \cos x - x$:

$$x_{i+1} = g(x_i),$$

where

$$g(x) = x - \frac{f(x)}{f'(x)}$$

$$= x - \frac{\cos x - x}{-\sin x - 1}$$

$$= \frac{x \sin x + \cos x}{1 + \sin x}.$$

Let the computer try this one. Results:

$$x_0 = 0.8$$

$$x_1 = 0.739853 \qquad x_3 = 0.739085$$

$$x_2 = 0.739085 \qquad x_4 = 0.739085.$$

The precision is amazing; just two iterations yield 6-place accuracy.

Just for fun, have the computer try some other values of x_0. Results:

$x_0 = 0$	$x_0 = 0.7$	$x_0 = 1$
$x_1 = 1.000000$	$x_1 = 0.739436$	$x_1 = 0.750364$
$x_2 = 0.750364$	$x_2 = 0.739085$	$x_2 = 0.739113$
$x_3 = 0.739113$	$x_3 = 0.739085$	$x_3 = 0.739085$
$x_4 = 0.739085$	$x_4 = 0.739085$	$x_4 = 0.739085$

Even the crude initial guesses, $x_0 = 0$ and $x_0 = 1$, yield 6-place accuracy after just 3 or 4 iterations.

Answer: 0.739085.

Generally, the Newton–Raphson Method is an effective procedure for finding roots. There are some cases, however, when the method fails. For example, if $f'(x)$ is zero or very small near a root, there may be trouble because of the denominator in the formula

$$x_{i+1} = x_i - \frac{f(x_i)}{f'(x_i)}.$$

In practice, the method usually works provided x_0 is close enough to the root. Still it is comforting that there is the bisection scheme to fall back on.

Computer Approximations

The approximation methods discussed in this chapter are well-adapted for computer use.

The program for the Bisection Method is straightforward (Fig. 5.7). For our flowchart, we assume that $f(x)$ has a zero between a and b, where $a < b$, and that $f(a) < 0 < f(b)$. The zero of $f(x)$ is always within the interval BOT $< 0 <$ TOP. The process terminates when the length of this interval is less than TEST.

For the Newton–Raphson Method, we need $f(x)$ and $f'(x)$, also an initial guess x_0. (There are several computer programs which can formally compute the derivative of a function. For example, such a program would accept "$3x^2 - 2x + 1$" as input, and produce "$6x - 2$" as output. However, since these programs are not available on all computers, the programmer must usually differentiate $f(x)$ himself.) Our flowchart is simplified since we assume that the method will not fail because of a zero derivative or any other reason (Fig. 5.8).

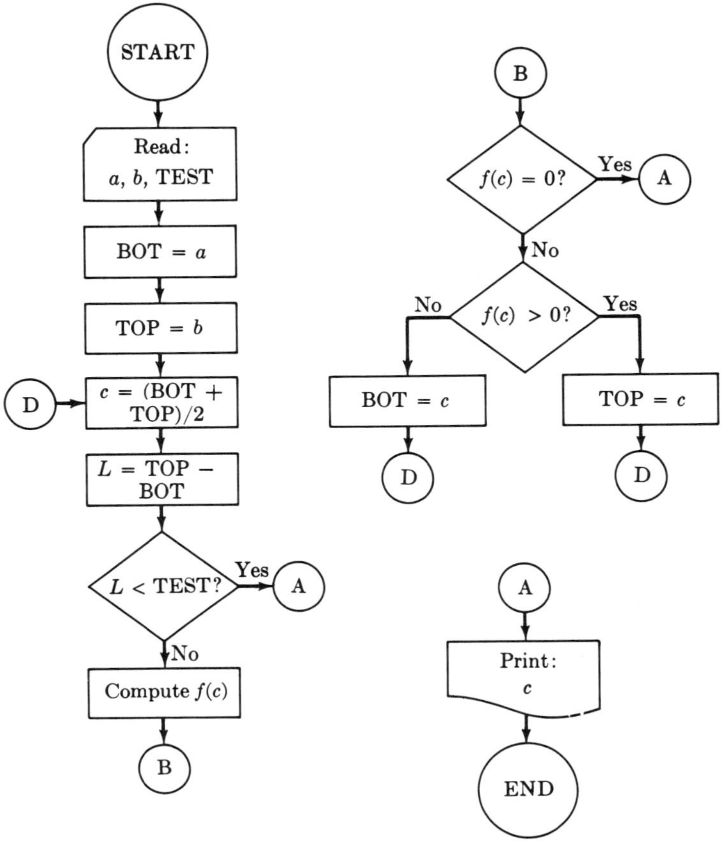

FIG. 5.8 Newton–Raphson Method (assuming $f'(x)$ never 0)

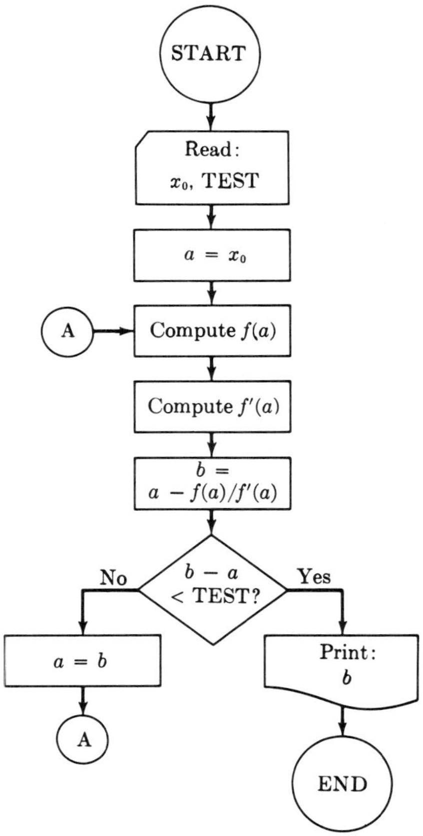

FIG. 5.7 Bisection Method (for $f(a) < 0 < f(b)$)

EXERCISES

Estimate to 2 places the root (or roots), using the Bisection Method:

1. $x^3 = 5$
2. $3x^3 = 7x + 3$
3. $x^3 + x^2 - x + 1 = 0$
4. $x^2 = 10$.

Estimate to 3 places the largest root, using Newton's Method:

5. $x^2 = 10$
6. $x^3 + x^2 - 4 = 0$
7. $x^3 - 2x^2 - x + 3 = 0$
8. $x^3 - 3x + 1 = 0$
9. $e^x = 2 \cos x$
10. $e^x = 3x$
11. $x = 2 \sin x$
12. $x = \cos 2x$.

13. Draw a flowchart for the Bisection Method, assuming only that the signs of $f(a)$ and $f(b)$ are different.

14. There are two main reasons for the failure of the Newton–Raphson Method: (1) the derivative is zero at some point near the root of $f(x) = 0$; (2) due to rounding within the computer, the estimates cycle: $x_i = x_{i+2} = x_{i+4} = \cdots$, and $x_{i+1} = x_{i+3} = x_{i+5} = \cdots$. Modify the flowchart of Fig. 5.8 to abort the computation if either of these events occurs.

6. TAYLOR POLYNOMIALS

Previously we approximated a function $f(x)$ near $x = a$ by a linear function $p_1(x) = f(a) + f'(a) (x - a)$. In geometric language, we approximated a curve by its tangent (Fig. 6.1).

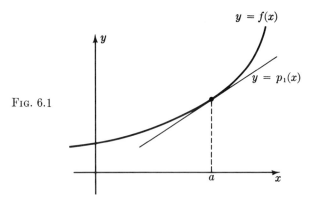

FIG. 6.1

Near $x = a$, the function $p_1(x)$ is a good approximation to $f(x)$ because $p_1(a) = f(a)$ and $p_1'(a) = f'(a)$; both graphs pass through the same point with the same slope. Farther from $x = a$, however, $p_1(x)$ may not be at all close to $f(x)$ since the graph of $y = f(x)$ may bend away from its tangent. The polynomial $p_1(x)$ is the **first degree Taylor polynomial** of $f(x)$ at $x = a$.

For greater accuracy, we shall approximate $f(x)$ by a function whose graph passes through $(a, f(a))$ with the same slope as $y = f(x)$, and which also curves in the same direction as $y = f(x)$. Now the curving of a graph is due to change in its slope. The slope is $f'(x)$, and the rate of change of the slope is the second derivative $f''(x)$. Therefore, we seek a function $p_2(x)$ such that

$$p_2(a) = f(a), \qquad p_2'(a) = f'(a), \qquad \text{and} \qquad p_2''(a) = f''(a).$$

Let us try a quadratic polynomial,

$$p_2(x) = A + B(x - a) + C(x - a)^2.$$

Then

$$p_2(a) = A, \qquad p_2'(a) = B, \qquad p_2''(a) = 2C.$$

(Verify these statements.) Since we want

$$p_2(a) = f(a), \qquad p_2'(a) = f'(a), \qquad p_2''(a) = f''(a),$$

there is no choice but

$$A = f(a), \qquad B = f'(a), \qquad C = \frac{1}{2} f''(a).$$

The polynomial

$$p_2(x) = f(a) + f'(a) \, (x - a) + \frac{1}{2} f''(a) \, (x - a)^2$$

agrees with $f(x)$ at $x = a$, and its derivative and second derivative agree with those of $f(x)$ at $x = a$. The polynomial $p_2(x)$ is the **second degree Taylor polynomial** of $f(x)$ at $x = a$.

The first two terms of $p_2(x)$ are $f(a) + f'(a) \, (x - a)$, which is $p_1(x)$. Thus $p_2(x)$ consists of the tangential linear approximation to $f(x)$ plus another term, $\frac{1}{2} f''(a) \, (x - a)^2$, which (we hope) corrects some of the error in linear approximation. (For a more precise treatment, see Chapter 21, Section 3.)

EXAMPLE 6.1

Approximate e^x near $x = 0$ by its first and second degree Taylor polynomials $p_1(x)$ and $p_2(x)$. Discuss their accuracy.

Solution: Use the formula

$$p_2(x) = f(a) + f'(a) \, (x - a) + \frac{1}{2} f''(a) \, (x - a)^2,$$

where $f(x) = e^x$ and $a = 0$. In this case $f(x) = f'(x) = f''(x) = e^x$, so $f(0) = f'(0) = f''(0) = 1$. Therefore,

$$p_2(x) = 1 + x + \frac{1}{2} x^2.$$

There is no need to compute $p_1(x)$ since it is the linear part of $p_2(x)$:

$$p_1(x) = 1 + x.$$

Table 6.1 compares e^x with $p_1(x)$ and $p_2(x)$ for various values of x.

TABLE 6.1

	Small values of x				Larger values of x		
x	e^x	$p_1(x)$	$p_2(x)$	x	e^x	$p_1(x)$	$p_2(x)$
-0.4	0.6703	0.6000	0.6800	-2.0	0.1353	-1.0000	1.0000
-0.3	0.7408	0.7000	0.7450	-1.5	0.2231	-0.5000	0.6250
-0.2	0.8187	0.8000	0.8200	-1.0	0.3679	0.0000	0.5000
-0.1	0.9048	0.9000	0.9050	-0.5	0.6065	0.5000	0.6250
0.0	1.0000	1.0000	1.0000	0.0	1.0000	1.0000	1.0000
0.1	1.1052	1.1000	1.1050	0.5	1.6487	1.5000	1.6250
0.2	1.2214	1.2000	1.2200	1.0	2.7183	2.0000	2.5000
0.3	1.3499	1.3000	1.3450	1.5	4.4817	2.5000	3.6250
0.4	1.4918	1.4000	1.4800	2.0	7.3891	3.0000	5.0000

From the table we see that $p_1(x)$ and $p_2(x)$ are good estimates of e^x for x near 0, but that $p_2(x)$ is considerably better than $p_1(x)$. Both estimates become poor as x moves away from 0, but $p_2(x)$ stays accurate in a wider range because its graph is curved like that of e^x near $x = 0$. See Fig. 6.2.

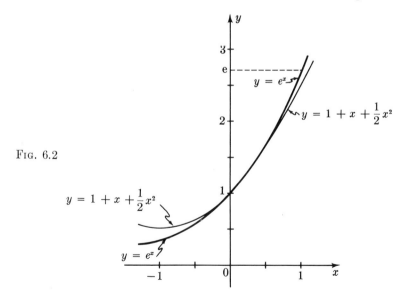

Fig. 6.2

EXAMPLE 6.2

Approximate $1/x$ near $x = 1$ by its first and second degree Taylor polynomials. Discuss their accuracy.

Solution: Use the formula

$$p_2(x) = f(a) + f'(a)\,(x-a) + \frac{1}{2}f''(a)\,(x-a)^2,$$

where $f(x) = 1/x$ and $a = 1$. Then $f'(x) = -1/x^2$ and $f''(x) = 2/x^3$ (a fact we shall prove later). Then $f(1) = 1$, $f'(1) = -1$, and $f''(1) = 2$. Hence

$$p_2(x) = 1 - (x-1) + (x-1)^2.$$

The polynomial $p_1(x)$ is the linear part of $p_2(x)$:

$$p_1(x) = 1 - (x-1).$$

Since we shall be dealing with numbers near 1, it is convenient to leave $p_1(x)$ and $p_2(x)$ in terms of $(x-1)$.

Table 6.2 compares $1/x$ with $p_1(x)$ and $p_2(x)$.

TABLE 6.2

	x near 1				Other values of x		
x	$1/x$	$p_1(x)$	$p_2(x)$	x	$1/x$	$p_1(x)$	$p_2(x)$
0.85	1.1765	1.1500	1.1725	0.25	4.0000	1.7500	2.3125
0.90	1.1111	1.1000	1.1100	0.50	2.0000	1.5000	1.7500
0.95	1.0526	1.0500	1.0525	0.75	1.3333	1.2500	1.3125
1.00	1.0000	1.0000	1.0000	1.00	1.0000	1.0000	1.0000
1.05	0.9524	0.9500	0.9525	1.25	0.8000	0.7500	0.8125
1.10	0.9091	0.9000	0.9100	1.50	0.6667	0.5000	0.7500
1.15	0.8696	0.8500	0.8725	1.75	0.5714	0.2500	0.8125

From the table, we see that $p_1(x)$ is a good approximation to $1/x$ provided x is near 1, but that $p_2(x)$ is much better. Both estimates become poor as x moves away from 1, but $p_2(x)$ is accurate in a wider range.

Cubic Approximation

The polynomial $p_2(x)$ was introduced in order to improve the tangential approximation $p_1(x)$. By the same token, we may try for greater precision by using a cubic polynomial

$$p_3(x) = A + B(x-a) + C(x-a)^2 + D(x-a)^3,$$

so chosen that

$$p_3(a) = f(a), \qquad p_3'(a) = f'(a), \qquad p_3''(a) = f''(a), \qquad p_3'''(a) = f'''(a).$$

Here $f'''(x)$ is the third derivative of $f(x)$, that is $f'''(x) = [f''(x)]'$. Differentiating $p_3(x)$ three times, we find

$$p_3(a) = A, \qquad p_3'(a) = B, \qquad p_3''(a) = 2C, \qquad p_3'''(a) = 6D.$$

(Verify these facts.) We are forced to choose

$$A = f(a), \qquad B = f'(a), \qquad C = \frac{1}{2}f''(a), \qquad D = \frac{1}{6}f'''(a).$$

The polynomial

$$p_3(x) = f(a) + f'(a)\,(x - a) + \frac{1}{2}f''(a)\,(x - a)^2 + \frac{1}{6}f'''(a)\,(x - a)^3$$

agrees with $f(x)$ at $x = a$, and its first, second and third derivatives agree with the corresponding derivatives of $f(x)$ at $x = a$. The polynomial $p_3(x)$ is the **third degree Taylor polynomial** of $f(x)$ at $x = a$.

The first two terms of $p_3(x)$ give $p_1(x)$, and the first three terms give $p_2(x)$. Thus $p_3(x)$ consists of $p_2(x)$ plus a term $\frac{1}{6}f'''(a)\,(x - a)^3$, which (we hope) corrects some of the error made in approximating $f(x)$ by $p_2(x)$.

EXAMPLE 6.3

Find $p_3(x)$, the third degree Taylor polynomial of e^x at $x = 0$. Compare its accuracy with that of $p_2(x)$.

Solution:

$$p_3(x) = p_2(x) + \frac{1}{6}f'''(a)\,(x - a)^3 = p_2(x) + \frac{1}{6}f'''(0)x^3.$$

But $f(x) = e^x$, so $f'''(x) = e^x$ and $f'''(0) = 1$. From Example 4.1,

$$p_2(x) = 1 + x + \frac{1}{2}x^2.$$

Conclusion:

$$p_3(x) = 1 + x + \frac{1}{2}x^2 + \frac{1}{6}x^3.$$

Table 6.3 shows $p_2(x)$ and $p_3(x)$ for several values of x.

TABLE 6.3

x	e^x	$p_2(x)$	$p_3(x)$
0.1	1.1052	1.1050	1.1052
0.2	1.2214	1.2200	1.2213
0.5	1.6487	1.6250	1.6458
1.0	2.7183	2.5000	2.6667
2.0	7.3891	5.0000	6.3333

The table reveals $p_3(x)$ to be more accurate than $p_2(x)$. Indeed, $p_3(x)$ is extremely precise for small values of x, and is more accurate for larger values of x than is $p_2(x)$.

EXAMPLE 6.4

Approximate $\sin x$ by its third degree Taylor polynomial at $x = 0$. Discuss the accuracy of this approximation.

Solution: Use the formula

$$p_3(x) = f(0) + f'(0)\,(x - 0) + \frac{1}{2}f''(0)\,(x - 0)^2 + \frac{1}{6}f'''(0)\,(x - 0)^3,$$

where $f(x) = \sin x$. Successive derivatives are

$$f'(x) = \cos x, \qquad f''(x) = -\sin x, \qquad f'''(x) = -\cos x;$$
$$f'(0) = 1, \qquad f''(0) = 0, \qquad f'''(0) = -1.$$

Hence,

$$p_3(x) = 0 + (x - 0) + 0 - \frac{1}{6}(x - 0)^3$$

$$= x - \frac{1}{6}x^3.$$

In Chapter 7 we saw that $\sin x \approx x$ if x is small. Now we have the approximation

$$\sin x \approx x - \frac{1}{6}x^3,$$

which is more precise (Table 6.4).

TABLE 6.4

	Small values of x			Larger values of x	
x	$\sin x$	$x - \dfrac{1}{6}x^3$	x	$\sin x$	$x - \dfrac{1}{6}x^3$
0.00	0.00000	0.00000	0.30	0.29552	0.29550
0.05	0.04998	0.04998	0.50	0.47943	0.47917
0.10	0.09983	0.09983	0.70	0.64422	0.64283
0.15	0.14944	0.14944	0.90	0.78333	0.77850
0.20	0.19867	0.19867	1.10	0.89121	0.87817
0.25	0.24740	0.24740	1.30	0.96356	0.93383

The approximation $\sin x \approx x - \frac{1}{6}x^3$ is extremely accurate. It gives 5-place accuracy for angles at least up to 0.25 radians ($\approx 14.3°$), and 3-place accuracy at least up to 0.5 radians ($\approx 28.6°$). Even the very simple formula

$\sin x \approx x$ is fairly accurate for small angles; it is correct to 3 places for angles up to 0.14 radians ($\approx 8°$).

Estimates Using Taylor Polynomials

Here are some common approximation formulas, all involving third degree Taylor polynomials at $x = 0$:

$$e^x \approx 1 + x + \frac{1}{2} x^2 + \frac{1}{6} x^3,$$

$$\sin x \approx x - \frac{1}{6} x^3,$$

$$\cos x \approx 1 - \frac{1}{2} x^2.$$

The approximation for $\cos x$ is actually $p_3(x)$ although no cubic term appears. That is because the third derivative of $\cos x$ is zero at $x = 0$.

EXERCISES

Sketch the graphs (on the same set of axes) of $y = f(x)$, of $p_1(x) = f(a) + f'(a) (x - a)$, and of $p_2(x) = f(a) + f'(a) (x - a) + \frac{1}{2}f''(a) (x - a)^2$:

1. $y = \sin 2x$;   near $a = 0$

2. $y = \frac{1}{2} (e^x + e^{-x})$;   near $a = 0$

3. $y = (x - 2)^3 + 3(x - 2)^2 - 4(x - 2) + 1$;   near $a = 2$

4. $y = \sin x$;   near $a = \frac{\pi}{4}$

5. $y = \cos x + 2 \cos \frac{x}{2} + 3 \cos \frac{x}{3}$;   near $a = 0$

6. $y = (x - 1)^2 + e^x$;   near $a = -1$.

Compute the third degree Taylor polynomial at the point specified:

7. $f(x) = e^{-x}$; $x = 0$ 8. $f(x) = e^x + \sin x$; $x = 0$

9. $f(x) = e^x + \sin x + \cos x$; $x = 0$

10. $f(x) = 2x^3 - x^2 + 5x - 1$; $x = 1$

11. $f(x) = \cos(20x)$; $x = \frac{\pi}{40}$ 12. $f(x) = e^x + e^{-x} + \cos x$; $x = 0$

13. $f(x) = e^{2x}$; $x = 0$.

14. Extend Table 6.3 to the corresponding negative values of x.

15. Extend Table 6.4 to the corresponding negative values of x.

16. Make the table for $\cos x$ corresponding to Table 6.4.

19. Interpolation and Numerical Integration

1. INTERPOLATION

We begin this chapter by considering an important scientific technique: fitting a curve to data.

Suppose in an accurate experiment, a quantity x is measured at 11 time readings. For example,

t	0	0.1	0.2	$\cdots$	0.8	0.9	1.0
x	2.783	3.142	4.003	$\cdots$	2.001	1.833	1.801

In order to find a mathematical relation between these readings, we seek a function which fits the data, that is, a function $x(t)$ defined for all values of t in the interval $0 \leq t \leq 1$, and satisfying the conditions $x(0) = 2.783$, $x(0.1) = 3.142$, $\cdots$, $x(1.0) = 1.801$. In other words, we want a function whose graph passes through 11 given points. Finding such a function is called **interpolation.**

The simple case of linear interpolation is familiar. For example, from a 5-place table,

$$\log 3.1920 \approx 0.50406 \quad \text{and} \quad \log 3.1930 \approx 0.50420.$$

To estimate $\log 3.1927$, add $\frac{7}{10}$ of the difference $(0.50420 - 0.50406)$ to 0.50406:

$$\log 3.1927 \approx 0.50416.$$

This is equivalent to finding the linear function $f(x)$ that fits the two points $(3.1920, 0.50406)$ and $(3.1930, 0.50420)$, and writing

$$\log 3.1927 \approx f(3.1927).$$

As is easily computed,

$$f(x) = 0.50406 + (0.14)\,(x - 3.1920).$$

Hence

$$\log 3.1927 \approx 0.50406 + (0.14)\,(3.1927 - 3.1920) \approx 0.50416.$$

In this example the data consist of only two points and we can fit a straight line graph (linear polynomial). In case the data consist of several points, we seek the polynomial of least degree that fits.

Polynomial Interpolation

Here is the basic problem. Given $n + 1$ points

$$(x_0, y_0), \quad (x_1, y_1), \quad (x_2, x_2), \quad \cdots, \quad (x_n, y_n),$$

where

$$x_0 < x_1 < x_2 < \cdots < x_n,$$

find a polynomial $y = p(x)$ of least degree whose graph passes through the given points, i.e.,

$$p(x_0) = y_0, \quad p(x_1) = y_1, \quad \cdots, \quad p(x_n) = y_n.$$

Let us start with three points. Suppose we wish to interpolate

$$(x_0, y_0), \quad (x_1, y_1), \quad (x_2, y_2), \qquad x_0 < x_1 < x_2,$$

by a polynomial of least degree. A first degree polynomial generally won't do since its graph is a straight line. So we try a quadratic polynomial

$$y = A + Bx + Cx^2$$

and hope to choose its three coefficients so that its graph passes through the three given points.

EXAMPLE 1.1

Fit a quadratic to the points $(0, 1)$, $(1, 2)$, $(2, 4)$.

Solution: Set $y = A + Bx + Cx^2$. Substitute $x = 0$, $y = 1$; $x = 1$, $y = 2$; $x = 2$, $y = 4$:

$$\begin{cases} A & = 1 \\ A + B + C & = 2 \\ A + 2B + 4C & = 4. \end{cases}$$

The solution of these simultaneous linear equations is $A = 1$, $B = C = \frac{1}{2}$.

$$\text{Answer:} \quad 1 + \frac{1}{2}x + \frac{1}{2}x^2.$$

This example illustrates the **method of undetermined coefficients**. The next example demonstrates the method for more than three points.

EXAMPLE 1.2

Fit a cubic to the four points $(-1, \frac{1}{2})$, $(0, 1)$, $(1, 2)$, $(2, 4)$.

Solution: Set

$$p(x) = A + Bx + Cx^2 + Dx^3.$$

The data yields four equations:

$$\begin{cases} A - B + C - D = \frac{1}{2} \\ A \qquad\qquad\qquad = 1 \\ A + B + C + D = 2 \\ A + 2B + 4C + 8D = 4. \end{cases}$$

After some labor one finds the solution:

$$A = 1, \quad B = \tfrac{2}{3}, \quad C = \tfrac{1}{4}, \quad D = \tfrac{1}{12}.$$

Answer: $1 + \tfrac{2}{3}x + \tfrac{1}{4}x^2 + \tfrac{1}{12}x^3.$

Fitting polynomials is important in approximation problems. For example, we may need many values of $f(x)$, a function difficult to compute. Then it is convenient to have a polynomial (easy to compute) which approximates $f(x)$. A basic method of finding one is fitting a polynomial to several points on the graph of $y = f(x)$.

EXAMPLE 1.3

Approximate $y = 2^x$, using the values at $x = 0, 1, 2$.

Solution: By Example 1.1, the quadratic polynomial $p(x) = 1 + \frac{1}{2}x + \frac{1}{2}x^2$ passes through the three points $(0, 2^0)$, $(1, 2^1)$, and $(2, 2^2)$.

REMARK: The approximation is quite good for $0 \le x \le 2$. One can show (not easily) that the error $\epsilon(x)$ in

$$2^x = 1 + \frac{1}{2}x + \frac{1}{2}x^2 + \epsilon(x)$$

satisfies

$$|\epsilon(x)| \le 0.05 \qquad \text{for} \quad -0.2 \le x \le 2.1,$$
$$|\epsilon(x)| \le 0.29 \qquad \text{for} \quad -0.5 \le x \le 2.5.$$

Figure 1.1 shows the error in the interval $0 \le x \le 2$.

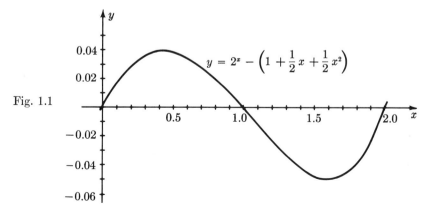

Fig. 1.1

EXERCISES

Fit a quadratic polynomial to the points:

1. $(0, 2)$, $(2, 0)$, $(3, 1)$
2. $(-2, 4)$, $(0, -1)$, $(1, 2)$
3. $(-2, -3)$, $(2, 0)$, $(5, 1)$
4. $(-4, 2)$, $(-3, 3)$, $(3, 9)$
5. $(-4, 1)$, $(-1, 2)$, $(2, 3)$
6. $(1, -2)$, $(2, 1)$, $(10, 1)$
7. $(2, 4)$, $(3, 1)$, $(4, -1)$
8. $(0, 7)$, $(2, 3)$, $(3, 1)$
9. $(-4, 4)$, $(0, 2)$, $(2, 1)$
10. $(-4, 2)$, $(-3, 5)$, $(3, 2)$.

Fit a cubic polynomial to the points:

11. $(-1, 1)$, $(0, 2)$, $(1, 4)$, $(2, 6)$
12. $(-2, -3)$, $(1, -1)$, $(2, 0)$, $(5, 4)$
13. $(-4, 4)$, $(0, 0)$, $(2, 2)$, $(4, -4)$
14. $(1, 5)$, $(2, 4)$, $(3, 1)$, $(4, -1)$
15. $(-2, -8)$, $(0, -4)$, $(2, 0)$, $(3, 2)$
16. $(-2, 0)$, $(-1, 0)$, $(1, 2)$, $(2, 2)$
17. $(-3, 1)$, $(-2, 3)$, $(-1, 0)$, $(0, -1)$
18. $(-1, -2)$, $(1, 0)$, $(3, 2)$, $(6, 5)$
19. $(-3, 4)$, $(2, 3)$, $(5, 0)$, $(7, -3)$.

Fit a quadratic polynomial to the function, using the values at $x = 0, 1, 2$:

20. $y = \dfrac{6}{1 + x}$

21. $y = e^x$

22. $y = x^3$

23. $y = \dfrac{x}{1 + x}$.

Fit a cubic polynomial to the function, using the values at $x = 0, 1, 2, 3$:

24. $y = 2^x$

25. $y = x^4 - x$

26. $y = \dfrac{6}{1 + x}$

27. $y = \dfrac{x^2}{1 + x}$

28. $y = \ln(x + 1)$.

29. During a three hour period, the distance from the tide line to a fixed mark is measured:

t	0	1	2	3	hr
s	20	10	8	15	ft

Estimate to 2 decimals the minimum distance from the tide line to the mark during this period.

30. A rocket is fired from zero altitude at time $t = 0$. Its altitude is 200 ft at $t = 5$ sec, 600 ft at $t = 10$ sec, and 3000 ft at $t = 15$ sec. Fit a polynomial to the data, and from it estimate the initial velocity of the rocket.

Estimate the integral by interpolating the integrand with a cubic polynomial; compute the answer to three decimal places:

31. $\displaystyle\int_0^3 x \sin^2 \frac{\pi x}{4}\, dx$

32. $\displaystyle\int_1^4 (\ln x)^2\, dx$.

2. LAGRANGE INTERPOLATION

We state the fundamental fact about polynomial fitting.

Given $n + 1$ points

$$(x_0, y_0), \quad (x_1, y_1), \quad \cdots, \quad (x_n, y_n),$$

with $x_0 < x_1 < \cdots < x_n$, there is precisely one polynomial of degree at most n that passes through these points.

This statement contains two important assertions. First, there is *some* polynomial of degree at most n which fits the given points. Second, this polynomial is *unique*, it is the only one. For us, the first assertion is the more important one. We shall verify it by actually writing down a polynomial that fills the bill. Fortunately we can avoid the method of undetermined coefficients, which becomes complicated for more than three or four points; a neater method is available.

Given $n + 1$ points as above, consider the polynomial

$$(x - x_1) (x - x_2) \cdots (x - x_n).$$

Its degree is n and it has zeros at $x = x_1, x = x_2, \cdots, x = x_n$. At $x = x_0$ its value is

$$(x_0 - x_1) (x_0 - x_2) \cdots (x_0 - x_n) \neq 0.$$

Consequently, the polynomial

$$p_0(x) = \frac{(x - x_1) (x - x_2) \cdots (x - x_n)}{(x_0 - x_1) (x_0 - x_2) \cdots (x_0 - x_n)}$$

has degree n, has value 1 at $x = x_0$, and has zeros at $x_1, x_2, \cdots, x_n$. Thus $p_0(x)$ solves the interpolation problem in the special case $y_0 = 1$, $y_1 = 0, \cdots, y_n = 0$.

Similarly, for each $j = 0, 1, \cdots, n$, set

$$p_j(x) = \frac{(x - x_0) (x - x_1) \cdots (x - x_{j-1}) (x - x_{j+1}) \cdots (x - x_n)}{(x_j - x_0) (x_j - x_1) \cdots (x_j - x_{j-1}) (x_j - x_{j+1}) \cdots (x_j - x_n)}.$$

(There is no factor $x - x_j$ in the numerator and no factor $x_j - x_j$ in the denominator.) Then $p_j(x)$ has degree n and

$$p_j(x_j) = 1, \quad \text{but} \quad p_j(x_i) = 0 \quad \text{if} \quad i \neq j.$$

Thus $p_j(x)$ solves the interpolation problem in the special case

$$y_0 = 0, \quad y_1 = 0, \quad \cdots, \quad y_{j-1} = 0, \quad y_j = 1, \quad y_{j+1} = 0, \quad \cdots, \quad y_n = 0.$$

Finally, set

$$p(x) = y_0 p_0(x) + y_1 p_1(x) + \cdots + y_n p_n(x).$$

This is it! Check:

$$p(x_0) = y_0 \cdot 1 + y_1 \cdot 0 + \cdots + y_n \cdot 0 = y_0,$$

$$p(x_1) = y_0 \cdot 0 + y_1 \cdot 1 + \cdots + y_n \cdot 0 = y_1,$$

$$\cdot \quad \cdot \quad \cdot \quad \cdot \quad \cdot \quad \cdot \quad \cdot \quad \cdot \quad \cdot \quad \cdot \quad \cdot \quad \cdot$$

$$p(x_n) = y_0 \cdot 0 + y_1 \cdot 0 + \cdots + y_n \cdot 1 = y_n.$$

Since $p(x)$ is the sum of n-th degree polynomials, $p(x)$ has degree at most n (some terms may drop out). The formula for $p(x)$ is the **Lagrange interpolation formula.**

Lagrange Interpolation Formula The polynomial of degree at most n that fits $n + 1$ points

$$(x_0, y_0), \quad (x_1, y_1), \quad \cdots, \quad (x_n, y_n), \quad x_0 < x_1 < \cdots < x_n,$$

is

$$p(x) = y_0 p_0(x) + y_1 p_1(x) + \cdots + y_n p_n(x),$$

where

$$p_j(x) = \frac{(x - x_0) \cdots (x - x_{j-1})(x - x_{j+1}) \cdots (x - x_n)}{(x_j - x_0) \cdots (x_j - x_{j-1})(x_j - x_{j+1}) \cdots (x_j - x_n)}$$

for $j = 0, 1, \cdots, n$.

EXAMPLE 2.1

Fit a quadratic to $(0, 1)$, $(1, 2)$, and $(2, 4)$.

Solution: Use the Lagrange interpolation formula:

$$p_0(x) = \frac{(x - 1)(x - 2)}{(0 - 1)(0 - 2)} = \frac{1}{2}(x^2 - 3x + 2),$$

$$p_1(x) = \frac{(x - 0)(x - 2)}{(1 - 0)(1 - 2)} = -x^2 + 2x,$$

$$p_2(x) = \frac{(x - 0)(x - 1)}{(2 - 0)(2 - 1)} = \frac{1}{2}(x^2 - x).$$

The desired polynomial is

$$p(x) = 1 \cdot p_0(x) + 2 \cdot p_1(x) + 4 \cdot p_2(x)$$

$$= \frac{1}{2}(x^2 - 3x + 2) + 2(-x^2 + 2x) + \frac{4}{2}(x^2 - x)$$

$$= \frac{1}{2}x^2 + \frac{1}{2}x + 1.$$

$$Answer: \quad \frac{1}{2}x^2 + \frac{1}{2}x + 1.$$

Lagrange's formula shows that there *is* a polynomial of degree at most n through $n + 1$ given points $(x_0, y_0), \cdots, (x_n, y_n)$. Now we must verify that there is *only one*.

Suppose there were two different ones, $p(x)$ and $q(x)$. Their difference $r(x)$ would be a non-zero polynomial of degree at most n. But

$$r(x_0) = p(x_0) - q(x_0) = 0, \cdots, r(x_n) = p(x_n) - q(x_n) = 0,$$

so $r(x)$ would have $n + 1$ *different* zeros. However, it is shown in algebra that this is impossible for a non-zero polynomial of degree *less than* $n + 1$. Consequently, there cannot be two different polynomials of degree less than $n + 1$ which fit $n + 1$ given points.

EXERCISES

Use Lagrange interpolation to fit a polynomial to the data:

1. $(-3, 4), (-2, 0), (0, -2), (1, 1)$
2. $(-2, -2), (-1, 2), (0, 3), (1, 0), (2, 1)$
3. $(0, 8), (2, 4), (4, 2), (6, 1)$
4. $(-3, -1), (-1, 0), (1, 0), (3, 1)$.
5. $(-2, -5), (0, 2), (2, 0), (4, -2), (6, 3)$
6. $(-1, 0), (1, 0), (2, 2), (5, 0), (8, -1), (10, 0)$

Use Lagrange interpolation to fit the function at the given points:

7. $y = \sin \dfrac{\pi x}{2}, \quad x = 0, 1, 2, 3, 4$

8. $y = e^{-x} \cos \dfrac{\pi x}{2}, \quad x = 0, 1, 2, 3$

9. $y = (1 + \sin \pi x) \left(\cos \dfrac{2\pi x}{3} \right), \quad x = \dfrac{1}{2}, \dfrac{3}{4}, 1$

10. $y = x^2(x + 1)^2, \quad x = -1, 0, 1, 2$.

Estimate the integral by fitting an interpolating polynomial to the integrand; give a 2-decimal answer:

11. $\displaystyle\int_{-1/2}^{1} x^3 \cos \pi x \, dx, \quad$ 4-point fit

12. $\displaystyle\int_{1}^{3} \dfrac{dx}{x\sqrt{1 + x}}, \quad$ 3-point fit

13. $\displaystyle\int_{0}^{4} e^{-x^2} \, dx, \quad$ 3-point fit.

3. SIMPSON'S RULE

Interpolation is used to derive numerical integration formulas. We know such a formula, the Trapezoidal Rule (Chapter 18):

$$\int_a^b f(x)\,dx \approx \frac{h}{2}\,[f(x_0) + 2f(x_1) + \cdots + 2f(x_{n-1}) + f(x_n)],$$

where $h = (b - a)/n$, and

$$x_0 = a, \quad x_1 = a + h, \quad x_2 = a + 2h, \quad \cdots, \quad x_{n-1} = a + (n-1)h, \quad x_n = b.$$

A convenient abbreviation is

$$\int_a^b f(x)\,dx \approx \frac{h}{2}\,[f_0 + 2f_1 + 2f_2 + \cdots + 2f_{n-1} + f_n],$$

where $f_i = f(x_i)$.

In this chapter, we derive several numerical integration formulas. In order to compare their usefulness, we test each of them on the integral

$$\int_0^2 e^{-x^2}\,dx.$$

Its exact value is not known, but from the U.S. Department of Commerce Table of Normal Distributions,

$$\int_0^2 e^{-x^2}\,dx \approx 0.88208\ 10350\ 6.$$

We shall carry our calculations to six significant figures since the C.R.C. table of the exponential function gives six places.

In Table 3.1 are listed the results of applying the Trapezoidal Rule to the above integral, using several values of n.

TABLE 3.1. TRAPEZOIDAL APPROXIMATIONS

n	$\int_0^2 e^{-x^2}\,dx$	n	$\int_0^2 e^{-x^2}\,dx$
2	0.877037	8	0.881704
4	0.880618	10	0.881837
6	0.881415	20	0.882020

Simpson's Rule

The idea behind numerical integration formulas is simple: in order to estimate

$$\int_a^b f(x)\,dx,$$

approximate $f(x)$ by a polynomial $p(x)$, then estimate the given integral by

$$\int_a^b p(x) \, dx.$$

Each choice of $p(x)$ gives rise to a different numerical integration formula.

Of particular importance is the following formula, obtained by using a *quadratic* $p(x)$.

Simpson's Three-Point Rule

$$\int_a^b f(x) \, dx \approx \frac{h}{3} \left[f(a) + 4f\left(\frac{a+b}{2}\right) + f(b) \right],$$

where $h = \dfrac{1}{2}(b - a)$.

The formula can be abbreviated

$$\int_a^b f(x) \, dx \approx \frac{h}{3} [f(x_0) + 4f(x_1) + f(x_2)],$$

where $x_0 = a$, $x_1 = \dfrac{a+b}{2}$, $x_2 = b$.

We obtain the rule by the following steps. First we approximate $f(x)$ by the quadratic $p(x)$ that fits the three points

$$(x_0, f(x_0)), \qquad (x_1, f(x_1)), \qquad (x_2, f(x_2)).$$

Then we show that

$$\int_a^b p(x) \, dx = \frac{h}{3} [f(x_0) + 4f(x_1) + f(x_2)].$$

Since $p(x_0) = f(x_0)$, $p(x_1) = f(x_1)$, and $p(x_2) = f(x_2)$, what we actually must do is show that the equation

$$\int_a^b p(x) \, dx = \frac{h}{3} [p(x_0) + 4p(x_1) + p(x_2)]$$

holds. In fact, this equation holds for each quadratic as we now show.

If $p(x) = A + Bx + Cx^2$, then

$$\int_a^b p(x) \, dx = \left(Ax + \frac{1}{2}Bx^2 + \frac{1}{3}Cx^3 \right) \Big|_a^b$$

$$= A(b-a) + \frac{1}{2}B(b^2 - a^2) + \frac{1}{3}C(b^3 - a^3)$$

$$= (b-a) \left[A + \frac{1}{2}B(b+a) + \frac{1}{3}C(b^2 + ba + a^2) \right].$$

Now $h = \frac{1}{2}(b - a)$, $x_0 = a$, $x_1 = \frac{1}{2}(a + b)$, and $x_2 = b$. Consequently,

$$\frac{h}{3} [p(x_0) + 4p(x_1) + p(x_2)]$$

$$= \frac{(b - a)}{6} \left\{ [A + Ba + Ca^2] \right.$$

$$+ 4 \left[A + B \left(\frac{a + b}{2} \right) + C \left(\frac{a + b}{2} \right)^2 \right] + \left. [A + Bb + Cb^2] \right\}$$

$$= \left(\frac{b - a}{6} \right) [6A + 3B(a + b) + 2C(a^2 + ab + b^2)]$$

$$= (b - a) \left[A + \frac{1}{2} B(a + b) + \frac{1}{3} C(a^2 + ab + b^2) \right].$$

This is equal to

$$\int_a^b p(x) \, dx,$$

which we wanted to show.

REMARK 1: If $p(x)$ is the cross-sectional area of a prismoid, then the formula

$$\int_a^b p(x) \, dx = \frac{h}{3} [p(x_0) + 4p(x_1) + p(x_2)]$$

is the Prismoidal Rule of Chapter 13.

REMARK 2: Surprisingly, this formula is correct not only for quadratics, but also for cubics.

Simpson's Three-Point Rule is exact for polynomials of degree three or less. In other words,

$$\int_a^b f(x) \, dx = \frac{h}{3} [f(x_0) + 4f(x_1) + f(x_2)]$$

if $f(x)$ is a polynomial of degree three or less.

The proof for cubics is similar to the proof for quadratics; we leave it as an exercise.

Does the Three-Point Rule provide a *good* approximation to

$$\int_a^b f(x) \, dx ?$$

That depends on the graph of $f(x)$. See Fig. 3.1.

The same interpolating quadratic $p(x)$ appears in Fig. 3.1a and Fig. 3.1b, since the three points which determine $p(x)$ are the same. Yet the

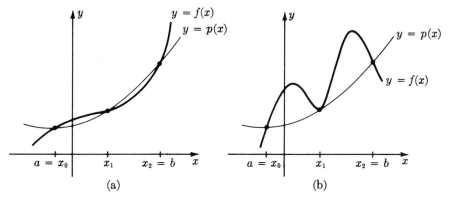

Fig. 3.1

approximation

$$\int_a^b f(x)\,dx \approx \int_a^b p(x)\,dx$$

is good in Fig. 3.1a and poor in Fig. 3.1b.

In the first case, $p(x)$ approximates $f(x)$ closely. Furthermore,

$$\int_{x_0}^{x_1} p(x)\,dx < \int_{x_0}^{x_1} f(x)\,dx,$$

whereas

$$\int_{x_1}^{x_2} p(x)\,dx > \int_{x_1}^{x_2} f(x)\,dx,$$

so the errors tend to cancel.

In Fig. 3.1b, however, $p(x)$ is a poor approximation to $f(x)$. To make matters worse, the errors do not cancel, they accumulate. The trouble is that the points x_0, x_1, x_2 are too widely spaced. It is much better to apply the Three-Point Rule *twice*, from x_0 to x_1 and from x_1 to x_2 (Fig. 3.2).

For greater accuracy divide the interval $a \le x \le b$ into an even number of equal pieces, and apply Simpson's Three-Point Rule to each pair of

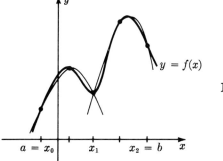

Fig. 3.2

consecutive subintervals:

$$\begin{array}{ccccccc} & h & h & & & h & h \\ \vdash\!\!\!-\!\!+\!\!-\!\!+\!\!-\!\!+\!\!-\!\!+\!\!\cdots\cdots\!\!-\!\!+\!\!-\!\!+\!\!-\!\!\dashv \\ a = x_0 & x_1 & x_2 & x_3 & x_4 \cdots\cdots x_{2n-2} & x_{2n-1} & x_{2n} = b. \end{array}$$

Set

$$h = \frac{b - a}{2n},$$

the length of each subinterval. Write

$$\int_a^b f(x)\, dx = \int_{x_0}^{x_2} + \int_{x_2}^{x_4} + \int_{x_4}^{x_6} + \cdots + \int_{x_{2n-2}}^{x_{2n}}.$$

Three-point approximation yields

$$\int_{x_0}^{x_2} f(x)\, dx \approx \frac{h}{3}\, [f_0 + 4f_1 + f_2],$$

$$\int_{x_2}^{x_4} f(x)\, dx \approx \frac{h}{3}\, [f_2 + 4f_3 + f_4],$$

$$\int_{x_4}^{x_6} f(x)\, dx \approx \frac{h}{3}\, [f_4 + 4f_5 + f_6],$$

$$\cdots \cdots \cdots \cdots \cdots \cdots \cdots$$

$$\int_{x_{2n-2}}^{x_{2n}} f(x)\, dx \approx \frac{h}{3}\, [f_{2n-2} + 4f_{2n-1} + f_{2n}].$$

Add these; the result is Simpson's Rule.

Simpson's Rule

$$\int_a^b f(x)\, dx \approx$$

$$\frac{h}{3}\, [f_0 + 4f_1 + 2f_2 + 4f_3 + 2f_4 + 4f_5 + \cdots + 2f_{2n-2} + 4f_{2n-1} + f_{2n}],$$

where $h = (b - a)/2n$ and $f_0, f_1, \cdots, f_{2n}$ are the values of f at the successive points of division of $a \le x \le b$ into $2n$ equal parts. The rule is exact whenever $f(x)$ is a polynomial of degree 3 or less.

Note that the sequence of coefficients is

$$1, \quad 4, \quad 2, \quad 4, \quad 2, \quad 4, \quad \cdots, \quad 4, \quad 2, \quad 4, \quad 1.$$

In Simpson's approximation, the number of subintervals of $a \le x \le b$ is $2n$ (even). The number of points of division, counting the end points, is $2n + 1$ (odd). These odd numbers are used to describe various versions of Simpson's

Rule. Thus a 7-point Simpson approximation refers to the division shown here:

$$a = x_0 \quad x_1 \quad x_2 \quad x_3 \quad x_4 \quad x_5 \quad x_6 = b.$$

In this case $n = 3$, $2n = 6$, $2n + 1 = 7$, and the rule states

$$\int_a^b f(x)\, dx \approx \frac{h}{3}[f_0 + 4f_1 + 2f_2 + 4f_3 + 2f_4 + 4f_5 + f_6].$$

We apply several versions of Simpson's Rule to our test integral

$$\int_0^2 e^{-x^2}\, dx.$$

See Table 3.2.

TABLE 3.2. $(2n + 1)$-POINT SIMPSON APPROXIMATIONS

$2n + 1$	$\int_0^2 e^{-x^2}\, dx$	$2n + 1$	$\int_0^2 e^{-x^2}\, dx$
3	0.829944	9	0.882066
5	0.881812	11	0.882073
7	0.882031	21	0.882081

Tables 3.1 and 3.2 show that Simpson's Rule is much more precise than the Trapezoidal Rule. For instance, with 5 points of subdivision, the errors are approximately 0.001463 (Trapezoidal) versus 0.000269 (Simpson); with 11 points of subdivision, 0.000244 (Trapezoidal) versus 0.000008 (Simpson).

EXERCISES

Use Simpson's Three-Point Rule to estimate the integral; give a 2-decimal answer:

1. $\displaystyle\int_3^5 x^3\, dx$

2. $\displaystyle\int_{-1}^1 \cos x\, dx$

3. $\displaystyle\int_0^2 xe^x\, dx$

4. $\displaystyle\int_1^5 \frac{dx}{x}$

5. $\displaystyle\int_{\pi/2}^{5\pi/2} \frac{\sin x}{x}\, dx$

6. $\displaystyle\int_1^2 e^{-x^2}\, dx$

7. $\displaystyle\int_{-1}^1 e^x \tan x\, dx$

8. $\displaystyle\int_2^4 \frac{dx}{x^2 + x + 1}.$

Use Simpson's Rule with 3, 5, and 9 points to estimate the integral. Give a 4-decimal answer (the different results show that you do *not* have 4-decimal accuracy):

9. $\displaystyle\int_0^4 x^2\sqrt{x + 1}\, dx$

10. $\displaystyle\int_0^8 \frac{dx}{x^3 + x + 1}$

11. $\displaystyle\int_2^6 x \ln x \, dx$

12. $\displaystyle\int_{0.6}^{1.4} \ln \tan x \, dx$

(*Hint:* Express ln in terms of $\log_{10}$.)

13. $\displaystyle\int_{-2}^2 x \sqrt{9 - x^3} \, dx$

14. $\displaystyle\int_0^2 \sin x \, dx.$

With a computer, use Simpson's Rule to estimate the integral; give a 6-decimal answer:

15. $\displaystyle\int_0^4 e^{-x^2} \, dx,$ 101 points

16. $\displaystyle\int_0^{\pi/2} \frac{dx}{\sqrt{1 - \frac{1}{2} \sin^2 x}},$ 21 points

17. $\displaystyle\int_1^3 \frac{\sin x}{x} \, dx,$ 101 points

18. $\displaystyle\int_0^{10} \frac{dx}{\sqrt{1 + x^3}},$ 101 points.

19. Verify that Simpson's Three-Point Rule is exact for cubics.

20. Show that Simpson's Three-Point Rule is exact for $\displaystyle\int_{-h}^h x^5 \, dx.$

21. (cont.) Does Ex. 20 mean Simpson's Three-Point Rule is exact for 5-th degree polynomials?

22. Draw a flowchart for Simpson's Rule with $2n + 1$ points.

4. NEWTON–COTES RULES   [optional]

The Trapezoidal Rule is based on linear interpolation, Simpson's Rule on quadratic interpolation. Rules based on interpolation of degree three or more are known as Newton–Cotes Rules.

The 4-point Newton–Cotes Rule is based on division of the interval $a \le x \le b$ into three equal parts:

$$a = x_0 \qquad x_1 \qquad x_2 \qquad x_3 = b.$$

The rule asserts that

$$\int_a^b f(x) \, dx \approx \int_a^b p_3(x) \, dx,$$

where $p_3(x)$ is the polynomial of degree at most three that agrees with $f(x)$ at x_0, x_1, x_2, x_3.

We need a formula for the integral on the right. We could find $p_3(x)$ explicitly by Lagrange interpolation and then integrate it. A quicker method, however, is this.

The answer will be of the form

$$\int_a^b p_3(x) \, dx = h[c_0 f_0 + c_1 f_1 + c_2 f_2 + c_3 f_3],$$

where c_0, c_1, c_2, c_3 are constants and $h = (b - a)/3$. (Why?) By symmetry (reverse the x-axis), we guess $c_0 = c_3$ and $c_1 = c_2$;

$$\int_a^b p_3(x)\,dx = h[c_0(f_0 + f_3) + c_1(f_1 + f_2)].$$

We find the constants c_0 and c_1 by examining special cases of this formula. First we take $x_0 = -3$, $x_1 = -1$, $x_2 = 1$, $x_3 = 3$ and $h = 2$:

$$\int_{-3}^3 p_3(x)\,dx = 2\left\{c_0[f(-3) + f(3)] + c_1[f(-1) + f(1)]\right\}.$$

Next we choose $p_3(x) = 1$, obtaining

$$6 = 2(2c_0 + 2c_1).$$

Last we choose $p_3(x) = x^2$:

$$18 = 2(18c_0 + 2c_1).$$

From these equations $c_0 = \frac{3}{8}$ and $c_1 = \frac{9}{8}$. The final result is the Three-Eighths Rule.

Three-Eighths Rule

$$\int_a^b f(x)\,dx \approx \frac{3h}{8}[f_0 + 3f_1 + 3f_2 + f_3],$$

where $h = \frac{1}{3}(b - a)$.

Just as Simpson's Three-Point Rule was extended to a more general rule, the Three-Eighths Rule can also be extended. For example, divide the interval into 6 subintervals:

$$a = x_0 \quad x_1 \quad x_2 \quad x_3 \quad x_4 \quad x_5 \quad x_6 = b.$$

Write

$$\int_a^b f(x)\,dx = \int_{x_0}^{x_3} + \int_{x_3}^{x_6}.$$

By the Three-Eighths Rule,

$$\int_{x_0}^{x_3} f(x)\,dx \approx \frac{3h}{8}[f_0 + 3f_1 + 3f_2 + f_3],$$

$$\int_{x_3}^{x_6} f(x)\,dx \approx \frac{3h}{8}[f_3 + 3f_4 + 3f_5 + f_6].$$

Add; the result is a 7-point rule:

$$\int_a^b f(x)\,dx \approx \frac{3h}{8}[f_0 + 3f_1 + 3f_2 + 2f_3 + 3f_4 + 3f_5 + f_6],$$

where $h = \frac{1}{6}(b - a)$.

Both the Three-Eighths Rule and Simpson's Rule are exact for cubic polynomials, but not for fourth degree polynomials. The two rules provide approximately the same degree of accuracy.

Interpolation with polynomials of degree 4 and 5 leads to the 5-point and 6-point Newton–Cotes Rules, etc. The coefficients that occur are tedious to compute; we simply state some of the more useful results.

Higher Order Newton–Cotes Rules

5-point:

$$\int_a^b f(x)\ dx \approx \frac{2h}{45}\ [7f_0 + 32f_1 + 12f_2 + 32f_3 + 7f_4],$$

where $h = \frac{1}{4}(b - a)$;

7-point:

$$\int_a^b f(x)\ dx \approx \frac{h}{140}\ [41f_0 + 216f_1 + 27f_2 + 272f_3 + 27f_4 + 216f_5 + 41f_6],$$

where $h = \frac{1}{6}(b - a)$;

9-point:

$$\int_a^b f(x)\ dx \approx \frac{4h}{14{,}175}\ [989f_0 + 5888f_1 - 928f_2 + 10{,}496f_3$$
$$- 4540f_4 + 10{,}496f_5 - 928f_6 + 5888f_7 + 989f_8],$$

where $h = \frac{1}{8}(b - a)$.

Repeated application of these rules produces further rules. For example, the 5-point rule applied twice produces a nine-point rule.

Nine-point 5-point Rule:

$$\int_a^b f(x)\ dx \approx \frac{2h}{45}\ [7f_0 + 32f_1 + 12f_2 + 32f_3 + 14f_4$$
$$+ 32f_5 + 12f_6 + 32f_7 + 7f_8],$$

where $h = \frac{1}{8}(b - a)$.

There are many other approximate integration rules based on rather complicated arguments. One stands out because of the simplicity of its coefficients; it is about as accurate as the 5-point rule.

Weddle's Rule

$$\int_a^b f(x)\ dx \approx \frac{3h}{10}\ [f_0 + 5f_1 + f_2 + 6f_3 + f_4 + 5f_5 + f_6],$$

where $h = \frac{1}{6}(b - a)$.

Applied to our test integral, these rules yield the estimates in Table 4.1.

TABLE 4.1. NEWTON–COTES APPROXIMATIONS

Rule	$\displaystyle\int_0^2 e^{-x^2}\,dx$
$\frac{3}{8}$-Rule	0.862224
5-point	0.885270
7-point	0.881916
Seven-point $\frac{3}{8}$-rule	0.881925
9-point	0.882087
Nine-point 5-point	0.882082
Weddle	0.882086

Comparing the results of Tables 3.1, 3.2, and 4.1 is instructive. (Recall that the true value of the integral is 0.8820810 to 7 places.) Most accurate is the Simpson 21-point approximation. Next is the 5-point rule applied to 9 division points.

The error in the various rules is discussed in Section 7.

EXERCISES

Estimate the integral, using the 5-point Simpson's Rule and the 5-point Newton–Cotes Rule; give a 2-decimal answer:

1. $\displaystyle\int_1^5 \frac{x^4 + 1}{x^5 + 1}\,dx$

2. $\displaystyle\int_{-4}^0 \sqrt{1 + x + 4x^2}\,dx$

3. $\displaystyle\int_0^4 \frac{e^x}{x + 1}\,dx$

4. $\displaystyle\int_0^8 x^2 e^{-x}\,dx$

5. $\displaystyle\int_{-2}^2 e^x \cos\frac{\pi x}{2}\,dx$

6. $\displaystyle\int_0^1 \ln\cos x\,dx.$

Estimate the integral using the 7-point Three-Eighths-Rule, the 7-point Newton–Cotes Rule, and Weddle's Rule; give a 4-decimal answer:

7. $\displaystyle\int_1^7 \frac{x + 1}{x^3 + x + 1}\,dx$

8. $\displaystyle\int_{-3}^3 \ln(x + 5)\,dx$

9. $\displaystyle\int_0^{1.5} \frac{\sin x}{x + 1}\,dx$

10. $\displaystyle\int_{-1.5}^{1.5} \sqrt{x^3 + 4}\,dx$

11. $\displaystyle\int_1^7 e^{-x} \ln x\,dx$

12. $\displaystyle\int_0^3 x \sin\frac{x}{2}\,dx.$

Values of a function are given at several points. Integrate the function numerically over the given range of points, using one of the rules of this section:

13. $(0, 0)$, $(1, 4)$, $(2, -1)$, $(3, 4)$
14. $(-1, 4)$, $(2, 7)$, $(5, 4)$, $(8, 0)$
15. $(-2, 3)$, $(-1, 1)$, $(0, 7)$, $(1, 5)$, $(2, -1)$
16. $(0, 3)$, $(1, -1)$, $(2, 0)$, $(3, 1)$, $(4, 5)$
17. $(0, 7)$, $(1, 5)$, $(2, 4)$, $(3, 1)$, $(4, -2)$, $(5, -3)$, $(6, -4)$
18. $(-3, -5)$, $(-2, -1)$, $(-1, 1)$, $(0, 1)$, $(1, 1)$, $(2, 4)$, $(3, 3)$.

In Ex. 19–23, use a computer to estimate $\int_{1}^{25} f(x)\, dx$ by Simpson's Rule, and by each of the rules of this section. Use $x = 1, 2, 3, \cdots, 25$:

19. $f(x) = e^{-x}\dfrac{x^3 + 1}{x^2 + 1}$

20. $f(x) = \dfrac{\sin x}{x}$

21. $f(x) = x \ln x$

22. $f(x) = \sqrt{1 + e^x}$

23. only the tabulated values of $f(x)$ are known:

x	$f(x)$	x	$f(x)$	x	$f(x)$	x	$f(x)$	x	$f(x)$
1	1	6	8	11	11	16	25	21	0
2	1	7	13	12	14	17	11	22	5
3	2	8	21	13	25	18	10	23	5
4	3	9	8	14	13	19	21	24	10
5	5	10	3	15	12	20	5	25	15

24. Carry out the details in the derivation of the 4-point Three-Eighths Rule.
25. Verify that the Three-Eighths Rule is exact for cubics in any interval $a \le x \le b$, not only $-3 \le x \le 3$ as discussed on p. 387.
26. Use Lagrange Interpolation to derive the Three-Eighths Rule. (Reread the first three paragraphs of the section.)
27. Draw a flowchart for the 5-point Newton–Cotes Rule.
28. Draw a flowchart for Weddle's Rule.

5. SYMMETRIES IN DEFINITE INTEGRALS

The rest of this chapter is devoted to certain techniques for evaluating and estimating definite integrals, and to discussion of the errors in various numerical integration formulas.

In this section, we discuss a few labor-saving methods for evaluating definite integrals.

Sometimes an integral

$$\int_{a}^{b} f(x)\, dx$$

can be simplified because the integrand $f(x)$ has certain symmetry. We look at several cases.

Even Functions

If $f(x)$ is an even function, i.e.,

$$f(x) = f(-x),$$

then

$$\int_{-a}^{a} f(x)\, dx = 2 \int_{0}^{a} f(x)\, dx.$$

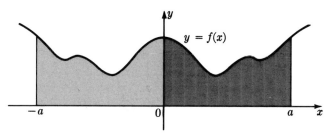

$y = f(x)$

Fɪɢ. 5.1

Look at a graph to see why this is so (Fig. 5.1). It can also be seen by a substitution:

$$\int_{-a}^{0} f(x)\, dx = \int_{a}^{0} f(-u)\,(-du) = \int_{a}^{0} f(u)\,(-du) = \int_{0}^{a} f(u)\, du.$$

(Justify each of these steps.) Hence,

$$\int_{-a}^{a} f(x)\, dx = \int_{-a}^{0} f(x)\, dx + \int_{0}^{a} f(x)\, dx = 2 \int_{0}^{a} f(x)\, dx.$$

EXAMPLE 5.1

Find $\displaystyle\int_{-\pi/2}^{\pi/2} \cos\frac{x}{3}\, dx.$

Solution: The integrand is an even function:

$$\cos\left(\frac{-x}{3}\right) = \cos\left(\frac{x}{3}\right).$$

Therefore,

$$\int_{-\pi/2}^{\pi/2} \cos\frac{x}{3}\, dx = 2 \int_{0}^{\pi/2} \cos\frac{x}{3}\, dx = 6 \sin\frac{x}{3}\Big|_{0}^{\pi/2} = 6 \sin\frac{\pi}{6} = 3.$$

Answer: 3.

Symmetry is useful in approximate integration also.

EXAMPLE 5.2

Estimate $\displaystyle\int_{-\pi/2}^{\pi/2} \cos \frac{x}{3}\, dx$, by Simpson's Rule with 3 points.

Solution:

$$\int_{-\pi/2}^{\pi/2} \cos \frac{x}{3}\, dx \approx \frac{\pi}{6}\left(\cos \frac{-\pi}{6} + 4\cos 0 + \cos \frac{\pi}{6}\right)$$

$$= \frac{\pi}{6}\left(\frac{\sqrt{3}}{2} + 4 + \frac{\sqrt{3}}{2}\right)$$

$$= \frac{\pi}{6}(4 + \sqrt{3}) \approx 3.0013.$$

(The exact value is 3.)

Alternate Solution: First observe $\cos (x/3)$ is even. Hence

$$\int_{-\pi/2}^{\pi/2} \cos \frac{x}{3}\, dx = 2\int_{0}^{\pi/2} \cos \frac{x}{3}\, dx.$$

Now use Simpson's Rule on the interval $0 \le x \le \pi/2$:

$$\int_{-\pi/2}^{\pi/2} \cos \frac{x}{3}\, dx \approx 2\left(\frac{1}{3}\right)\left(\frac{\pi}{4}\right)\left(\cos 0 + 4\cos \frac{\pi}{12} + \cos \frac{\pi}{6}\right)$$

$$\approx \frac{\pi}{6}\left[1 + 4(0.96593) + (0.86603)\right]$$

$$\approx \frac{\pi}{6}(5.72975) \approx 3.0000.$$

(There is a cumulative round-off error here. Using 7-place tables we get 3.00007.)

Answer: 3.0000.

REMARK: In the second solution we exploited the evenness of $\cos (x/3)$. That enabled us to apply Simpson's Rule on a smaller interval and obtain greater accuracy.

Sometimes a function may be "even" with respect to an axis other than the y-axis. For example,

$$\int_{4}^{6} (x - 5)^2\, dx = 2\int_{5}^{6} (x - 5)^2\, dx$$

because the function $(x - 5)^2$ is symmetric about the line $x = 5$. See Fig. 5.2.

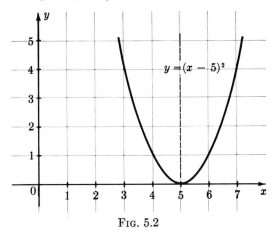

FIG. 5.2

Odd Functions

If $f(x)$ is an odd function, i.e.,
$$f(-x) = -f(x),$$
then
$$\int_{-a}^{a} f(x)\, dx = 0.$$

This can be seen from a graph (Fig. 5.3). It also can be derived by a substitution:

$$\int_{-a}^{a} f(x)\, dx = \int_{a}^{-a} f(-x)\,(-dx) = \int_{a}^{-a} [-f(x)]\,[-dx]$$
$$= \int_{a}^{-a} f(x)\, dx = -\int_{-a}^{a} f(x)\, dx.$$

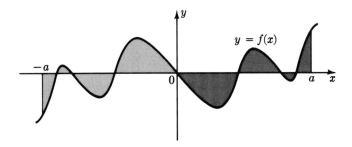

FIG. 5.3

(Justify each of these steps.) Hence,

$$2 \int_{-a}^{a} f(x) \, dx = 0, \qquad \int_{-a}^{a} f(x) \, dx = 0.$$

This property of odd functions can save a lot of computation. For example,

$$\int_{-\pi/4}^{\pi/4} \sin^9 x \, dx = 0, \qquad \int_{-2}^{2} \frac{x^3 \, dx}{x^4 + x^2 + 1} = 0,$$

by inspection.

The graph of an odd function is symmetric with respect to the origin. A function may be symmetric with respect to some other point of the x-axis.

EXAMPLE 5.3

Find $\displaystyle\int_{0}^{6} x(x-1)\,(x-2)\,(x-3)\,(x-4)\,(x-5)\,(x-6)\,dx.$

Solution: The point of symmetry is $(3, 0)$. To exploit this make the change of variable $x = u + 3$. Then

$$x(x-1) \cdots (x-6) = g(u),$$

where

$$g(u) = (u+3)\,(u+2)\,(u+1)u(u-1)\,(u-2)\,(u-3).$$

Thus

$$\int_{0}^{6} x(x-1) \cdots (x-6) \, dx = \int_{-3}^{3} g(u) \, du.$$

But $g(-u) = -g(u)$, so the integral is 0.

Answer: **0.**

Periodic Functions

Suppose $f(x)$ is periodic of period 2π. That is,

$$f(x + 2\pi) = f(x)$$

for each value of x. The first relation we notice is

$$\int_{a}^{b} f(x) \, dx = \int_{a+2\pi}^{b+2\pi} f(x) \, dx.$$

This follows from the substitution $x = u + 2\pi$:

$$\int_{a+2\pi}^{b+2\pi} f(x) \, dx = \int_{a}^{b} f(u + 2\pi) \, du = \int_{a}^{b} f(u) \, du.$$

It can also be seen from a graph (Fig. 5.4).

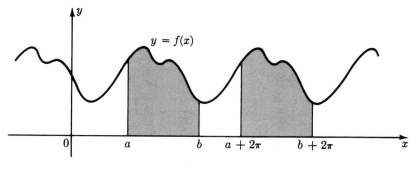

FIG. 5.4

The next relation says that the integral can be evaluated over a full period by evaluating it over *any* full period:

$$\int_a^{a+2\pi} f(x) \; dx = \int_0^{2\pi} f(x) \; dx.$$

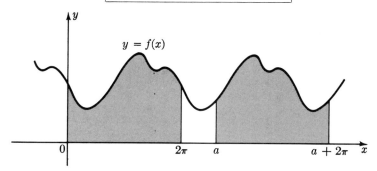

FIG. 5.5

This again is clear from a graph (Fig. 5.5). It can also be justified by shorthand:

$$\int_a^{a+2\pi} = \int_0^{a+2\pi} - \int_0^a$$

$$= \int_0^{2\pi} + \int_{2\pi}^{a+2\pi} - \int_0^a$$

$$= \int_0^{2\pi} + \int_0^a - \int_0^a$$

$$= \int_0^{2\pi}.$$

EXAMPLE 5.4

Show that $\displaystyle\int_0^{2\pi} \sqrt{1 + \sin^3 x}\, dx = \int_0^{2\pi} \sqrt{1 + \cos^3 x}\, dx.$

Solution: In the integral on the left, replace $\sin x$ by $\cos(\pi/2 - x)$. Then make the substitution $u = \pi/2 - x$:

$$\int_0^{2\pi} \sqrt{1 + \sin^3 x}\, dx = \int_0^{2\pi} \sqrt{1 + \cos^3 \left(\frac{\pi}{2} - x\right)}\, dx$$

$$= \int_{\pi/2}^{-3\pi/2} \sqrt{1 + \cos^3 u}\,(-du)$$

$$= \int_{-3\pi/2}^{\pi/2} \sqrt{1 + \cos^3 u}\, du = \int_0^{2\pi} \sqrt{1 + \cos^3 u}\, du.$$

The next example uses the same idea.

EXAMPLE 5.5

Suppose n is a positive integer and $f(t)$ is any function defined for $-1 \leq t \leq 1$. Show that

$$\int_0^{2\pi} f(\sin nx)\, dx = \int_0^{2\pi} f(\cos nx)\, dx.$$

Solution: Substitute

$$x = \frac{\pi}{2n} - u$$

into the integral on the left. Then

$$\sin nx = \sin\left(\frac{\pi}{2} - nx\right) = \cos nu, \qquad dx = -du,$$

$$\int_0^{2\pi} f(\sin nx)\, dx = -\int_{\pi/2n}^{(\pi/2n)-2\pi} f(\cos nu)\, du$$

$$= \int_{(\pi/2n)-2\pi}^{\pi/2n} f(\cos nu)\, du = \int_0^{2\pi} f(\cos nu)\, du.$$

We have used two facts:

(i) $f(\cos nu)$ has period 2π,

(ii) $\displaystyle\int_a^{a+2\pi} = \int_0^{2\pi}$,   where $a = \dfrac{\pi}{2n} - 2\pi$.

EXAMPLE 5.6

Compute $\displaystyle\int_0^{2\pi} \sin^2(100x)\, dx.$

Solution: Set

$$A = \int_0^{2\pi} \cos^2(100x)\, dx \qquad \text{and} \qquad B = \int_0^{2\pi} \sin^2(100x)\, dx.$$

By the last example, $A = B$. On the other hand,

$$
\begin{aligned}
A + B &= \int_0^{2\pi} \cos^2(100x)\, dx + \int_0^{2\pi} \sin^2(100x)\, dx \\
&= \int_0^{2\pi} [\cos^2(100x) + \sin^2(100x)]\, dx \\
&= \int_0^{2\pi} 1 \cdot dx = 2\pi.
\end{aligned}
$$

Hence, $A = \pi$.

Alternate Solution: Use the identity

$$\sin^2 \theta = \frac{1}{2} + \frac{1}{2} \cos 2\theta.$$

$$\int_0^{2\pi} \sin^2(100x)\, dx = \frac{1}{2} \int_0^{2\pi} dx + \frac{1}{2} \int_0^{2\pi} \cos(200x)\, dx.$$

The first integral on the right is π. The second is zero because $\cos 200x$ makes a whole number of complete cycles from 0 to 2π.

Answer: **π.**

A function $f(x)$ is called **periodic with period** p if

$$f(x + p) = f(x).$$

Each statement about functions of period 2π can be modified to a statement about functions of any period p.

EXERCISES

Determine if the function is even, odd, or neither:

1. $y = e^{-x^2}$
2. $y = x \sin x$
3. $y = x^3 - 5x$
4. $y = x \cos x$
5. $y = \ln(x^2)$
6. $y = \ln(x^3)$
7. $y = \sin x + \cos x$
8. $y = e^{x^2} \cos x.$

Find a line $x = k$ of even or odd symmetry:

9. $y = (x^2 - 1)(x + 3)$
10. $y = (x^2 + 2x)(x + 3)(x + 5)$

11. $y = \sin(x + 1)$

12. $y = e^{-(x+1)^2}$

13. $y = \sin x + \cos x$

14. $y = \dfrac{1}{x^2 + x + 1}$

15. $y = \sqrt{1 + x^2}$

16. $y = e^{\sin x}$.

Reduce the given integral by symmetry to one over a shorter interval; do not evaluate:

17. $\displaystyle\int_{-1}^{2} (x^3 - 5x)\, dx$

18. $\displaystyle\int_{-4}^{4} \sin(x^2)\, dx$

19. $\displaystyle\int_{-2}^{3} \dfrac{2x - 1}{x^2 - x + 1}\, dx$

20. $\displaystyle\int_{-4}^{0} \sqrt{x^2 + 4x + 6}\, dx$.

Reduce the given integral by symmetry and periodicity to one over a shorter interval; do not evaluate:

21. $\displaystyle\int_{0}^{3\pi} (\sin x + \cos x)\, dx$

22. $\displaystyle\int_{0}^{\pi} (\sin x + \cos 2x)\, dx$

23. $\displaystyle\int_{0}^{2\pi} \sin^2 x\, dx$

24. $\displaystyle\int_{0}^{3\pi} \dfrac{\sin x}{2 + \cos x}\, dx$

25. $\displaystyle\int_{-100\pi}^{100\pi} \sin\left(\dfrac{x}{12} - 4\right) dx$

26. $\displaystyle\int_{1}^{4} \sin(\pi x + 3)\, dx$.

(*Hint:* Use the addition formula for the sine.)

6. ESTIMATES OF INTEGRALS

In applications, important quantities may occur as definite integrals which are difficult or impossible to compute. In such cases, one can use numerical integration formulas. But if only a rough estimate is needed, there are some simple quick techniques worth knowing. Here are a few of the most basic ones.

Inequalities for Definite Integrals

(1) If $f(x) \geq 0$ for $a \leq x \leq b$, then $\displaystyle\int_{a}^{b} f(x)\, dx \geq 0$.

(2) If $f(x) \leq g(x)$ for $a \leq x \leq b$, then $\displaystyle\int_{a}^{b} f(x)\, dx \leq \int_{a}^{b} g(x)\, dx$.

(3) If $m \leq f(x) \leq M$ for $a \leq x \leq b$, then

$$m(b - a) \leq \int_{a}^{b} f(x)\, dx \leq M(b - a).$$

(4) $$\left| \int_{a}^{b} f(x)\, dx \right| \leq \int_{a}^{b} |f(x)|\, dx \qquad (a < b).$$

(5) If $|f(x)| \leq M$, and either $g(x) \geq 0$ for all x or $g(x) \leq 0$ for all x, where $a \leq x \leq b$, then $\left| \displaystyle\int_{a}^{b} f(x)g(x)\, dx \right| \leq M \left| \displaystyle\int_{a}^{b} g(x)\, dx \right|$.

COMMENTS: Inequality (1) goes back to the definition of the definite integral of a nonnegative function as an area. In fact, with area in mind a bit more can be said:

If $f(x)$ is a smooth function and $f(x) \geq 0$ for $a \leq x \leq b$, then actually

$$\int_a^b f(x)\,dx > 0$$

unless $f(x) = 0$ for all x.

Inequality (2) follows from (1). If $f(x) \leq g(x)$, then $[g(x) - f(x)] \geq 0$. From (1),

$$\int_a^b [g(x) - f(x)]\,dx \geq 0.$$

Hence

$$\int_a^b g(x)\,dx - \int_a^b f(x)\,dx \geq 0,$$

which implies (2). Notice that the sharpened version of (1) implies a sharpened version of (2):

If $f(x) \leq g(x)$ for $a \leq x \leq b$, then actually

$$\int_a^b f(x)\,dx < \int_a^b g(x)\,dx$$

unless $f(x) = g(x)$ for all x.

Inequality (3) follows from (2). Let $g(x)$ be the constant function $g(x) = M$. If $f(x) \leq M$, then

$$\int_a^b f(x)\,dx \leq \int_a^b g(x)\,dx = \int_a^b M\,dx = M(b - a).$$

The other half of (3) is proved in a similar way.

Inequality (3) has a simple geometric meaning for positive functions (Fig. 6.1). The area of the region under $y = f(x)$ between a and b is larger than that of a rectangle, base $b - a$, height m, and smaller than that of a rectangle, base $b - a$, height M.

Inequality (4) follows from (2), and from simple properties of absolute values:

$$|a| = +a \quad \text{or} \quad -a; \qquad a \leq |a|, \qquad -a \leq |a|.$$

Thus

$$\left| \int_a^b f(x)\,dx \right| = + \int_a^b f(x)\,dx \quad \text{or} \quad - \int_a^b f(x)\,dx.$$

But $f(x) \leq |f(x)|$ and $-f(x) \leq |f(x)|$. Hence, from (2),

$$\left| \int_a^b f(x)\,dx \right| = \int_a^b \pm f(x)\,dx \leq \int_a^b |f(x)|\,dx.$$

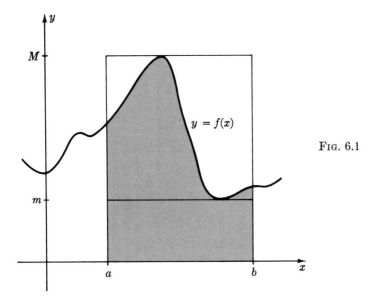

FIG. 6.1

This inequality also has a geometric meaning. The integral

$$\int_a^b f(x)\ dx$$

is an algebraic sum of areas (Fig. 6.2a). But the integral

$$\int_a^b |f(x)|\ dx$$

counts all areas positive; it allows no cancellation (Fig. 6.2b). Therefore its value is greater than or equal to the absolute value of

$$\int f(x)\ dx.$$

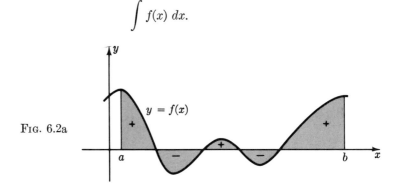

FIG. 6.2a

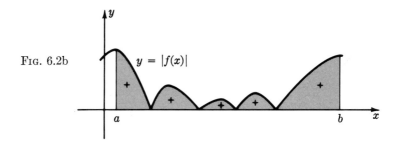

Fig. 6.2b

The integrals are unequal when there is cancellation, equal otherwise:

$$\left| \int_a^b f(x)\ dx \right| < \int_a^b |f(x)|\ dx$$

if $f(x)$ changes sign in the interval $a \leq x \leq b$. Otherwise,

$$\left| \int_a^b f(x)\ dx \right| = \int_a^b |f(x)|\ dx.$$

Inequality (5) follows from (2) and (4): If $|f(x)| \leq M$, and $g(x)$ does not change sign, then

$$\left| \int_a^b f(x)g(x)\ dx \right| \leq \int_a^b |f(x)| \cdot |g(x)|\ dx$$

$$\leq \int_a^b M|g(x)|\ dx = M \left| \int_a^b g(x)\ dx \right|.$$

Final comment: In each of the five integral inequalities, it is assumed that $a < b$. If $a > b$, the rule

$$\int_a^b f(x)\ dx = - \int_a^b f(x)\ dx$$

converts the integral into one whose upper limit is larger than its lower limit. Using this rule, we see that the inequalities are reversed in (1), (2), (3), and (4) if $a > b$. Inequality (5) is valid in all cases. (For further information, see Chapter 21, Section 4.)

Applications

EXAMPLE 6.1

Show that $\displaystyle\int_1^3 \frac{dx}{1 + x^4} < \frac{1}{3}.$

Solution: Since

$$\frac{1}{1 + x^4} < \frac{1}{x^4},$$

it follows from inequality (2) that

$$\int_1^3 \frac{dx}{1+x^4} < \int_1^3 \frac{dx}{x^4} = -\frac{1}{3x^3}\Big|_1^3 = \frac{1}{3} - \frac{1}{81} < \frac{1}{3}.$$

REMARK: This example illustrates an important technique: replacing the integrand $f(x)$ by a slightly larger one, $g(x)$, which is easily integrated. Generally, this technique yields better results than does use of inequality (3). For instance, all we can deduce from (3) is

$$\int_1^3 \frac{dx}{1+x^4} < 1.$$

(Here $a = 1$, $b = 3$, and $M = \frac{1}{2}$, the largest value of $1/(1+x^4)$ in the interval $1 \le x \le 3$.) Nevertheless, (3) is effective for very quick estimates, especially when great accuracy is not needed.

EXAMPLE 6.2

Estimate $\displaystyle\int_6^8 \frac{dx}{x^3 + x + \sin 2x}$.

Solution: Find bounds for the integrand. Since $-1 \le \sin 2x \le 1$ and $x^3 + x$ is increasing,

$$6^3 + 6 - 1 < x^3 + x + \sin 2x < 8^3 + 8 + 1$$

in the range $6 \le x \le 8$. Take reciprocals (and reverse inequalities):

$$\frac{1}{521} < \frac{1}{x^3 + x + \sin 2x} < \frac{1}{221}.$$

Use inequality (3) with $a = 6$, $b = 8$, $m = \frac{1}{521}$, $M = \frac{1}{221}$:

$$\frac{2}{521} < \int_6^8 \frac{dx}{x^3 + x + \sin 2x} < \frac{2}{221}.$$

Answer:

$$0.0038 < \int_6^8 \frac{dx}{x^3 + x + \sin 2x} < 0.0091.$$

EXAMPLE 6.3

Show that $\displaystyle\left| \int_0^{2\pi} \frac{\sin x \, dx}{1 + x^2} \right| < \frac{\pi}{2}$.

Solution: Regard the integral as

$$\int_0^{2\pi} f(x)g(x) \, dx, \qquad f(x) = \sin x, \qquad g(x) = \frac{1}{1 + x^2}.$$

Since $|f(x)| \leq 1$ and $g(x) > 0$, use inequality (5):

$$\left| \int_0^{2\pi} \frac{\sin x \, dx}{1 + x^2} \right| \leq \int_0^{2\pi} \frac{dx}{1 + x^2} = \left. \text{arc tan } x \right|_0^{2\pi} = \text{arc tan } 2\pi.$$

But arc tan $x < \pi/2$ for all values of x, hence

$$\left| \int_0^{2\pi} \frac{\sin x \, dx}{1 + x^2} \right| < \frac{\pi}{2}.$$

EXAMPLE 6.4

Show that $\int_0^3 e^{-x^2} \, dx$ is a good approximation for $\int_0^{100} e^{-x^2} \, dx$. How good?

Solution: The error in this approximation is

$$\int_0^{100} e^{-x^2} \, dx - \int_0^3 e^{-x^2} \, dx = \int_3^{100} e^{-x^2} \, dx.$$

Since e^{-x^2} is extremely small even for moderate values of x, the integral on the right is small. Estimate the integral by (3). Because e^{-x^2} is a decreasing function, its largest value in the interval $3 \leq x \leq 100$ occurs at the left end point; this value is e^{-9}. By (3),

$$\int_3^{100} e^{-x^2} \, dx < (100 - 3)e^{-9} < 97(0.000124) < 0.0124.$$

A better estimate can be obtained using (2). Note that $x^2 \geq 3x$ when $x \geq 3$. In this range therefore, $e^{-x^2} \leq e^{-3x}$ (which can be integrated). Hence

$$\int_3^{100} e^{-x^2} \, dx \leq \int_3^{100} e^{-3x} \, dx = \left. \frac{e^{-3x}}{-3} \right|_3^{100} = \frac{e^{-9}}{3} - \frac{e^{-300}}{3} < \frac{e^{-9}}{3} < 0.000042.$$

Answer:

$$\int_0^{100} e^{-x^2} \, dx - \int_0^3 e^{-x^2} \, dx < 4.2 \times 10^{-5}.$$

REMARK: This example illustrates an important labor-saving device. If you intend to estimate

$$\int_0^{100} e^{-x^2} \, dx$$

by use of a numerical integration formula, you can save a great deal of work by applying the formula to

$$\int_0^3 e^{-x^2} \, dx.$$

By ignoring the rest of the integral, you introduce an error less than 0.000042. If that is not precise enough, you might apply numerical integration to

$$\int_0^4 e^{-x^2}\, dx.$$

Then by the same argument as in the example, the error you introduce by ignoring the rest of the integral will be less than $e^{-16}/4 < 3 \times 10^{-8}$.

EXERCISES

In the following exercises you are asked to find bounds for certain integrals. There are generally several ways to estimate each integral. Try to obtain the bound given or to improve on it. If you cannot, at least find *some* bound.

Show:

1. $\dfrac{\pi}{2} < \displaystyle\int_0^{\pi/2} \dfrac{d\theta}{\sqrt{1 - k^2 \sin^2 \theta}} < \dfrac{\pi}{2\sqrt{1 - k^2}}$ $(0 < k^2 < 1)$

2. $\displaystyle\int_0^1 x \ln(1 + x)\, dx < \dfrac{\ln 2}{2}$

3. $\displaystyle\int_1^2 \dfrac{dx}{x^3 + 3x + 1} < \dfrac{1}{5}$

4. $\displaystyle\int_1^3 \dfrac{x\, dx}{(1 + x)^3} < \dfrac{1}{4}$

5. $\displaystyle\int_0^{100} e^{-x} \sin^2 x\, dx < 1$

6. $\displaystyle\int_0^{\pi/3} \sin 2\theta \cos \theta\, d\theta < \dfrac{\sqrt{3}}{2}$

7. $\displaystyle\int_5^{10} \dfrac{x^2\, dx}{3 + 2x} < \dfrac{75}{4}$

8. $\displaystyle\int_0^1 \dfrac{dx}{4 + x^3} > \ln \dfrac{5}{4}.$

Without evaluating the integral, prove:

9. $\dfrac{3}{10} < \displaystyle\int_1^4 \dfrac{dx}{x^2 + x + 1} < \dfrac{3}{4}$

10. $3\sqrt{23} < \displaystyle\int_2^5 \sqrt{3x^3 - 1}\, dx < 10\sqrt{15} - \dfrac{8}{5}\sqrt{6}$

11. $3 \ln \dfrac{5}{3} < \displaystyle\int_3^5 \dfrac{\sqrt{3 + 2x}}{x}\, dx < \sqrt{13} \ln \dfrac{5}{3}$

12. $\dfrac{8}{\sqrt{13}} < \displaystyle\int_3^5 \dfrac{x\, dx}{\sqrt{3 + 2x}} < \dfrac{8}{3}$

13. $2 < \displaystyle\int_0^4 \dfrac{dx}{1 + \sin^2 x} < 4$

14. $\dfrac{99\pi}{400} < \displaystyle\int_1^{100} \dfrac{\arctan x}{x^2}\, dx < \dfrac{99\pi}{200}$

15. $\dfrac{609(\ln 2)^2}{4} < \displaystyle\int_2^5 x^3 (\ln x)^2\, dx < \dfrac{609(\ln 5)^2}{4}$

16. $(1 - e^{-1}) \ln 10 < \displaystyle\int_1^{10} \dfrac{1 - e^{-x}}{x}\, dx < \ln 10.$

17. Estimate how closely $\int_0^{10} e^{-x} \sin^2 x \, dx$ approximates $\int_0^{100} e^{-x} \sin^2 x \, dx$.

18. Find b such that $\int_b^1 \dfrac{\sin x}{x} \, dx$ approximates $\int_0^1 \dfrac{\sin x}{x} \, dx$ to within 5×10^{-5}. (Recall $\sin x < x$ for $x > 0$.)

7. ERRORS IN NUMERICAL INTEGRATION   [optional]

It is important to have some idea of the error made when using a numerical integration formula. Often the error is expressed as an integral which can be estimated by techniques of the last section. We shall illustrate by a discussion of the error in the Trapezoidal Rule.

All of the results in this section depend on integration by parts. (For a precise statement, see Chapter 21, Section 5.) First we prove a preliminary result:

> If $f(a) = 0$ and $f(b) = 0$, then
> $$\int_a^b f(x) \, dx = -\frac{1}{2} \int_a^b (x - a)(b - x) f''(x) \, dx.$$

We derive this formula by two applications of integration by parts; in each case the "uv" part drops out.

$$\int_a^b [(x - a)(b - x)] f''(x) \, dx = -\int_a^b [(b - x) - (x - a)] f'(x) \, dx$$
$$= +\int_a^b (-2) f(x) \, dx = -2 \int_a^b f(x) \, dx.$$

Now follows another preliminary result:

> Suppose $f(a) = 0$ and $f(b) = 0$, and suppose
> $$|f''(x)| \le M, \qquad a \le x \le b.$$
> Then
> $$\left| \int_a^b f(x) \, dx \right| \le \frac{M}{12} (b - a)^3.$$

Indeed, from the preceding result,

$$\left| \int_a^b f(x) \, dx \right| = \frac{1}{2} \left| \int_a^b (x - a)(b - x) f''(x) \, dx \right|.$$

But $(x - a)(b - x) \ge 0$ between a and b, so we can use inequality (5) of the last section:

$$\left| \int_a^b f(x) \, dx \right| \le \frac{1}{2} M \int_a^b (x - a)(b - x) \, dx.$$

A routine computation shows that the integral on the right is $\frac{1}{6}(b-a)^3$. Conclusion:

$$\left| \int_a^b f(x)\,dx \right| \le \frac{M}{12}(b-a)^3.$$

We are now ready for the basic error estimate in the Trapezoidal Rule.

Two-Point Trapezoidal Rule with Error   Suppose $|f''(x)| \le M$ for $a \le x \le b$. Set $h = b - a$. Then

$$\int_a^b f(x)\,dx = \frac{h}{2}[f(a) + f(b)] + \epsilon,$$

where

$$|\epsilon| \le \frac{Mh^3}{12}.$$

The trapezoidal approximation was obtained by fitting a *linear* function $p(x)$ to the points $(a, f(a))$ and $(b, f(b))$, then writing

$$\int_a^b f(x)\,dx \approx \int_a^b p(x)\,dx = \frac{h}{2}[f(a) + f(b)].$$

The error to be estimated is therefore

$$\epsilon = \int_a^b f(x)\,dx - \int_a^b p(x)\,dx = \int_a^b [f(x) - p(x)]\,dx.$$

But look at the function $g(x) = f(x) - p(x)$. Note two of its properties:

(i) $g(a) = g(b) = 0$,

(ii) $g''(x) = f''(x)$.

(Verify these.) From (ii), $|g''(x)| \le M$. Now the preceding result applies to $g(x)$:

$$\left| \int_a^b g(x)\,dx \right| \le \frac{M}{12}(b-a)^3,$$

that is,

$$|\epsilon| = \left| \int_a^b [f(x) - p(x)]\,dx \right| \le \frac{M}{12}h^3.$$

This is the stated error estimate.

Now we estimate the error in the n-point trapezoidal approximation.

Trapezoidal Rule with Error Divide the interval $a \leq x \leq b$ into n equal parts by inserting points:

$$a = x_0 < x_1 < x_2 < \cdots < x_n = b.$$

Set

$$h = \frac{b - a}{n}.$$

Suppose $|f''(x)| \leq M$ for all x. Then

$$\int_a^b f(x) \, dx = \frac{h}{2} [f_0 + 2f_1 + 2f_2 + \cdots + 2f_{n-1} + f_n] + \epsilon,$$

where

$$|\epsilon| \leq \frac{M(b - a)}{12} h^2.$$

Write

$$\int_a^b f(x) \, dx = \int_{x_0}^{x_1} + \int_{x_1}^{x_2} + \cdots + \int_{x_{n-1}}^{x_n},$$

and apply the two-point estimate to each integral on the right. The error in each case is at most $Mh^3/12$, so the total error is at most n times this:

$$|\epsilon| \leq n \frac{Mh^3}{12} = \frac{M}{12} (nh)h^2 = \frac{M(b - a)}{12} h^2.$$

EXAMPLE 7.1

Suppose you estimate ln 2, approximating $\int_1^2 \frac{dx}{x}$ by the Trapezoidal Rule with $h = 0.1$. Find a bound for the error.

Solution:

$$|\text{error}| \leq \frac{M(b - a)}{12} h^2,$$

where $a = 1$, $b = 2$, $h = 0.1$, and M is a bound for the second derivative of $f(x) = 1/x$. But $f''(x) = 2/x^3$, hence $|f''(x)| \leq 2$ for $1 \leq x \leq 2$. Therefore

$$|\text{error}| \leq \frac{2(2 - 1)}{12} (0.1)^2 = \frac{1}{6} (0.01).$$

Answer: $|\text{error}| < 0.0017.$

In some cases the actual error is much smaller than the trapezoidal estimate indicates. For example, if $f(x)$ has a point of inflection (change of concavity) in the interval, the trapezoidal errors tend to cancel (Fig. 7.1a).

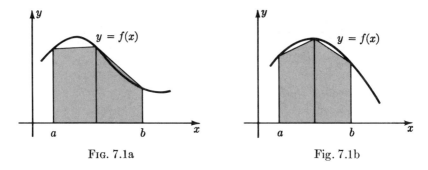

Fɪɢ. 7.1a   Fig. 7.1b

In Fig. 7.1b, however, there is no cancellation: all errors have the same sign. Since the estimate $M(b - a)h^2/12$ was made assuming all errors accumulate, the trapezoidal error estimate exceeds the actual error more in Fig. 7.1a than in Fig. 7.1b.

Other Error Estimates

By similar (although much harder) methods one finds the following estimates for the errors in other numerical integration methods.

THREE-POINT SIMPSON'S RULE

$$\int_a^b f(x)\ dx = \frac{h}{3}\left[f_0 + 4f_1 + f_2\right] + \epsilon,$$

$$|\epsilon| \leq \frac{Mh^5}{90}, \qquad \text{where}\quad |f^{(4)}(x)| \leq M.$$

THREE-EIGHTHS RULE

$$\int_a^b f(x)\ dx = \frac{3h}{8}\left[f_0 + 3f_1 + 3f_2 + f_3\right] + \epsilon,$$

$$|\epsilon| \leq \frac{3Mh^5}{80}, \qquad \text{where}\quad |f^{(4)}(x)| \leq M.$$

5-POINT NEWTON–COTES

$$\int_a^b f(x)\ dx = \frac{2h}{45}\left[7f_0 + 32f_1 + 12f_2 + 32f_3 + 7f_4\right] + \epsilon,$$

$$|\epsilon| \leq \frac{8Mh^7}{945}, \qquad \text{where}\quad |f^{(6)}(x)| \leq M.$$

7-POINT NEWTON–COTES

$$\int_a^b f(x)\,dx = \frac{h}{140}[41f_0 + 216f_1 + 27f_2 + 272f_3 + 27f_4 + 216f_5 + 41f_6] + \epsilon,$$

$$|\epsilon| \le \frac{9Mh^9}{1400}, \qquad \text{where} \quad |f^{(8)}(x)| \le M.$$

9-POINT NEWTON–COTES

$$\int_a^b f(x)\,dx = \frac{4h}{14175}[989f_0 + 5888f_1 - 928f_2 + 10496f_3 - 4540f_4$$
$$+ 10496f_5 - 928f_6 + 5888f_7 + 989f_8] + \epsilon,$$

$$|\epsilon| \le \frac{2368Mh^{11}}{467775}, \qquad \text{where} \quad |f^{(10)}(x)| \le M.$$

WEDDLE'S RULE

$$\int_a^b f(x)\,dx = \frac{3h}{10}[f_0 + 5f_1 + f_2 + 6f_3 + f_4 + 5f_5 + f_6] + \epsilon,$$

$$|\epsilon| \le \frac{h^7}{1400}(10M + 9h^2N), \qquad \text{where} \quad |f^{(6)}(x)| \le M, \quad |f^{(8)}(x)| \le N.$$

EXAMPLE 7.2

Suppose you estimate ln 2 as in Example 7.1, but use Simpson's Rule with $h = 0.1$. Find a bound for the error.

Solution: Divide the interval $1 \le x \le 2$ into 5 equal parts. Write

$$\ln 2 = \int_1^2 \frac{dx}{x} = \int_{1.0}^{1.2} + \int_{1.2}^{1.4} + \int_{1.4}^{1.6} + \int_{1.6}^{1.8} + \int_{1.8}^{2.0},$$

and apply the three-point Simpson's Rule to each integral on the right. In each case the error is at most

$$\frac{M(0.1)^5}{90},$$

where M is a bound for the fourth derivative of $f(x) = 1/x$. Since

$$f^{(4)}(x) = \frac{2 \cdot 3 \cdot 4}{x^5} \qquad \text{and} \qquad 1 \le x \le 2,$$

take $M = 2 \cdot 3 \cdot 4 = 24$. Thus each of the 5 errors is at most

$$\frac{24(0.1)^5}{90},$$

and the combined error is at most 5 times this much.

$Answer:$ $|\text{error}| < 1.4 \times 10^{-5}.$

REMARK: We were wasteful using the same value of M in each of the 5 integrals. For a sharper estimate, we can use

$$M = \frac{24}{1^5}, \quad \frac{24}{(1.2)^5}, \quad \frac{24}{(1.4)^5}, \quad \frac{24}{(1.6)^5}, \quad \frac{24}{(1.8)^5},$$

respectively. Then we find

$$|\text{error}| < 4.7 \times 10^{-6}.$$

EXERCISES

Estimate the error in using the Trapezoidal Rule, Simpson's Rule, and the Three-Eighths Rule to approximate the integral:

1. $\int_0^1 \sin x \, dx, \quad h = \frac{1}{6}$

2. $\int_{\pi/4}^{\pi/2} x \sin x \, dx, \quad h = \pi/24$

3. $\int_1^3 \ln x \, dx, \quad h = \frac{1}{3}$

4. $\int_0^1 e^{-x} \, dx, \quad h = \frac{1}{6}.$

Estimate the error in using the 7-point Newton–Cotes Rule and Weddle's Rule to approximate the integral:

5. $\int_0^2 \cos x \, dx, \quad h = \frac{1}{3}$

6. $\int_1^4 \ln x \, dx, \quad h = \frac{1}{2}$

7. $\int_{-2}^1 x^2 e^x \, dx, \quad h = \frac{1}{2}$

8. $\int_0^{\pi/2} \sin x \cos 2x \, dx, \quad h = \pi/12.$

9. Suppose you are to estimate $\int_0^6 x^2 e^{-x} \, dx$, using $h = 0.25$. Find one of the methods of this chapter which will guarantee an error of at most $5 \times 10^{-5}.$

10, Write a program to carry out the estimation chosen in Ex. 9.

11. Show that multiplying the number of points by a factor of 10 in the Trapezoidal Rule improves the error estimate by a factor of 100.

12. Suppose $f(-1) = f(0) = f(1) = 0$. Show (integration by parts) that

$$\int_{-1}^1 f(x) \, dx = -\frac{1}{6}\left[\int_{-1}^0 x(x+1)^2 f'''(x) \, dx + \int_0^1 x(x-1)^2 f'''(x) \, dx \right].$$

13. (cont.) Show further that

$$72 \int_{-1}^1 f(x) \, dx$$
$$= \int_{-1}^0 (x+1)^3(3x-1)f^{(4)}(x) \, dx + \int_0^1 (x-1)^3(3x+1)f^{(4)}(x) \, dx.$$

14. (cont.)   Conclude that if $f(-1) = f(0) = f(1) = 0$ and $f^{(4)}(x) = 0$ for $-1 < x < 1$, then $\int_{-1}^1 f(x) \, dx = 0.$

15. (cont.) Suppose $f(-1) = f(0) = f(1) = 0$ and $|f^{(4)}(x)| \leq M$ for $-1 \leq x \leq 1$. Use Ex. 13 to prove that $\left| \int_{-1}^{1} f(x)\, dx \right| \leq \dfrac{M}{90}$.

16. (cont.) Deduce the error estimate in the three-point Simpson's Rule.

17. Suppose Simpson's Rule is used with 5, 9, or $2n + 1$ points. Find an error estimate.

18. Do the same for the $(3n + 1)$-point Three-Eighths Rule.

19. Do the same for the $(4n + 1)$-point 5-point Newton–Cotes Rule.

20. Consider the estimate in the second box on p. 405. Stretching the interval $a \leq x \leq b$ by a factor c appears to divide the left-hand side of the inequality by c and the right-hand side by c^3, or does it?

20. Theory of Limits and Continuity

1. INTRODUCTION

In this book we presented calculus as a working tool. Our presentation was intuitive rather than rigorous, because we were more concerned with the use of calculus than with its foundations. Now, in these final two chapters, we shall give some of the main theoretical considerations behind calculus. This theory is covered in more detail in courses on Functions of Real Variables or Mathematical Analysis.

Any mathematical theory consists of a sequence of precise definitions, assumptions (axioms), theorems, and proofs. Such theory is necessarily more formal than applications. Often the proofs are subtle and require careful study. Also, mathematical knowledge is cumulative; it is necessary to know all preceding results before going on to the next one. So again, careful study of this theoretical chapter is necessary. Yet, in time it becomes easier to learn theory than to learn applications, perhaps because theory is very orderly and application so diverse.

Real and Rational Numbers

The two basic processes of calculus are differentiation and integration. Both are applied to functions. Calculus really begins with a study of basic properties of functions. This study requires a thorough knowledge of the real number system and the notion of a limit.

The basic number system of science is the real number system. It has two operations, addition and multiplication (and their inverses, subtraction and division). The system is a **field,** meaning roughly that all the usual rules of arithmetic hold (see Section 1.2†).

Among the real numbers are the **rational numbers,** those real numbers expressible as quotients of integers, for example, 6/1, 2/3, −9/5, 37/2965, 3.1416 = 31,416/10,000. The rational numbers form a field. Most computations in real life can be carried out entirely within the rational field.

---

† Section 1.2 means Chapter 1, Section 2; Theorem 21.4.2 means Chapter 21, Section 4, Theorem 2; Theorem 4.2 means Section 4, Theorem 2, present chapter, etc.

The rational numbers are thick in the real number system (**dense** is the technical term) in the sense that between any two reals there is a rational number, actually many.

Each real number can be written as an unending decimal. The rational numbers are precisely the decimals which repeat from some point on. (See Exs. 5.25–26.) For example,

$$0.125000 \cdots = \frac{1}{8}, \qquad 0.257000 \cdots = \frac{257}{1000},$$

$$1.333 \cdots = \frac{4}{3}, \qquad 0.09090909 \cdots = \frac{1}{11},$$

$$2.53697697697697 \cdots = \frac{253{,}444}{99{,}900} = \frac{63{,}361}{24{,}975}.$$

Not all decimals repeat, for instance

$$0.101001000100001000001 \cdots ,$$

where each string of zeros is one longer than the preceding string. Thus not all real numbers are rational. Many numbers are known to be irrational, for example $\sqrt{2}$. Similarly, $\sqrt{3}$, $\sqrt{5}$, and $\sqrt[3]{2}$ are irrational, as are π, e, and $\ln 17$.

Although the rational number system and the real number system are similar in many ways, there is an important distinction between them: the rational number system is full of "gaps" or "holes" while the real system is not; it is "complete". To understand this, consider the sequence of rational numbers

$$1, \quad 1.4, \quad 1.41, \quad 1.414, \quad 1.4142, \quad 1.41421, \quad 1.414213, \quad \cdots .$$

Their squares approach 2 as closely as we wish, so the sequence seems to be approaching a number whose square is 2. But there is no rational number whose square is exactly 2; there is a "hole" in the rational numbers where $\sqrt{2}$ should be. In the real number system, there *is* a number $\sqrt{2}$.

REMARK: There are many proofs that $2 \neq a^2/b^2$, where a and b are integers. For example, start with $a^2 = 2b^2$. Suppose 2 divides a exactly m times so $a = 2^m c$, where c is odd, and likewise $b = 2^n d$, where d is odd. Then $2^{2m}c^2 = 2^{2n+1}d^2$ by substitution. Since c^2 and d^2 are odd, this implies $2m = 2n + 1$; an even number equals an odd number. Nonsense!

Similarly,

$$3, \quad 3.1, \quad 3.14, \quad 3.141, \quad 3.1415, \quad 3.14159, \quad 3.141592, \quad \cdots$$

is a sequence of rational numbers approximating the circumference of a circle of unit diameter. But there is no rational number exactly equal to the circumference; there is a "hole" in the rational numbers where π should be.

The real numbers can be constructed rigorously by "filling in the holes" or "completing the rational numbers". Or the real numbers can be described by a set of axioms, the critical one being an axiom of completeness.

Set Theory Notation

We shall use the language of sets, and we recall that

$$S = \{x \mid x \text{ has property } P\}$$

reads "S is the set of all x with property P". The empty set will not enter our discussion; we decree that each time we say "set" we mean "non-empty set".

We use the notation $x \in S$ for "x belongs to S" or simply "x in S". We recall that "set S is a subset of set T" is written $S \subseteq T$ and that **union** of two sets is

$$S \cup T = \{x \mid x \in S \quad \text{or} \quad x \in T \quad \text{or both}\}.$$

Triangle Inequality

In the proofs that follow we shall use the *triangle inequality* time and again. It is important to be fluent in its various forms:

$$|a + b| \leq |a| + |b|,$$
$$\big||a| - |b|\big| \leq |a - b|,$$
$$|a_1 + a_2 + \cdots + a_n| \leq |a_1| + |a_2| + \cdots + |a_n|.$$

2. COMPLETENESS

In this section, we introduce an axiom of completeness for the real number system. In order to understand the axiom, we begin with a few remarks about sets of real numbers.

Any finite set of real numbers has a largest member (maximum). We take this as obvious, but it can be proved by induction. An infinite set, however, may not have a largest member. For example, the set of positive integers has minimum 1, but no maximum. The set of *all* integers has neither a maximum nor a minimum.

These sets contain numbers that are as big as you please; it is hopeless to look for a maximum. On the other hand, the set $S = \{x \mid 0 < x < 1\}$, even though confined between 0 and 1, has neither maximum nor minimum. Still, in this case something can be salvaged: the number 1 is "nearly" a maximum for S, and the number 0 is "nearly" a minimum. The completeness axiom guarantees that this is a typical case: any bounded set of real numbers either has a largest element, or there is a real number that "acts" like a largest element (and similarly for a smallest element.)

We need some precise terminology to state these ideas. Suppose **S** is any set of real numbers. A number B is an **upper bound** for **S** if $x \le B$ for each $x \in$ **S**. A number A is a **lower bound** for **S** if $A \le x$ for each $x \in$ **S**. A set that has an upper bound is **bounded above**; a set that has a lower bound is **bounded below.** A set that is bounded both above and below is **bounded.**

Examples:

1. The set $\{1, 2, 3, \cdots\}$ of positive integers is bounded below but not bounded above. For if $A \le 1$, then A is a lower bound, but there is no upper bound.

2. The set $\{0, \pm 1, \pm 2, \cdots\}$ of all integers is neither bounded above nor below.

3. The set **S** $= \{r \mid r$ is rational and $r^2 < 2\}$ is bounded. If $r \in$ **S**, then $-2 < r < 2$, otherwise $r^2 \ge 4$.

We can now state a completeness axiom for the real numbers:

Completeness Axiom   Any set of real numbers that is bounded above has a **least** (smallest) **upper bound.** Any set of real numbers that is bounded below has a **greatest lower bound.**

Thus if there is any upper bound at all, then there is a *least* upper bound.

REMARK: The second part of the axiom actually follows from the first. For if **S** is bounded below, then the set **S**$^* = \{x \mid -x \in$ **S**$\}$ is bounded above, hence has a least upper bound B. Then $-B$ is the greatest lower bound of **S**. (Try to justify this argument.)

We denote the least upper bound of **S** by sup **S**, where "sup" stands for **supremum.** We denote the greatest lower bound of **S** by inf **S**, where "inf" stands for **infimum.**

For applications, it is convenient to have the following characterization of the least upper bound (supremum):

Theorem 2.1   Given a set **S** of real numbers, sup **S** $= B$ if and only if

(1)   for each $x \in$ **S**, we have $x \le B$,

(2)   if $B_1 < B$, then there is an $x \in$ **S** such that $x > B_1$.

This criterion is very simple; (1) says that B is *an* upper bound, and (2) says that no smaller number is an upper bound. Of course, there is a similar criterion for the inf **S**.

EXAMPLE 2.1

Suppose **S** $= \{0, \frac{1}{2}, \frac{2}{3}, \frac{3}{4}, \cdots, (n-1)/n, \cdots\}$. Prove that sup **S** $= 1$.

Solution: We use the preceding criterion with $B = 1$.

(1)   Each element of **S** is of the form $(n - 1)/n$ for some positive integer n, and $(n - 1)/n = 1 - 1/n < 1$.

(2)   Suppose $B_1 < 1$. Then $B_1 = 1 - \epsilon$ for some positive ϵ. For n large enough, $1/n < \epsilon$; hence

$$1 - \frac{1}{n} > 1 - \epsilon = B_1.$$

This completes the proof that sup **S** $= 1$.

Filling Gaps in the Rational Numbers

The completeness axiom is used to fill in the "gaps" in the rational number system. We leave the full treatment of this theory to a more advanced course. We shall simply illustrate the ideas involved by showing how completeness guarantees the existence of a real number x for which $x^2 = 2$. (There is no such *rational* number.)

Let

$$\mathbf{S} = \{r \mid r \text{ is rational} \quad \text{and} \quad r^2 < 2\}.$$

We noted above that **S** is bounded; indeed, $-2 < r < 2$ whenever $r \in \mathbf{S}$. The completeness axiom assures the existence of $B = \sup \mathbf{S}$. This number B is characterized by two properties:

(1)   If r is rational and $r^2 < 2$, then $r \leq B$.

(2)   If $A < B$, then there is a rational r satisfying $r^2 < 2$ and $r > A$.

We shall prove that $B^2 = 2$. First we suppose that $B^2 < 2$. We look for a number $B + \epsilon$, slightly larger than B, whose square is also less than 2. Thus we seek ϵ with $0 < \epsilon < 1$ and

(3) $(B + \epsilon)^2 < 2$.

This is satisfied provided $B^2 + 2B\epsilon + \epsilon^2 < 2$, that is, $(2B + \epsilon)\epsilon < (2 - B^2)$. Now $2 - B^2 > 0$ by assumption, so we satisfy the inequality (3) by choosing any ϵ in the interval $0 < \epsilon < 1$ that satisfies

$$\epsilon < \frac{2 - B^2}{2B + 1}.$$

Now we choose a rational number r such that $B < r < B + \epsilon$. Then

$$B < r \quad \text{and} \quad r^2 < (B + \epsilon)^2 < 2.$$

This contradicts (1), so $B^2 < 2$ is ruled out.

Now suppose $B^2 > 2$. As above, we can find ϵ with $\epsilon > 0$ and $(B - \epsilon)^2 > 2$. Hence if $r^2 < 2$, then $r < B - \epsilon$, which contradicts (2). So $B^2 > 2$ is also ruled out. Only $B^2 = 2$ is possible.

EXERCISES

State whether the set is bounded above or bounded below:

1. the set of rational numbers
2. $\{x \mid x > 4\}$
3. $\{x \mid 0 \leq x \leq 1\} \cup \{3\}$
4. the set of real solutions of the equation

$$x^{15} - 4x^9 + 6x^8 - 3x^2 - 5 = 0$$

5. the set of numbers 2^n for $n = 1, 2, 3, \cdots$
6. the set of all numbers $1 + \dfrac{1}{2} + \dfrac{1}{4} + \cdots + \dfrac{1}{2^n}$, for $n = 1, 2, 3, \cdots$
7. the set $\left\{\dfrac{1}{2}, -1, \dfrac{3}{4}, -2, \dfrac{7}{8}, -3, \cdots\right\}$
8*. the set of prime numbers
9. $\{y \mid y = 1/(1 + x^2), \ -\infty < x < \infty\}$
10. $\{y \mid y = 1/x, \ 0 < x < \infty\}$.

Find the least upper bound (supremum) of **S**:

11. **S** is the set of all distances between pairs of points *inside* a circle of radius r.
12. **S** $= \{r \mid r$ is rational and $r^2 < 7\}$
13. **S** $= \{r \mid r$ is rational and $r^3 > 2\}$
14. **S** is the set of areas of all circles inside the unit circle.

Find the greatest lower bound (infinum) of **S**:

15. **S** $= \{x - y \mid 3 < x < 4$ and $0 < y < 1\}$
16. **S** $= \{r \mid r$ is rational and $r^2 > 2\}$
17. **S** $= \left\{2, \dfrac{3}{2}, \dfrac{4}{3}, \dfrac{5}{4}, \cdots\right\}$
18. **S** is the set of vertical distances between the x-axis and the graph of $y = 1/(1 + x^2)$.
19. Assume **S** is bounded and prove that inf **S** $\leq$ sup **S**. When are the two equal?
20. If **S** $\subseteq$ **T** and **T** has an upper bound, prove that sup **S** $\leq$ sup **T**.
21. Prove Theorem 2.1.
22. (cont.) State and prove an analogous characterization of the infinum.

3. SEQUENCES AND THEIR LIMITS

Let x_1, x_2, x_3, $\cdots$, x_n, $\cdots$ be a sequence of real numbers. Standard notation for such a sequence is

$$\{x_n\} \qquad \text{or} \qquad \{x_n\}_{n=1}^{\infty} \qquad \text{or} \qquad \{x_n\}_1^{\infty}.$$

Sometimes the first term of a sequence is some x_n other than x_1; for instance if the sequence starts with x_0, then we write $\{x_n\}_0^{\infty}$ for x_0, x_1, x_2, $\cdots$.

A **subsequence** of x_n is a sequence $\{x_{n_j}\}_{j=1}^{\infty}$, where $\{n_j\}_{j=1}^{\infty}$ is a strictly increasing sequence of positive integers: $1 \leq n_1 < n_2 < n_3 < \cdots$. For example,

$$x_1, x_3, x_5, \cdots, \qquad x_4, x_5, x_6, \cdots, \qquad x_1, x_4, x_9, x_{16}, \cdots$$

are subsequences of $\{x_n\}$.

REMARK: We must distinguish between the sequence $\{x_n\}$ and the set $\mathbf{S} = \{x_1, x_2, \cdots\}$ of values of the sequence, first because *sequence* requires a definite order while *set* doesn't. Also, there can be repetitions in the sequence. As an extreme case take $x_1 = 1$, $x_2 = x_3 = \cdots = 0$. Then $\mathbf{S} = \{0, 1\}$.

Limit of Sequences

One of the most far-reaching concepts in mathematics is that of limit. In order to formulate the definition of limit, let us look at an example. Consider the sequence $\{x_n\}$ where $x_n = (n+1)/n$, that is, the sequence

$$2, \frac{3}{2}, \frac{4}{3}, \frac{5}{4}, \cdots, \frac{n+1}{n}, \cdots.$$

In some sense, these numbers "approach" the number 1. But what does that mean exactly? We need a precise way of stating the idea, saying "x_n approaches 1" in mathematical terms.

By "x_n approaches 1" we mean that the numbers get close to 1. How close? To within 0.01? That is not good enough; the sequence

$$1.005, \quad 1.005, \quad 1.005, \cdots$$

gets within 0.01 of the number 1, yet this sequence does not "approach" 1. To within 0.001? Again not good enough; the sequence

$$0.9999, \quad 0.9999, \quad 0.9999, \cdots$$

gets within 0.001, yet does not "approach" 1. No matter what accuracy we specify, examples like these show that it is not good enough. The trick is to require that the numbers x_n approximate 1 to within *every possible degree* of accuracy.

Let us try to say that "in math". We specify a "degree of accuracy" by a positive number ϵ (usually very small). Given ϵ, we want x_n eventually to come within ϵ of 1; written "in math", we want $|1 - x_n| < \epsilon$. Now we should clarify the vague word "eventually". This should mean "from a certain point on in the sequence". Now a "point in the sequence" is indicated by a subscript, so we want $|1 - x_n| < \epsilon$ starting with a certain subscript N.

With these ideas in mind we formulate the general definition:

Definition 3.1 A sequence $\{x_n\}$ has **limit** L, if for each positive ϵ, there exists an integer N such that

$$|L - x_n| < \epsilon \qquad \text{for all} \quad n \geq N.$$

The definition requires all terms beyond some point to be within ϵ of L. For example, the sequence

$$0, \frac{1}{2}, 0, \frac{3}{4}, 0, \frac{7}{8}, \cdots$$

does not have limit 1; although it does contain numbers close to 1, not *all* terms of the sequence are near 1 from some point on. In fact this sequence has no limit. We should emphasize that having a limit is a very special privilege, not a right. You should not assume that a given sequence will necessarily have a limit.

We write

$$\lim_{n \to \infty} x_n = L, \qquad \text{or simply} \qquad \lim x_n = L.$$

We also write

$$x_n \longrightarrow L \qquad \text{as} \quad n \longrightarrow \infty, \qquad \text{or simply} \qquad x_n \longrightarrow L.$$

If $x_n \longrightarrow L$, we also say that $\{x_n\}$ **converges** to L. A sequence that has a limit is called **convergent**, and a sequence without a limit is called **divergent**.

If a given sequence $\{x_n\}$ does have a limit, then it has only one limit, so that when $x_n \longrightarrow L$ we are justified in saying L is *the* limit of $\{x_n\}$. Let us state this as a formal theorem and prove it.

Theorem 3.1 If $x_n \longrightarrow L_1$ and $x_n \longrightarrow L_2$, then $L_1 = L_2$.

Proof: Let $\epsilon > 0$. Then there exists an N_1 so that $|x_n - L_1| < \frac{1}{2}\epsilon$ for all $n \geq N_1$, and there exists an N_2 so that $|x_n - L_2| < \frac{1}{2}\epsilon$ for all $n \geq N_2$. These statements are both consequences of Definition 3.1 and the hypotheses.

Choose $N = \max\{N_1, N_2\}$, the larger of N_1 and N_2. Then $|x_N - L_1| < \frac{1}{2}\epsilon$ and $|x_N - L_2| < \frac{1}{2}\epsilon$. By the triangle inequality,

$$|L_1 - L_2| = |(L_1 - x_N) + (x_N - L_2)| \leq |L_1 - x_N| + |x_N - L_2|$$
$$< \tfrac{1}{2}\epsilon + \tfrac{1}{2}\epsilon = \epsilon.$$

Therefore $|L_1 - L_2|$ is smaller than every positive ϵ, so $L_1 = L_2$.

Proving that $x_n \longrightarrow L$ is a kind of game; I challenge you with an ϵ, and you must find some appropriate N. It is not necessary to find the *smallest N* such that $|L - x_n| < \epsilon$ for all $n \geq N$; that may be hard. But for each ϵ, you must produce *some* N.

Sometimes it is helpful to interpret the definition this way; $x_n \longrightarrow L$ if for each $\epsilon > 0$, the inequality $|L - x_n| < \epsilon$ holds *with only a finite number of exceptions.*

EXAMPLE 3.1

If $x_n = (n + 1)/n$, prove that $x_n \longrightarrow 1$.

Solution: Let $\epsilon > 0$ be given. Since $x_n = 1 + 1/n$, we have

$$|1 - x_n| = \frac{1}{n}.$$

Hence $|1 - x_n| < \epsilon$ provided $1/n < \epsilon$, that is, $n > 1/\epsilon$. Choose for N any integer larger than $1/\epsilon$. Then

$$|1 - x_n| < \epsilon \qquad \text{for all} \quad n \geq N.$$

This completes the proof.

REMARK 1: The proof is valid for *each* choice of ϵ. If you produce an N that works only for $\epsilon = 0.1$ or $\epsilon = 0.001$, that is not sufficient.

REMARK 2: In general the smaller ϵ is, the larger N must be. That makes sense: the closer you want to approximate the limit, the farther out in the sequence you must go.

EXAMPLE 3.2

Show that $\lim \dfrac{(-1)^n n}{n^3 + 1} = 0$.

Solution: Let us write out a few terms:

$$\frac{-1}{1 + 1}, \quad \frac{2}{2^3 + 1}, \quad \frac{-3}{3^3 + 1}, \quad \frac{4}{4^3 + 1}, \dots$$

Let $\epsilon > 0$ be given. If x_n denotes the general term, we must find a positive integer N such that $|0 - x_n| < \epsilon$ for all $n \geq N$. Now

$$|0 - x_n| = |x_n| = \frac{n}{n^3 + 1} < \frac{n}{n^3} = \frac{1}{n^2}.$$

Choose any integer N such that $N^2 > 1/\epsilon$. If $n \geq N$, then $n^2 \geq N^2 > 1/\epsilon$.

Therefore

$$|0 - x_n| < \frac{1}{n^2} < \epsilon \quad \text{if} \quad n \geq N.$$

This completes the proof.

Before ending this section we wish to dispel two old-wive's tales concerning limits of sequences:

TALE 1:   If $x_n \longrightarrow L$, then the numbers x_n get closer and closer to L without ever reaching L. Not necessarily! Examples:

$$3, 3, 3, 3, \cdots, \qquad 0, \frac{1}{2}, 0, \frac{1}{3}, 0, \frac{1}{4}, \cdots$$

The first sequence converges to 3, the second to 0. Each "reaches its limit" infinitely often.

TALE 2:   If $x_n \longrightarrow L$, the numbers increase towards L or decrease towards L. Not necessarily! Example:

$$1, -\frac{1}{2}, \frac{1}{3}, -\frac{1}{4}, + - \cdots$$

This sequence converges to 0 but jumps around. In fact, take the sequence

$$1, \frac{1}{2}, \frac{1}{3}, \frac{1}{4}, \cdots$$

and sprinkle in minus signs at random. The resulting irregular sequence still converges to zero.

An even more striking example is this one:

$$\frac{1}{10}, \quad \frac{1}{10^2}, \frac{2}{10^2}, \quad \frac{1}{10^3}, \frac{2}{10^3}, \frac{3}{10^3}, \quad \frac{1}{10^4}, \frac{2}{10^4}, \frac{3}{10^4}, \frac{4}{10^4}, \cdots$$

This sequence converges to zero, yet it has longer and longer strings of terms that move *away* from zero!

EXERCISES

1. Under what circumstances can a sequence of *integers* have a limit?
2. Show by examples that a sequence may diverge yet contain subsequences which converge.

Find lim x_n and prove your answer if $x_n =$

3. $\dfrac{1}{n}$

4. $\dfrac{1}{\sqrt{n}}$

5. $\dfrac{3n}{4n - 1}$

6. $\dfrac{n^2}{3n^2 + 2}$

7. $\dfrac{\sin n}{n}$

8. $\dfrac{1}{1 + \log n}$

9. $\sqrt{n + 1} - \sqrt{n}$

10. $1 + \dfrac{1}{3} + \dfrac{1}{3^2} + \cdots + \dfrac{1}{3^n}$

11. $0.11111 \cdots 1$ (n ones)

12. $\dfrac{(-1)^n}{n!}$.

Prove that the sequence converges:

13. $\dfrac{1}{10}, \dfrac{1}{10^2}, \dfrac{2}{10^2}, \dfrac{1}{10^3}, \dfrac{2}{10^3}, \dfrac{3}{10^3}, \dfrac{1}{10^4}, \cdots$

14. $1, -\frac{1}{2}, -\frac{1}{2}, \frac{1}{3}, \frac{1}{3}, \frac{1}{3}, -\frac{1}{4}, -\frac{1}{4}, -\frac{1}{4}, -\frac{1}{4}, \cdots$.

15. Show that the limit of a sequence of rational numbers can be irrational.

16. (cont.) Show that the limit of a sequence of irrational numbers can be rational.

17. If $\{x_n\}$ converges and $x_n \geq 0$ for $n \geq 1$, prove that $\lim x_n \geq 0$.

18. If $\{x_n\}$ and $\{y_n\}$ converge, and if $x_n \geq y_n$ for $n \geq 1$, prove that $\lim x_n \geq \lim y_n$. Explain how Ex. 17 follows from this result.

19. Prove that $x_n \longrightarrow L$ if and only if $(L - x_n) \longrightarrow 0$.

20. Prove that changing a finite number of terms does not affect the convergence of a sequence.

21. Prove that inserting or deleting a finite number of terms does not affect the convergence of a sequence.

22. If $a_n \longrightarrow L$ and $b_n \longrightarrow L$, show that the sequence

$$a_1, b_1, a_2, b_2, a_3, b_3, \cdots$$

also converges to L.

4. THEOREMS ON LIMITS

The ϵ, N definition is important in making the concept of limit precise, but it is tedious to apply. In practice we use certain theorems about limits which allow us to derive the convergence of many sequences from that of known convergent sequences.

Theorem 4.1   If $x_n \longrightarrow L$, then any subsequence of $\{x_n\}$ also converges to L.

The proof is not hard; we leave it as an exercise. From the theorem we deduce, for example, that the following sequences $\{y_n\}$ all converge to zero because each is a subsequence of $\{1/n\}$, which we know converges to zero.

(1) $1, \dfrac{1}{3}, \dfrac{1}{5}, \dfrac{1}{7}, \cdots$ $y_n = \dfrac{1}{2n - 1}$

(2) $\dfrac{1}{2}, \dfrac{1}{2^2}, \dfrac{1}{2^3}, \dfrac{1}{2^4}, \cdots$ $y_n = \dfrac{1}{2^n}$

(3) $1, \dfrac{1}{2^2}, \dfrac{1}{3^2}, \dfrac{1}{4^2}, \cdots$ $y_n = \dfrac{1}{n^2}$

(4) $1, \dfrac{1}{2^3}, \dfrac{1}{3^3}, \dfrac{1}{4^3}, \cdots$ $y_n = \dfrac{1}{n^3}.$

The next result says that a sequence between two sequences that converge to the same limit is itself squeezed to the same limit.

Theorem 4.2   Suppose $\{a_n\}$ and $\{c_n\}$ are convergent sequences with the same limit L, and suppose $\{b_n\}$ is a sequence such that $a_n \le b_n \le c_n$ for $n \ge 1$. Then $\{b_n\}$ also converges to L.

Proof: Let $\epsilon > 0$ be given. There exist integers N_1 and N_2 such that

$$|L - a_n| < \epsilon \quad \text{for all} \quad n \ge N_1, \qquad |L - c_n| < \epsilon \quad \text{for all} \quad n \ge N_2.$$

If $N = \max\{N_1, N_2\}$, the larger of N_1 and N_2, then both inequalities hold for all $n \ge N$. In particular,

$$L - \epsilon < a_n \quad \text{and} \quad c_n < L + \epsilon.$$

Since $a_n \le b_n \le c_n$,

$$L - \epsilon < a_n \le b_n \le c_n < L + \epsilon.$$

Hence

$$|L - b_n| < \epsilon \quad \text{for all} \quad n \ge N.$$

This proves that $b_n \longrightarrow L$.

Corollary   Suppose $0 \le b_n \le c_n$, and $c_n \longrightarrow 0$. Then $b_n \longrightarrow 0$.

Proof: Apply Theorem 4.2 with $a_n = 0$.

As applications of the corollary, we deduce immediately that the following sequences $\{b_n\}$ all converge to zero:

$$\{1/n^{3/2}\}, \qquad \{1/n^2\}, \qquad \{(\sin^2 n)/n\}.$$

In each case, $0 < b_n \le 1/n$. Since $1/n \longrightarrow 0$, the corollary shows that $b_n \longrightarrow 0$.

Before we discuss arithmetic operations on convergent sequences, we need the fact that a convergent sequence is bounded. A sequence $\{x_n\}$ is called **bounded** if the *set* $\mathbf{S} = \{x_1, x_2, \cdots\}$ is a bounded set. This simply means there exists a number B such that $|x_n| \le B$ for all n.

Theorem 4.3   Let $\{x_n\}$ be a convergent sequence. Then $\{x_n\}$ is a bounded sequence.

Proof: Suppose $x_n \longrightarrow L$. Apply the definition of convergence with $\epsilon = 1$: there exists an integer N such that $|L - x_n| < 1$ for all $n \geq N$. Write $x_n = L - (L - x_n)$. By the triangle inequality,

$$|x_n| \leq |L| + |L - x_n| < |L| + 1 \qquad \text{for all} \quad n \geq N.$$

Now take B to be the largest of the numbers

$$|x_1|, |x_2|, \cdots, |x_{N-1}|, |L| + 1.$$

Then $|x_n| \leq B$ for all $n \geq 1$.

Arithmetic of Convergent Sequences

Given a sequence $\{a_n\}$ we can form a new sequence $\{|a_n|\}$ by taking absolute values and another new sequence $\{ca_n\}$ by multiplying each term by a number c. Given two sequences $\{a_n\}$ and $\{b_n\}$ we can form new sequences $\{a_n + b_n\}$, $\{a_n b_n\}$, $\{a_n/b_n\}$ by adding, multiplying, or dividing termwise.

Theorem 4.4   Suppose $a_n \longrightarrow A$ and $b_n \longrightarrow B$. Then

(1) $|a_n| \longrightarrow |A|$

(2) $ca_n \longrightarrow cA$

(3) $a_n \pm b_n \longrightarrow A \pm B$

(4) $a_n b_n \longrightarrow AB$

(5) $\dfrac{a_n}{b_n} \longrightarrow \dfrac{A}{B} \qquad (b_n \neq 0, B \neq 0).$

Proof: Given $\epsilon > 0$, choose N so $|a_n - A| < \epsilon$ for all $n \geq N$. By the triangle inequality,

$$\big||a_n| - |A|\big| \leq |a_n - A| < \epsilon,$$

hence $|a_n| \longrightarrow |A|$, which proves (1). We leave the proof of (2) as an exercise.

Let us prove (3) for the "$+$" case. Let $\epsilon > 0$ be given. By hypothesis, there exist integers N_1 and N_2 such that

$$|A - a_n| < \frac{1}{2}\epsilon \qquad \text{for all} \quad n \geq N_1; \qquad |B - b_n| < \frac{1}{2}\epsilon \qquad \text{for all} \quad n \geq N_2.$$

Set $N = \max\{N_1, N_2\}$. If $n \geq N$, then both inequalities hold, so

$$|(A + B) - (a_n + b_n)| = |(A - a_n) + (B - b_n)|$$
$$\leq |A - a_n| + |B - b_n| < \frac{1}{2}\epsilon + \frac{1}{2}\epsilon = \epsilon.$$

Therefore $\lim(a_n + b_n) = A + B$.

Let us now prove (4). We need to show that $|AB - a_nb_n|$ is small when n is large enough. By hypothesis we have the power to make $|A - a_n|$ and $|B - b_n|$ small. To exploit this power, we use a trick; we add and subtract Ab_n:

$$AB - a_nb_n = AB - (Ab_n + Ab_n) - a_nb_n = A(B - b_n) + (A - a_n)b_n.$$

By the triangle inequality,

$$|AB - a_nb_n| \leq |A|\,|B - b_n| + |A - a_n|\,|b_n|.$$

By Theorem 4.3, the sequence $\{b_n\}$ is bounded; choose $C > 0$ such that $|b_n| \leq C$ for all $n \geq 1$. Then we have

$$|AB - a_nb_n| \leq |A|\,|B - b_n| + C|A - a_n|.$$

Now set $D = \max\{A, C\} > 0$. Then

$$|AB - a_nb_n| \leq D(|B - b_n| + |A - a_n|)$$

for all $n \geq 1$.

Suppose we are given $\epsilon > 0$. Then $\epsilon/2D > 0$, so we can choose N such that

$$|A - a_n| < \frac{\epsilon}{2D} \qquad \text{and} \qquad |B - b_n| < \frac{\epsilon}{2D}$$

for all $n \geq N$. Then

$$|AB - a_nb_n| < D\left(\frac{\epsilon}{2D} + \frac{\epsilon}{2D}\right) = \epsilon$$

for all $n \geq N$. This completes the proof of (4).

To prove (5), it is enough to prove the special case $\lim 1/b_n = 1/B$. The general case then follows from (4). Now

$$\left|\frac{1}{B} - \frac{1}{b_n}\right| = \left|\frac{b_n - B}{Bb_n}\right| = \frac{|b_n - B|}{|B|\,|b_n|}.$$

We can make the numerator as small as we like. We must be sure however, that the denominator is not too small. Since $b_n \longrightarrow B$, we know that $|b_n| \longrightarrow |B|$ from (1). Now apply the definition of $|b_n| \longrightarrow |B|$ with $\epsilon_1 = \frac{1}{2}|B|$: there exists an integer N_1 such that

$$\big||b_n| - |B|\big| < \epsilon_1 = \tfrac{1}{2}|B| \qquad \text{for all} \quad n \geq N_1,$$

that is, $-\frac{1}{2}|B| < |b_n| - |B| < \frac{1}{2}|B|$. We use only the left side of this inequality; it implies $|b_n| > \frac{1}{2}|B|$. Therefore

$$\left|\frac{1}{B} - \frac{1}{b_n}\right| \leq \frac{|b_n - B|}{\frac{1}{2}|B|^2}$$

for all $n \geq N_1$.

Now suppose $\epsilon > 0$ is given. We choose N_2 so that $|b_n - B| < \frac{1}{2}|B|^2\epsilon$ for all $n \geq N_2$. Now we set $N = \max\{N_1, N_2\}$. Then for all $n \geq N$ we have *both*

$$\left| \frac{1}{B} - \frac{1}{b_n} \right| \leq \frac{|b_n - B|}{\frac{1}{2}|B|^2} \qquad and \qquad |b_n - B| \leq \frac{1}{2}|B|^2\epsilon.$$

It follows that

$$\left| \frac{1}{B} - \frac{1}{b_n} \right| < \frac{\frac{1}{2}|B|^2\epsilon}{\frac{1}{2}|B|^2} = \epsilon$$

for all $n \geq N$. Therefore $1/b_n \longrightarrow 1/B$.

EXAMPLE 4.1

Find $\lim \dfrac{n^2 - 2n + 4}{n^3}$.

Solution: Write

$$x_n = \frac{n^2 - 2n + 4}{n^3} = \frac{1}{n} - 2 \cdot \frac{1}{n^2} + 4 \cdot \frac{1}{n^3}.$$

The sequences $\{1/n\}$, $\{1/n^2\}$, and $\{1/n^3\}$ all converge to zero. Apply Theorem 4.4:

$$\lim x_n = \lim \frac{1}{n} - \lim 2 \cdot \frac{1}{n^2} + \lim 4 \cdot \frac{1}{n^3}$$

$$= \lim \frac{1}{n} - 2 \lim \frac{1}{n^2} + 4 \lim \frac{1}{n^3} = 0 - 0 + 0 = 0.$$

Answer: 0.

REMARK: In practice, we skip many of the steps illustrated in the solution of Example 4.1. For example, to find

$$\lim \frac{3n^2 + n - 7}{4n^2 + 3n + 6},$$

we divide all terms by n^2, then use Theorem 4.4, combining some obvious steps:

$$\lim \frac{3n^2 + n - 7}{4n^2 + 3n + 6} = \lim \frac{3 + \dfrac{1}{n} - \dfrac{7}{n^2}}{4 + \dfrac{3}{n} + \dfrac{6}{n^2}} = \frac{3 + 0 - 0}{4 + 0 + 0} = \frac{3}{4}.$$

EXAMPLE 4.2

If $0 < a < 1$, prove that $a^n \longrightarrow 0$.

Solution: Since $a < 1$, we may write $a = 1/(1 + p)$ where $p > 0$. From the binomial theorem,

$$a^n = \frac{1}{(1 + p)^n} = \frac{1}{1 + np + \text{(positive terms)}} < \frac{1}{np}.$$

Therefore

$$0 < a^n < \frac{1}{p} \cdot \frac{1}{n}.$$

But $1/pn \longrightarrow 0$ because $1/n \longrightarrow 0$ and $1/p$ is a constant. Hence $a^n \longrightarrow 0$ by the corollary to Theorem 4.2.

EXERCISES

1. If $\lim x_n = L$ and $\{y_n\}$ is a subsequence of $\{x_n\}$, prove that $\lim y_n = L$.
2. If $\lim a_n = 0$ and if $\{b_n\}$ is a bounded sequence (not necessarily convergent), prove that $\{a_n b_n\}$ is convergent and that $\lim a_n b_n = 0$.
3. If $\lim(a_n/n) > 0$, prove that $\{a_n\}$ is unbounded.
4. Prove that $\lim c a_n = c \lim a_n$.

Find $\lim x_n$ if $x_n =$

5. $\dfrac{n + 1}{2n + 3}$

6. $\dfrac{4n}{n^2 + 1}$

7. $\dfrac{n^2 + 2n - 8}{n^3 + 7n + 9}$

8. $\dfrac{n^2 + 5}{3n^2 + 12n + 5}$

9. $\dfrac{n}{\sqrt{n^2 + 1}}$

10. $\dfrac{2n}{\sqrt{n^3 + 6}}$

11. $\dfrac{\sqrt{n}}{3 + 2\sqrt{n}}$

12. $\dfrac{1}{n^2 + \sin n}$

13. $\left(1 + \dfrac{2}{n}\right)^3$

14. $\left(1 + \dfrac{3n}{n^2 + 5}\right)^4$

15. $\dfrac{10^n}{n!}$

16. $\dfrac{(n + 1)\,(n + 2)\,(n + 3)}{(n + 4)\,(n + 5)\,(n + 6)}$

17. $\left[\dfrac{3n}{n + 7}\right]\left[1 - \left(\dfrac{1}{2}\right)^n\right]$

18. $\dfrac{7^n + 1}{8^n}$.

19. If $|a_n| \longrightarrow |a|$, does $a_n \longrightarrow a$?
20. If $\{a_n\}$ and $\{b_n\}$ diverge, does $\{a_n + b_n\}$ diverge?
21. If $\{a_n\}$ and $\{b_n\}$ diverge, does $\{a_n b_n\}$ diverge?
22. If $\lim a_n = 0$, prove that $\lim a_n^2 = 0$.

23*. If $a > 1$, prove that $\lim a^{1/n} = 1$. [*Hint:* Adapt the trick used in Example 4.2.]

24*. If $b > 1$, prove that

$$\lim \frac{n}{b^n} = \lim \frac{n^2}{b^n} = 0.$$

[*Hint:* Extend the trick in Example 4.2.]

5. EXISTENCE OF LIMITS

Until now, we have established the convergence of various sequences by finding in each case a number that appears to be the limit, then proving it is so. It often happens, however, that a given sequence is so complicated that it is hard to find its limit, but it is adequate to know that the sequence converges without actually knowing the limit.

For this reason, we shall discuss "intrinsic" criteria for convergence, that is, conditions that ensure the convergence of a sequence from the nature of the sequence itself, but do not require knowledge of the limit.

Monotone Sequences

We start with increasing and decreasing sequences. A sequence $\{x_n\}$ is called **strictly increasing** if

$$x_1 < x_2 < x_3 < \cdots$$

and is called **increasing** if

$$x_1 \leq x_2 \leq x_3 \leq \cdots.$$

Similarly $\{x_n\}$ is **strictly decreasing** if $x_1 > x_2 > x_3 > \cdots$ and simply **decreasing** if $x_1 \geq x_2 \geq x_3 \geq \cdots$. A sequence that is either increasing or is decreasing is called a **monotone** sequence (moving in one direction).

Theorem 5. 1   Any bounded increasing sequence converges; any bounded decreasing sequence converges.

If $x_1 \leq x_2 \leq \cdots \leq B$,   then $\lim x_n \leq B$.

If $x_1 \geq x_2 \geq \cdots \geq A$,   then $\lim x_n \geq A$.

Proof: First suppose $x_1 \leq x_2 \leq \cdots \leq B$. Then the set $\mathsf{S} = \{x_1, x_2, \cdots\}$ has upper bound B, hence S has a least upper bound $L = \sup \mathsf{S}$. Clearly $L \leq B$. We claim that $x_n \longrightarrow L$.

Let $\epsilon > 0$ be given. Since $L = \sup \mathsf{S}$ there is an N such that $L - \epsilon < x_N \leq L$. But $x_N \leq x_{N+1} \leq x_{N+2} \leq \cdots \leq L$, hence

$$L - \epsilon < x_N \leq x_n < L \qquad \text{for all} \quad n \geq N.$$

Therefore $|L - x_n| < \epsilon$ for all $n \geq N$. This proves $x_n \longrightarrow L$. The proof for decreasing sequences is similar. We illustrate the situation in the decreasing case (Fig. 5.1).

FIG. 5.1.   a bounded decreasing sequence

EXAMPLE 5.1

Let $0 < a < 1$. Prove that $a^n \longrightarrow 0$ using Theorem 5.1. (Cf. Example 4.2.)

Solution: The sequence $\{a^n\}$ is bounded and decreasing; clearly $0 < a^n < 1$, and $a^{n+1} = a \cdot a^n < a^n$. Therefore $a^n \longrightarrow L \geq 0$ by Theorem 5.1.

To find L, we note that $\{a^{n+1}\}$ is a subsequence of $\{a^n\}$; by Theorem 4.1 we have $a^{n+1} \longrightarrow L$. But $a^{n+1} = a \cdot a^n$, so by Theorem 4.4, part (2), we have $L = aL$. Since $a \neq 1$, this implies $L = 0$.

EXAMPLE 5.2

Define a sequence $\{x_n\}$ by

$$x_1 = 2, \qquad x_{n+1} = \frac{1}{2}\left(x_n + \frac{2}{x_n}\right).$$

Prove that $\{x_n\}$ is a decreasing sequence and find $\lim x_n$.

Solution: First we prove by induction that $x_n^2 > 2$. Certainly $x_1^2 > 2$. Now we assume $x_n^2 > 2$ and show that $x_{n+1}^2 > 2$ by means of the relation $(a + b)^2 = (a - b)^2 + 4ab \geq 4ab$:

$$x_{n+1}^2 = \left(\frac{x_n}{2} + \frac{1}{x_n}\right)^2 \geq 4\left(\frac{x_n}{2}\right)\left(\frac{1}{x_n}\right) = 2.$$

Next we prove that $x_{n+1} < x_n$. From $x_n^2 > 2$ we have $2/x_n < x_n$, hence

$$x_{n+1} = \frac{1}{2}\left(x_n + \frac{2}{x_n}\right) < \frac{1}{2}\left(x_n + x_n\right) = x_n.$$

Therefore $\{x_n\}$ is a decreasing sequence of positive numbers. By Theorem 5.1, we have $x_n \longrightarrow L \geq 0$. Now we want the value of L. Since

$$x_{n+1} = \frac{1}{2}\left(x_n + \frac{2}{x_n}\right)$$

and $x_{n+1} \longrightarrow L$, we have (by Theorem 4.4)

$$L = \frac{1}{2}\left(L + \frac{2}{L}\right).$$

It follows that $L^2 = 2$. Since $L \geq 0$ we have $L = \sqrt{2}$.

Answer: $x_n \longrightarrow \sqrt{2}$.

EXAMPLE 5.3

Define a sequence $\{x_n\}$ by

$$x_n = 1 + \frac{1}{1!} + \frac{1}{2!} + \cdots + \frac{1}{n!}.$$

Prove that $\{x_n\}$ converges.

Solution: Clearly $x_{n+1} = x_n + 1/(n+1)! > x_n$, so the sequence is increasing. To prove the sequence converges by Theorem 5.1, we must prove the sequence is bounded above. Now $n! \geq 2^{n-1}$ for $n \geq 1$, hence

$$x_n \leq 1 + \left(1 + \frac{1}{2} + \frac{1}{2^2} + \cdots + \frac{1}{2^{n-1}}\right)$$

$$= 1 + \frac{1 - 1/2^n}{1 - 1/2} = 1 + 2\left(1 - \frac{1}{2^n}\right) < 3.$$

Therefore $\{x_n\}$ converges and we can say (from this proof) that $\lim x_n \leq 3$, no more.

Nested Intervals

If $a < b$, we define the **closed interval** $[a, b]$ by

$$[a, b] = \{x \mid a \leq x \leq b\}.$$

The word "closed" means the interval contains its end points; this contrasts with the **open interval** $(a, b) = \{x \mid a < x < b\}$, where the end points are excluded. The importance of closed intervals in the theory of limits is illustrated by several important results. We begin with an easy one.

Theorem 5.2   Let $[a, b]$ be a closed interval and $\{x_n\}$ a convergent sequence such that $x_n \in [a, b]$ for all n. Then $\lim x_n \in [a, b]$.

Proof: Set $L = \lim x_n$. We have $a \leq x_n \leq b$ for all n, and we wish to prove that $a \leq L \leq b$. Suppose not; then either $L < a$ or $L > b$, say $L < a$. Set $\epsilon = a - L > 0$. Since $x_n \longrightarrow L$, there is an N such that $|x_N - L| < \epsilon$. Hence $x_N < L + \epsilon = a$; impossible. Similarly $L > b$ is impossible; done.

The next result is sometimes called the **nested interval theorem.**

Theorem 5.3 Let $[a_n, b_n]$ be a nested sequence of closed intervals; that is,

$$[a_1, b_1] \supseteq [a_2, b_2] \supseteq [a_3, b_3] \supseteq \cdots ,$$

each is a subset of the previous one. Then these intervals have *at least* one common point. If in addition $(b_n - a_n) \longrightarrow 0$, then the intervals have *exactly* one common point.

Proof: Clearly $a_1 \le a_2 \le a_3 \le \cdots \le b_1$, so $\{a_n\}$ is a bounded increasing sequence. By Theorem 5.1, $a_n \longrightarrow L$. Now fix N. The subsequence $a_N, a_{N+1}, a_{N+2}, \cdots$ also converges to L by Theorem 4.1; but the points of this subsequence all lie in $[a_N, b_N]$. Hence $L \in [a_N, b_N]$. This is true for each N, hence L belongs to all $[a_n, b_n]$.

If L' is another point in all of the intervals, then for each n we have $|L - L'| \le (b_n - a_n)$. If $(b_n - a_n) \longrightarrow 0$, this obviously forces $|L - L'| = 0$, so $L' = L$. The proof is complete.

The next result is called the **Bolzano–Weierstrass Theorem.**

Theorem 5.4 Each bounded sequence contains a convergent subsequence.

Proof: Let $\{x_n\}$ be a bounded sequence. Then there is a closed interval $[a_1, b_1]$ such that $a_1 \le x_n \le b_1$ for all n. We shall construct a nested sequence

$$[a_1, b_1] \supseteq [a_2, b_2] \supseteq [a_3, b_3] \supseteq \cdots$$

of closed intervals such that (1) each $[a_p, b_p]$ contains x_n for infinitely many values of n and (2) $b_p - a_p = (b_1 - a_1)/2^{p-1}$.

We have $[a_1, b_1]$ and it certainly fits the bill. Suppose we have constructed $[a_1, b_1], \cdots, [a_p, b_p]$ satisfying (1) and (2). We divide $[a_p, b_p]$ into two halves by inserting the midpoint. If the left half contains x_n for infinitely many values of n, choose it for $[a_{p+1}, b_{p+1}]$. If not, then the right half *must* contain x_n for infinitely many values of n, because the union of the two halves is $[a_p, b_p]$, which contains infinitely many x_n. We take the right half for $[a_{p+1}, b_{p+1}]$ in this case. In either case,

$$b_{p+1} - a_{p+1} = \tfrac{1}{2}(b_p - a_p) = \frac{\tfrac{1}{2}(b_1 - a_1)}{2^p} = \frac{b_1 - a_1}{2^{p+1}} .$$

See Fig. 5.2. The sequence $\{[a_p, b_p]\}$ of closed intervals is nested, and $b_p - a_p \longrightarrow 0$. By Theorem 5.3, there is exactly one point L common to all $[a_p, b_p]$.

Now we shall find a subsequence $\{x_{n_p}\}$ of $\{x_n\}$ that converges to L. To do this we shall find a strictly increasing sequence of integers $n_1 < n_2 < n_3 < \cdots$ such that $x_{n_p} \in [a_p, b_p]$.

We choose $x_{n_1} = x_1$. Suppose we have constructed $n_1 < n_2 < \cdots <$
n_{p-1} so that $x_{n_j} \in [a_j, b_j]$ for $j = 1, 2, \cdots, p - 1$. The interval $[a_p, b_p]$
contains x_n for *infinitely* many values of n, so it must contain some x_n with
$n > n_{p-1}$. For n_p, we choose the *first* $n > n_{p-1}$ with $x_n \in [a_p, b_p]$. By mathematical induction, this gives us the desired subsequence. Since x_{n_p} and L are
both in $[a_p, b_p]$, we have

$$|x_{n_p} - L| \le b_p - a_p.$$

But $b_p - a_p \longrightarrow 0$, hence $\lim x_{n_p} = L$. The proof is complete.

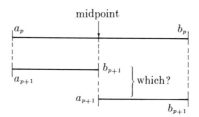

FIG. 5.2.   choice of $[a_{p+1}, b_{p+1}]$

It is worthwhile comparing three theorems we have proved; they are
related, but they say very different things:

(4.3)   Each convergent sequence is bounded.

(5.1)   Each bounded monotone sequence is convergent.

(5.4)   Each bounded sequence contains a convergent subsequence.

We need one more thing now, a way of testing any sequence for convergence (not just a monotone one) without knowing in advance a possible
limit, that is, an intrinsic criterion that applies to all sequences.

Cauchy Sequences

We observe that if $\lim x_n = L$, then the numbers x_n get close to L,
hence close to each other. More precisely, suppose $\epsilon > 0$ is given. There
exists an N such that if $m \ge N$ and $n \ge N$, then both $|L - x_m| < \frac{1}{2}\epsilon$ and
$|L - x_n| < \frac{1}{2}\epsilon$. Consequently

$$|x_m - x_n| = |(x_m - L) - (x_n - L)| \le |x_m - L| + |x_n - L| < \tfrac{1}{2}\epsilon + \tfrac{1}{2}\epsilon = \epsilon.$$

Definition 5.1   A sequence $\{x_n\}$ is a **Cauchy sequence** if for each $\epsilon > 0$,
there is a positive integer N such that

$$|x_m - x_n| < \epsilon \qquad \text{for all} \quad m \ge N \quad \text{and all} \quad n \ge N.$$

(A Cauchy sequence is sometimes called a **fundamental sequence**.)

We just proved that each convergent sequence is a Cauchy sequence; that is the "only if" part of the following theorem. The "if" part is somewhat harder.

Theorem 5.5 A sequence $\{x_n\}$ converges if and only if it is a Cauchy sequence.

Proof: Let $\{x_n\}$ be a Cauchy sequence. We must prove that $\{x_n\}$ is a convergent sequence. First, we prove it is bounded. Choose $\epsilon = 1$. Then there is an N such that $|x_m - x_n| < 1$ for all $m \geq N$ and $n \geq N$. Therefore

$$|x_n| = |x_N + (x_n - x_N)| \leq |x_N| + |x_n - x_N| < |x_N| + 1$$

for all $n \geq N$. Set

$$B = \max\{|x_1|, |x_2|, \cdots, |x_{N-1}|, |x_N| + 1\}.$$

Then $|x_n| \leq B$ for all n.

Now we can apply Theorem 5.4; the sequence $\{x_n\}$ contains a convergent subsequence $\{x_{n_p}\}$. We set $L = \lim x_{n_p}$ and shall prove that $\{x_n\}$ itself converges to L.

Let $\epsilon > 0$. Since $\{x_n\}$ is a Cauchy sequence, there is an integer N such that $|x_m - x_n| < \tfrac{1}{2}\epsilon$ for all $m \geq N$ and $n \geq N$. Since $x_{n_p} \longrightarrow L$, there is an integer P such that $|x_{n_p} - L| < \tfrac{1}{2}\epsilon$ for all $p \geq P$.

Suppose $n \geq N$. We want to prove that $|x_n - L| < \epsilon$. To do so, choose *any* p such that (1) $p \geq P$ and (2) $n_p \geq N$. Then

$$|x_n - L| = |(x_n - x_{n_p}) + (x_{n_p} - L)| \leq |x_n - x_{n_p}| + |x_{n_p} - L| < \tfrac{1}{2}\epsilon + \tfrac{1}{2}\epsilon = \epsilon.$$

This completes the proof.

REMARK: The statement of Theorem 5.5 is often taken as an axiom of completeness for the real numbers. Roughly speaking, it says that if any sequence of real numbers "looks as if it should converge," then it does converge: there is a real number available as its limit.

It can be shown that Theorems 5.1, 5.3, 5.4, 5.5, and the completeness axiom stated in Section 2 are all equivalent. There exist other equivalent forms as well. In a systematic development of the real numbers, any one of them may be used as a completeness axiom. Of course, the others must then be proved as theorems.

EXERCISES

Prove the convergence of $\{x_n\}$ by showing the sequence is monotone and bounded.

1. $x_n = \dfrac{1 \cdot 4 \cdot 7 \cdots (3n - 2)}{2 \cdot 5 \cdot 8 \cdots (3n - 1)}$
2. $x_n = \left(1 - \dfrac{1}{4}\right)\left(1 - \dfrac{1}{9}\right) \cdots \left(1 - \dfrac{1}{n^2}\right)$

3. $x_n = 1 + \dfrac{1}{(2!)^2} + \dfrac{1}{(3!)^2} + \cdots + \dfrac{1}{(n!)^2}$

4. $x_n = \dfrac{1}{n+1} + \dfrac{1}{n+2} + \cdots + \dfrac{1}{2n}$

5. $x_0 = 1$, $x_1 = \sqrt{5}$, $\cdots$, $x_{n+1} = \sqrt{5x_n}$

6. $x_0 = 1$, $x_1 = \frac{3}{2}$, $\cdots$, $x_{n+1} = 1 + \frac{1}{2}x_n$.

7. Given an infinite decimal $0.d_1\,d_2\,d_3\,\cdots$, where $d_i = 0, 1, 2, \cdots, 9$, define $x_n = 0.d_1\,d_2\,\cdots\,d_n$. Prove that $\{x_n\}$ is a Cauchy sequence.

8. Suppose $0 < a < 1$ and that $|x_{n+1} - x_n| < a^n$ for all n. Prove $\{x_n\}$ is a Cauchy sequence, hence convergent.

9. Define $\{x_n\}$ by $x_0 = 0$, $x_1 = 1$, and $x_{n+2} = \frac{1}{2}(x_n + x_{n+1})$. Prove $\{x_n\}$ is convergent. [*Hint:*   Ex. 8.]

10*. (cont.) Find $\lim x_n$ in Ex. 9.

11. Consider the nested sequence of open intervals $(0, 1) \supseteq (0, \frac{1}{2}) \supseteq (0, \frac{1}{3}) \supseteq \cdots$. Find their common points. Does the answer contradict Theorem 5.3?

12*. (cont.) Where does the proof of Theorem 5.3 break down for this example?

13. A bounded sequence must contain a convergent subsequence. Can it contain two convergent subsequences converging to different limits?

14*. Let $\{x_n\}$ be a bounded sequence. Suppose all convergent subsequences converge to the same limit. Prove $\{x_n\}$ is convergent.

15. If an increasing sequence contains a convergent subsequence, prove that the full sequence converges.

16*. In the proof of Theorem 5.5, suppose ϵ is given and N is chosen so that $|x_m - x_n| < \epsilon$ for all $m \geq N$ and all $n \geq N$. Prove that $|x_n - L| \leq \epsilon$ for all $n \geq N$.

17*. Prove that $(n + 1)^n \leq n^{n+1}$ for $n \geq 3$. [*Hint:*   First prove $(n + 2)/(n + 1) \leq (n + 1)/n$ and then use induction.]

18. (cont.) Prove that $\{n^{1/n}\}$ is convergent.

19. Prove the inequality of James Bernoulli: If $n \geq 2$ and $-1 < x$, then $(1 + x)^n \geq 1 + nx$, with equality only for $x = 0$.

Set $a_n = \left(1 + \dfrac{1}{n}\right)^n$ and $b_n = \left(1 + \dfrac{1}{n}\right)^{n+1}$. Use Ex. 19 in the next three exercises:

20*. (cont.) Prove $\{a_n\}$ is a strictly increasing sequence. [*Hint:*   Prove $a_n/a_{n-1} = (1 - n^{-2})^n[n/(n - 1)]$ and use Bernoulli's inequality.]

21*. (cont.) Prove $\{b_n\}$ is a strictly decreasing sequence.

22*. (cont.) Prove that $a_1 < a_2 < a_3 < \cdots < b_3 < b_2 < b_1$ and that $\lim a_n = \lim b_n$. Can you identify this common limit?

23*. In Theorem 5.3, prove $\bigcap_{n=1}^{\infty} [a_n, b_n] = [\sup a_n, \inf b_n]$.

24. Let $\{a_n\}$ be a sequence of integers, where $0 \leq a_n \leq 9$. Set $b_n = a_1 \cdot 10^{-1} + a_2 \cdot 10^{-2} + \cdots + a_n \cdot 10^{-n}$. Prove that $\{b_n\}$ converges.

25*. (cont.) Let $L = \lim b_n$ in Ex. 24. Suppose $\{a_n\}$ is eventually periodic, that is, there are positive integers N and p such that $a_n = a_{n+p}$ for all $n \geq N$. Prove L is a rational number.

26*. (cont.) Prove the converse to Ex. 25. That is, assume L is rational and prove $\{a_n\}$ is eventually periodic.

6. FUNCTIONS AND THEIR LIMITS

In this section we introduce limits of functions. First we need some terminology. The **domain** of a real function f is the set **D** of real numbers x for which $f(x)$ is defined. The domain of nearly every function used in calculus is a union of finitely many sets of the following six types, called **intervals**:

(1)   the whole real line: $(-\infty, \infty) = \{x \mid -\infty < x < \infty\}$,

(2)   a **closed half-line**:

$$[a, \infty) = \{x \mid a \le x < \infty\} \quad \text{or} \quad (-\infty, b] = \{x \mid -\infty < x \le b\},$$

(3)   an **open half-line**:

$$(a, \infty) = \{x \mid a < x < \infty\} \quad \text{or} \quad (-\infty, b) = \{x \mid -\infty < x < b\},$$

(4)   a **closed interval**: $[a, b] = \{x \mid a \le x \le b\}$,

(5)   an **open interval**: $(a, b) = \{x \mid a < x < b\}$,

(6)   a **half-open interval**:

$$(a, b] = \{x \mid a < x \le b\} \quad \text{or} \quad [a, b) = \{x \mid a \le x < b\}.$$

For example, the domain of $\ln x$ is $(0, \infty)$, the domain of $1/x(x - 1)$ is $(-\infty, 0) \cup (0, 1) \cup (1, \infty)$, the domain of $\sqrt{x^2 - 1}$ is $(-\infty, -1] \cup [1, \infty)$, the domain of $1/\sqrt{1 - x^2}$ is $(-1, 1)$, the domain of $\sqrt{x}/(1 - x) + \sqrt{1 - x}$ is $[0, 1)$, etc.

Note that the sets in (2), (4), and (6) have one or two end-points included. Points of these sets that are not end-points are called **interior points.** An interior point of a set is completely surrounded by other points of the set.

Limits of Functions

We wish to express the idea that the values of a given function f "approach" c. We require for each $\epsilon > 0$, no matter how small, that $|f(x) - L| < \epsilon$ provided x is sufficiently close to c.

Before stating the definition formally, let us describe some situations the definition ought to cover. Certainly the function $f(x) = x/x$ "approaches" 1 as x "approaches" 0, even though $f(x)$ is not defined at the point 0 itself. The limit of $f(x)$ at c should not demand anything at all about $f(c)$, not even that $f(c)$ be defined.

If, however, c is not in the domain of f, then c should be "close" to the domain so that x can "approach" c through points of the domain. For example, c could be an end point of a domain (a, c), which is an open interval.

Definition 6.1   Let f be defined on the domain **D** and let c be a point such that there are points of **D** different from c as close to c as we please. We write

$$\lim_{x \to c} f(x) = L$$

$$(\text{or } f(x) \longrightarrow L \text{ as } x \longrightarrow c)$$

if for each $\epsilon > 0$, there exists a $\delta > 0$ such that

$$|f(x) - L| < \epsilon$$

for all $x \in$ **D** that satisfy

$$0 < |x - c| < \delta.$$

Proving that $f(x) \longrightarrow L$ as $x \longrightarrow c$ is an ϵ, δ-game. I challenge you with an ϵ, and you must produce an acceptable δ. Notice that if one δ is acceptable, so is any smaller positive number.

The existence or non-existence of $\lim_{x \to c} f(x)$ is a *local property;* it depends only on the values of $f(x)$ in the immediate vicinity of c. For instance, it is perfectly legal to restrict attention to the range $0 < |x - c| < 10^{-10}$. Why?—we can choose δ' so that both $\delta' \le \delta$ and $\delta' < 10^{-10}$. In this way, only those points x come into play for which $|x - c| < 10^{-10}$.

If $f(x)$ has a limit as $x \longrightarrow c$, this limit is unique. We state this as a formal theorem, but save the proof for an exercise, because it is very similar to the proof of Theorem 3.1.

Theorem 6.1   If $f(x) \longrightarrow L$ and $f(x) \longrightarrow M$ as $x \longrightarrow c$, then $L = M$.

EXAMPLE 6.1

Prove   (a) $\lim_{x \to 1} (x^2 + x + 3) = 5$

(b) $\lim_{x \to 9} \sqrt{x} = 3.$

Solution: (a) Here $f(x) = x^2 + x + 3$ and $L = 5$. Let $\epsilon > 0$ be given. We must make $|f(x) - L| < \epsilon$. Now

$$|f(x) - L| = |(x^2 + x + 3) - 5| = |x^2 + x - 2| = |x + 2|\,|x - 1|.$$

The presence of the factor $|x - 1|$ is good news; we can make it as small as we like by taking x close enough to 1. However, the factor $|x + 2|$ must not be too big. We can prevent that by restricting x to the interval $[0, 2]$. (This means we agree to choose $\delta \le 1$.) Then $|x + 2| \le 4$, hence $|x + 2|\,|x - 1| \le 4|x - 1|$. Therefore if $\delta = \min\{1, \tfrac{1}{4}\epsilon\}$, then for $0 < |x - 1| < \delta$ we have

$$|f(x) - 5| = |x + 2|\,|x - 1| < 4(\tfrac{1}{4}\epsilon) = \epsilon.$$

(b) This time $f(x) = \sqrt{x}$, defined for $x \geq 0$, and $L = 3$:

$$|f(x) - L| = |\sqrt{x} - 3| = \frac{|(\sqrt{x} - 3)(\sqrt{x} + 3)|}{|\sqrt{x} + 3|} = \frac{|x - 9|}{\sqrt{x} + 3} \leq \frac{|x - 9|}{3}.$$

Therefore given $\epsilon > 0$, we have $|f(x) - L| < \epsilon$ provided x is in the domain of f and $|x - 9| < 3\epsilon$. Hence we choose for δ any number less than 3ϵ.

Theorem 6.2 Suppose $f(x) \longrightarrow L$ and $g(x) \longrightarrow M$ as $x \longrightarrow c$. Then

(1) $|f(x)| \longrightarrow |L|$

(2) $af(x) \longrightarrow aL$

(3) $f(x) \pm g(x) \longrightarrow L \pm M$

(4) $f(x)g(x) \longrightarrow LM$

(5) $\dfrac{f(x)}{g(x)} \longrightarrow \dfrac{L}{M} \qquad (M \neq 0).$

Step-by-step, the proof mimics the proof of Theorem 4.4. Instead of finding N sufficiently large, we find δ sufficiently small. In (5), if x is sufficiently close to c, then $|g(x)| > \frac{1}{2}M$, so $g(x) \neq 0$ and it is meaningful to consider $\lim_{x \to c} f(x)/g(x)$. We leave the details as exercises.

Corollary If $f(x)$ is a polynomial and c is any real number, then $f(x) \longrightarrow f(c)$ as $x \longrightarrow c$.

Proof: First try $f(x) = 1$. Then $f(c) = 1$, so obviously $f(x) \longrightarrow f(c)$ as $x \longrightarrow c$. Next try $f(x) = x$. Again it is obvious that $f(x) = x \longrightarrow c = f(c)$ as $x \longrightarrow c$.

Now take $f(x) = g(x) = x$ in (4). Then

$$f(x)g(x) = x^2 \qquad \text{and} \qquad f(c)g(c) = c^2,$$

so $f(x)g(x) \longrightarrow f(c)g(c)$ as $x \longrightarrow c$.

Next by (4) again, $x^3 = x^2 x \longrightarrow c^2 c = c^3$. Continuing, we conclude by induction that $x^n \longrightarrow c^n$. By (2) $ax^n \longrightarrow ac^n$. But each polynomial $f(x)$ is a finite sum of monomials ax^n, hence $f(x) \longrightarrow f(c)$ as $x \longrightarrow c$ by (3).

One-Sided Limits

Sometimes it is useful to examine $\lim_{x \to c} f(x)$ where x is restricted to one side of c, for instance $x > c$. This is possible provided there are points of the domain of f to the right of c as close as we please to c. Then we define the **right-hand limits,** written

$$\lim_{x \to c+} f(x) = L,$$

provided for any $\epsilon > 0$ there is a $\delta > 0$ and that $|f(x) - L| < \epsilon$ for all x in the domain of f that satisfy $c < x < c + \delta$. We also write

$$f(x) \longrightarrow L \qquad \text{as} \quad x \longrightarrow c+.$$

The **left-hand limit** is defined similarly. Then we require $c - \delta < x < c$.

These definitions are really special cases of Definition 6.1 because we cut down the domain of f to the (possibly) smaller domains $\mathbf{D}' = \{x \mid x \in \mathbf{D}$ and $x > c\}$ and $\mathbf{D}'' = \{x \mid x \in \mathbf{D}$ and $x < c\}$, then operate with the new domains. So Theorems 6.1 and 6.2 hold for $x \longrightarrow c+$ and $x \longrightarrow c-$ just as they hold for $x \longrightarrow c$.

Limits at ∞

Suppose a function f is defined on a half-line, say for $a < x < \infty$. It may be useful to study $f(x)$ for very large values of x and to ask whether there is a "limiting value". This requires an obvious modification of Definition 6.1.

Definition 6.2 Suppose f is defined for $a < x < \infty$. We write

$$\lim_{x \to \infty} f(x) = L$$

(or $f(x) \longrightarrow L$ as $x \longrightarrow \infty$)

if given $\epsilon > 0$, there is an x_0 such that

$$|f(x) - L| < \epsilon$$

for all x in the domain of f that satisfy

$$x > x_0.$$

Of course, limits as $x \longrightarrow -\infty$ are defined similarly. Theorems 6.1 and 6.2 are valid for limits at $\pm \infty$, with the obvious modifications.

Infinite Limits

It is convenient to write

$$\frac{1}{x} \longrightarrow \infty \qquad \text{as} \quad x \longrightarrow 0+$$

to express the fact that $1/x$ becomes larger and larger as x becomes smaller and smaller. Such a use of ∞ (and $-\infty$) is valuable in comparing the rates of growth of functions.

We shall give a formal definition for $\lim_{x \to c} f(x) = \infty$. It can be easily modified for such limits as

$$\lim_{x \to c+} f(x) = \infty, \qquad \lim_{x \to \infty} f(x) = -\infty, \qquad \text{etc.}$$

Definition 6.3 We write

$$f(x) \longrightarrow \infty \qquad \text{as} \quad x \longrightarrow c$$

if for each real number A, there exists a $\delta > 0$ such that

$$f(x) > A$$

for all x in the domain of f that satisfy

$$0 < |x - c| < \delta.$$

EXERCISES

Find the limit and prove your answer:

1. $\lim_{x \to 2} \dfrac{1}{x}$

2. $\lim_{x \to 11} \sqrt{2x + 3}$

3. $\lim_{x \to -2} \dfrac{1}{x^2 + 1}$

4. $\lim_{x \to 0} |x|$

5. $\lim_{x \to 0} \dfrac{x^2}{x^2}$

6. $\lim_{x \to 1} \dfrac{x^2 - 1}{x - 1}$

7. $\lim_{x \to 0} \dfrac{x^2}{x}$

8. $\lim_{x \to 1} (3x^5 - 7x^3 + 2x^2 + x - 5)$

9. $\lim_{x \to 0} x \sin x$

10. $\lim_{x \to 0} (\sqrt{x} - x)$.

11. Prove Theorem 6.1.

Prove the following part of Theorem 6.2:

12. (1)   13. (2)   14. (3)   15. (4)   16. (5).

17*. Let $f(x) = \begin{cases} 1 & \text{if } x \text{ is rational} \\ 0 & \text{if } x \text{ is irrational.} \end{cases}$

Show there is no point c for which $\lim_{x \to c} f(x)$ exists.

18*. (cont.) Prove that

$$f(x) = \lim_{m \to \infty} \{ \lim_{n \to \infty} [\cos(m!\pi x)]^n \}.$$

19*. Let $f(x)$ be defined on $[0, 1]$ by

$$f(x) = \begin{cases} \dfrac{1}{q} & \text{if} \quad x = \dfrac{p}{q} \text{ is rational in lowest terms} \\ 0 & \text{if} \quad x \text{ is irrational.} \end{cases}$$

Prove that $\lim\limits_{x \to c} f(x)$ exists and has value 0 for each c.

20. Suppose $f(x) \longrightarrow L$ as $x \longrightarrow c$. Let $\{x_n\}$ be any sequence such that $x_n \longrightarrow c$. Prove that the sequence $\{f(x_n)\}$ converges to L.

21*. (cont.) Suppose for *any* sequence $\{x_n\}$ such that $x_n \longrightarrow c$ but $x_n \neq c$ for all n, we have $f(x_n) \longrightarrow L$. Prove that $f(x) \longrightarrow L$ as $x \longrightarrow c$.

22*. (cont.) In Ex. 21, replace "$f(x_n) \longrightarrow L$" by "$f(x_n)$ is a convergent sequence". Show that the conclusion $f(x) \longrightarrow L$ (for some L) as $x \longrightarrow c$ still holds. (Different $\{x_n\}$ *may* lead to different L.) [*Hint:* If $x_n \longrightarrow c$ and $y_n \longrightarrow c$, consider the sequence $x_1, y_1, x_2, y_2, x_3, y_3, \cdots \cdot$.]

23*. *A Cauchy condition.* Prove that $f(x)$ has a limit as $x \longrightarrow c$ if and only if given any $\epsilon > 0$, there is a $\delta > 0$ such that $|f(x) - f(x')| < \epsilon$ whenever $0 < |x - c| < \delta$ and $0 < |x' - c| < \delta$. [*Hint:* Either modify the proof of Theorem 5.5, or use Theorem 5.5 and Exs. 20–22.]

24. Let $f(x) = \begin{cases} 1 & \text{if} \quad x \geq 0 \\ 0 & \text{if} \quad x < 0. \end{cases}$

For $x \longrightarrow 0$, prove that the right-hand limit and the left-hand limit of $f(x)$. exist, but that $\lim\limits_{x \to 0} f(x)$ does not exist.

25. If the right-hand and left-hand limits exist, prove that $\lim\limits_{x \to c} f(x)$ exists if and only if the one-sided limits are equal.

26*. Let $f(x)$ be an increasing function on (a, b), that is, $f(x_1) \leq f(x_2)$ whenever $x_1 \leq x_2$. Prove that the one-sided limits of f exist as $x \longrightarrow c-$ and $x \longrightarrow c+$ for each $c \in (a, b)$. [*Hint:* Either use the results of Exs. 21, 22 and Theorem 5.1, or adjust the proof of Theorem 5.1 to this problem.]

27. Write down the definition for $x \longrightarrow -\infty$ that corresponds to Definition 6.2.

28. Give a full proof that $1/(1 + \sqrt{x}) \longrightarrow 0$ as $x \longrightarrow \infty$.

29. Prove that $1/\sqrt{x} \longrightarrow \infty$ as $x \longrightarrow 0+$.

30*. State and prove the result corresponding to Ex. 21 for $x \longrightarrow \infty$.

31*. Prove that $f(x) \longrightarrow L$ as $x \longrightarrow \infty$ if and only if $f(1/x) \longrightarrow L$ as $x \longrightarrow 0+$.

32*. Suppose $g(x) \longrightarrow M$ as $x \longrightarrow c$ and that $f(x) \longrightarrow L$ as $x \longrightarrow M$. Is it correct that $f[g(x)] \longrightarrow L$ as $x \longrightarrow c$? Explain.

Find $\lim f(x)$ as $x \longrightarrow \infty$:

33. $\dfrac{x}{x + 1}$

34. $\dfrac{x}{x^2 + 1}$

35. $\dfrac{3x + 1}{4x - 5}$

36. $\dfrac{1 + x}{1 - x}$

37. $x^2 e^{-x}$

38. $\dfrac{\cos 3x}{1 + 4x}$

39. $\sqrt{x^2 + x} - x$

40. $\tan\left(\dfrac{\pi x^3}{2x^3 + 7}\right).$

7. CONTINUITY

We all have an instinctive idea of what a continuous function is: one whose graph is a smooth curve that can be drawn without lifting the pencil off the paper. We want to formulate this notion more precisely.

Perhaps it's easier to see what a continuous function is *not*. Consider the function $f(x)$ shown in Fig. 7.1. Certainly $f(x)$ is not continuous at $x = 0$. Suppose the graph represents the altitude of a plane flying from

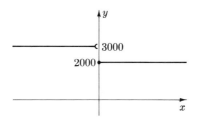

FIG. 7.1.

left to right above the x-axis. The altimeter reads a steady 3000 ft, so the pilot radios that he will be passing over the point 0 at 3000 ft. But due to an air pocket, he suddenly finds his altitude above the point is 2000 ft! His altitude function is discontinuous; it was not predictable at $x = 0$ from readings taken as $x \longrightarrow 0$. We want a continuous function to be predictable, that is, we want $\lim_{x \to c} f(x)$ to agree with $f(c)$.

Definition 7.1 Let c be a point of the domain of f. We say that f is **continuous** at c if

$$f(x) \longrightarrow f(c) \qquad \text{as} \quad x \longrightarrow c.$$

We say that the function f is **continuous** if it is continuous at each point of its domain.

It is worthwhile to go right back to fundamentals, and state the definition of continuity in ϵ, δ-terms.

The function f is **continuous** at c provided that given $\epsilon > 0$, there exists a $\delta > 0$ such that

$$|f(x) - f(c)| < \epsilon$$

for all x in the domain of f that satisfy $|x - c| < \delta$.

NOTE: We need not require $0 < |x - c|$ because f is defined at c and certainly $|f(c) - f(c)| = 0$.

Continuity at c means that the value $f(c)$ is consistent with the values of $f(x)$ for x near c: that $\lim f(x)$ exists as $x \longrightarrow c$ and is the "right number",

$f(c)$. Continuity is a local property; a function can be continuous at some points and discontinuous at others. The graph in Fig. 7.1 shows a function discontinuous at $x = 0$ but continuous at all other values of x.

Let us consider a few examples where continuity breaks down.

Example 1. $f(x) = \begin{cases} x + 1, & x \neq 3 \\ 47, & x = 3. \end{cases}$

As $x \longrightarrow 3$, we see that $f(x) \longrightarrow 4$. But $f(3) = 47$. Thus $\lim f(x)$ exists but is the "wrong value". The value of $f(3)$ is inconsistent with the values of $f(x)$ for x near 3.

Example 2. $f(x) = \begin{cases} 1, & x > 0 \\ 0, & x = 0 \\ -1, & x < 0. \end{cases}$

Here $f(x)$ is discontinuous at $x = 0$ because $\lim f(x)$ as $x \longrightarrow 0$ does not exist.

Example 3. $f(x) = \sin \dfrac{1}{x}, \quad x \neq 0.$

This function is not defined for $x = 0$. What is worse is the strange behavior of $f(x)$ near $x = 0$. The closer x moves towards 0, the larger $1/x$ becomes, and $\sin(1/x)$ oscillates more and more between $+1$ and -1. Hence $\lim_{x \to 0} f(x)$ does not exist; there is no way to define $f(0)$ so that $f(x)$ will be continuous at 0. See Fig. 7.2.

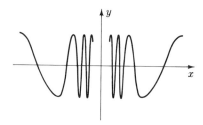

FIG. 7.2.   graph of $y = \sin 1/x$

Contrast this situation with the much simpler function $f(x) = x/x$. Since $f(x) \longrightarrow 1$ as $x \longrightarrow 0$, we may define $f(0) = 1$, and then the function will be continuous at $x = 0$.

Proof "by Continuity"

There is an argument used repeatedly in proofs. We have a function f continuous at a point c. Somehow we find a sequence x_n that converges to c. Then we say "$f(x_n) \longrightarrow f(c)$ by continuity". It pays to formalize this result.

> **Theorem 7.1** Suppose f is continuous at a point c. Suppose $x_n \longrightarrow c$ with each x_n in the domain of f. Then $f(x_n) \longrightarrow f(c)$.
> Conversely, suppose $f(x_n) \longrightarrow f(c)$ for each sequence $\{x_n\}$ with $x_n \longrightarrow c$. Then f is continuous at c.

Proof: Let $\epsilon > 0$. Then there exists $\delta > 0$ such that $|f(x) - f(c)| < \epsilon$ whenever $|x - c| < \delta$ and x lies in the domain of f. Since $x_n \longrightarrow c$ and $\delta > 0$, there exists an integer N such that $|x_n - c| < \delta$ for all $n \geq N$. Therefore $|f(x_n) - f(c)| < \epsilon$ for all $n \geq N$. This proves $\{f(x_n)\}$ converges to $f(c)$.

Proof of the converse is left as for Ex. 22.

REMARK: Discontinuities occur in nature, or at least in useful mathematical models of nature. For instance, consider the electric field strength $E(x)$ at distance x from the center of a uniformly charged spherical shell of radius R. See Fig. 7.3. Inside the shell, the field is 0, but outside it obeys the inverse square law. At $x = R$ it is not well defined.

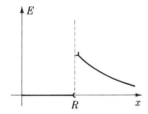

FIG. 7.3. electric field strength for a uniformly charged spherical shell

Construction of Continuous Functions

The next two theorems help us create new continuous functions out of known ones. They also help us prove that a given function is continuous by referring back to functions already known to be continuous.

The corollary to Theorem 6.2 says precisely that all polynomials are continuous functions. That is because $f(x) = x$ is continuous, and so are sums and products of continuous functions. Let us restate Theorem 6.2 in terms of continuity as a formal theorem.

> **Theorem 7.2** Let f and g be continuous at c. Then so are (1) $|f|$, (2) af, (3) $f \pm g$, (4) fg, and (5) f/g provided $g(c) \neq 0$.

From this result it follows that each rational function (quotient of polynomials) is continuous on its domain (i.e., where the denominator is not zero). All of the functions we have used in calculus are continuous, and we shall discuss some of the basic ones later.

> **Theorem 7.3**   Suppose all values of $g(t)$ are in the domain of $f(x)$; suppose g is continuous at $t = c$ and f is continuous at $x = g(c)$. Then the composite function $f[g(t)]$ is continuous at $t = c$.

Proof: Let $\epsilon > 0$. Then there exists $\eta > 0$ such that $|f(x) - f[g(c)]| < \epsilon$ whenever $|x - g(c)| < \eta$ (and x is in the domain of f—let's stop saying it each time). Since $\eta > 0$, there exists $\delta > 0$ such that $|g(t) - g(c)| < \eta$ whenever $|t - c| < \delta$. But then $|f[g(t)] - f[g(c)]| < \epsilon$; done.

For example, once we have the continuity of e^x, $\sin x$, $\sqrt{x}$ we can infer the continuity of

$$\sin(e^x), \qquad e^{\sin x}, \qquad e^{\sqrt{x}}, \qquad \sqrt{e^x + 1}, \qquad \text{etc.}$$

Uniform Continuity

Suppose $f(x)$ is continuous at all points of its domain. Given $\epsilon > 0$ and a point c in the domain of f, there is a $\delta > 0$ such $|f(x) - f(c)| < \epsilon$ whenever $|x - c| < \delta$. Given the same ϵ but a different point c', it is conceivable that a different δ will be needed. Question: given ϵ, does there exist a single δ that works for *all* c in the domain of f? Answer: not necessarily. Here is an example.

Take $f(x) = x^2$. Suppose $c > 0$ and $x > c$. In order that $|f(x) - f(c)| < \epsilon$, we must have

$$x^2 - c^2 = (x - c)(x + c) < \epsilon, \qquad x - c < \frac{\epsilon}{x + c} < \frac{\epsilon}{2c}.$$

Thus at c, a suitable δ *must be* less than $\epsilon/2c$. The larger c is, the smaller δ must be; there is no positive δ that is *simultaneously* acceptable for all values of c.

On the other hand, try $f(x) = x$. Given $\epsilon > 0$, then $|f(x) - f(c)| < \epsilon$, provided $|x - c| < \epsilon$. Here the number $\delta = \epsilon$, works for *all* points x. We say that $f(x) = x$ is "uniformly continuous". Here is the definition of this new concept.

> **Definition 7.2**   A function f is **uniformly continuous** on its domain **D** if for each $\epsilon > 0$ there exists a $\delta > 0$ such that for each $c \in$ **D**
>
> $$|f(x) - f(c)| < \epsilon$$
>
> for all $x \in$ **D** satisfying $|x - c| < \delta$.

The point of this definition is that δ is independent of the choice of $x \in$ **D**.

If you look closely at the definition, you see there is completely symmetry between x and c. It is useful to restate the definition to take this symmetry into account.

Definition 7.2′   A function f is **uniformly continuous** on its domain **D** if for each $\epsilon > 0$ there exists a $\delta > 0$ such that

$$|f(x) - f(z)| < \epsilon$$

for all $x, z \in$ **D** satisfying $|x - z| < \delta$.

REMARK: Uniform continuity is a global property while continuity is a local property. Thus a perfectly decent function like $f(x) = x^2$ is continuous at each point of its domain $(-\infty, \infty)$, but is not uniformly continuous. (Of course uniform continuity implies continuity.)

EXAMPLE 7.1

Show that $f(x) = 1/x^2$ is uniformly continuous on the domain **D** $= [1, \infty)$.

Solution: Let $x, z \geq 1$. Then

$$|f(x) - f(z)| = \left| \frac{1}{x^2} - \frac{1}{z^2} \right| = \frac{|z^2 - x^2|}{x^2 z^2} = \frac{x + z}{x^2 z^2} |x - z|.$$

But

$$\frac{x + z}{x^2 z^2} = \frac{1}{xz^2} + \frac{1}{x^2 z} \leq 1 + 1 = 2,$$

hence

$$|f(x) - f(z)| \leq 2|x - z|.$$

Given $\epsilon > 0$, we choose $\delta = \frac{1}{2}\epsilon$. This choice of δ depends *only* on ϵ, not on x or z. Then if $|z - x| < \delta$, we have

$$|f(x) - f(z)| \leq 2|x - z| < 2(\tfrac{1}{2}\epsilon) = \epsilon.$$

Therefore f is uniformly continuous on **D** $= [1, \infty)$.

EXERCISES

Show directly from the definition that $f(x)$ is continuous for all x:

1. $f(x) = |x|$

2. $f(x) = x^2 + 3x$

3. $f(x) = x^3 - 4x + 6$

4. $f(x) = \dfrac{x}{x^2 + 3}$

5. $f(x) = \sqrt[3]{x}$

6. $f(x) = \sqrt{1 + x^2}$.

7. Let $f(x) = \begin{cases} x \sin \dfrac{1}{x}, & x \neq 0 \\ 0, & x = 0. \end{cases}$

Prove that $f(x)$ is continuous at 0.

8. Let $f(x) = \begin{cases} 1, & x \text{ rational} \\ 0, & x \text{ irrational.} \end{cases}$

Show $f(x)$ is discontinuous at every point.

Prove that the function is uniformly continuous on the domain indicated:

9. $f(x) = x^2, \quad 0 \le x \le 3$

10. $f(x) = \dfrac{1}{3x + 4}, \quad 0 \le x$

11. $f(x) = \dfrac{1}{1 + x^2}, \quad -\infty < x < \infty$

12. $f(x) = \dfrac{x}{1 + x^2}, \quad -\infty < x < \infty.$

Prove that the function is not uniformly continuous:

13. $f(x) = x^3, \quad -\infty < x < \infty$

14. $f(x) = 1/x, \quad 0 < x.$

15. If $f(x)$ is continuous and $f(c) > 0$, show that $f(x) > 0$ for all x sufficiently near c.

16. If $f(x)$ is continuous at $x = c$ and $f(x) < B$ when $x < c$, prove that $f(c) \le B$.

17. Suppose f is uniformly continuous on **D**. Prove that $|f|$ is uniformly continuous in **D**.

18. Suppose f and g are both uniformly continuous on **D**. Prove that $f + g$ is uniformly continuous on **D**.

19*. Suppose f and g are both uniformly continuous on **D**. Is fg uniformly continuous?

20*. Suppose f and g have domain **D**. Define a new function h on **D** by $h(x) = \max\{f(x), g(x)\}$. Prove that h is continuous (uniformly continuous) if both f and g are so.

21. (cont.) Define $f_+(x) = \max\{f(x), 0\}$ and $f_-(x) = \min\{f(x), 0\}$. Express f_+ and f_- in terms of f and $|f|$.

22. Prove the converse part of Theorem 7.1.

8. PROPERTIES OF CONTINUOUS FUNCTIONS

In this section we discuss certain fundamental properties of continuous functions, each essential both in theory and application.

Existence of Zeros

The first property asserts that a continuous function that is positive someplace and negative someplace else, must have a zero in between.

Theorem 8.1 Let f be continuous on a closed interval $[a, b]$. Suppose $f(a)$ and $f(b)$ have opposite signs. Then there exists a point c such that $a < c < b$ and $f(c) = 0$.

Proof: We shall take the case $f(a) < 0$, $f(b) > 0$. (The other case follows from this one on replacing f by $-f$.) The proof will use the nested interval theorem (Theorem 5.3) and is much like the proof of Theorem 5.4.

Set $a_0 = a$, $b_0 = b$. We shall construct a nested sequence of closed intervals

$$[a_0, b_0] \supseteq [a_1, b_1] \supseteq [a_3, b_3] \supseteq \cdots$$

such that $b_n - a_n = (b_0 - a_0)/2^n \to 0$ and $f(a_n) < 0$, $f(b_n) > 0$. The construction stops if at some step $f(a_n) = 0$ or $f(b_n) = 0$—then our goal is achieved—otherwise the construction goes on forever.

Suppose we have reached $[a_n, b_n]$. Let $c = \frac{1}{2}(a_n + b_n)$. If $f(c) < 0$, choose $a_{n+1} = c$, $b_{n+1} = b_n$; if $f(c) > 0$, choose $a_{n+1} = a_n$, $b_{n+1} = c$ (and if $f(c) = 0$, stop!). Then $[a_{n+1}, b_{n+1}] \subseteq [a_n, b_n]$, $f(a_{n+1}) < 0$, $f(b_{n+1}) > 0$, and $b_{n+1} - a_{n+1} = \frac{1}{2}(b_n - a_n) = (b_0 - a_0)/2^{n+1}$, as desired.

By Theorem 5.3, there is a unique point c in all of the intervals $[a_n, b_n]$. Clearly $a_n \longrightarrow c$ and $b_n \longrightarrow c$. By continuity (Theorem 7.1), $f(a_n) \longrightarrow f(c)$ and $f(b_n) \longrightarrow f(c)$. Now $f(a_n) < 0$, so the limit $f(c) \leq 0$. But $f(b_n) > 0$, so the limit $f(c) \geq 0$. Hence $f(c) = 0$.

REMARK: This is not the only way to prove the theorem, but it has the advantage of being constructive. By the method used in the proof we can approximate a zero of f as closely as we please. See the bisection method, Section 18.5.

An easy corollary is called the **Intermediate Value Theorem.**

Theorem 8.2 Let f be continuous on a closed interval $[a, b]$. Suppose C is any number between $f(a)$ and $f(b)$. Then there exists a point c with $a < c < b$ and $f(c) = C$.

Proof: Set $g = f - C$. Then $g(a) = f(a) - C$ and $g(b) = f(b) - C$, have opposite signs. Apply Theorem 8.1 to g.

Inverse Functions

Let f be a strictly increasing continuous function on a closed interval $[a, b]$. If $x \in [a, b]$, then $f(x) \in [f(a), f(b)]$. Furthermore, if $y \in [f(a), f(b)]$, then by Theorem 8.2, there is a point $x \in [a, b]$ for which $y = f(x)$. In fact, there is only one such x. For if $x_1 \neq x_2$, then either $x_1 < x_2$ or $x_1 > x_2$; since f is strictly increasing, either $f(x_1) < f(x_2)$ or $f(x_1) > f(x_2)$, certainly not $f(x_1) = f(x_2)$.

We conclude that f sets up a one-one correspondence between the points of $[a, b]$ and those of $[f(a), f(b)]$. We say that f is a **one-one function** on $[a, b]$ onto $[f(a), f(b)]$.

From a different point of view we can say that to each $y \in [f(a), f(b)]$ corresponds a unique $x \in [a, b]$ for which $y = f(x)$. We write $x = g(y)$.

Then $g(y)$ is a one-one increasing function on $[f(a), f(b)]$ onto $[a, b]$. The function g is the **inverse function** of f. (Compare Section 14.1.)

By definition of g, the statements

$$y = f(x) \qquad \text{and} \qquad x = g(y)$$

are equivalent; they say exactly the same thing. From them follow

$$y = f[g(y)] \qquad \text{and} \qquad x = g[f(x)].$$

Thus the actions of f and g neutralize each other. We remark that precisely the same ideas apply if f is a strictly a decreasing function.

Theorem 8.3   Let f be a continuous strictly increasing or strictly decreasing function on a closed interval $[a, b]$. Then its inverse function is continuous on $[f(a), f(b)]$.

Proof: We shall give the proof for f increasing. Suppose C is an interior point of $[f(a), f(b)]$. Given $\epsilon > 0$, we want to find δ such that $|g(y) - g(C)| < \epsilon$ when $|y - C| < \delta$.

Let $g(C) = c$, that is, $f(c) = C$. Then $a < c < b$, so we may assume, by decreasing ϵ if necessary, that $a < c - \epsilon < c + \epsilon < b$. Because f is continuous and strictly increasing, it sets up a one-one correspondence on $[c - \epsilon, c + \epsilon]$ onto $[f(c - \epsilon), f(c + \epsilon)]$, and $f(c - \epsilon) < C < f(c + \epsilon)$. For δ sufficiently small, $[C - \delta, C + \delta] \subseteq [f(c - \epsilon), f(c + \epsilon)]$. Therefore if $y \in (C - \delta, C + \delta)$, then $f(c - \epsilon) < y < f(c + \epsilon)$, so $y = f(x)$ with $c - \epsilon < x < c + \epsilon$. That is, if $|y - C| < \delta$, then $|g(y) - g(C)| = |x - c| < \epsilon$.

If C is an end point of $[f(a), f(b)]$, then a slight modification of this argument shows that g is continuous at C. For example, if $C = f(a)$, then we demonstrate a one-one correspondence between the intervals $[a, a + \epsilon]$ and $[f(a), f(a + \epsilon)]$. This completes the proof.

Theorem 8.3 was stated in terms of closed intervals, but the result is actually true for any interval.

Theorem 8.4   Let f be a continuous strictly increasing or strictly decreasing function on an interval **D**. Then the **image** of f,

$$f(\mathbf{D}) = \{f(x) \mid x \in \mathbf{D}\}$$

is an interval and the inverse function g is continuous on $f(\mathbf{D})$.

Proof: The assertion that $f(\mathbf{D})$ is an interval, while intuitively obvious, requires a proof, but we leave it for Exs. 22, 23.

Suppose C is an interior point (not an end point) of the interval $f(\mathbf{D})$. Then $c = g(C)$ is an interior point of **D**. Choose a and b such that $[a, b] \subseteq \mathbf{D}$ and $c \in [a, b]$. Then $C \in [f(a), f(b)]$. By Theorem 8.3, applied to the function f considered only on the closed interval $[a, b]$, the inverse function g is continuous at C.

If C is an end point of $f(\mathbf{D})$, then a slight modification of the argument is needed. See the last part of the proof of Theorem 8.3.

Existence of Maxima and Minima

One of the principal concerns of calculus is finding the maximum and minimum values of various continuous functions. Whether the problem can be solved depends very much on the domain. For example, the function $f(x) = x$ on $[0, 1)$ does not have a maximum. Its values get closer and closer to 1 as $x \longrightarrow 1-$, but never quite reach 1. On $[0, 1]$ however, $f(x) = x$ does achieve its maximum. The function $f(x) = 1/x$ on $(0, b]$ does not have a maximum; it just gets too big. (It has a maximum on each interval $[a, b]$ where $0 < a < b$.) The first requirement for a maximum is that the function should not have arbitrarily large values.

Definition 8.1   A function f with domain $\mathbf{D}$ is **bounded** if there exists a number B such that $|f(x)| \le B$ for all $x \in \mathbf{D}$.

We shall prove that a continuous function on a *closed interval* has a maximum and minimum. First we shall prove it is bounded.

Theorem 8.5   A continuous function on a closed interval is bounded.

Proof: This proof will be based on the Bolzano–Weierstrass Theorem, 5.4. Suppose f is continuous on $[a, b]$, but unbounded. Then for each n, there exists a point $x_n \in [a, b]$ such that $|f(x_n)| > n$; otherwise f would be bounded.

By Theorem 5.4, the sequence $\{x_n\}$ has a convergent subsequence y_n; say $y_n \longrightarrow c \in [a, b]$. By continuity, $f(y_n) \longrightarrow f(c)$. But this is impossible. Since $y_n = x_m$ for some $m \ge n$, we have

$$|f(y_n)| = |f(x_m)| > m \ge n, \qquad \text{so} \quad |f(y_n)| \longrightarrow \infty.$$

Now we come to the key result of this subject.

Theorem 8.6   A continuous function on a closed interval has a maximum and a minimum on the interval.
More precisely, if f is continuous on $[a, b]$, then there exist points c_0 and $c_1 \in [a, b]$ such that
$$f(c_0) \le f(x) \le f(c_1)$$
for all $x \in [a, b]$.

Proof: We shall prove the maximum part only. The trick of replacing f by $-f$ gives the minimum. Since f is bounded by Theorem 8.5, the set

S $= \{f(x) \mid a \le x \le b\}$ of values of f has a least upper bound $M = \sup$ **S**. Then $f(x) \le M$ for all $x \in [a, b]$, and no smaller number M_1 enjoys this property.

Suppose $f(x) < M$ for all $x \in [a, b]$, just what we don't want! Then $M - f(x) > 0$ for all x, so $g(x) = 1/(M - f(x))$ is continuous on $[a, b]$ by Theorem 7.1. Now apply Theorem 8.5 to g: there is a B such that $g(x) \le B$ for all $x \in [a, b]$.

Clearly $B > 0$ because $g(x) > 0$. Therefore

$$\frac{1}{M - f(x)} \le B, \qquad M - f(x) \ge \frac{1}{B}, \qquad f(x) \le M - \frac{1}{B}$$

for all $x \in [a, b]$. But $M - B^{-1} < M$, contradicting the minimal property of M. Conclusion: it is false that $f(x) < M$ for all $x \in [a, b]$. So $f(c_0) = M$ for some $c_0 \in [a, b]$.

Uniform Continuity

We have seen examples of perfectly decent continuous functions which are not uniformly continuous on their domains. Here is a theorem that guarantees uniform continuity when the domain is a *closed* interval.

Theorem 8.7   A continuous function on a closed interval is uniformly continuous.

Proof: Suppose f is continuous on $[a, b]$, but not uniformly continuous. Now "uniformly continuous" means that for *each* $\epsilon > 0$ certain things happen, so "not uniformly continuous" means there is *some* $\epsilon > 0$ for which these certain things do not happen. Precisely, there exists a positive ϵ such that for *each* $\delta > 0$ there are points $x, z \in [a, b]$ with $|x - z| < \delta$, but $|f(x) - f(z)| \ge \epsilon$.

Apply this to $\delta = 1/n$: There are points $x_n, z_n \in [a, b]$ such that

$$|x_n - z_n| < \frac{1}{n} \qquad \text{and} \qquad |f(x_n) - f(z_n)| \ge \epsilon.$$

By Theorem 5.4, the sequence $\{x_n\}$ has a convergent subsequence, so we might as well assume $\{x_n\}$ itself converges, say $x_n \longrightarrow c$. But $|x_n - z_n| \longrightarrow 0$, so we also have $z_n = x_n + (z_n - x_n) \longrightarrow c + 0 = c$.

The situation is this. We have found sequences $\{x_n\}$ and $\{z_n\}$ in $[a, b]$ such that $x_n \longrightarrow c$ and $z_n \longrightarrow c$, but $|f(x_n) - f(z_n)| \ge \epsilon$. By the continuity of f at c, we have $f(x_n) \longrightarrow f(c)$ and $f(z_n) \longrightarrow f(c)$. Therefore

$$|f(x_n) - f(z_n)| \longrightarrow |f(c) - f(c)| = 0.$$

But this clearly contradicts

$$|f(x_n) - f(z_n)| \ge \epsilon > 0.$$

EXERCISES

Find an example of a continuous function f on an open interval (a, b) with the property:

1. f has a maximum and a minimum

2. f has neither a maximum nor a minimum

3. f has a maximum but no minimum

4. f is uniformly continuous.

Find an example of a continuous function f on $(-\infty, \infty)$ with the property:

5. f is uniformly continuous

6. f is bounded but has neither a maximum nor a minimum.

7. Suppose f and g are continuous and $f(x) > g(x)$ for each $x \in [a, b]$. Prove that there exists a positive number p such that $f(x) \geq g(x) + p$ for each x in $[a, b]$.

8. (cont.) Show that the assertion of Ex. 7 is false if the domain is $(-\infty, \infty)$.

Locate a solution of the equation between two integers:

9. $x^5 - 8x^4 + x^2 - 1 = 0$ 10. $x^5 + 3x^3 + 7x^2 + 2 = 0$

11. $2^{-x} = x - 1$ 12. $3^x = 5x^2 \sqrt{x + 1}$.

13. Let f be continuous on $[0, 1]$ and suppose $0 \leq f(x) \leq 1$ for each $x \in [0, 1]$. Prove that there exists a point $c \in [0, 1]$ such that $f(c) = c$, and interpret graphically.

14. Let f be continuous on an interval **D** and suppose $f(r) = 0$ for each rational number r. Prove $f = 0$.

15. Let n be a positive integer. Prove the existence and continuity of the n-th root function $R_n(x) = x^{1/n} \geq 0$ for $x \geq 0$.

16. (cont.) Prove the laws of radicals:
    (1) $R_n(xz) = R_n(x) R_n(z)$,   (2) $R_m \circ R_n = R_{mn}$,
    (3) $R_m \cdot R_n = (R_{mn})^{m+n}$.

17*. Let f be continuous on an interval **D** and suppose f is one-one. Prove that either f is strictly increasing or f is strictly decreasing.

18*. Suppose f is continuous on $[0, 1]$ and $f(0) = f(1)$. Prove there exists a point $c \in [0, \frac{1}{2}]$ such that $f(c) = f(c + \frac{1}{2})$. Interpret graphically.

19*. (cont.) Prove there exists a point $c \in [0, \frac{2}{3}]$ such that $f(c) = f(c + \frac{1}{3})$. Now generalize.

20*. Give a proof for Theorem 8.1 based on the Completeness Axiom rather than on Theorem 5.3. [*Hint:* Take **S** $= \{x \mid f(x) \leq 0\}$.]

21*. At the beginning of Section 6 we listed the six types of intervals. Prove that a set **S** is an interval if and only if whenever $x < y < z$ and $x, z \in$ **S**, then $y \in$ **S**. [*Hint:* Examine inf **S** and sup **S**. What if one of them doesn't exist?— etc.]

22*. (cont.) Complete the first step in the proof of Theorem 8.4.

23*. (cont.) Let f be continuous on an interval **D**. Prove that the image $f($**D**$) = \{f(x) \mid x \in$ **D**$\}$ is an interval.

24. Suppose f is continuous on $(-\infty, \infty)$ and that f satisfies $f(x + \pi) = -f(x)$. Prove that f has period 2π and that $f(x) = 0$ has a solution.

25. Suppose f is continuous on $(-\infty, \infty)$ and periodic of positive period p, that is, $f(x + p) = f(x)$. Prove that f is bounded and has a max and a min.

26*. (cont.) Suppose f is continuous on $[0, \infty)$ and satisfies $f(x + p) = f(x) + k$ where p and k are constants with $p > 0$. Prove that $\lim_{x \to \infty} f(x)/x$ exists and find it.

27*. (Horizontal Chord Theorem) Suppose $f(x)$ is continuous on $(-\infty, \infty)$ and periodic of period 1, that is, $f(x + 1) = f(x)$. Let $h > 0$. Prove there exists a c such that $f(c + h) = f(c)$. Interpret graphically.

21. Calculus Theory

1. THE DERIVATIVE

In earlier chapters we discussed the derivative from an intuitive point of view. Now we are in a position to give an accurate account of the main theoretical aspects of differential calculus.

Definition 1.1 Let f be a function defined on an interval including a point c. We say that f is **differentiable** at c provided the limit

$$\lim_{x \to c} \frac{f(x) - f(c)}{x - c}$$

exists. The value of this limit is written $f'(c)$ and called the **derivative** of f at c.

REMARK 1: Sometimes it is convenient to write $x = c + h$ and take the limit as $h \longrightarrow 0$. Then we obtain the equivalent formula

$$f'(c) = \lim_{h \to 0} \frac{f(c + h) - f(c)}{h}.$$

REMARK 2: The existence of $f'(c)$ is a local property of f; it depends only on values of f at points arbitrarily close to c.

REMARK 3: In case c is an end point, the defining relation is a one-sided limit. Thus if the domain is $[a, b]$ we sometimes write

$$f'(a+) = \lim_{x \to a+} \frac{f(x) - f(a)}{x - a}, \qquad f'(b-) = \lim_{x \to b-} \frac{f(x) - f(b)}{x - b}.$$

We know that the existence of a derivative is connected with linear approximation. We have frequently written

$$f(x) \approx f(x) + f'(c) (x - c)$$

without being 100% accurate about the meaning of " $\approx$ ". Let us now state this properly.

Theorem 1.1   Suppose f is differentiable at $x = c$. Then

$$f(x) = f(c) + f'(c)\,(x - c) + e(x)\,(x - c),$$

where $e(x) \longrightarrow 0$ as $x \longrightarrow c$ and $e(c) = 0$.

Conversely, let f be defined on an interval **D** and let $c \in$ **D**. Suppose there is a constant K such that

$$f(x) = f(c) + K(x - c) + e(x)\,(x - c),$$

where $e(x) \longrightarrow 0$ as $x \longrightarrow c$. Then f is differentiable at c and $f'(c) = K$.

Proof: If

$$\lim_{x \to c} \frac{f(x) - f(c)}{x - c} = f'(c)$$

exists, then

$$e(x) = \frac{f(x) - f(c)}{x - c} - f'(c) \longrightarrow 0 \qquad \text{as} \quad x \longrightarrow c.$$

Conversely, given $f(x) = f(c) + K(x - c) + e(x)\,(x - c)$, where $e(x) \longrightarrow 0$, then

$$\frac{f(x) - f(c)}{x - c} = K + e(x) \longrightarrow K.$$

Hence the derivative exists and equals K.

Theorem 1.2   If f is differentiable at $x = c$, then f is continuous at c.

Proof: We may write

$$f(x) = f(c) + f'(c)\,(x - c) + e(x)\,(x - c)$$

where $e(x) \longrightarrow 0$ as $x \longrightarrow c$. Both $f'(c)\,(x - c) \longrightarrow 0$ and $(x - c)e(x) \longrightarrow 0$ as $x \longrightarrow c$, hence $f(x) \longrightarrow f(c)$ as $x \longrightarrow c$. This is continuity.

REMARK: The theorem says that differentiability implies continuity. The converse is false! For example, $f(x) = |x|$ is continuous at 0 but not differentiable there. For,

$$\frac{f(x) - f(0)}{x - 0} = \frac{f(x)}{x} = \begin{cases} \dfrac{x}{x} = 1, & x > 0 \\[2mm] \dfrac{-x}{x} = -1, & x < 0. \end{cases}$$

As $x \longrightarrow 0$, this expression has left-hand limit 1 and right-hand limit -1, but no limit. Hence $f(x)$ has no derivative at $x = 0$.

If a function has a derivative at each point of its domain, it is simply called a **differentiable** function.

Rules for Derivatives

In Chapter 9 we gave rules for computing the derivatives of algebraic combinations of functions. The justifications given there for these rules are easily made into real proofs by using the converse part of Theorem 1.1. Therefore we shall simply state these rules accurately.

Theorem 1.3 Suppose f and g have the same domain and both are differentiable at $x = c$. Then $af, f \pm g, fg$ and f/g (if $g(c) \neq 0$) are differentiable at c and

(1) $(af)'(c) = af'(c)$

(2) $(f \pm g)'(c) = f'(c) \pm g'(c)$

(3) $(fg)'(c) = f'(c)g(c) + f(c)g'(c)$

(4) $\left(\dfrac{f}{g}\right)'(c) = \dfrac{f'(c)g(c) - f(c)g'(c)}{g(c)^2}.$

In (4), since g is continuous at c and $g(c) \neq 0$, we know that $g(x) \neq 0$ for all x sufficiently near c. Therefore f/g is defined for x near c.

Chain Rule

The *chain rule* is the formula for differentiating composite functions.

Theorem 1.4 Let the set of values of g be contained in the domain of f. Suppose that g is differentiable at c and that f is differentiable at $g(c)$. Then the composite function $f[g(x)]$ is differentiable at $x = c$ and

$$\{f[g(c)]\}' = f'[g(c)]g'(c).$$

Proof: Set $b = g(c)$. By Theorem 1.1,

$$f(y) = f(b) + f'(b)\ (y - b) + e_1(y)\ (y - b),$$
$$g(x) = b + g'(c)\ (x - c) + e_2(x)\ (x - c),$$

where $e_1(y) \longrightarrow 0 = e_1(b)$ as $y \longrightarrow b$ and $e_2(x) \longrightarrow 0 = e_2(c)$ as $x \longrightarrow c$. Substitute $g(x)$ for y:

$$f[g(x)] = f(b) + \{f'(b) + e_1[g(x)]\}\ [g'(c) + e_2(x)]\ (x - c)$$
$$= f(b) + f'(b)g'(c)\ (x - c)$$
$$+ \{f'(b)e_2(x) + g'(c)e_1[g(x)] + e_1[g(x)]e_2(x)\}\ (x - c).$$

Let us abbreviate this awkward formula to

$$f[g(x)] = f[g(c)] + K(x - c) + e(x) (x - c),$$

where

$$K = f'(b)g'(c), \qquad e(x) = f'(b)e_2(x) + g'(c)e_1[g(x)] + e_1[g(x)]e_2(x).$$

From the converse part of Theorem 1.1, it will follow that K is the derivative of $f[g(x)]$ at c, provided we can show that $e(x) \longrightarrow 0$ as $x \longrightarrow c$.

Let us examine $e(x)$. We know that $e_2(x) \longrightarrow 0$ as $x \longrightarrow c$. We know also that $g(x) \longrightarrow b$ as $x \longrightarrow c$ and that $e_1(y) \longrightarrow 0$ as $y \longrightarrow b$. Hence $e_1[g(x)] \longrightarrow 0$ as $x \longrightarrow c$. Therefore all three terms in the formula for $e(x)$ approach 0 as $x \longrightarrow c$, so $e(x) \longrightarrow 0$ as $x \longrightarrow c$. Therefore $\{f[g(c)]\}' = K = f'[g(c)]g'(c)$.

Inverse Functions

There is one more formal rule for differentiating that is quite useful; it expresses the derivative of an inverse function in terms of the derivative of the function. (See Sections 14.1 and 14.2 for an intuitive discussion.) Recall that Theorem 20.8.4 guarantees the existence of the inverse function of a strictly increasing (decreasing) continuous function.

Theorem 1.5   Let f be a strictly increasing (or strictly decreasing) continuous function on an open interval (a, b). Suppose that $c \in (a, b)$, that f is differentiable at c, and that $f'(c) \neq 0$. Let g be the inverse function of f. Then g is differentiable at $y = f(c)$ and

$$g'[f(c)] = \frac{1}{f'(c)}.$$

Proof: Write $y = f(x)$ and $b = f(c)$ so that $x = g(y)$ and $c = g(b)$. If $y \neq b$, then $x \neq c$, and

$$\frac{g(y) - g(b)}{y - b} = \frac{x - c}{f(x) - f(c)} = \left(\frac{f(x) - f(c)}{x - c}\right)^{-1}.$$

The function g is continuous at b by Theorem 20.8.4, hence $x = g(y) \longrightarrow c$ as $y \longrightarrow b$. Therefore

$$\frac{f(x) - f(c)}{x - c} \longrightarrow f'(c) \qquad \text{as} \quad y \longrightarrow b.$$

But $f'(c) \neq 0$, so (5) of Theorem 20.6.2 applies:

$$\frac{g(y) - g(b)}{y - b} \longrightarrow \frac{1}{f'(c)} \qquad \text{as} \quad y \longrightarrow b.$$

This completes the proof.

1. Let

$$f(x) = \begin{cases} x^2 & x \leq 0 \\ -x^2 & x > 0. \end{cases}$$

Prove that f is differentiable. Is f' continuous?

2. Let

$$f(x) = \begin{cases} 0 & x < 0 \\ x^2 & x \geq 0. \end{cases}$$

Prove that f is differentiable. Is f' continuous?

3. The function $f(x) = x^3$ is strictly increasing and is differentiable with $f'(x) = 3x^2$. Use Theorem 1.5 to find the derivative of the inverse function.

4. Define f by $f(0) = 0$ and $f(x) = x \sin (1/x)$ for $x \neq 0$. Is f differentiable?

5. Define f by $f(0) = 0$ and $f(x) = x^2 \sin(1/x)$ for $x \neq 0$. Is f differentiable at 0?

6. Let f be differentiable on (a, b) and suppose $a < c < b$. Define g by $g(c) = f'(c)$ and $g(x) = [f(x) - f(c)]/(x - c)$ if $x \neq c$. Prove g is continuous.

7. Suppose f is defined on (a, b) and $a < c < b$. Suppose f is differentiable at c. Prove that

$$\frac{f(c + h) - f(c - h)}{2h} \longrightarrow f'(c)$$

as $h \longrightarrow 0$.

8*. Let f be defined on (a, b) and differentiable at c, where $a < c < b$. Suppose $x_n \longrightarrow c$ and $z_n \longrightarrow c$, where $x_n < c < z_n$ for all n. Prove

$$\frac{f(x_n) - f(z_n)}{x_n - z_n} \longrightarrow f'(c).$$

Find the $e(x)$ of Theorem 1.1:

9. $f(x) = x^2$, $c = 3$
10. $f(x) = 1/x$, $c = 2$.

Use Theorem 1.1 to prove:

11. Theorem 1.3 (2)
12. Theorem 1.3 (3).

13. Write the equation for the line tangent to the graph of $y = f(x)$ at $(c, f(c))$. (Assume f is differentiable at c.) Explain the relation between this equation and the formula in Theorem 1.1.

14. A physicist spends a year of hard work measuring certain velocities. Just as he is about to publish his findings, he discovers that his clock has been running at 1.01 times normal speed during the experiments. How can he salvage his data? Find a connection between this problem and the Chain Rule.

2. PROPERTIES OF DERIVATIVES

The derivative of a function measures how the function changes. For example, the sign of the derivative at a point provides important information.

Theorem 2.1   Suppose $f'(c) > 0$ at an interior point c of the domain of f. Then there exists $\delta > 0$ such that

$$\begin{cases} f(x) > f(c) \\ f(x) < f(c) \end{cases} \quad \text{for} \quad \begin{array}{l} c < x < c + \delta \\ c - \delta < x < c. \end{array}$$

Proof: Take $\epsilon = f'(c)$ in the definition of derivative. Then there exists $\delta > 0$ such that

$$-f'(c) < \frac{f(x) - f(c)}{x - c} - f'(c) < f'(c)$$

for $0 < |x - c| < \delta$. The left half of the inequality implies

$$\frac{f(x) - f(c)}{x - c} > 0 \qquad \text{for} \quad 0 < |x - c| < \delta.$$

The conclusion of the theorem follows easily.

Theorem 2.2   Suppose $f'(c) < 0$ at an interior point c of the domain of f. Then there exists $\delta > 0$ such that

$$\begin{cases} f(x) < f(c) \\ f(x) > f(c) \end{cases} \quad \text{for} \quad \begin{array}{l} c < x < c + \delta \\ c - \delta < x < c. \end{array}$$

This is proved in the same way as Theorem 2.1, or by simply applying that theorem to $-f$. The results are easily modified to apply at end-points.

Maxima and Minima

Derivatives are indispensable in many applications; one of the most important is locating maximum and minimum values of differentiable functions. The basic fact along these lines is expressed by the following theorem.

Theorem 2.3   Let f be differentiable on $[a, b]$. Suppose $c \in [a, b]$ and $f(c)$ is a maximum or minimum value of f. Then either $c = a$, or $c = b$, or $f'(c) = 0$.

Proof: Suppose $c \neq a$ and $c \neq b$, so that c is an interior point of $[a, b]$. If either $f'(c) > 0$ or $f'(c) < 0$, then Theorems 2.1 and 2.2 imply that $f(c)$ is neither a maximum nor a minimum value of f.

See Section 10.2 for the dangers of overlooking the end points in extrema problems. In general, a point c where $f'(c) = 0$ is called a **stationary point** for f, but it does not necessarily yield a max or a min. For instance take $f(x) = x^3$ and $c = 0$.

Mean Value Theorem

We proceed now to the Mean Value Theorem, a very important result. First we prove a special case known as **Rolle's Theorem.**

Theorem 2.4 Suppose f is continuous on $[a, b]$ and differentiable on (a, b) and $f(a) = f(b)$. Then there exists $c \in (a, b)$ such that $f'(c) = 0$.

Proof: If f is a constant function, then $f'(x) = 0$ for all $x \in (a, b)$. Suppose f is not constant. Since f is continuous on $[a, b]$, it has maximum and minimum values on $[a, b]$ by Theorem 20.8.6, and at least one of these must occur at an interior point c. By Theorem 2.3, we have $f'(c) = 0$.

Rolle's Theorem guarantees the existence of a horizontal tangent to the graph of f. The Mean Value Theorem is a kind of "tilted" Rolle's Theorem. It guarantees the existence of a tangent parallel to the chord through $[a, f(a)]$ and $[b, f(b)]$. See Fig. 2.1.

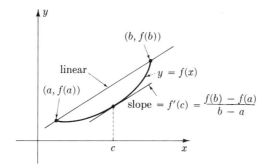

FIG. 2.1. Mean Value Theorem

Theorem 2.5 (Mean Value Theorem) Suppose f is continuous on $[a, b]$ and differentiable on (a, b). Then there exists $c \in (a, b)$ such that

$$f'(c) = \frac{f(b) - f(a)}{b - a}.$$

Proof: The idea is to subtract from f the linear function that passes through $(a, f(a))$ and $(b, f(b))$, and then apply Rolle's Theorem to the difference. Thus we set

$$g(x) = f(x) - \left[\left(\frac{f(b) - f(a)}{b - a}\right)(x - a) + f(a)\right].$$

Then g satisfies the hypotheses of Rolle's Theorem; it inherits continuity and differentiability from f and from the linear function in brackets, and an easy computation shows that $f(a) = f(b) = 0$. By Rolle's Theorem, there exists a point c with $a < c < b$ for which $g'(c) = 0$. But

$$g'(c) = f'(c) - \frac{f(b) - f(a)}{b - a}$$

so the conclusion of the theorem follows.

Derivative Zero

The following basic fact was discussed intuitively in Section 6.1.

Theorem 2.6   Assume f is continuous on $[a, b]$ and $f' = 0$ on (a, b). Then f is constant.

Proof: Let $a < x \leq b$. Apply the Mean Value Theorem to $[a, x]$: there exists $c \in (a, x)$ such that

$$f(x) - f(a) = (x - a)f'(c) = 0.$$

Therefore $f(x) = f(a)$ for all $x \in [a, b]$.

Theorem 2.7   Suppose f and g are continuous on $[a, b]$ and $f' = g'$ on (a, b). Then $f = g + c$, where c is a constant.

Proof: Apply Theorem 2.6 to $f - g$.

Monotone Functions

We showed in Theorem 2.1 that if $f'(c) > 0$ at one point c, then in a certain sense f is increasing at c. If we assume $f'(x) > 0$ on an interval, we can say more.

Theorem 2.8   Suppose f is continuous on $[a, b]$ and $f'(x) > 0$ ($f'(x) < 0$) for all $x \in (a, b)$. Then f is a strictly increasing (strictly decreasing) function on $[a, b]$.

Proof: Take the case $f' > 0$. Suppose $a \leq x < z \leq b$. We must prove $f(x) < f(z)$. By the Mean Value Theorem, there is $c \in (x, z)$ such that

$$f(z) - f(x) = (z - x)f'(c) > 0.$$

If we assume less, then of course we expect to prove less.

Theorem 2.9   Suppose f is continuous on $[a, b]$ and $f'(x) \geq 0$ ($f'(x) \leq 0$) for all $x \in (a, b)$. Then f is an increasing (decreasing) function on $[a, b]$.

General Mean Value Theorem

Theorem 2.10 Suppose f and g are continuous on $[a, b]$ and differentiable on (a, b). Then there exists $c \in (a, b)$ such that

$$f'(c) [g(b) - g(a)] = g'(c) [f(b) - f(a)].$$

Proof: Set

$$h(x) = [f(x) - f(a)] [g(b) - g(a)] - [g(x) - g(a)] [f(b) - f(a)].$$

The function h satisfies all the hypotheses of Rolle's Theorem, hence $h'(c) = 0$ for some $c \in (a, b)$. The conclusion follows.

EXERCISES

1. State and prove Theorem 2.1 for the case of a left end point.

2. State and prove Theorem 2.2 for the case of a right end point.

3. Extend the conclusion of Theorem 2.1 as follows. With the same hypothesis, prove there exists $\delta > 0$ such that

$$f(x) > f(c) + \frac{9}{10} f'(c) (x - c) \qquad \text{for} \quad c < x < c + \delta$$

and

$$f(x) < f(c) - \frac{9}{10} f'(c) (c - x) \qquad \text{for} \quad c - \delta < x < c.$$

4. Give an example of a continuous function on $[0, 2]$, differentiable except at $x = 1$, and with maximum only at $x = 1$.

5. Find the max and min of $f(x) = x^2 - ax + 1$ on $[0, 3]$.

6. Find the max and min of $f(x) = x - (a/x)$ on $[1, 2]$.

7. Suppose f is differentiable on $[a, b]$ and increasing. Prove $f'(x) \geq 0$.

8. (cont.) If f is strictly increasing, do you conclude $f'(x) > 0$ for all x?

Prove by the Mean Value Theorem:

9. If $|f'(x)| \leq B$ on a domain **D**, then f is uniformly continuous on **D**.

10. $|\cos z - \cos x| \leq |z - x|$

11. $10 < \sqrt{101} < 10.05$

12. $\pi/36 < \sin 55° - \sin 45° < \pi \sqrt{2}/36$.

13. Prove Theorem 2.9.

14. Suppose you assume in Theorem 2.9 that $f'(x) \geq 0$ and $f'(c) > 0$ for some c. Prove that $f(b) > f(a)$.

In Exs. 15–26 assume f, g, etc. are continuous on $[a, b]$ and differentiable on (a, b).

15. Suppose $f'(x) \geq 0$ on (a, b) and $f(a) = f(b)$. Prove f is constant.

16. Suppose $f'(x) \geq g'(x)$ on (a, b) and $f(a) = g(a)$. Prove $f(x) \geq g(x)$ on $[a, b]$.

17. (cont.) Suppose also $f(b) = g(b)$. Prove $f = g$.

18. Suppose $|f'(x)| \leq g'(x)$ on (a, b). Prove $|f(b) - f(a)| \leq g(b) - g(a)$. What do you conclude if $|f(b) - f(a)| = g(b) - g(a)$?

19. Suppose $f'(x) \leq B$ on (a, b) and $f(b) - f(a) = B(b - a)$. Prove $f(x)$ is linear. [*Hint:* Use Ex. 15.]

20. Suppose $f'(x) \geq A$ on (a, b) and $f(b) - f(a) = A(b - a)$. Prove $f(x)$ is linear. [*Hint:* Use Ex. 15.]

21. Suppose $f(a) = f(b) = 0$. Prove there exists $c \in (a, b)$ such that $f(c) + cf'(c) = 0$. [*Hint:* Is $f(x) + xf'(x)$ possibly a derivative?]

22. Suppose $0 < a$ and $f(a) = f(b) = 0$. Prove there exists $c \in (a, b)$ such that $f'(c) = f(c)/c$. Interpret graphically. [*Hint:* Consider $g(x) = f(x)/x$.]

23. Suppose $f(a) = f(b) = 0$ and k is a constant. Prove there exists $c \in (a, b)$ such that $f'(c) + kf(c) = 0$.

24*. Prove there exists $c \in (a, b)$ such that

$$\begin{vmatrix} f(a) & g(a) & h(a) \\ f(b) & g(b) & h(b) \\ f'(c) & g'(c) & h'(c) \end{vmatrix} = 0.$$

25. (cont.) Interpret Ex. 24 when $g = x$ and $h = 1$.

26. (cont.) Interpret Ex. 24 when $h = 1$.

27. Suppose

$$\frac{a_0}{n + 1} + \frac{a_1}{n} + \cdots + \frac{a_{n-1}}{2} + a_n = 0.$$

Prove that $f(x) = a_0 x^n + a_1 x^{n-1} + \cdots + a_n$ has a zero in $(0, 1)$.

28. Suppose f is differentiable on (a, b) and that $a < c < b$. Suppose $f'(x) \longrightarrow L$ as $x \longrightarrow c$. Prove $L = f'(c)$.

29. Prove $e^x \leq 1/(1 - x)$ for $-\infty < x < 1$ with equality only for $x = 0$. [*Hint:* maximize $(1 - x)e^x$.]

30. Prove $\ln x \leq x - 1$ for $x > 0$ with equality only for $x = 1$.

31*. Suppose f is continuous on (a, b) and that $a < c < b$. Suppose f is differentiable on (a, c) and on (c, b), but not necessarily at c. Suppose $f'(x) \longrightarrow L$ as $x \longrightarrow c$. Prove f is differentiable at c and find $f'(c)$.

32. Let f and g be differentiable in $[a, b]$. Suppose $f(a) = f(b) = 0$ and suppose $f'g - fg'$ is never zero in $[a, b]$. Prove that g has a zero in (a, b).

33*. Suppose f is differentiable on $[a, b]$, and that $f'(a)$ and $f'(b)$ have opposite signs. Prove there exists $c \in (a, b)$ such that $f'(c) = 0$. [*Note:* continuity of f' is *not* assumed. *Hint:* Use Exs. 1, 2 to prove f has an interior min or max.]

34. (cont.) Suppose f is differentiable on $[a, b]$ and $f'(a) < k < f'(b)$ or $f'(a) > k > f'(b)$. Prove there exists $c \in (a, b)$ such that $f'(c) = k$. [*Hint:* Consider $g(x) = f(x) - kx$.]

35. (cont.) By Ex. 34, each derivative function has the intermediate value property. Does this mean every derivative is continuous? Try $f(x) = x^2 \sin(1/x)$ for $x \neq 0$, $f(0) = 0$.

36*. (cont.) Give an example of a differentiable function on the closed interval $[-1, 1]$ whose derivative is unbounded.

37*. (cont.) Suppose f is continuous on $[a, b]$ and $f'(x) \neq 0$ for each $x \in (a, b)$. Prove f is strictly monotone on $[a, b]$.

38*. Suppose f is differentiable in $[a, b]$ and $f'(a) = f'(b) = 0$. Prove there exists $c \in (a, b)$ such that

$$\frac{f(c) - f(a)}{c - a} = f'(c).$$

[*Hint:* Consider $g(x) = [f(x) - f(a)]/(x - a)$ for $x > a$, $g(a) = 0$.]

39*. (cont.) Prove the conclusion only assuming $f'(a) = f'(b)$. Interpret graphically. [*Hint:* Consider $g(x) = f(x) - f'(a)x$.]

40*. Let f be a polynomial such that $f(a) = f(b) = 0$, but $f(x) \neq 0$ for all $x \in (a, b)$. Prove that the number of zeros of f' on (a, b), counting multiplicities, is odd. [*Hint:* What goes up must come down.]

41*. (cont.) Same hypothesis and k a constant. Prove that the number of zeros of $f' + kf$ on (a, b) is odd. [*Hint:* Consider $e^{kx}f(x)$.]

In Exs. 42–50, assume f is differentiable on $[0, \infty)$.

42. Find an f such that $f'(x) \longrightarrow 0$ as $x \longrightarrow \infty$, but f is unbounded.

43. Suppose $f'(x) \longrightarrow \infty$ as $x \longrightarrow \infty$. Prove $f(x) \longrightarrow \infty$ as $x \longrightarrow \infty$.

44*. (cont.) Prove $f(x)/x \longrightarrow \infty$ as $x \longrightarrow \infty$.

45*. Suppose $f(x) \longrightarrow L$ as $x \longrightarrow \infty$. Prove there exists a sequence $\{a_n\}$ such that $a_n \longrightarrow \infty$ and $f'(a_n) \longrightarrow 0$.

46. (cont.) Suppose $f(x) \longrightarrow L$ and $f'(x) \longrightarrow M$ as $x \longrightarrow \infty$. Prove $M = 0$.

47. Suppose $f'(x)/e^x$ is bounded. Prove that $f(x)/e^x$ is bounded.

48*. Suppose $f'(x)/e^x \longrightarrow 0$ as $x \longrightarrow \infty$. Prove $f(x)/e^x \longrightarrow 0$ as $x \longrightarrow \infty$.

49*. (cont.) Suppose $f(x) + f'(x) \longrightarrow 0$ as $x \longrightarrow \infty$. Prove $f(x) \longrightarrow 0$.

50*. (cont.) Suppose $f(x) + f'(x) \longrightarrow L$ as $x \longrightarrow \infty$. Prove $f(x) \longrightarrow L$.

3. FURTHER DIFFERENTIAL CALCULUS

If f is differentiable on an interval **D**, and c is a point of **D**, then f' may or may not be differentiable at c. If it is, we call its derivative the **second derivative** of f at c and write it $f''(c)$. Thus

$$f''(c) = \frac{d}{dx} f'(x) \bigg|_{x=c} = \lim_{x \to c} \frac{f'(x) - f'(c)}{x - c}.$$

It follows from Theorem 1.2 that f' is continuous at $x = c$. [Note that f' must exist in an interval before we can begin to talk about $f''(c)$. If f' exists only at $x = c$, it is senseless to ask about $f''(c)$.]

There is a formula for $f''(c)$ that generalizes the formula

$$f'(c) = \lim_{h \to 0} \frac{f(c + h) - f(c)}{h}.$$

Theorem 3.1   Suppose f'' exists on (a, b) and is continuous at an interior point c. Then

$$\lim_{h \to 0} \left[\frac{f(c + h) - 2f(c) + f(c - h)}{h^2} \right] = f''(c).$$

Proof: Fix h and set $g(x) = f(x) - f(x - h)$. Then $f(c + h) - 2f(c) + f(c - h) = g(c + h) - g(c)$. By the Mean Value Theorem,

$$g(c + h) - g(c) = hg'(z),$$

where z is between c and $c + h$. But

$$g'(z) = f'(z) - f'(z - h) = hf''(w),$$

where w is between $z - h$ and z, hence between $c - h$ and $c + h$. The result is

$$\frac{f(c + h) - 2f(c) + f(c - h)}{h^2} = f''(w),$$

where $|c - w| < h$. Let $h \longrightarrow 0$. Then $w \longrightarrow c$, so $f''(w) \longrightarrow f''(c)$ since we assumed f'' is continuous at c.

Second Order Approximation

In Section 18.6, we introduced second (and third) order approximations to a function. Now we can make this idea precise.

Theorem 3.2   Let c be an interior point of the domain of f. Suppose f'' exists near c and is continuous at c. Then

$$f(x) = f(c) + f'(c) (x - c) + \tfrac{1}{2}f''(c) (x - c)^2 + e(x) (x - c)^2,$$

where $e(x) \longrightarrow 0$ as $x \longrightarrow c$.

Proof: Define $e(x)$ by the formula above and $e(c) = 0$. Now fix $x \neq c$, and define a new function g by

$$g(t) = f(x) - f(t) - f'(t) (x - t) - \tfrac{1}{2}f''(c) (x - t)^2.$$

This function is defined on $[c, x]$ (or $[x, c]$ if $x < c$) and is differentiable. Note carefully where each c, x, and t enters the formula.

By the definitions of $e(x)$ and $g(t)$ and by the Mean Value Theorem,

$$e(x) (x - c)^2 = f(x) - f(c) - f'(c) (x - c) - \tfrac{1}{2}f''(c) (x - c)^2$$
$$= g(c) - g(x) = (c - x)g'(z),$$

where z is between c and x. But $g'(z) = -f''(z) (x - z) + f''(c) (x - z)$, hence $e(x) (x - c)^2 = (c - x) (x - z) [-f''(z) + f''(c)]$,

$$|e(x)| = \left| \frac{x - z}{x - c} \right| |f''(z) - f''(c)|.$$

Since z is between c and x, we have $|x - z| < |x - c|$, hence $|e(x)| \leq |f''(z) - f''(c)|$. As $x \longrightarrow c$, then $z \longrightarrow c$, hence $f''(z) \longrightarrow f''(c)$ since f'' is continuous at c. Therefore $e(x) \longrightarrow 0$ as $x \longrightarrow c$.

Max and Min

In Section 10.2 we used the second derivative as an aid in curve sketching and in finding maxima and minima. Now we shall give the theoretical basis for those discussions.

Theorem 3.3 Suppose f'' exists on an open interval and is continuous at $x = c$. Suppose $f'(c) = 0$ and $f''(c) < 0$. Then there exists $\delta > 0$ such that

$$f(x) < f(c) \qquad \text{for} \quad 0 < |x - c| < \delta.$$

(If instead $f''(c) > 0$, the conclusion is $f(x) > f(c)$.)

Proof: By Theorem 3.2,

$$f(x) = f(c) + \tfrac{1}{2}f''(c) (x - c)^2 + e(x) (x - c)^2,$$

where $e(x) \longrightarrow 0$ as $x \longrightarrow c$. Choose $\delta > 0$ so that $\tfrac{1}{2}f''(c) + e(x) < 0$ for $|x - c| < \delta$. Then for $0 < |x - c| < \delta$ we have

$$f(x) = f(c) + [\tfrac{1}{2}f''(c) + e(x)] (x - c)^2 < f(c).$$

For an alternative proof using a weaker hypothesis, see Ex. 16.

Convexity

In Section 5.2 we used the second derivative to characterize convexity and concavity of graphs. Let us consider first the case $f'' > 0$ (or $f'' \geq 0$). Such a function is called **strictly convex (convex)**. The basic facts are that such functions lie below their chords and above their tangents (Fig. 3.1). First we take care of the chord.

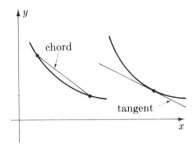

FIG. 3.1.   convex function: $f'' > 0$

Theorem 3.4   Suppose that f is continuous on $[a, b]$, that f'' exists on (a, b), and that $f''(x) > 0$ for all $x \in (a, b)$. Then

$$f(x) < f(a) + \frac{f(b) - f(a)}{b - a} (x - a)$$

for all $x \in (a, b)$. If we replace $f''(x) > 0$ by $f''(x) \geq 0$, then the conclusion holds with "$\leq$".

Proof: We can simplify the notation by subtracting from f the linear function through $(a, f(a))$ and $(b, f(b))$. Thus we set

$$g(x) = f(x) - \left[f(a) + \frac{f(b) - f(a)}{b - a} (x - a) \right].$$

Then $g(a) = g(b) = 0$ and $g''(x) = f''(x) > 0$. We must prove $g(x) < 0$ for $a < x < b$.

Fix x, with $a < x < b$. By the Mean Value Theorem, applied to $[a, x]$ and also to $[x, b]$, we have

$$\frac{g(x)}{x - a} = f'(z), \qquad \frac{-g(x)}{b - x} = f'(w)$$

where $a < z < x < w < b$. But f' is strictly increasing by Theorem 2.8, hence $f'(z) - f'(w) < 0$,

$$g(x) \left[\frac{1}{x - a} + \frac{1}{b - x} \right] < 0,$$

so $g(x) < 0$.

The case $f'' \geq 0$ requires only a slight modification of the proof.

Now we come to the tangent.

Theorem 3.5 Suppose that f is continuous on $[a, b]$, that f'' exists on (a, b), and that $f''(x) > 0$ for all $x \in (a, b)$. Let $c \in (a, b)$. Then

$$f(x) \geq f(c) + f'(c) \, (x - c)$$

for all $x \in [a, b]$, with equality only for $x = c$. If $f''(x) > 0$ is replaced by $f''(x) \geq 0$, there may be equality for other values of x.

Proof: Define

$$g(x) = f(x) - f(c) - f'(c) \, (x - c).$$

Then

$$g(c) = 0, \qquad g'(c) = 0, \qquad g''(x) = f''(x) > 0$$

for $a < x < b$. The function $g'(x)$ is strictly increasing on $[a, b]$ by Theorem 2.8. Therefore $g'(x) > 0$ for $c < x < b$ and $g'(x) < 0$ for $a < x < c$. Suppose $c < x < b$. Then $g(x) - g(c) = (x - c)g'(z)$, where $c < z < x$. Therefore $g(x) - g(c) > 0$, $g(x) > g(c)$. Likewise $g(x) > g(c)$ for $a < x < c$.

This proof is easily modified to cover the case $f'' \geq 0$.

Both Theorems 3.4 and 3.5 are readily adapted to **strictly concave** ($f'' < 0$) and **concave** ($f'' \leq 0$) functions.

Newton–Raphson Method

We shall prove the convergence of this approximation method (Chapter 18, Section 5) in one case, adequate for most purposes, and then briefly discuss the rate of convergence.

Theorem 3.6 Suppose that f is continuous on $[a, b]$ and that $f(a) < 0$ and $f(b) > 0$. Suppose that f'' exists on (a, b) and both $f'(x) > 0$ and $f''(x) > 0$ on (a, b). Define a sequence $\{b_n\}$ by

$$b_0 = b, \qquad b_{n+1} = b_n - \frac{f(b_n)}{f'(b_n)}.$$

Then $b_n \longrightarrow c$ and $f(c) = 0$.

Proof: By Theorem 20.8.1, there exists $c \in (a, b)$ such that $f(c) = 0$. Since $f' > 0$, we know that f is strictly increasing (Theorem 2.8), so c is the only zero of f on $[a, b]$.

We shall prove that

$$b_0 > b_1 > b_2 > \cdots > c$$

by induction. Suppose we have $b_0 > \cdots > b_n > c$. Then $f(b_n) > f(c) = 0$, hence

$$b_{n+1} = b_n - \frac{f(b_n)}{f'(b_n)} < b_n .$$

Furthermore, by Theorem 3.5,

$$0 = f(c) > f(b_n) + f'(b_n) (c - b_n),$$

$$-\frac{f(b_n)}{f'(b_n)} > c - b_n .$$

Therefore $b_{n+1} > c$.

The sequence $\{b_n\}$ converges (Theorem 20.5.1) to a limit p with $p \geq c$. But

$$b_{n+1} = b_n - \frac{f(b_n)}{f'(b_n)} .$$

Since $f(x)/f'(x)$ is continuous (f and f' are differentiable), we may take limits as $n \longrightarrow \infty$:

$$p = p - \frac{f(p)}{f'(p)} .$$

Hence $f(p) = 0$, so $p = c$.

It is useful to know how fast $\{b_n\}$ converges to c, how many times must the process be repeated to ensure a given degree of accuracy. This depends on how small f'' is and how large f' is.

Theorem 3.6'   Suppose $f'(x) \geq m > 0$ and $f''(x) \leq M$ on (a, b). Set $K = \frac{1}{2}M/m$. Then

$$b_n - c \leq \frac{1}{K} [K(b - a)]^{2^n}.$$

Proof: First we apply Theorem 3.5 to the function

$$g(x) = f(e) + f'(e) (x - e) + \tfrac{1}{2}M(x - e)^2 - f(x),$$

which satisfies $g(e) = 0$, $g'(e) = 0$, $g''(x) \geq 0$. The result (without the conclusion about equality since we don't have $g'' > 0$) is $g(x) \geq 0$, that is

$$f(x) \leq f(e) + f'(e) (x - e) + \tfrac{1}{2}M(x - e)^2.$$

Take $x = c$ and $e = b_{n-1}$. Then

$$0 \leq f(b_{n-1}) + f'(b_{n-1})\,(c - b_{n-1}) + \tfrac{1}{2}M(c - b_{n-1})^2,$$

$$-\frac{f(b_{n-1})}{f'(b_{n-1})} \leq c - b_{n-1} + \frac{1}{2}\frac{M}{f'(b_{n-1})}\,(c - b_{n-1})^2,$$

$$b_n - c \leq \frac{1}{2}\frac{M}{f'(b_{n-1})}\,(c - b_{n-1})^2 \leq K(c - b_{n-1})^2.$$

Temporarily set $a_n = K(b_n - c)$, so this inequality is $a_n \leq a_{n-1}^2$. Hence

$$\ln a_n \leq 2 \ln a_{n-1} \leq 2^2 \ln a_{n-2} \leq \cdots \leq 2^n \ln a_0,$$

so

$$a_n \leq a_0^{2^n}, \qquad b_n - c \leq \frac{1}{K}\,[K(b_0 - c)]^{2^n}.$$

Since $b_0 - c = b - c < b - a$, the estimate follows.

This estimate shows that once the zero has been confined to a sufficiently small interval relative to the sizes of f' and f'', once $\tfrac{1}{2}(M/m)\,(b - a) < 1$, then the convergence of b_n to c is rapid.

Lhospital's Rule

We have seen examples of functions such as x/x and $(\sin x)/x$ which have limits as $x \longrightarrow 0$ even though the fractions appear to approach "0/0". Lhospital's Rule helps evaluate such limits; in many situations, it allows us to replace $f(x)/g(x)$ by $f'(x)/g'(x)$.

Theorem 3.7   (Lhospital's Rule)   Let f and g be continuous on $[a, b]$ and differentiable on (a, b). Suppose $c \in [a, b]$ and $f(c) = g(c) = 0$, but $g(x) \neq 0$ and $g'(x) \neq 0$ for all $x \neq c$. Finally suppose

$$\frac{f'(x)}{g'(x)} \longrightarrow L \qquad \text{as} \quad x \longrightarrow c,$$

where L is finite or $L = \pm\infty$. Then

$$\frac{f(x)}{g(x)} \longrightarrow L \qquad \text{as} \quad x \longrightarrow c.$$

Proof: Suppose $x \neq c$. There exists a z between x and c such that

$$\frac{f(x)}{g(x)} = \frac{f(x) - f(c)}{g(x) - g(c)} = \frac{f'(z)}{g'(z)}$$

by Theorem 2.10. If $x \longrightarrow c$, then $z \longrightarrow c$, so $f(x)/g(x) = f'(z)/g'(z) \longrightarrow L$.

EXAMPLE 3.1

Find the limit as $x \longrightarrow 0$ of   (a) $(\sin x)/x$ (b) $(1 - \cos x)/x^2$.

Solution: By Theorem 3.7,

$$\lim_{x \to 0} \frac{\sin x}{x} = \lim_{x \to 0} \frac{(\sin x)'}{(x)'} = \lim_{x \to 0} \frac{\cos x}{1} = 1,$$

$$\lim_{x \to 0} \frac{1 - \cos x}{x^2} = \lim_{x \to 0} \frac{(1 - \cos x)'}{(x^2)'} = \lim_{x \to 0} \frac{\sin x}{2x} = \frac{1}{2}.$$

Answer: (a)   1   (b) $\frac{1}{2}$.

Lhospital's Rule can be extended to cover limits as $x \longrightarrow \infty$ and limits of the form " ∞ / ∞ ", for example

$$\lim_{x \to \infty} \frac{\sqrt{x^2 + 1}}{x}, \qquad \lim_{x \to \frac{1}{2}\pi -} \frac{\text{arc tan } x}{(\frac{1}{2}\pi - x)^{-1}}, \qquad \lim_{x \to \infty} \frac{e^{-x^2}}{1/x}.$$

We state the corresponding results, but not every conceivable case.

Theorem 3.8   Suppose that f and g are differentiable on (a, b), that $f(x) \longrightarrow \infty$ and $g(x) \longrightarrow \infty$ as $x \longrightarrow a$, that $g(x) \neq 0$ and $g'(x) \neq 0$ for all $x \in (a, b)$, and that

$$\frac{f'(x)}{g'(x)} \longrightarrow L \qquad \text{as} \quad x \longrightarrow a+,$$

where L is finite or $L = \pm \infty$. Then

$$\frac{f(x)}{g(x)} \longrightarrow L \qquad \text{as} \quad x \longrightarrow a+.$$

Proof: First we take L finite. Let $\epsilon > 0$. Choose $y > a$ so that

$$\left| \frac{f'(x)}{g'(x)} - L \right| < \frac{1}{2} \epsilon$$

for $a < x < y$. If $a < x < y$, then

$$\left| \frac{f(x) - f(y)}{g(x) - g(y)} - L \right| = \left| \frac{f'(z)}{g'(z)} - L \right| < \frac{1}{2} \epsilon,$$

where $x < z < y$. By a little manipulation, we obtain

$$|[f(x) - f(y)] - L[g(x) - g(y)]| < \frac{1}{2} \epsilon |g(x) - g(y)|,$$

$$|f(x) - Lg(x)| < |f(y) - Lg(y)| + \frac{1}{2} \epsilon |g(x) - g(y)|,$$

$$\left| \frac{f(x)}{g(x)} - L \right| < \frac{|f(y) - Lg(y)| + \frac{1}{2}\epsilon|g(y)|}{g(x)} + \frac{1}{2} \epsilon.$$

Since $g(x) \longrightarrow \infty$, the first term on the right is less than $\frac{1}{2}\epsilon$ provided x is close enough to a. Hence there exists $\delta > 0$ such that $|f(x)/g(x) - L| < \epsilon$ for $a < x < a + \delta$.

If $L = \infty$, the proof must be modified. We start with any A. Then there exists $y > a$ such that $f'(x)/g'(x) > 2A$ for $a < x < y$. The rest of the proof is left as an exercise.

EXAMPLE 3.2

Find $\lim\limits_{x \to 0+} x^x$.

Solution: We have

$$\ln x^x = x \ln x = \frac{\ln x}{1/x}.$$

Apply Theorem 3.8 with $f(x) = \ln x$ and $g(x) = 1/x$. The result is

$$\lim_{x \to 0+} \frac{\ln x}{1/x} = \lim_{x \to 0+} \frac{1/x}{-1/x^2} = \lim_{x \to 0+} (-x) = 0.$$

Therefore $\ln x^x \longrightarrow 0$ as $x \longrightarrow 0+$. We conclude that $x^x \longrightarrow e^0 = 1$ as $x \longrightarrow 0+$.

Answer: 1.

Theorem 3.9 Let f and g be differentiable on (a, ∞). Suppose that either

$$f(x) \longrightarrow 0 \quad \text{and} \quad g(x) \longrightarrow 0 \quad \text{as} \quad x \longrightarrow \infty$$

or

$$f(x) \longrightarrow \infty \quad \text{and} \quad g(x) \longrightarrow \infty \quad \text{as} \quad x \longrightarrow \infty.$$

Assume that $g(x) \neq 0$ and $g'(x) \neq 0$ on (a, ∞), and that

$$\frac{f'(x)}{g'(x)} \longrightarrow L \quad \text{as} \quad x \longrightarrow \infty.$$

Then

$$\frac{f(x)}{g(x)} \longrightarrow L \quad \text{as} \quad x \longrightarrow \infty.$$

The proof is similar to that of the last theorem.

REMARK: In all of these theorems, f'/g' may itself lead to "0/0" or "∞/∞". Then you can try f''/g'', etc.

EXERCISES

1. Prove the Leibniz formula

$$\frac{d^n}{dx^n}(fg) = \sum_{j=0}^{n} \binom{n}{j} f^{(n-i)} g^{(i)}.$$

[*Hint:* Try $n = 2$ and $n = 3$.]

2. Find

$$\frac{d^n}{dx^n}\left[\frac{x^3}{1-x^2}\right]\bigg|_{x=0}$$

3*. Prove

$$\frac{d^n}{dx^n}(x^{n-1}e^{1/x}) = (-1)^n\frac{e^{1/x}}{x^{n+1}}.$$

4. Suppose f is continuous on $[0, b]$, $f(0) = 0$, and $f'' \geq 0$ on $(0, b)$. Prove that $f(x)/x \leq f'(x)$ for all $x \in (0, b]$.

5*. Suppose f'' exists on (a, b) and $f'''(c)$ exists. Suppose

$$\frac{1}{2h}[f(c + h) - f(c - h)] = f'(c)$$

for all h sufficiently small. Prove $f'''(c) = 0$. [*Hint:* First prove $f'(c + x) + f'(c - x) = 2f'(c)$ and $f''(c + x) - f''(c - x) = 0$.]

6. Let f be a polynomial. Suppose f has a zero of multiplicity $m > 1$ at $x = c$. Prove that f' has a zero of multiplicity $m - 1$ at $x = c$.

7*. (cont.) Suppose f is a polynomial of degree n with n real zeros (counting multiplicities). Prove that f' has $n - 1$ real zeros.

8*. (cont.) Prove that

$$\frac{d^n}{dx^n}[(x^2 - 1)^n]$$

has n distinct real zeros in $(-1, 1)$.

9*. Suppose $f(x) \longrightarrow A$ and $f''(x) \longrightarrow 0$ as $x \longrightarrow \infty$. Prove $f'(x) \longrightarrow 0$. [*Hint:* Look carefully at Ex. 2.45.]

10*. Prove Theorem 3.1 assuming only that f' exists on (a, b) and $f''(c)$ exists. [*Hint:* Use Ex. 1.8.]

11*. Prove that

$$\frac{f(c + 2h) - 2f(c + h) + f(c)}{h^2} \longrightarrow f''(c)$$

under suitable hypotheses.

12*. Suppose that f is continuous on $[a, b]$, that $f(a) = f(b) = 0$, and that for each $x \in (a, b)$,

$$\frac{f(x + h) - 2f(x) + f(x - h)}{h^2} \longrightarrow 0$$

as $h \longrightarrow 0$. Prove $f = 0$. [*Hint:* Set $g(x) = \pm f(x) + k^2(x - a)(b - x)$ and consider $\lim_{h\to 0}[g(x + h) - 2g(x) + g(x - h)]/h^2$.]

13. State the third order approximation result analogous to Theorem 3.2.

14*. (cont.) Suppose $f'(c) = f''(c) = 0$ but $f'''(c) \neq 0$. Prove $f(c)$ is neither a max nor a min.

15*. (cont.) Suppose $f'(c) = f''(c) = f'''(c) = 0$, but $f^{(4)}(c) > 0$. Prove $f(c)$ is a minimum. Assume a suitable approximation formula.

16*. Prove Theorem 3.3 assuming only that f' exists on the open interval, $f'(c) = 0$, f'' exists at c, and $f''(c) < 0$. [*Hint:* Use the Mean Value Theorem and Theorem 2.2.]

17. With the hypotheses of Theorem 3.4, prove that the function g defined by $g(x) = [f(x) - f(a)]/(x - a)$ is strictly increasing on $(a, b]$.

18. Complete the proof of Theorem 3.4 for "≥ 0".

19. Complete the proof of Theorem 3.5 for "≥ 0".

20. State and prove Theorem 3.5 for $f'' < 0$.

21. Suppose f is continuous on $[a, b]$, $f(a) = f(b) = 0$, and f'' exists on $[a, b)$. Suppose $f(c) > 0$ for some c. Prove $f''(c) < 0$ for some $c \in (a, b)$.

22*. Prove the "$<$" conclusion in Theorem 3.4 under the hypothesis $f''(x) \geq 0$ for all $x \in (a, b)$ and $f''(z) > 0$ for some $z \in (a, x)$.

23. Suppose f and g are convex on $[a, b]$. Prove that $f + g$ is convex.

24. Find a necessary and sufficient condition for $\ln f$ to be convex (where $f > 0$).

25. (cont.) Suppose $f > 0$ on (a, b) and $\ln f$ is convex. Prove f is convex.

26. Let f be continuous on $[a, b]$ and $f'' \geq 0$ on (a, b). Suppose $p \geq 0$, $q \geq 0$ and $p + q = 1$. Prove that

$$f(pa + qb) \leq pf(a) + qf(b).$$

27. (cont.) Assume $x_1, \cdots, x_n \in [a, b]$, $p_i > 0$, and $p_1 + \cdots + p_n = 1$. Prove

$$f(p_1x_1 + \cdots + p_nx_n) \leq p_1f(x_1) + \cdots + p_nf(x_n).$$

[*Hint:* Use induction.]

28. Let $0 < x < y$ and $0 < p < 1$. Prove $x^py^{1-p} < px + (1 - p)y$ with equality only if $x = y$. [*Hint:* Apply Ex. 26 to $\ln x$.]

Find the limit:

29. $\lim\limits_{x \to 0} \dfrac{x - \sin x}{x^3}$

30. $\lim\limits_{x \to 0} \dfrac{\cos x - 1 + \frac{1}{2}x^2}{x^4}$

31. $\lim\limits_{x \to \frac{1}{2}\pi -} (x - \frac{1}{2}\pi)\tan x$

32. $\lim\limits_{x \to \pi +} (x - \pi)\csc x$

33. $\lim\limits_{x \to 0+} x^{\tan x}$

34. $\lim\limits_{x \to 0+} x^{\ln(1+x)}$

35. $\lim\limits_{x \to 0+} [\ln(1 + x)]^x$

36. $\lim\limits_{x \to 0+} x^{x^2}$

37. $\lim\limits_{x \to \infty} (\ln x)^2/x$

38. $\lim\limits_{x \to \infty} e^x/x^{10}$

39. $\lim\limits_{x \to \infty} x(\frac{1}{2}\pi - \arctan x)$

40*. $\lim\limits_{x \to \infty} x^2(\text{arc cot } x)^3$

41. $\lim\limits_{x \to \infty} (\sqrt{x^2 + 1} - x)$

42. $\lim\limits_{x \to \infty} [(\sqrt{x^2 + 1})/x]$.

43. $\lim\limits_{x \to \infty} (1 + x^{-1})^x$

44. $\lim\limits_{x \to 0} x^2(1 - e^{-1/x^2})$.

45*. Complete the proof of Theorem 3.8 for the case $L = \infty$.

46*. Prove Theorem 3.9 for the case $f \longrightarrow 0$, $g \longrightarrow 0$, and $f'/g' \longrightarrow \infty$.

47. Suppose $f^{(n)}$ and $g^{(n)}$ exist in $[a, b]$ and $f(a) = g(a)$, $f'(a) = g'(a)$, $\cdots$, $f^{(n-1)}(a) = g^{(n-1)}(a)$, and $f^{(n)}(x) \leq g^{(n)}(x)$ on (a, b). Prove $f(x) \leq g(x)$ on $[a, b]$.

48*. Suppose f is differentiable on $(0, b)$ and $f(x) > 0$, $f'(x) > 0$ for all x. Suppose $f(x) \longrightarrow 0$, $f'(x) \longrightarrow 0$, and $f(x)/f'(x) \longrightarrow L$ as $x \longrightarrow 0+$. Prove $L = 0$. [*Hint:* Consider $g(x) = \ln f(x)$.]

49*. (cont.) Under the same hypotheses, prove that $x^{f(x)} \longrightarrow 1$.

50*. (cont.) Suppose $f(x) > 0$, $f(x) \longrightarrow 0$ as $x \longrightarrow 0+$. Does it follow that

$$x^{f(x)} \longrightarrow 1 \qquad \text{as} \quad x \longrightarrow 0+?$$

4. INTEGRATION

Our first problem is to formulate an accurate definition of the integral of a function. The definition should be broad enough to include all the functions needed in applications of calculus, in particular the continuous functions. We should be able to prove as theorems all the main properties of integrals taken for granted in our earlier intuitive approach (Chapter 11, Sections 1, 2; Chapter 16, Sections 1, 2; Chapter 18, Sections 1, 2; Chapter 19, Sections 3–7).

We begin with the (relatively small) class of functions whose graphs consist of a finite number of horizontal segments. We define the integral in the obvious way for these functions, and then we attempt to approximate arbitrary functions by these special functions. That is our strategy.

Step Functions

We work on a fixed closed interval $[a, b]$.

Definition 4.1   A **step function** on $[a, b]$ is a function $s(x)$ that is piecewise constant. That is, there is a partition

$$a = x_0 < x_1 < \cdots < x_{n-1} < x_n = b$$

of $[a, b]$ into a finite number of subintervals such that $s(x)$ is constant on each *open* interval (x_{i-1}, x_i) for $i = 1, \cdots, n$. The values $s(x_i)$ at the partition points can be anything.

See Fig. 4.1 for an illustration of a step function.

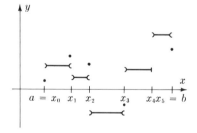

FIG. 4.1.   step function

Theorem 4.1 Let s_1 and s_2 be step functions on $[a, b]$ and k a constant. Then each of the following is a step function:

$$s_1 + s_2, \quad ks_1, \quad |s_1|, \quad s_1 s_2,$$

$$S(x) = \max\{s_1(x),\, s_2(x)\}, \quad s(x) = \min\{s_1(x),\, s_2(x)\}.$$

The proof of this theorem is quite routine. The idea is to lump together all of the partition points for s_1 with all of those for s_2 into one long string

$$a = z_0 < z_1 < z_2 < \cdots < z_m = b.$$

Then s_1 and s_2 are both constant on each (z_{i-1}, z_i), etc.

Definition 4.2 Let s be a step function on $[a, b]$, with partition points

$$a = x_0 < x_1 < \cdots < x_n = b.$$

Let $s(x) = B_i$ for $x \in (x_{i-1}, x_i)$. The **integral** of s on $[a, b]$ is

$$\int_a^b s(x)\, dx = \sum_{i=1}^n B_i(x_i - x_{i-1}).$$

Note that the values $s(x_i)$ at the partition points do not enter the formula. Note also that if some additional partition points are inserted, then the integral does not change. In particular, if s is constant so that $B_1 = B_2 = \cdots = B_n = B$, then $\int_a^b s(x)\, dx = B(b - a)$.

Theorem 4.2 Let s, s_1, and s_2 be step functions on $[a, b]$. Then:

(1) $\displaystyle\int_a^b (s_1 + s_2)(x)\, dx = \int_a^b s_1(x)\, dx + \int_a^b s_2(x)\, dx.$

(2) $\displaystyle\int_a^b ks(x)\, dx = k \int_a^b s(x)\, dx.$

(3) If $s(x) \geq 0$ for all $x \in [a, b]$, then

$$\int_a^b s(x)\, dx \geq 0.$$

(4) If $s_1(x) \leq s_2(x)$ for all $x \in [a, b]$, then

$$\int_a^b s_1(x)\, dx \leq \int_a^b s_2(x)\, dx.$$

(5) If $a < c < b$, then

$$\int_a^b s(x)\, dx = \int_a^c s(x)\, dx + \int_c^b s(x)\, dx.$$

These are the main properties of the integral of a step function. The proofs are left as exercises.

The Riemann Integral

We deal only with *bounded* functions f on $[a, b]$. If $|f(x)| \leq B$ for all $x \in [a, b]$, then we can find *some* step functions s and S such that

(*) $s(x) \leq f(x) \leq S(x)$ for all x.

For example $s(x) = -B$ and $S(x) = B$. We are interested in *all* step functions that satisfy (*). By studying the integrals of all such functions we hope to squeeze down on the "area" under the graph of f. See Fig. 4.2.

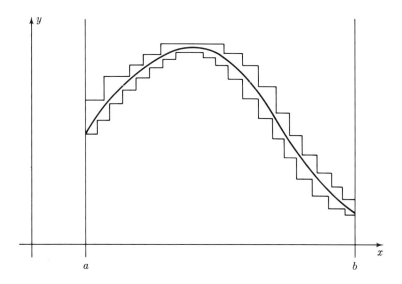

FIG. 4.2.   squeezing a function between step functions

Definition 4.3 A bounded function f on $[a, b]$ is **integrable** if for each $\epsilon > 0$ there exist step functions s and S such that

(1) $s(x) \leq f(x) \leq S(x)$ for all $x \in [a, b]$,

(2) $\displaystyle\int_a^b S(x)\, dx - \int_a^b s(x)\, dx < \epsilon.$

If f is integrable on $[a, b]$, we shall assign to f a number called its integral.

> **Theorem 4.3** Suppose f is integrable on $[a, b]$. Consider all step functions s and S such that
> $$s(x) \leq f(x) \leq S(x)$$
> for all x. Then
> $$\sup_s \left\{ \int_a^b s(x)\, dx \right\} = \inf_S \left\{ \int_a^b S(x)\, dx \right\}.$$
> The common value is called the **integral** of f, and it is written
> $$\int_a^b f(x)\, dx.$$

Proof: If $s(x) \leq f(x) \leq S(x)$, then
$$\int_a^b s(x)\, dx \leq \int_a^b S(x)\, dx$$

by Theorem 4.2 (4). Fix S and let s vary. Then the set of integrals $\{\int_a^b s(x)\, dx\}$ has $\int_a^b S(x)\, dx$ as an upper bound. Hence $\sup_s\{\int_a^b s\, dx\} \leq \int_a^b S\, dx$. Now let S vary. We easily conclude that

$$(3) \qquad \sup_s \left\{ \int_a^b s\, dx \right\} \leq \inf_S \left\{ \int_a^b S\, dx \right\}.$$

To complete the proof, we shall prove the reverse inequality. By definition, given $\epsilon > 0$, there exist s_1 and S_1 satisfying $s_1(x) \leq f(x) \leq S_1(x)$ and $\int_a^b S_1\, dx < \int_a^b s_1\, dx + \epsilon$. Hence

$$\inf_S \left\{ \int_a^b S\, dx \right\} \leq \int_a^b S_1\, dx < \int_a^b s_1\, dx + \epsilon \leq \sup_s \left\{ \int_a^b s\, dx \right\} + \epsilon.$$

Since this is true for all $\epsilon > 0$, we conclude that

$$(4) \qquad \inf_S \left\{ \int_a^b S\, dx \right\} \leq \sup_s \left\{ \int_a^b s\, dx \right\}.$$

By (3) and (4) the inf and sup are equal.

REMARK 1: It follows from Theorem 4.3 that if f is integrable and s and S are step functions satisfying $s(x) \leq f(x) \leq S(x)$ for all x, then

$$\int_a^b s(x)\, dx \leq \int_a^b f(x)\, dx \leq \int_a^b S(x)\, dx.$$

This relation determines $\int_a^b f\, dx$. It is the only number between all pairs $\int_a^b s\, dx$ and $\int_a^b S\, dx$.

REMARK 2: The integral we have defined is called the **Riemann integral** and integrable functions are also called **R-integrable**. There are other integrals that apply to even more functions than does the R-integral.

Continuous Functions

Theorem 4.4   Every continuous function is integrable.

Proof: Let f be continuous on $[a, b]$. By Theorem 20.8.5, f is bounded. Now let $\epsilon > 0$. By Theorem 20.8.7, f is uniformly continuous, hence there exists $\delta > 0$ such that $|f(x) - f(z)| < \epsilon/(b - a)$ whenever $|x - z| < \delta$.

Choose a partition $a = x_0 < x_1 < \cdots < x_n = b$ so that $x_i - x_{i-1} < \delta$. Set

$$m_i = \inf\{f(x) \mid x \in [x_{i-1}, x_i]\}$$
$$M_i = \sup\{f(x) \mid x \in [x_{i-1}, x_i]\}.$$

Then $m_i \leq f(x) \leq M_i$ for $x \in [x_{i-1}, x_i]$ and $M_i - m_i < \epsilon/(b - a)$.

Now choose step functions s and S such that $s(x) = m_i$ and $S(x) = M_i$ on (x_{i-1}, x_i) and $s(x_i) = S(x_i) = f(x_i)$. Then

$$s(x) \leq f(x) \leq S(x) \qquad \text{on} \quad [a, b]$$

and

$$\int_a^b S \, dx - \int_a^b s \, dx = \int_a^b (S - s) \, dx < \int_a^b \frac{\epsilon}{b - a} \, dx = \epsilon.$$

Therefore f satisfies Definition 4.3.

Sums and Multiples

Theorem 4.5   Suppose f and g are integrable on $[a, b]$ and k is a constant. Then kf and $f + g$ are integrable, and

$$\int_a^b kf \, dx = k \int_a^b f \, dx, \qquad \int_a^b (f + g) \, dx = \int_a^b f \, dx + \int_a^b g \, dx.$$

Proof: The statement about kf is left as an exercise. Note that the case $k < 0$ requires some care because inequalities are reversed.

Suppose $\epsilon > 0$. Choose step functions such that

(1) $s_1(x) \leq f(x) \leq S_1(x)$, $s_2(x) \leq g(x) \leq S_2(x)$,

(2) $\displaystyle\int_a^b S_1 \, dx < \int_a^b s_1 \, dx + \tfrac{1}{2}\epsilon$, $\displaystyle\int_a^b S_2 \, dx < \int_a^b s_2 \, dx + \tfrac{1}{2}\epsilon$.

Set $s = s_1 + s_2$ and $S = S_1 + S_2$. Then $s(x) \leq f(x) + g(x) \leq S(x)$ and $\int_a^b S \, dx < \int_a^b s \, dx + \epsilon$. We conclude that $f + g$ is integrable and that for any step functions satisfying (1) *only*, $s_1(x) + s_2(x) \leq f(x) + g(x) \leq S_1(x) + S_2(x)$, hence

$$\int_a^b s_1 \, dx + \int_a^b s_2 \, dx \leq \int_a^b (f + g) \, dx \leq \int_a^b S_1 \, dx + \int_a^b S_2 \, dx.$$

Hold s_2, S_1, and S_2 fixed, and take the sup as s_1 varies. Then take the sup over s_2, the inf over S_1, and finally the inf over S_2. We obtain

$$\int_a^b f\,dx + \int_a^b g\,dx \leq \int_a^b (f+g)\,dx \leq \int_a^b f\,dx + \int_a^b g\,dx,$$

and $\int(f+g) = \int f + \int g$ follows.

Inequalities

> **Theorem 4.6**   Let f and g be integrable on $[a, b]$.
>
> If $f(x) \geq 0$ for all x, then
>
> $$\int_a^b f\,dx \geq 0.$$
>
> If $g(x) \leq f(x)$ for all x, then
>
> $$\int_a^b g\,dx \leq \int_a^b f\,dx.$$
>
> If $m \leq f(x) \leq M$ for all x, then
>
> $$m(b-a) \leq \int_a^b f(x)\,dx \leq M(b-a).$$

Proof: Suppose $f(x) \geq 0$. Set $s(x) = 0$ on $[a, b]$, a *step function*. Then $f(x) \geq s(x)$ implies

$$\int_a^b f(x)\,dx \geq \int_a^b s(x)\,dx = 0.$$

The second statement follows from this, from $f(x) - g(x) \geq 0$, and from the last theorem. The last statement now follows.

The following corollary is referred to as the **Mean Value Theorem** of integral calculus.

> **Corollary**   Let f be continuous on $[a, b]$. Then there exists $c \in [a, b]$ such that
>
> $$\frac{1}{b-a}\int_a^b f(x)\,dx = f(c).$$

Proof: By Theorem 20.8.6, there exist c_1 and c_2 on $[a, b]$ such that $f(c_1) \leq f(x) \leq f(c_2)$ for all $x \in [a, b]$. It follows that

$$f(c_1) \leq \frac{1}{b-a}\int_a^b f\,dx \leq f(c_2).$$

By Theorem 20.8.2, the continuous function f takes every value between $f(c_1)$ and $f(c_2)$, in particular the one just displayed.

> **Theorem 4.7** Let f and g be integrable on $[a, b]$. Define M and m by $M(x) = \max\{f(x), g(x)\}$ and $m(x) = \min\{f(x), g(x)\}$. Then M and m are integrable. What is more
>
> $$\max\left\{\int_a^b f\,dx, \int_a^b g\,dx\right\} \le \int_a^b \max\{f, g\}\,dx,$$
>
> $$\int_a^b \min\{f, g\}\,dx \le \min\left\{\int_a^b f\,dx, \int_a^b g\,dx\right\}.$$

Proof: Let $\epsilon > 0$ and choose s_1, s_2, S_1, S_2 as in (1) and (2) in the proof of Theorem 4.5. Set $s(x) = \max\{s_1(x), s_2(x)\}$ and $S(x) = \max\{S_1(x), S_2(x)\}$. Then

$$s(x) \le M(x) \le S(x).$$

We now claim that

$$S(x) - s(x) \le [S_1(x) - s_1(x)] + [S_2(x) - s_2(x)]$$

for all x. In fact, for each x, either

$$S(x) - s(x) \le S_1(x) - s_1(x) \qquad \text{or} \qquad S(x) - s(x) \le S_2(x) - s_2(x)$$

or both; just check cases.

Therefore

$$\int_a^b S\,dx - \int_a^b s\,dx = \int_a^b (S - s)\,dx < \tfrac{1}{2}\epsilon + \tfrac{1}{2}\epsilon.$$

It follows that M is integrable; similarly m is integrable. Since $f(x) \le M(x)$ and $g(x) \le M(x)$, we have

$$\int_a^b f\,dx \le \int_a^b M\,dx, \qquad \int_a^b g\,dx \le \int_a^b M\,dx,$$

so $\max\{\int_a^b f\,dx, \int_a^b g\,dx\} \le \int_a^b M\,dx$, etc.

> **Theorem 4.8** If f is integrable on $[a, b]$, then $|f|$ is integrable and
>
> $$\left|\int_a^b f\,dx\right| \le \int_a^b |f|\,dx.$$

Proof: The integrability of $|f|$ follows from the formula

$$|f(x)| = \max\{f(x), 0\} - \min\{f(x), 0\}$$

and previous theorems. Since $f \le |f|$ and $-f \le |f|$ we have $\int_a^b f\,dx \le \int_a^b |f|\,dx$ and $-\int_a^b f\,dx \le \int_a^b |f|\,dx$, hence $|\int_a^b f\,dx| \le \int_a^b |f|\,dx$.

Subintervals

> **Theorem 4.9** Suppose f is a bounded function on $[a, b]$ and $a < c < b$. Then f is integrable on $[a, b]$ if and only if f is integrable both on $[a, c]$ and on $[c, b]$. If so, then
> $$\int_a^b f \, dx = \int_a^c f \, dx + \int_c^b f \, dx.$$

Proof: Suppose first that f is integrable on $[a, c]$ and on $[c, b]$. Let $\epsilon > 0$. Choose step functions satisfying $s_1(x) \le f(x) \le S_1(x)$ on $[a, c]$ and $s_2(x) \le f(x) \le S_2(x)$ on $[c, b]$ such that

$$\int_a^c S_1 \, dx - \int_a^c s_1 \, dx < \tfrac{1}{2}\epsilon, \qquad \int_c^b S_2 \, dx - \int_c^b s_2 \, dx < \tfrac{1}{2}\epsilon.$$

Now piece together these step functions. Define

$$s(x) = \begin{cases} s_1(x) & \text{on} \quad [a, c) \\ f(c) & \text{at} \quad x = c \\ s_2(x) & \text{on} \quad (c, b] \end{cases} \qquad S(x) = \begin{cases} S_1(x) & \text{on} \quad [a, c) \\ f(c) & \text{at} \quad x = c \\ S_2(x) & \text{on} \quad (c, b]. \end{cases}$$

Then $s(x) \le f(x) \le S(x)$ on $[a, b]$ and $\int_a^b S \, dx - \int_a^b s \, dx < \tfrac{1}{2}\epsilon + \tfrac{1}{2}\epsilon = \epsilon$, by Theorem 4.2 (5).

Therefore f is integrable on $[a, b]$ and

$$\int_a^b s \, dx \le \int_a^b f \, dx \le \int_a^b S \, dx.$$

But

$$\int_a^b s \, dx = \int_a^c s_1 \, dx + \int_c^b s_2 \, dx \le \int_a^c f \, dx + \int_c^b f \, dx$$

$$\le \int_a^c S_1 \, dx + \int_c^b S_2 \, dx = \int_a^b S \, dx.$$

It follows easily that

$$\left| \int_a^b f \, dx - \left(\int_a^c f \, dx + \int_c^b f \, dx \right) \right| < \epsilon.$$

Since ϵ is arbitrary, $\int_a^b = \int_a^c + \int_c^b$ follows.

Conversely suppose f is integrable on $[a, b]$. We shall prove f is integrable on $[a, c]$. Indeed, if $\epsilon > 0$, choose s and S so that $s(x) \le f(x) \le S(x)$ on $[a, b]$ and $\int_a^b S \, dx - \int_a^b s \, dx < \epsilon$. Then s and S, considered only on $[a, c]$, are step functions and $\int_a^c S \, dx - \int_a^c s \, dx \le \int_a^b S \, dx - \int_a^b s \, dx$ since $S(x) - s(x) \ge 0$. Therefore f is integrable on $[a, c]$. Likewise f is integrable on $[c, b]$; the first part of the proof now implies $\int_a^b = \int_a^c + \int_c^b$ again.

1. Prove Theorem 4.2, part (1).

2. Prove Theorem 4.2, part (5).

3. Suppose f is a bounded function on $[a, b]$ that can be **uniformly approximated** by step functions. That is, given $\epsilon > 0$, there exists a step function s such that $|f(x) - s(x)| < \epsilon$ for all $x \in [a, b]$. Prove f is integrable.

4*. (cont.) Suppose f can be uniformly approximated by integrable functions. Prove f is integrable.

5. Prove the first statement in Theorem 4.5.

6. Suppose f is continuous on $[a, b]$ and $f(x) \geq 0$ for all x. Prove $\int_a^b f\, dx > 0$ unless $f = 0$.

7. Suppose f is integrable on $[a, b]$ and $[c, d] \subseteq [a, b]$. Prove f is integrable on $[c, d]$.

8. Suppose f is integrable on $[a, b]$ and $g(x) = f(x)$ except for a finite set of x's. Prove g is integrable and find $\int_a^b g\, dx$.

9. Prove in complete detail the assertion $S(x) - s(x) \leq [S_1(x) - s_1(x)] + [S_2(x) - s_2(x)]$ in the proof of Theorem 4.7.

10*. Suppose f is bounded on $[a, b]$. Suppose for each $\epsilon > 0$, there exist *integrable* functions g and G such that (1) $g(x) \leq f(x) \leq G(x)$ for all x and (2) $\int_a^b G\, dx - \int_a^b g\, dx < \epsilon$. Prove that f is integrable.

11*. Let f and g be integrable functions on $[a, b]$ with $f(x) \geq 0$ and $g(x) \geq 0$ for all x. Prove fg is integrable. [*Hint:* First take the case where g is a step function; then use Ex. 10.]

12*. (cont.) Prove the same thing without assuming $f(x) \geq 0$ or $g(x) \geq 0$, that is, prove the product of integrable functions is integrable.

13. Prove that the function of Ex. 20.7.8 is not integrable on any interval $[a, b]$.

14*. Prove that the function of Ex. 20.6.19 is integrable on $[0, 1]$ and find its integral.

15*. Let f be integrable on $[a, b]$. For each n, partition $[a, b]$ into n equal parts by

$$x_0 = a, \qquad x_1 = a + \frac{1}{n}(b - a), \qquad x_2 = a + \frac{2}{n}(b - a), \qquad \cdots, \qquad x_n = b.$$

Form

$$T_n = \frac{b - a}{n} \sum_{i=1}^{n} \sup\{f(x) \mid x_{i-1} \leq x \leq x_i\},$$

$$t_n = \frac{b - a}{n} \sum_{i=1}^{n} \inf\{f(x) \mid x_{i-1} \leq x \leq x_i\}.$$

Prove $\lim T_n = \lim t_n = \int_a^b f\, dx$. [*Hint:* First try f a step function.]

16. (cont.) Choose any z_i with $x_{i-1} \leq z_i \leq x_i$ and set $U_n = [(b - a)/n] \sum_{i=1}^{n} f(z_i)$. Prove $U_n \longrightarrow \int_a^b f\, dz$.

17*. (cont.) Suppose g is also integrable on $[a, b]$. Choose w_i so that $x_{i-1} \leq w_i \leq x_i$

and set

$$V_n = \frac{b-a}{n} \sum_{i=1}^{n} f(z_i)g(w_i).$$

Prove that $V_n \longrightarrow \int_a^b fg\, dx$. You may assume $g \geq 0$. [*Hint:* First take the case g a step function, and use the solution of Ex. 11.]

18*. Find

$$\lim_{n \to \infty} \left(\frac{1}{n+1} + \frac{1}{n+2} + \frac{1}{n+3} + \cdots + \frac{1}{2n} \right).$$

[*Hint:* Use Ex. 15.]

19. Find $\int_0^b x\, dx$ by the methods of this section.

20. In the Corollary to Theorem 4.6, prove you can choose $c \in (a, b)$. [*Hint:* Use Ex. 6.]

21*. Suppose f is continuous on $[a, b]$ and g is integrable, $g(x) \geq 0$ for all x. By Ex. 12, fg is integrable. Prove there exists $c \in [a, b]$ such that

$$\int_a^b f(x)g(x)\, dx = f(c) \int_a^b g(x)\, dx.$$

22*. Suppose f and g are integrable on $[a, b]$. By Ex. 12, so are f^2, g^2, and fg. Prove

$$\left(\int_a^b fg\, dx \right)^2 \leq \left(\int_a^b f^2\, dx \right) \left(\int_a^b g^2\, dx \right).$$

[*Hint:* Use $\int_a^b (sf - tg)^2 \geq 0$ with suitable constants s and t.]

5. EVALUATION OF INTEGRALS

The definition of integral given in the last section is important theoretically, but difficult or impossible to use in practice. This section contains theorems that are indispensable in the actual computation of integrals.

It is convenient to assign a meaning to $\int_a^b f\, dx$ when $b = a$, or $b < a$, namely

$$\int_a^a f\, dx = 0, \qquad \int_b^a f\, dx = - \int_a^b f\, dx.$$

(See Section 11.4.) The advantage of this notation is that the formula

$$\int_a^b f\, dx = \int_a^c f\, dx + \int_c^b f\, dx$$

is valid for any three points a, b, c on the interval where f is integrable, *regardless of their order*. This follows easily from Theorem 4.9.

Next a remark about notation. The integral of $f(x)$ on $[a, b]$ can be denoted by

$$\int_a^b f(x)\, dx \quad \text{or} \quad \int_a^b f(y)\, dy \quad \text{or} \quad \int_a^b f(t)\, dt, \quad \text{etc.}$$

We may rename the variable under the integral sign at will.

Fundamental Theorem of Calculus

The **Fundamental Theorem of Calculus** describes a vital connection between integrals and derivatives.

Theorem 5.1 Let f be continuous on $[a, b]$. Define a new function F by

$$F(x) = \int_a^x f(t)\, dt, \quad a \le x \le b.$$

Then F is differentiable on $[a, b]$ and

$$F'(x) = f(x), \quad a \le x \le b.$$

Proof: From the definition of derivative,

$$F'(x) = \lim_{h \to 0} \frac{F(x + h) - F(x)}{h}.$$

By the definition of $F(x)$ and by simple properties of the integral,

$$\frac{F(x + h) - F(x)}{h} = \frac{1}{h} \left[\int_a^{x+h} f(t)\, dt - \int_a^x f(t)\, dt \right] = \frac{1}{h} \int_x^{x+h} f(t)\, dt.$$

By the corollary to Theorem 4.6,

$$\frac{F(x + h) - F(x)}{h} = f(z),$$

where z is between x and $x + h$. (This is right whether $h > 0$ or $h < 0$ as is easily verified.) If $h \longrightarrow 0$, then $z \longrightarrow x$, so $f(z) \longrightarrow f(x)$ by continuity. Therefore

$$\lim_{h \to 0} \frac{F(x + h) - F(x)}{h} = f(x).$$

Therefore F is differentiable at x and $F'(x) = f(x)$. This is true for each $x \in [a, b]$, even the end-points. (At $x = a$ we only allow $h > 0$ and at $x = b$ only $h < 0$.)

Corollary Each continuous function on $[a, b]$ is a derivative.

The Fundamental Theorem makes it easy to evaluate the integral of a continuous function when that function is the derivative of a known function.

Theorem 5.2 Let f be differentiable on $[a, b]$ and suppose f' is continuous on $[a, b]$. Then

$$\int_a^b f'(x)\ dx = f(b) - f(a)$$

Proof: Define

$$F(x) = f(a) + \int_a^x f'(t)\ dt.$$

Then $F(a) = f(a)$ and $F'(x) = f'(x)$ for all x on $[a, b]$ by the Fundamental Theorem. By Theorem 2.7, we have $F = f$. In particular $F(b) = f(b)$; that is the content of the theorem.

It is now easy to derive the rule for **integration by parts.**

Theorem 5.3 Let f and g be differentiable on $[a, b]$ and suppose f' and g' both continuous on $[a, b]$. Then

$$\int_a^b f'(x)g(x)\ dx + \int_a^b f(x)g'(x)\ dx = f(b)g(b) - f(a)g(a).$$

Prove: Apply Theorem 5.2 to fg and use the product rule: $(fg)' = f'g + fg'$. This function is continuous because f, g, f', and g' are.

REMARK: We can now give completely rigorous proofs of the various error estimates in numerical integration. See Section 19.7 and the exercises there.

Change of Variable

In Section 16.5 we stated and proved the following result concerning change of variable. The proof there is correct; it only remains to state the theorem with precise hypotheses.

Theorem 5.3 Let f be continuous on an interval **D**. Suppose g is differentiable on $[c, d]$, and its derivative g' is continuous. Suppose $g(t) \in$ **D** for each $t \in [c, d]$. Then

$$\int_{g(c)}^{g(d)} f(x)\ dx = \int_c^d f[g(t)]g'(t)\ dt.$$

Note that the composite function $f \circ g$ is continuous, so the integrand on the right is a continuous function, hence integrable. The values of the function $g(t)$, for $t \in [c, d]$, may not all lie between $g(c)$ and $g(d)$, but the formula is still true. Just check the proof.

1. Let f be continuous on $[a, b]$ and $\int_a^x f(t)\, dt = 0$ for all $x \in [a, b]$. Prove $f = 0$.

2. Prove
$$\frac{d}{dx} \int_a^{g(x)} f(t)\, dt = f[g(x)]g'(x).$$

[*Hint:* Use Theorem 5.1 and the Chain Rule.]

Differentiate:

3. $\displaystyle\int_0^x \frac{dt}{\sqrt{t^3 + 1}}$

4. $\displaystyle\int_0^{x^2} \frac{dt}{\sqrt{t^3 + 1}}$

5. $\displaystyle\int_x^1 e^{-t^2}\, dt$

6. $\displaystyle\int_x^{x+1} e^{-t^2}\, dt.$

7. Find $f(x)$ if $[f(x)]^2 = 2 \int_0^x f(t)\, dt$. [*Hint:*   Differentiate.]

8. Suppose f continuous on $(-\infty, \infty)$ with period p. Suppose f' and f'' are also continuous. Prove that
$$\int_a^{a+p} f''(x)\, dx = \int_a^{a+p} f'(x)\, dx = 0.$$

9. Suppose f and g are continuous and $f(a) = f(b) = 0$. Prove
$$\int_a^b f(x)g(x)\, dx = -\int_a^b f'(x)G(x)\, dx,$$
where $G(x) = \int_a^x g(t)\, dt$.

10*. Suppose f is continuous and g is differentiable on $[a, b]$. Set $h = f + g'$. Show that h has the intermediate value property: if k is between $h(a)$ and $h(b)$, then $h(x) = k$ has a solution. [*Hint:*   Use Ex. 2.34.]

11*. (cont.) Let f be differentiable on $(-\infty, \infty)$ and periodic of period 1. Let h and B be constants with $h > 0$. Prove there exists a number c such that $f(c + h) - f(c) = Bf'(c)$. Interpret this graphically when $B = h$. [*Hint:*   Use Ex. 20.8.25.]

12*. Prove Theorem 5.2 under the weaker assumption that f' is merely R-integrable on $[a, b]$ rather than continuous. [*Hint:*   Use Ex. 4.16 and the Mean Value Theorem.]

13*. Let $f(a) = f(b) = 0$ and $|f'(x)| \leq M$ for $a \leq x \leq b$. Prove that
$$\left| \int_a^b f(x)\, dx \right| \leq \frac{M}{4} (b - a)^2.$$

[*Hint:*   Compare Section 19.7.]

14*. Suppose $f'(x) > 0$ for $a \leq x \leq b$. Let $g(y)$ be the inverse function of $f(x)$. Prove that
$$\int_a^b f(x)\, dx + \int_{f(a)}^{f(b)} g(y)\, dy = bf(b) - af(a).$$

[*Hint:*   Use Ex. 2.]

6. LOGARITHMS AND EXPONENTIALS

Now we shall face squarely the unpleasant fact that we have never *proved* the existence of the elementary transcendental functions ln x, e^x, sin x, arc tan x, etc. Our treatment so far has been intuitive, based on values in tables and educated guesses. It might be well before proceeding to review our introduction to the trigonometric functions (Sections 7.1–7.3, 15.1–15.3, 15.5, 15.6) and the exponential and logarithm functions (Sections 8.1–8.3, 14.3, 14.4, 14.6).

We begin with the logarithm. We want to find a function ln x for which

$$\frac{d}{dx}\ln x = \frac{1}{x}, \qquad \ln 1 = 0.$$

Therefore we *define*

$$\ln x = \int_1^x \frac{dt}{t}, \qquad x > 0.$$

By Theorem 5.1, ln x is a differentiable function in $(0, \infty)$ and

$$\frac{d}{dx}\ln x = \frac{1}{x}.$$

Obviously, ln $1 = 0$.

Theorem 6.1   If $x > 0$, $y > 0$, and n is an integer, then

$$\ln(xy) = \ln x + \ln y,$$
$$\ln(x/y) = \ln x - \ln y$$
$$\ln x^n = n \ln x.$$

Proof: Fix y. By the Chain Rule

$$\frac{d}{dx}\ln(xy) = y \cdot \frac{1}{xy} = \frac{1}{x} = \frac{d}{dx}\ln x.$$

Therefore $\ln(xy) = \ln x + f(y)$, where $f(y)$ is a constant as far as x is concerned. Set $x = 1$: $\ln y = 0 + f(y)$. Hence $\ln(xy) = \ln x + \ln y$.
In particular, $\ln x = \ln[(x/y)y] = \ln(x/y) + \ln y$, so

$$\ln(x/y) = \ln x - \ln y.$$

It follows from the first formula that $\ln x^2 = \ln x + \ln x = 2 \ln x$, $\ln x^3 = \ln(x \cdot x^2) = \ln x + 2 \ln x = 3 \ln x$, and by induction, $\ln x^n = n \ln x$ for n a positive integer. For $n = 0$, we have $\ln x^0 = \ln 1 = 0 = 0 \cdot \ln x$. For $n < 0$, we have $-n > 0$, hence

$$\ln x^n = \ln(1/x^{-n}) = \ln 1 - \ln x^{-n} = 0 - (-n)\ln x = n \ln x.$$

> **Theorem 6.2**   The function ln is strictly increasing on $(0, \infty)$. Its set of values is $(-\infty, \infty)$.

Proof: Since $(\ln x)' = 1/x > 0$, Theorem 2.8 implies ln is strictly increasing. By the last theorem, $\ln 2^n = n \ln 2$. Hence, $\ln x$ takes on arbitrarily large values for $x > 1$. For $0 < x < 1$, $\ln x = -\ln(1/x)$, so $\ln x$ takes on arbitrarily large negative values. Since the set of values of ln is an interval (Theorem 20.8.4), it must be $(-\infty, \infty)$.

In Section 14.7, we discussed the growth rate of ln. We can give precise proofs now.

> **Theorem 6.3**   Let n be a positive integer. Then
>
> $$\lim_{x \to \infty} \frac{(\ln x)^n}{x} = 0, \qquad \lim_{x \to 0+} x(\ln x)^n = 0.$$

Proof: The statements are equivalent via the change of variables $x = 1/t$, so we prove only the first. Set $f(x) = (\ln x)^n$ and $g(x) = x$. Then $f'(x) = n(\ln x)^{n-1}/x$ and $g'(x) = 1$. Therefore

$$\frac{f'(x)}{g'(x)} = n \frac{(\ln x)^{n-1}}{x} \cdot$$

By Lhospital's Rule (Theorem 3.9),

$$\lim_{x \to \infty} \frac{f(x)}{g(x)} = \lim_{x \to \infty} \frac{f'(x)}{g'(x)} = n \lim_{x \to \infty} \frac{(\ln x)^{n-1}}{x},$$

provided the limit on the right exists. But this is the same problem again, with n reduced by one! We repeat the argument, by induction, and eventually come to

$$\lim_{x \to \infty} \frac{(\ln x)^n}{x} = (n!) \lim_{x \to \infty} \frac{1}{x} = 0.$$

REMARK: We haven't defined x^p yet for arbitrary p, but we might as well observe now that if $p > 0$, then $(\ln x)^p/x \longrightarrow 0$ as $x \longrightarrow \infty$. We simply choose an integer $n \geq p$. Then for $x > 1$, $(\ln x)^p/x \leq (\ln x)^n/x \longrightarrow 0$.

The Exponential Function

By Theorem 6.2, the function ln maps $(0, \infty)$ onto $(-\infty, \infty)$. It is strictly increasing and has positive derivative everywhere. By Theorem 1.5, its inverse function exists and has positive derivative everywhere. The inverse function of ln is called exp; we write e^x for exp x.

Theorem 6.4 The exponential function satisfies

(1) e^x is strictly increasing on $(-\infty, \infty)$ and
$$\{e^x \mid x \in (-\infty, \infty)\} = (0, \infty).$$
(2) $e^{\ln x} = x$ for $x > 0$.
(3) $\ln e^x = x$ for all x.
(4) $e^0 = 1$.
(5) $\dfrac{d}{dx} e^x = e^x$.

Proof: Properties (1), (2), (3) follow by definition, and (4) is obvious. By Theorem 1.5,

$$\frac{d}{dx} e^x = \left(\frac{d}{dy} \ln y \Big|_{y=e^x}\right)^{-1} = \left(\frac{1}{e^x}\right)^{-1} = e^x.$$

Theorem 6.5 If x and y are real and n is an integer, then
$$e^{x+y} = e^x e^y, \qquad e^{x-y} = \frac{e^x}{e^y}, \qquad e^{nx} = (e^x)^n.$$

This theorem is a direct translation of Theorem 6.1, and the proof is left for the exercises.

REMARK: The last relation fully justifies the notation e^x for exp x. In fact, if we *define* the number e by $e = \exp 1$, then we have $\exp n = (e)^n$, the nth power of e. We also can prove in a few more steps that $\exp(m/n) = [(e)^m]^{1/n}$. (See Ex. 20.8.15.) We shall not give details because we shall soon define a^b for *any* $a > 0$ and b.

Theorem 6.6 Let n be a positive integer. Then
$$\lim_{x \to \infty} \frac{e^x}{x^n} = \infty, \qquad \lim_{x \to \infty} x^n e^{-x} = 0.$$

This result can be proved directly by Lhospital's Rule, or by translating Theorem 6.3. Compare Section 14.8.

Exponential Functions

If $a > 0$, we *define* a^x by
$$a^x = e^{x \ln a}.$$

This function is discussed in Section 8.3, and its properties are easy consequences of the properties of e^x. In particular

$$a^0 = 1, \qquad \frac{d}{dx} a^x = (\ln a)a^x.$$

Power Functions

Let p be *any* real number. We *define* x^p for $x > 0$ by

$$x^p = e^{p \ln x}.$$

By Theorem 6.5,

$$x^{p+q} = e^{(p+q)\ln x} = e^{p \ln x} e^{q \ln x} = x^p x^q,$$

and

$$(xy)^p = e^{p \ln (xy)} = e^{p(\ln x + \ln y)}$$
$$= e^{p \ln x} e^{p \ln y} = x^p y^p.$$

We also have

$$(x^p)^q = e^{q \ln x^p}$$

But $\ln x^p = \ln e^{p \ln x} = p \ln x$. Hence

$$(x^p)^q = e^{pq \ln x} = x^{pq}.$$

The function x^p is a composite function of two differentiable functions, so the Chain Rule applies:

$$\frac{d}{dx} x^p = (e^{p \ln x}) \frac{d}{dx} (p \ln x)$$

$$= x^p \left(\frac{p}{x} \right) = px^{p-1}.$$

We summarize:

Theorem 6.7 The functions x^p, defined for $x > 0$, are differentiable and satisfy

(1) $\quad x^p = e^{p \ln x}$

(2) $\quad x^{p+q} = x^p x^q$

(3) $\quad (xy)^p = x^p y^p$

(4) $\quad (x^p)^q = x^{pq}$

(5) $\quad \dfrac{d}{dx} x^p = px^{p-1}.$

Finally we give a formula for the number e.

Theorem 6.8 $\quad \lim\limits_{x \to \infty} \left(1 + \dfrac{1}{x} \right)^x = e.$

Proof: We can do this by Lhospital's Rule, or more directly as follows. Start with

$$1 = \frac{d}{dx} \ln x \bigg|_{x=1} = \lim_{t \to 0} \frac{\ln(1+t) - 0}{t} = \lim_{t \to 0} \frac{\ln(1+t)}{t}.$$

Replace t by $1/x$:

$$\lim_{x \to \infty} \frac{\ln\left(1 + \frac{1}{x}\right)}{\frac{1}{x}} = 1,$$

$$\lim_{x \to \infty} \ln\left(1 + \frac{1}{x}\right)^x = 1.$$

But ln has a continuous inverse function, exp, hence

$$\lim_{x \to \infty} \left(1 + \frac{1}{x}\right)^x = \lim_{x \to \infty} \exp\left[\ln\left(1 + \frac{1}{x}\right)^x\right]$$

$$= \exp\left[\lim_{x \to \infty} \ln\left(1 + \frac{1}{x}\right)^x\right] = e^1 = e.$$

EXERCISES

1. Prove Theorem 6.5.
2. Prove Theorem 6.6 by Lhospital's Rule.
3. Prove Theorem 6.6 by using Theorem 6.3.
4. Prove $a^{x+y} = a^x a^y$, $a^x b^x = (ab)^x$, and $(a^x)^y = a^{xy}$.
5. Find a step function $S(x)$ on $[1, 2.5]$ such that $1/x \le S(x)$ and

$$\int_1^{2.5} S(x) \, dx < 1.$$

Conclude that $e > 2.5$.

6. (cont.) By a similar method show that $e < 3$.
7. Let $0 < x < y$. Prove

$$\frac{1}{y} < \frac{\ln y - \ln x}{y - x} < \frac{1}{x} \qquad \text{(Napier)}.$$

8. (cont.) Prove

$$\frac{1}{n+1} < \ln\left(1 + \frac{1}{n}\right) < \frac{1}{n}.$$

9. Let $0 < x < y$. Prove

$$\frac{\ln y - \ln x}{y - x} < \frac{1}{\sqrt{xy}} \qquad \text{(Kepler)}.$$

[*Hint:* Start by proving $\ln x < \sqrt{x} - 1/\sqrt{x}$ for $x > 1$.]

10. Find $\lim\limits_{x \to \infty} [(x + \sqrt{x})^{1/2} - \sqrt{x}]$.

11. Find

$$\lim_{x \to \infty} \left(\frac{x^{x+1} + x + 1}{x^{x+1}}\right)^x.$$

12*. Prove $(1 + x^{-1})^x$ is steadily increasing for $x > 0$.

13*. Prove $(1 + x^{-1})^{1+x}$ is a steadily decreasing function for $x > 0$ with limit e as $x \longrightarrow \infty$. (Cf. Exs. 20.5.20–23.)

14. Let $A > 0$ and define $f(x) = \log_x A$ for $x > 1$. Find $f'(x)$.

Find the limit:

15. $\lim\limits_{x \to \infty} \left(1 + \dfrac{a}{x}\right)^x$

16. $\lim\limits_{x \to \infty} \left(1 + \dfrac{a}{x^2}\right)^x.$

17. Find the inverse function of $\exp(\exp x)$.

7. TRIGONOMETRIC FUNCTIONS

In this section we shall sketch a logical approach to the trigonometric functions. We shall not push the matter too far because there are better approaches through the theory of differential equations. For the sake of brevity, we shall omit quoting previous theorems as we use them.

We want to define $\sin x$, $\cos x$, and $\tan x$, and establish their basic properties: periodicity, algebraic identities, addition formulas, and differentiation formulas. It seems reasonable that if we get our hands on one of these functions, the others will soon follow.

Where do we start? In the last section we developed the exponential function by first defining its inverse function ln in terms of an integral. We could use the same strategy here, approaching the function sin through its inverse function, defined by

$$\arcsin x = \int_0^x \frac{dt}{\sqrt{1 - t^2}}, \qquad -1 \le x \le 1.$$

This must surely work, but it is unpleasant both because of the radical and because of the abrupt stop at the end points ± 1.

Arc tan

It is much more pleasant to use an integral formula for arc tan. So we *define*

$$(1) \quad \arctan x = \int_0^x \frac{dt}{1 + t^2}, \qquad x \in (-\infty, \infty).$$

A number of properties of arc tan follow directly from the definition:

> (2)   arc tan $0 = 0$
>
> (3)   arc tan$(-x) = -$arc tan x
>
> (4) $\dfrac{d}{dx}$ arc tan $x = \dfrac{1}{1 + x^2}$.

Thus arc tan x is an odd function and is increasing for all x.

One property, not obvious from the definition, is that arc tan x is a bounded function. Proof: for $x > 1$,

$$\text{arc tan } x = \int_0^x \frac{dt}{1 + t^2} = \int_0^1 \frac{dt}{1 + t^2} + \int_1^x \frac{dt}{1 + t^2}$$

$$< \int_0^1 dt + \int_1^x \frac{dt}{t^2} = 1 + \left(1 - \frac{1}{x}\right) < 2.$$

Since arc tan x is increasing and bounded, it approaches a limit as $x \longrightarrow \infty$. We call this limit $\frac{1}{2}\pi$, defining a number π. The crude estimate above shows that $\frac{1}{2}\pi < 2$. By symmetry, arc tan $x \longrightarrow -\frac{1}{2}\pi$ as $x \longrightarrow -\infty$. We write

> (5) $\displaystyle \int_0^\infty \frac{dt}{1 + t^2} = \lim_{x \to \infty} \text{arc tan } x = \lim_{x \to \infty} \int_0^x \frac{dt}{1 + t^2} = \tfrac{1}{2}\pi.$

We show next that arc tan $1 = \frac{1}{4}\pi$. We have

$$\frac{\pi}{2} = \int_0^\infty \frac{dt}{1 + t^2} = \int_0^1 \frac{dt}{1 + t^2} + \int_1^\infty \frac{dt}{1 + t^2}.$$

If the two integrals on the right are equal, then the value of each is $\frac{1}{4}\pi$. The substitution $t = 1/u$ yields

$$\int_\epsilon^1 \frac{dt}{1 + t^2} = \int_1^{1/\epsilon} \frac{du}{1 + u^2}.$$

Let $\epsilon \longrightarrow 0+$:

$$\int_0^1 \frac{dt}{1 + t^2} = \int_1^\infty \frac{du}{1 + u^2}.$$

Hence

> (6)   arc tan $1 = \displaystyle\int_0^1 \frac{dt}{1 + t^2} = \frac{\pi}{4}$.

We may approximate π as closely as we wish by using numerical integration in (6).

We can now make a reasonable sketch of the graph $y = \text{arc tan } x$. See Fig. 7.1.

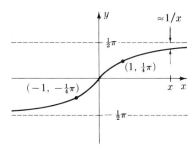

FIG. 7.1.   graph of $y = \text{arc tan } x$

We may ask at what rate the graph approaches its horizontal asymptotes $y = \pm\frac{1}{2}\pi$ as $x \longrightarrow \pm\infty$. The answer is that for x large, the vertical distance between the curve and the line is approximately $1/x$. More precisely, we have

$$
\begin{aligned}
(7) \quad & x(\tfrac{1}{2}\pi - \text{arc tan } x) \longrightarrow 1 && \text{as} && x \longrightarrow \infty, \\
& x(\tfrac{1}{2}\pi + \text{arc tan } x) \longrightarrow -1 && \text{as} && x \longrightarrow -\infty.
\end{aligned}
$$

These formulas are equivalent by symmetry. The first follows from Lhospital's Rule applied to $f(x) = \frac{1}{2}\pi - \text{arc tan } x$ and $g(x) = 1/x$.

Tangent

We have seen that arc tan is a strictly increasing function on $(-\infty, \infty)$ whose values fill out the interval $(-\frac{1}{2}\pi, \frac{1}{2}\pi)$. We now define tan to be the inverse function of arc tan. Then tan is defined on $(-\frac{1}{2}\pi, \frac{1}{2}\pi)$ and takes all real values.

A number of properties of tan follow easily from corresponding properties of arc tan:

$$
\begin{aligned}
(8) \quad & \tan 0 = 0 \\
(9) \quad & \tan(-x) = -\tan x \\
(10) \quad & \tan \tfrac{1}{4}\pi = 1 \\
(11) \quad & \tan x \longrightarrow \infty \text{ as } x \longrightarrow \tfrac{1}{2}\pi - \\
& \tan x \longrightarrow -\infty \text{ as } x \longrightarrow -\tfrac{1}{2}\pi + \\
(12) \quad & \frac{d}{dx} \tan x = 1 + \tan^2 x.
\end{aligned}
$$

The information in (7) tells us the rate at which $\tan x \longrightarrow \infty$ as $x \longrightarrow \frac{1}{2}\pi -$.

$$(13) \quad (\tfrac{1}{2}\pi - x)\tan x \longrightarrow 1 \qquad \text{as} \quad x \longrightarrow \tfrac{1}{2}\pi -,$$
$$(\tfrac{1}{2}\pi + x)\tan x \longrightarrow -1 \qquad \text{as} \quad x \longrightarrow -\tfrac{1}{2}\pi +.$$

Roughly speaking, for x just to the left of $\frac{1}{2}\pi$, we have $\tan x \approx 1/(\frac{1}{2}\pi - x)$.

We now extend the definition of $\tan x$ by making it periodic of period π. In this way, $\tan x$ is defined for all x except $x = \frac{1}{2}\pi + n\pi$.

$$(14) \quad \tan(x + \pi) = \tan x.$$

Sines and Cosines

We may now introduce the functions sin and cos in terms of tan. We are motivated by the half-angle formulas of trigonometry. We set

$$t = \tan \tfrac{1}{2}x, \qquad x \neq (2n + 1)\pi,$$

then define

$$(15) \quad \sin x = \frac{2t}{1 + t^2}, \qquad \cos x = \frac{1 - t^2}{1 + t^2}, \qquad x \neq (2n + 1)\pi.$$

We define $\sin(2n + 1)\pi$ and $\cos(2n + 1)\pi$ so that sin and cos are continuous. If $x \longrightarrow (2n + 1)\pi$, then $t \longrightarrow \pm \infty$. From (15) we see that $\sin x \longrightarrow 0$ and $\cos x \longrightarrow -1$. Therefore we define

$$(16) \quad \sin(2n + 1)\pi = 0, \qquad \cos(2n + 1)\pi = -1.$$

From the definitions and basic facts about tan we easily derive the following properties:

$$(17) \quad \sin(x + 2\pi) = \sin x, \qquad \cos(x + 2\pi) = \cos x$$
$$(18) \quad \sin^2 x + \cos^2 x = 1$$
$$(19) \quad \sin(-x) = -\sin x, \qquad \cos(-x) = \cos x.$$

Furthermore, sin and cos are differentiable for $x \neq (2n + 1)\pi$. Their derivatives can be computed from (15) and (12) by the Chain Rule. For $x = (2n + 1)\pi$ the functions are still differentiable; this can be proved from the definition of the derivative as limit of a quotient. We leave the proofs as exercises. The results are familiar formulas:

$$(20) \quad \frac{d}{dx}\sin x = \cos x, \qquad \frac{d}{dx}\cos x = -\sin x.$$

To complete the story, two important things remain: the addition laws and the relation $\tan x = \sin x/\cos x$.

Addition Formulas

Fix y and define four functions of x:

$$\begin{cases} f_1(x) = \cos(x - y) \\ f_2(x) = \sin(x - y) \end{cases} \qquad \begin{cases} g_1(x) = \cos x \cos y + \sin x \sin y \\ g_2(x) = \sin x \cos y - \cos x \sin y. \end{cases}$$

We are going to show that $(f_1 - g_1)^2 + (f_2 - g_2)^2 = 0$ for all x. That will prove at one fell swoop that $f_1 = g_1$ and $f_2 = g_2$.

By a routine computation, we see that

$$f_1{}^2 + f_2{}^2 = 1, \qquad g_1{}^2 + g_2{}^2 = 1.$$

Hence

$$(f_1 - g_1)^2 + (f_2 - g_2)^2 = (f_1{}^2 + f_2{}^2) + (g_1{}^2 + g_2{}^2) - 2(f_1g_1 + f_2g_2)$$
$$= 2 - 2(f_1g_1 + f_2g_2).$$

Therefore, it will be enough to show that $f_1g_1 + f_2g_2 = 1$ for all x.

Using (20) we find

$$\begin{cases} f_1' = -f_2 \\ f_2' = f_1 \end{cases} \qquad \begin{cases} g_1' = -g_2 \\ g_2' = g_1. \end{cases}$$

It follows that

$$(f_1g_1 + f_2g_2)' = -(f_2g_1 + f_1g_2) + (f_2g_1 + f_1g_2) = 0.$$

Hence $f_1g_1 + f_2g_2$ is a constant. To find that constant, take $x = y$. The result is $f_1g_1 + f_2g_2 = 1$.

Relation between Sin, Cos, and Tan

Suppose we set $f(x) = \sin x/\cos x$ for $x \neq (n + \tfrac{1}{2})\pi$. We shall show that $f(x) = \tan x$. By (20),

$$f'(x) = \frac{1}{\cos^2 x} = 1 + f(x)^2.$$

Therefore $f(x)$ is strictly increasing on $(-\tfrac{1}{2}\pi, \tfrac{1}{2}\pi)$. Also $f(x) \longrightarrow \infty$ as $x \longrightarrow \tfrac{1}{2}\pi-$, and $f(x) \longrightarrow -\infty$ as $x \longrightarrow -\tfrac{1}{2}\pi+$. It follows that the inverse function $g(x)$ is defined on $(-\infty, \infty)$, takes values on $(-\tfrac{1}{2}\pi, \tfrac{1}{2}\pi)$, and satisfies

$$g(0) = 0, \qquad g'(x) = \frac{1}{1 + x^2}.$$

Hence $g(x) = \arctan x$, so $f(x) = \tan x$ on $(-\tfrac{1}{2}\pi, \tfrac{1}{2}\pi)$.

Now $\tan x$ is periodic of period π. We observe that $f(x)$ has this property also. For,

$$\sin(x + \pi) = -\sin x, \qquad \cos(x + \pi) = -\cos x,$$

as is easily seen from the addition formulas. Hence

$$f(x + \pi) = \frac{\sin(x + \pi)}{\cos(x + \pi)} = \frac{-\sin x}{-\cos x} = f(x).$$

It follows that $f(x) = \tan x$ for all x where $\tan x$ is defined:

$$(21) \quad \tan x = \frac{\sin x}{\cos x}.$$

EXERCISES

1. Prove $\arctan[2x/(1 - x^2)] = 2 \arctan x$ for $-1 < x < 1$. Find similar expressions for $\arctan[2x/(1 - x^2)]$ for $x > 1$ and for $x < 1$. [*Hint:* Compare derivatives on both sides.]

2. Find $\arctan x + \arctan(1/x)$ for $x \neq 0$.

3. (cont.) Discuss the relation $\arctan[(x + y)/(1 - xy)] = \arctan x + \arctan y$. [*Hint:* Consider the cases $y < 0$, $y = 0$, $y > 0$.]

4. Prove (20) for $x \neq (2n + 1)\pi$.

5. Prove (20) for $x = (2n + 1)\pi$.

6. Let $0 < x < y < \pi$. Prove $(\sin x)/x > (\sin y)/y$.

7. Prove $\frac{1}{4}\pi = \arctan \frac{1}{2} + \arctan \frac{1}{3}$. [*Hint:* Use Ex. 3.]

8. (cont.) Prove $\frac{1}{4}\pi = 2 \arctan \frac{1}{3} + \arctan \frac{1}{7}$.

9. (cont.) Prove $\frac{1}{4}\pi = 2 \arctan \frac{1}{5} + \arctan \frac{1}{7} + 2 \arctan \frac{1}{8}$.

10. Show that $x/(1 + x^2) < \arctan x < x$ for $x > 0$. Use this and Ex. 7 to prove $\frac{14}{5} < \pi < \frac{10}{3}$.

11. (cont.) Use Exs. 8 and 10 to prove $\frac{74}{25} < \pi < \frac{68}{21}$.

12. (cont.) Use Ex. 9 to estimate π.

13. Prove $(\sin x)/x \longrightarrow 1$ as $x \longrightarrow 0$.

14. Prove $(1 - \cos x)/x^2 \longrightarrow \frac{1}{2}$ as $x \longrightarrow 0$.

15. Prove $t = \sin x/(1 + \cos x)$ in (15).

16. Prove $\sin x < x < 1 - \cos x + \sin x$ for $0 < x < \frac{1}{2}\pi$.

TABLE 1 Trigonometric Functions

Degrees	sin	cos	tan	cot	
0°	.0000	1.000	.0000	—	90°
1°	.0175	.9998	.0175	57.29	89°
2°	.0349	.9994	.0349	28.64	88°
3°	.0523	.9986	.0524	19.08	87°
4°	.0698	.9976	.0699	14.30	86°
5°	.0872	.9962	.0875	11.43	85°
6°	.1045	.9945	.1051	9.514	84°
7°	.1219	.9925	.1228	8.144	83°
8°	.1392	.9903	.1405	7.115	82°
9°	.1564	.9877	.1584	6.314	81°
10°	.1736	.9848	.1763	5.671	80°
11°	.1908	.9816	.1944	5.145	79°
12°	.2079	.9781	.2126	4.705	78°
13°	.2250	.9744	.2309	4.331	77°
14°	.2419	.9703	.2493	4.011	76°
15°	.2588	.9659	.2679	3.732	75°
16°	.2756	.9613	.2867	3.487	74°
17°	.2924	.9563	.3057	3.271	73°
18°	.3090	.9511	.3249	3.078	72°
19°	.3256	.9455	.3443	2.904	71°
20°	.3420	.9397	.3640	2.747	70°
21°	.3584	.9336	.3839	2.605	69°
22°	.3746	.9272	.4040	2.475	68°
23°	.3907	.9205	.4245	2.356	67°
24°	.4067	.9135	.4452	2.246	66°
25°	.4226	.9063	.4663	2.145	65°
26°	.4384	.8988	.4877	2.050	64°
27°	.4540	.8910	.5095	1.963	63°
28°	.4695	.8829	.5317	1.881	62°
29°	.4848	.8746	.5543	1.804	61°
30°	.5000	.8660	.5774	1.732	60°
31°	.5150	.8572	.6009	1.664	59°
32°	.5299	.8480	.6249	1.600	58°
33°	.5446	.8387	.6494	1.540	57°
34°	.5592	.8290	.6745	1.483	56°
35°	.5736	.8192	.7002	1.428	55°
36°	.5878	.8090	.7265	1.376	54°
37°	.6018	.7986	.7536	1.327	53°
38°	.6157	.7880	.7813	1.280	52°
39°	.6293	.7771	.8098	1.235	51°
40°	.6428	.7660	.8391	1.192	50°
41°	.6561	.7547	.8693	1.150	49°
42°	.6691	.7431	.9004	1.111	48°
43°	.6820	.7314	.9325	1.072	47°
44°	.6947	.7193	.9657	1.036	46°
45°	.7071	.7071	1.000	1.000	45°
	cos	sin	ctn	tan	Degrees

TABLE 2 Trigonometric Functions for Angles in Radians*

Rad.	Sin	Tan	Cot	Cos	Rad.	Sin	Tan	Cot	Cos
.00	.00000	.00000	∞	1.00000	.50	.47943	.54630	1.8305	.87758
.01	.01000	.01000	99.997	0.99995	.51	.48818	.55936	1.7878	.87274
.02	.02000	.02000	49.993	.99980	.52	.49688	.57256	1.7465	.86782
.03	.03000	.03001	33.323	.99955	.53	.50553	.58592	1.7067	.86281
.04	.03999	.04002	24.987	.99920	.54	.51414	.59943	1.6683	.85771
.05	.04998	.05004	19.983	.99875	.55	.52269	.61311	1.6310	.85252
.06	.05996	.06007	16.647	.99820	.56	.53119	.62695	1.5950	.84726
.07	.06994	.07011	14.262	.99755	.57	.53963	.64097	1.5601	.84190
.08	.07991	.08017	12.473	.99680	.58	.54802	.65517	1.5263	.83646
.09	.08988	.09024	11.081	.99595	.59	.55636	.66956	1.4935	.83094
.10	.09983	.10033	9.9666	.99500	.60	.56464	.68414	1.4617	.82534
.11	.10978	.11045	9.0542	.99396	.61	.57287	.69892	1.4308	.81965
.12	.11971	.12058	8.2933	.99281	.62	.58104	.71391	1.4007	.81388
.13	.12963	.13074	7.6489	.99156	.63	.58914	.72911	1.3715	.80803
.14	.13954	.14092	7.0961	.99022	.64	.59720	.74454	1.3431	.80210
.15	.14944	.15114	6.6166	.98877	.65	.60519	.76020	1.3154	.79608
.16	.15932	.16138	6.1966	.98723	.66	.61312	.77610	1.2885	.78999
.17	.16918	.17166	5.8256	.98558	.67	.62099	.79225	1.2622	.78382
.18	.17903	.18197	5.4954	.98384	.68	.62879	.80866	1.2366	.77757
.19	.18886	.19232	5.1997	.98200	.69	.63654	.82534	1.2116	.77125
.20	.19867	.20271	4.9332	.98007	.70	.64422	.84229	1.1872	.76484
.21	.20846	.21314	4.6917	.97803	.71	.65183	.85953	1.1634	.75836
.22	.21823	.22362	4.4719	.97590	.72	.65938	.87707	1.1402	.75181
.23	.22798	.23414	4.2709	.97367	.73	.66687	.89492	1.1174	.74517
.24	.23770	.24472	4.0864	.97134	.74	.67429	.91309	1.0952	.73847
.25	.24740	.25534	3.9163	.96891	.75	.68164	.93160	1.0734	.73169
.26	.25708	.26602	3.7591	.96639	.76	.68892	.95045	1.0521	.72484
.27	.26673	.27676	3.6133	.96377	.77	.69614	.96967	1.0313	.71791
.28	.27636	.28755	3.4776	.96106	.78	.70328	.98926	1.0109	.71091
.29	.28595	.29841	3.3511	.95824	.79	.71035	1.0092	.99084	.70385
.30	.29552	.30934	3.2327	.95534	.80	.71736	1.0296	.97121	.69671
.31	.30506	.32033	3.1218	.95233	.81	.72429	1.0505	.95197	.68950
.32	.31457	.33139	3.0176	.94924	.82	.73115	1.0717	.93309	.68222
.33	.32404	.34252	2.9195	.94604	.83	.73793	1.0934	.91455	.67488
.34	.33349	.35374	2.8270	.94275	.84	.74464	1.1156	.89635	.66746
.35	.34290	.36503	2.7395	.93937	.85	.75128	1.1383	.87848	.65998
.36	.35227	.37640	2.6567	.93590	.86	.75784	1.1616	.86091	.65244
.37	.36162	.38786	2.5782	.93233	.87	.76433	1.1853	.84365	.64483
.38	.37092	.39941	2.5037	.92866	.88	.77074	1.2097	.82668	.63715
.39	.38019	.41105	2.4328	.92491	.89	.77707	1.2346	.80998	.62941
.40	.38942	.42279	2.3652	.92106	.90	.78333	1.2602	.79355	.62161
.41	.39861	.43463	2.3008	.91712	.91	.78950	1.2864	.77738	.61375
.42	.40776	.44657	2.2393	.91309	.92	.79560	1.3133	.76146	.60582
.43	.41687	.45862	2.1804	.90897	.93	.80162	1.3409	.74578	.59783
.44	.42594	.47078	2.1241	.90475	.94	.80756	1.3692	.73034	.58979
.45	.43497	.48306	2.0702	.90045	.95	.81342	1.3984	.71511	.58168
.46	.44395	.49545	2.0184	.89605	.96	.81919	1.4284	.70010	.57352
.47	.45289	.50797	1.9686	.89157	.97	.82489	1.4592	.68531	.56530
.48	.46178	.52061	1.9208	.88699	.98	.83050	1.4910	.67071	.55702
.49	.47063	.53339	1.8748	.88233	.99	.83603	1.5237	.65631	.54869
.50	.47943	.54630	1.8305	.87758	1.00	.84147	1.5574	.64209	.54030
Rad.	Sin	Tan	Cot	Cos	Rad.	Sin	Tan	Cot	Cos

* Tables 2–5 are reproduced from "Handbook of Tables for Mathematics" (R. C. Weast and S. M. Selby, eds.), 3rd ed., Chemical Rubber Co., Cleveland, Ohio, and used by permission.

TABLE 2   Trigonometric Functions for Angles in Radians (Continued)

Rad.	Sin	Tan	Cot	Cos	Rad.	Sin	Tan	Cot	Cos
1.00	.84147	1.5574	.64209	.54030	1.50	.99749	14.101	.07091	.07074
1.01	.84683	1.5922	.62806	.53186	1.51	.99815	16.428	.06087	.06076
1.02	.85211	1.6281	.61420	.52337	1.52	.99871	19.670	.05084	.05077
1.03	.85730	1.6652	.60051	.51482	1.53	.99917	24.498	.04082	.04079
1.04	.86240	1.7036	.58699	.50622	1.54	.99953	32.461	.03081	.03079
1.05	.86742	1.7433	.57362	.49757	1.55	.99978	48.078	.02080	.02079
1.06	.87236	1.7844	.56040	.48887	1.56	.99994	92.621	.01080	.01080
1.07	.87720	1.8270	.54734	.48012	1.57	1.00000	1255.8	.00080	.00080
1.08	.88196	1.8712	.53441	.47133	1.58	.99996	−108.65	−.00920	−.00920
1.09	.88663	1.9171	.52162	.46249	1.59	.99982	−52.067	−.01921	−.01920
1.10	.89121	1.9648	.50897	.45360	1.60	.99957	−34.233	−.02921	−.02920
1.11	.89570	2.0143	.49644	.44466	1.61	.99923	−25.495	−.03922	−.03919
1.12	.90010	2.0660	.48404	.43568	1.62	.99879	−20.307	−.04924	−.04918
1.13	.90441	2.1198	.47175	.42666	1.63	.99825	−16.871	−.05927	−.05917
1.14	.90863	2.1759	.45959	.41759	1.64	.99761	−14.427	−.06931	−.06915
1.15	.91276	2.2345	.44753	.40849	1.65	.99687	−12.599	−.07937	−.07912
1.16	.91680	2.2958	.43558	.39934	1.66	.99602	−11.181	−.08944	−.08909
1.17	.92075	2.3600	.42373	.39015	1.67	.99508	−10.047	−.09953	−.09904
1.18	.92461	2.4273	.41199	.38092	1.68	.99404	− 9.1208	−.10964	−.10899
1.19	.92837	2.4979	.40034	.37166	1.69	.99290	− 8.3492	−.11977	−.11892
1.20	.93204	2.5722	.38878	.36236	1.70	99166	− 7.6966	−.12993	−.12884
1.21	.93562	2.6503	.37731	.35302	1.71	.99033	− 7.1373	−.14011	−.13875
1.22	.93910	2.7328	.36593	.34365	1.72	.98889	− 6.6524	−.15032	−.14865
1.23	.94249	2.8198	.35463	.33424	1.73	.98735	− 6.2281	−.16056	−.15853
1.24	.94578	2.9119	.34341	.32480	1.74	.98572	− 5.8535	−.17084	−.16840
1.25	.94898	3.0096	.33227	.31532	1.75	.98399	− 5.5204	−.18115	−.17825
1.26	.95209	3.1133	.32121	.30582	1.76	.98215	− 5.2221	−.19149	−.18808
1.27	.95510	3.2236	.31021	.29628	1.77	.98022	− 4.9534	−.20188	−.19789
1.28	.95802	3.3413	.29928	.28672	1.78	.97820	− 4.7101	−.21231	−.20768
1.29	.96084	3.4672	.28842	.27712	1.79	.97607	− 4.4887	−.22278	−.21745
1.30	.96356	3.6021	.27762	.26750	1.80	.97385	− 4.2863	−.23330	−.22720
1.31	.96618	3.7471	.26687	.25785	1.81	.97153	− 4.1005	−.24387	−.23693
1.32	.96872	3.9033	.25619	.24818	1.82	.96911	− 3.9294	−.25449	−.24663
1.33	.97115	4.0723	.24556	.23848	1.83	.96659	− 3.7712	−.26517	−.25631
1.34	.97348	4.2556	.23498	.22875	1.84	.96398	− 3.6245	−.27590	−.26596
1.35	.97572	4.4552	.22446	.21901	1.85	.96128	− 3.4881	−.28669	−.27559
1.36	.97786	4.6734	.21398	.20924	1.86	.95847	− 3.3608	−.29755	−.28519
1.37	.97991	4.9131	.20354	.19945	1.87	.95557	− 2.2419	−.30846	−.29476
1.38	.98185	5.1774	.19315	.18964	1.88	.95258	− 3.1304	−.31945	−.30430
1.39	.98370	5.4707	.18279	.17981	1.89	.94949	− 3.0257	−.33051	−.31381
1.40	.98545	5.7979	.17248	.16997	1.90	.94630	− 2.9271	−.34164	−.32329
1.41	.98710	6.1654	.16220	.16010	1.91	.94302	− 2.8341	−.35284	−.33274
1.42	.98865	6.5811	.15195	.15023	1.92	.93965	− 2.7463	−.36413	−.34215
1.43	.99010	7.0555	.14173	.14033	1.93	.93618	− 2.6632	−.37549	−.35153
1.44	.99146	7.6018	.13155	.13042	1.94	.93262	− 2.5843	−.38695	−.36087
1.45	.99271	8.2381	.12139	.12050	1.95	.92896	− 2.5095	−.39849	−.37018
1.46	.99387	8.9886	.11125	.11057	1.96	.92521	− 2.4383	−.41012	−.37945
1.47	.99492	9.8874	.10114	.10063	1.97	.92137	− 2.3705	−.42185	−.38868
1.48	.99588	10.983	.09105	.09067	1.98	.91744	− 2.3058	−.43368	−.39788
1.49	.99674	12.350	.08097	.08071	1.99	.91341	− 2.2441	−.44562	−.40703
1.50	.99749	14.101	.07091	.07074	2.00	.90930	− 2.1850	−.45766	−.41615
Rad.	Sin	Tan	Cot	Cos	Rad.	Sin	Tan	Cot	Cos

TABLE 3 Four-Place Mantissas for Common Logarithms

N	0	1	2	3	4	5	6	7	8	9	Proportional Parts								
											1	2	3	4	5	6	7	8	9
10	0000	0043	0086	0128	0170	0212	0253	0294	0334	0374	*4	8	12	17	21	25	29	33	37
11	0414	0453	0492	0531	0569	0607	0645	0682	0719	0755	4	8	11	15	19	23	26	30	34
12	0792	0828	0864	0899	0934	0969	1004	1038	1072	1106	3	7	10	14	17	21	24	28	31
13	1139	1173	1206	1239	1271	1303	1335	1367	1399	1430	3	6	10	13	16	19	23	26	29
14	1461	1492	1523	1553	1584	1614	1644	1673	1703	1732	3	6	9	12	15	18	21	24	27
15	1761	1790	1818	1847	1875	1903	1931	1959	1987	2014	*3	6	8	11	14	17	20	22	25
16	2041	2068	2095	2122	2148	2175	2201	2227	2253	2279	3	5	8	11	13	16	18	21	24
17	2304	2330	2355	2380	2405	2430	2455	2480	2504	2529	2	5	7	10	12	15	17	20	22
18	2553	2577	2601	2625	2648	2672	2695	2718	2742	2765	2	5	7	9	12	14	16	19	21
19	2788	2810	2833	2856	2878	2900	2923	2945	2967	2989	2	4	7	9	11	13	16	18	20
20	3010	3032	3054	3075	3096	3118	3139	3160	3181	3201	2	4	6	8	11	13	15	17	19
21	3222	3243	3263	3284	3304	3324	3345	3365	3385	3404	2	4	6	8	10	12	14	16	18
22	3424	3444	3464	3483	3502	3522	3541	3560	3579	3598	2	4	6	8	10	12	14	15	17
23	3617	3636	3655	3674	3692	3711	3729	3747	3766	3784	2	4	6	7	9	11	13	15	17
24	3802	3820	3838	3856	3874	3892	3909	3927	3945	3962	2	4	5	7	9	11	12	14	16
25	3979	3997	4014	4031	4048	4065	4082	4099	4116	4133	2	3	5	7	9	10	12	14	15
26	4150	4166	4183	4200	4216	4232	4249	4265	4281	4298	2	3	5	7	8	10	11	13	15
27	4314	4330	4346	4362	4378	4393	4409	4425	4440	4456	2	3	5	6	8	9	11	13	14
28	4472	4487	4502	4518	4533	4548	4564	4579	4594	4609	2	3	5	6	8	9	11	12	14
29	4624	4639	4654	4669	4683	4698	4713	4728	4742	4757	1	3	4	6	7	9	10	12	13
30	4771	4786	4800	4814	4829	4843	4857	4871	4886	4900	1	3	4	6	7	9	10	11	13
31	4914	4928	4942	4955	4969	4983	4997	5011	5024	5038	1	3	4	6	7	8	10	11	12
32	5051	5065	5079	5092	5105	5119	5132	5145	5159	5172	1	3	4	5	7	8	9	11	12
33	5185	5198	5211	5224	5237	5250	5263	5276	5289	5302	1	3	4	5	6	8	9	10	12
34	5315	5328	5340	5353	5366	5378	5391	5403	5416	5428	1	3	4	5	6	8	9	10	11
35	5441	5453	5465	5478	5490	5502	5514	5527	5539	5551	1	2	4	5	6	7	9	10	11
36	5563	5575	5587	5599	5611	5623	5635	5647	5658	5670	1	2	4	5	6	7	8	10	11
37	5682	5694	5705	5717	5729	5740	5752	5763	5775	5786	1	2	3	5	6	7	8	9	10
38	5798	5809	5821	5832	5843	5855	5866	5877	5888	5899	1	2	3	5	6	7	8	9	10
39	5911	5922	5933	5944	5955	5966	5977	5988	5999	6010	1	2	3	4	5	7	8	9	10
40	6021	6031	6042	6053	6064	6075	6085	6096	6107	6117	1	2	3	4	5	6	8	9	10
41	6128	6138	6149	6160	6170	6180	6191	6201	6212	6222	1	2	3	4	5	6	7	8	9
42	6232	6243	6253	6263	6274	6284	6294	6304	6314	6325	1	2	3	4	5	6	7	8	9
43	6335	6345	6355	6365	6375	6385	6395	6405	6415	6425	1	2	3	4	5	6	7	8	9
44	6435	6444	6454	6464	6474	6484	6493	6503	6513	6522	1	2	3	4	5	6	7	8	9
45	6532	6542	6551	6561	6571	6580	6590	6599	6609	6618	1	2	3	4	5	6	7	8	9
46	6628	6637	6646	6656	6665	6675	6684	6693	6702	6712	1	2	3	4	5	6	7	7	8
47	6721	6730	6739	6749	6758	6767	6776	6785	6794	6803	1	2	3	4	5	5	6	7	8
48	6812	6821	6830	6839	6848	6857	6866	6875	6884	6893	1	2	3	4	4	5	6	7	8
49	6902	6911	6920	6928	6937	6946	6955	6964	6972	6981	1	2	3	4	4	5	6	7	8
50	6990	6998	7007	7016	7024	7033	7042	7050	7059	7067	1	2	3	3	4	5	6	7	8
51	7076	7084	7093	7101	7110	7118	7126	7135	7143	7152	1	2	3	3	4	5	6	7	8
52	7160	7168	7177	7185	7193	7202	7210	7218	7226	7235	1	2	2	3	4	5	6	7	7
53	7243	7251	7259	7267	7275	7284	7292	7300	7308	7316	1	2	2	3	4	5	6	6	7
54	7324	7332	7340	7348	7356	7364	7372	7380	7388	7396	1	2	2	3	4	5	6	6	7
N	0	1	2	3	4	5	6	7	8	9	1	2	3	4	5	6	7	8	9

* Interpolation in this section of the table is inaccurate.

TABLE 3 Four-Place Mantissas for Common Logarithms (Continued)

N	0	1	2	3	4	5	6	7	8	9	|	1	2	3	4	5	6	7	8	9
												\multicolumn{9}{Proportional Parts}								
55	7404	7412	7419	7427	7435	7443	7451	7459	7466	7474		1	2	2	3	4	5	5	6	7
56	7482	7490	7497	7505	7513	7520	7528	7536	7543	7551		1	2	2	3	4	5	5	6	7
57	7559	7566	7574	7582	7589	7597	7604	7612	7619	7627		1	2	2	3	4	5	5	6	7
58	7634	7642	7649	7657	7664	7672	7679	7686	7694	7701		1	1	2	3	4	4	5	6	7
59	7709	7716	7723	7731	7738	7745	7752	7760	7767	7774		1	1	2	3	4	4	5	6	7
60	7782	7789	7796	7803	7810	7818	7825	7832	7839	7846		1	1	2	3	4	4	5	6	6
61	7853	7860	7868	7875	7882	7889	7896	7903	7910	7917		1	1	2	3	4	4	5	6	6
62	7924	7931	7938	7945	7952	7959	7966	7973	7980	7987		1	1	2	3	3	4	5	6	6
63	7993	8000	8007	8014	8021	8028	8035	8041	8048	8055		1	1	2	3	3	4	5	5	6
64	8062	8069	8075	8082	8089	8096	8102	8109	8116	8122		1	1	2	3	3	4	5	5	6
65	8129	8136	8142	8149	8156	8162	8169	8176	8182	8189		1	1	2	3	3	4	5	5	6
66	8195	8202	8209	8215	8222	8228	8235	8241	8248	8254		1	1	2	3	3	4	5	5	6
67	8261	8267	8274	8280	8287	8293	8299	8306	8312	8319		1	1	2	3	3	4	5	5	6
68	8325	8331	8338	8344	8351	8357	8363	8370	8376	8382		1	1	2	3	3	4	4	5	6
69	8388	8395	8401	8407	8414	8420	8426	8432	8439	8445		1	1	2	2	3	4	4	5	6
70	8451	8457	8463	8470	8476	8482	8488	8494	8500	8506		1	1	2	2	3	4	4	5	6
71	8513	8519	8525	8531	8537	8543	8549	8555	8561	8567		1	1	2	2	3	4	4	5	5
72	8573	8579	8585	8591	8597	8603	8609	8615	8621	8627		1	1	2	2	3	4	4	5	5
73	8633	8639	8645	8651	8657	8663	8669	8675	8681	8686		1	1	2	2	3	4	4	5	5
74	8692	8698	8704	8710	8716	8722	8727	8733	8739	8745		1	1	2	2	3	4	4	5	5
75	8751	8756	8762	8768	8774	8779	8785	8791	8797	8802		1	1	2	2	3	3	4	5	5
76	8808	8814	8820	8825	8831	8837	8842	8848	8854	8859		1	1	2	2	3	3	4	5	5
77	8865	8871	8876	8882	8887	8893	8899	8904	8910	8915		1	1	2	2	3	3	4	4	5
78	8921	8927	8932	8938	8943	8949	8954	8960	8965	8971		1	1	2	2	3	3	4	4	5
79	8976	8982	8987	8993	8998	9004	9009	9015	9020	9025		1	1	2	2	3	3	4	4	5
80	9031	9036	9042	9047	9053	9058	9063	9069	9074	9079		1	1	2	2	3	3	4	4	5
81	9085	9090	9096	9101	9106	9112	9117	9122	9128	9133		1	1	2	2	3	3	4	4	5
82	9138	9143	9149	9154	9159	9165	9170	9175	9180	9186		1	1	2	2	3	3	4	4	5
83	9191	9196	9201	9206	9212	9217	9222	9227	9232	9238		1	1	2	2	3	3	4	4	5
84	9243	9248	9253	9258	9263	9269	9274	9279	9284	9289		1	1	2	2	3	3	4	4	5
85	9294	9299	9304	9309	9315	9320	9325	9330	9335	9340		1	1	2	2	3	3	4	4	5
86	9345	9350	9355	9360	9365	9370	9375	9380	9385	9390		1	1	2	2	3	3	4	4	5
87	9395	9400	9405	9410	9415	9420	9425	9430	9435	9440		0	1	1	2	2	3	3	4	4
88	9445	9450	9455	9460	9465	9469	9474	9479	9484	9489		0	1	1	2	2	3	3	4	4
89	9494	9499	9504	9509	9513	9518	9523	9528	9533	9538		0	1	1	2	2	3	3	4	4
90	9542	9547	9552	9557	9562	9566	9571	9576	9581	9586		0	1	1	2	2	3	3	4	4
91	9590	9595	9600	9605	9609	9614	9619	9624	9628	9633		0	1	1	2	2	3	3	4	4
92	9638	9643	9647	9652	9657	9661	9666	9671	9675	9680		0	1	1	2	2	3	3	4	4
93	9685	9689	9694	9699	9703	9708	9713	9717	9722	9727		0	1	1	2	2	3	3	4	4
94	9731	9736	9741	9745	9750	9754	9759	9763	9768	9773		0	1	1	2	2	3	3	4	4
95	9777	9782	9786	9791	9795	9800	9805	9809	9814	9818		0	1	1	2	2	3	3	4	4
96	9823	9827	9832	9836	9841	9845	9850	9854	9859	9863		0	1	1	2	2	3	3	4	4
97	9868	9872	9877	9881	9886	9890	9894	9899	9903	9908		0	1	1	2	2	3	3	4	4
98	9912	9917	9921	9926	9930	9934	9939	9943	9948	9952		0	1	1	2	2	3	3	4	4
99	9956	9961	9965	9969	9974	9978	9983	9987	9991	9996		0	1	1	2	2	3	3	3	4
N	0	1	2	3	4	5	6	7	8	9		1	2	3	4	5	6	7	8	9

TABLE 4   Antilogarithms

	0	1	2	3	4	5	6	7	8	9	Proportional Parts								
											1	2	3	4	5	6	7	8	9
.00	1000	1002	1005	1007	1009	1012	1014	1016	1019	1021	0	0	1	1	1	1	2	2	2
.01	1023	1026	1028	1030	1033	1035	1038	1040	1042	1045	0	0	1	1	1	1	2	2	2
.02	1047	1050	1052	1054	1057	1059	1062	1064	1067	1069	0	0	1	1	1	1	2	2	2
.03	1072	1074	1076	1079	1081	1084	1086	1089	1091	1094	0	0	1	1	1	1	2	2	2
.04	1096	1099	1102	1104	1107	1109	1112	1114	1117	1119	0	1	1	1	1	2	2	2	2
.05	1122	1125	1127	1130	1132	1135	1138	1140	1143	1146	0	1	1	1	1	2	2	2	2
.06	1148	1151	1153	1156	1159	1161	1164	1167	1169	1172	0	1	1	1	1	2	2	2	2
.07	1175	1178	1180	1183	1186	1189	1191	1194	1197	1199	0	1	1	1	1	2	2	2	2
.08	1202	1205	1208	1211	1213	1216	1219	1222	1225	1227	0	1	1	1	1	2	2	2	3
.09	1230	1233	1236	1239	1242	1245	1247	1250	1253	1256	0	1	1	1	1	2	2	2	3
.10	1259	1262	1265	1268	1271	1274	1276	1279	1282	1285	0	1	1	1	1	2	2	2	3
.11	1288	1291	1294	1297	1300	1303	1306	1309	1312	1315	0	1	1	1	2	2	2	3	3
.12	1318	1321	1324	1327	1330	1334	1337	1340	1343	1346	0	1	1	1	2	2	2	3	3
.13	1349	1352	1355	1358	1361	1365	1368	1371	1374	1377	0	1	1	1	2	2	2	3	3
.14	1380	1384	1387	1390	1393	1396	1400	1403	1406	1409	0	1	1	1	2	2	2	3	3
.15	1413	1416	1419	1422	1426	1429	1432	1435	1439	1442	0	1	1	1	2	2	2	3	3
.16	1445	1449	1452	1455	1459	1462	1466	1469	1472	1476	0	1	1	1	2	2	2	3	3
.17	1479	1483	1486	1489	1493	1496	1500	1503	1507	1510	0	1	1	1	2	2	2	3	3
.18	1514	1517	1521	1524	1528	1531	1535	1538	1542	1545	0	1	1	1	2	2	2	3	3
.19	1549	1552	1556	1560	1563	1567	1570	1574	1578	1581	0	1	1	1	2	2	3	3	3
.20	1585	1589	1592	1596	1600	1603	1607	1611	1614	1618	0	1	1	1	2	2	3	3	3
.21	1622	1626	1629	1633	1637	1641	1644	1648	1652	1656	0	1	1	2	2	2	3	3	3
.22	1660	1663	1667	1671	1675	1679	1683	1687	1690	1694	0	1	1	2	2	2	3	3	3
.23	1698	1702	1706	1710	1714	1718	1722	1726	1730	1734	0	1	1	2	2	2	3	3	4
.24	1738	1742	1746	1750	1754	1758	1762	1766	1770	1774	0	1	1	2	2	2	3	3	4
.25	1778	1782	1786	1791	1795	1799	1803	1807	1811	1816	0	1	1	2	2	2	3	3	4
.26	1820	1824	1828	1832	1837	1841	1845	1849	1854	1858	0	1	1	2	2	3	3	3	4
.27	1862	1866	1871	1875	1879	1884	1888	1892	1897	1901	0	1	1	2	2	3	3	3	4
.28	1905	1910	1914	1919	1923	1928	1932	1936	1941	1945	0	1	1	2	2	3	3	4	4
.29	1950	1954	1959	1963	1968	1972	1977	1982	1986	1991	0	1	1	2	2	3	3	4	4
.30	1995	2000	2004	2009	2014	2018	2023	2028	2032	2037	0	1	1	2	2	3	3	4	4
.31	2042	2046	2051	2056	2061	2065	2070	2075	2080	2084	0	1	1	2	2	3	3	4	4
.32	2089	2094	2099	2104	2109	2113	2118	2123	2128	2133	0	1	1	2	2	3	3	4	4
.33	2138	2143	2148	2153	2158	2163	2168	2173	2178	2183	0	1	1	2	2	3	3	4	4
.34	2188	2193	2198	2203	2208	2213	2218	2223	2228	2234	1	1	2	2	3	3	4	4	5
.35	2239	2244	2249	2254	2259	2265	2270	2275	2280	2286	1	1	2	2	3	3	4	4	5
.36	2291	2296	2301	2307	2312	2317	2323	2328	2333	2339	1	1	2	2	3	3	4	4	5
.37	2344	2350	2355	2360	2366	2371	2377	2382	2388	2393	1	1	2	2	3	3	4	4	5
.38	2399	2404	2410	2415	2421	2427	2432	2438	2443	2449	1	1	2	2	3	3	4	4	5
.39	2455	2460	2466	2472	2477	2483	2489	2495	2500	2506	1	1	2	2	3	3	4	5	5
.40	2512	2518	2523	2529	2535	2541	2547	2553	2559	2564	1	1	2	2	3	4	4	5	5
.41	2570	2576	2582	2588	2594	2600	2606	2612	2618	2624	1	1	2	2	3	4	4	5	5
.42	2630	2636	2642	2649	2655	2661	2667	2673	2679	2685	1	1	2	2	3	4	4	5	6
.43	2692	2698	2704	2710	2716	2723	2729	2735	2742	2748	1	1	2	3	3	4	4	5	6
.44	2754	2761	2767	2773	2780	2786	2793	2799	2805	2812	1	1	2	3	3	4	4	5	6
.45	2818	2825	2831	2838	2844	2851	2858	2864	2871	2877	1	1	2	3	3	4	5	5	6
.46	2884	2891	2897	2904	2911	2917	2924	2931	2938	2944	1	1	2	3	3	4	5	5	6
.47	2951	2958	2965	2972	2979	2985	2992	2999	3006	3013	1	1	2	3	3	4	5	5	6
.48	3020	3027	3034	3041	3048	3055	3062	3069	3076	3083	1	1	2	3	4	4	5	6	6
.49	3090	3097	3105	3112	3119	3126	3133	3141	3148	3155	1	1	2	3	4	4	5	6	6
	0	1	2	3	4	5	6	7	8	9	1	2	3	4	5	6	7	8	9

TABLE 4 Antilogarithms (Continued)

	0	1	2	3	4	5	6	7	8	9	1	2	3	4	5	6	7	8	9
.50	3162	3170	3177	3184	3192	3199	3206	3214	3221	3228	1	1	2	3	4	4	5	6	7
.51	3236	3243	3251	3258	3266	3273	3281	3289	3296	3304	1	2	2	3	4	5	5	6	7
.52	3311	3319	3327	3334	3342	3350	3357	3365	3373	3381	1	2	2	3	4	5	5	6	7
.53	3388	3396	3404	3412	3420	3428	3436	3443	3451	3459	1	2	2	3	4	5	6	6	7
.54	3467	3475	3483	3491	3499	3508	3516	3524	3532	3540	1	2	2	3	4	5	6	6	7
.55	3548	3556	3565	3573	3581	3589	3597	3606	3614	3622	1	2	2	3	4	5	6	7	7
.56	3631	3639	3648	3656	3664	3673	3681	3690	3698	3707	1	2	3	3	4	5	6	7	8
.57	3715	3724	3733	3741	3750	3758	3767	3776	3784	3793	1	2	3	3	4	5	6	7	8
.58	3802	3811	3819	3828	3837	3846	3855	3864	3873	3882	1	2	3	4	4	5	6	7	8
.59	3890	3899	3908	3917	3926	3936	3945	3954	3963	3972	1	2	3	4	5	5	6	7	8
.60	3981	3990	3999	4009	4018	4027	4036	4046	4055	4064	1	2	3	4	5	6	6	7	8
.61	4074	4083	4093	4102	4111	4121	4130	4140	4150	4159	1	2	3	4	5	6	7	8	9
.62	4169	4178	4188	4198	4207	4217	4227	4236	4246	4256	1	2	3	4	5	6	7	8	9
.63	4266	4276	4285	4295	4305	4315	4325	4335	4345	4355	1	2	3	4	5	6	7	8	9
.64	4365	4375	4385	4395	4406	4416	4426	4436	4446	4457	1	2	3	4	5	6	7	8	9
.65	4467	4477	4487	4498	4508	4519	4529	4539	4550	4560	1	2	3	4	5	6	7	8	9
.66	4571	4581	4592	4603	4613	4624	4634	4645	4656	4667	1	2	3	4	5	6	7	9	10
.67	4677	4688	4699	4710	4721	4732	4742	4753	4764	4775	1	2	3	4	5	7	8	9	10
.68	4786	4797	4808	4819	4831	4842	4853	4864	4875	4887	1	2	3	4	6	7	8	9	10
.69	4898	4909	4920	4932	4943	4955	4966	4977	4989	5000	1	2	3	5	6	7	8	9	10
.70	5012	5023	5035	5047	5058	5070	5082	5093	5105	5117	1	2	4	5	6	7	8	9	11
.71	5129	5140	5152	5164	5176	5188	5200	5212	5224	5236	1	2	4	5	6	7	8	10	11
.72	5248	5260	5272	5284	5297	5309	5321	5333	5346	5358	1	2	4	5	6	7	9	10	11
.73	5370	5383	5395	5408	5420	5433	5445	5458	5470	5483	1	3	4	5	6	8	9	10	11
.74	5495	5508	5521	5534	5546	5559	5572	5585	5598	5610	1	3	4	5	6	8	9	10	12
.75	5623	5636	5649	5662	5675	5689	5702	5715	5728	5741	1	3	4	5	7	8	9	10	12
.76	5754	5768	5781	5794	5808	5821	5834	5848	5861	5875	1	3	4	5	7	8	9	11	12
.77	5888	5902	5916	5929	5943	5957	5970	5984	5998	6012	1	3	4	5	7	8	10	11	12
.78	6026	6039	6053	6067	6081	6095	6109	6124	6138	6152	1	3	4	6	7	8	10	11	13
.79	6166	6180	6194	6209	6223	6237	6252	6266	6281	6295	1	3	4	6	7	9	10	11	13
.80	6310	6324	6339	6353	6368	6383	6397	6412	6427	6442	1	3	4	6	7	9	10	12	13
.81	6457	6471	6486	6501	6516	6531	6546	6561	6577	6592	2	3	5	6	8	9	11	12	14
.82	6607	6622	6637	6653	6668	6683	6699	6714	6730	6745	2	3	5	6	8	9	11	12	14
.83	6761	6776	6792	6808	6823	6839	6855	6871	6887	6902	2	3	5	6	8	9	11	13	14
.84	6918	6934	6950	6966	6982	6998	7015	7031	7047	7063	2	3	5	6	8	10	11	13	15
.85	7079	7096	7112	7129	7145	7161	7178	7194	7211	7228	2	3	5	7	8	10	12	13	15
.86	7244	7261	7278	7295	7311	7328	7345	7362	7379	7396	2	3	5	7	8	10	12	13	15
.87	7413	7430	7447	7464	7482	7499	7516	7534	7551	7568	2	3	5	7	9	10	12	14	16
.88	7586	7603	7621	7638	7656	7674	7691	7709	7727	7745	2	4	5	7	9	11	12	14	16
.89	7762	7780	7798	7816	7834	7852	7870	7889	7907	7925	2	4	5	7	9	11	13	14	16
.90	7943	7962	7980	7998	8017	8035	8054	8072	8091	8110	2	4	6	7	9	11	13	15	17
.91	8128	8147	8166	8185	8204	8222	8241	8260	8279	8299	2	4	6	8	9	11	13	15	17
.92	8318	8337	8356	8375	8395	8414	8433	8453	8472	8492	2	4	6	8	10	12	14	15	17
.93	8511	8531	8551	8570	8590	8610	8630	8650	8670	8690	2	4	6	8	10	12	14	16	18
.94	8710	8730	8750	8770	8790	8810	8831	8851	8872	8892	2	4	6	8	10	12	14	16	18
.95	8913	8933	8954	8974	8995	9016	9036	9057	9078	9099	2	4	6	8	10	12	15	17	19
.96	9120	9141	9162	9183	9204	9226	9247	9268	9290	9311	2	4	6	8	11	13	15	17	19
.97	9333	9354	9376	9397	9419	9441	9462	9484	9506	9528	2	4	7	9	11	13	15	17	20
.98	9550	9572	9594	9616	9638	9661	9683	9705	9727	9750	2	4	7	9	11	13	16	18	20
.99	9772	9795	9817	9840	9863	9886	9908	9931	9954	9977	2	5	7	9	11	14	16	18	20
	0	1	2	3	4	5	6	7	8	9	1	2	3	4	5	6	7	8	9

TABLE 5   Exponential Functions

x	e^x	$\text{Log}_{10}(e^x)$	e^{-x}	x	e^x	$\text{Log}_{10}(e^x)$	e^{-x}
0.00	1.0000	0.00000	1.000000	**0.50**	1.6487	0.21715	0.606531
0.01	1.0101	.00434	0.990050	0.51	1.6653	.22149	.600496
0.02	1.0202	.00869	.980199	0.52	1.6820	.22583	.594521
0.03	1.0305	.01303	.970446	0.53	1.6989	.23018	.588605
0.04	1.0408	.01737	.960789	0.54	1.7160	.23452	.582748
0.05	1.0513	0.02171	0.951229	**0.55**	1.7333	0.23886	0.576950
0.06	1.0618	.02606	.941765	0.56	1.7507	.24320	.571209
0.07	1.0725	.03040	.932394	0.57	1.7683	.24755	.565525
0.08	1.0833	.03474	.923116	0.58	1.7860	.25189	.559898
0.09	1.0942	.03909	.913931	0.59	1.8040	25623	.554327
0.10	1.1052	0.04343	0.904837	**0.60**	1.8221	0.26058	0.548812
0.11	1.1163	.04777	.895834	0.61	1.8404	.26492	.543351
0.12	1.1275	.05212	.886920	0.62	1.8589	.26926	.537944
0.13	1.1388	.05646	.878095	0.63	1.8776	.27361	.532592
0.14	1.1503	.06080	.869358	0.64	1.8965	27795	.527292
0.15	1.1618	0.06514	0.860708	**0.65**	1.9155	0.28229	0.522046
0.16	1.1735	.06949	.852144	0.66	1.9348	.28663	.516851
0.17	1.1853	.07383	.843665	0.67	1.9542	.29098	.511709
0.18	1.1972	.07817	.835270	0.68	1.9739	.29532	.506617
0.19	1.2092	.08252	.826959	0.69	1.9937	.29966	.501576
0.20	1.2214	0.08686	0.818731	**0.70**	2.0138	0.30401	0.496585
0.21	1.2337	.09120	.810584	0.71	2.0340	.30835	.491644
0.22	1.2461	.09554	.802519	0.72	2.0544	.31269	.486752
0.23	1.2586	.09989	.794534	0.73	2.0751	.31703	.481909
0.24	1.2712	.10423	.786628	0.74	2.0959	.32138	.477114
0.25	1.2840	0.10857	0.778801	**0.75**	2.1170	0.32572	0.472367
0.26	1.2969	.11292	.771052	0.76	2.1383	.33006	.467666
0.27	1.3100	.11726	.763379	0.77	2.1598	.33441	.463013
0.28	1.3231	.12160	.755784	0.78	2.1815	.33875	.458406
0.29	1.3364	.12595	.748264	0.79	2.2034	.34309	.453845
0.30	1.3499	0.13029	0.740818	**0.80**	2.2255	0.34744	0.449329
0.31	1.3634	.13463	.733447	0.81	2.2479	.35178	.444858
0.32	1.3771	.13897	.726149	0.82	2.2705	.35612	.440432
0.33	1.3910	.14332	.718924	0.83	2.2933	.36046	.436049
0.34	1.4049	.14766	.711770	0.84	2.3164	.36481	.431711
0.35	1.4191	0.15200	0.704688	**0.85**	2.3396	0.36915	0.427415
0.36	1.4333	.15635	.697676	0.86	2.3632	.37349	.423162
0.37	1.4477	.16069	.690734	0.87	2.3869	.37784	.418952
0.38	1.4623	.16503	.683861	0.88	2.4109	.38218	.414783
0.39	1.4770	.16937	.677057	0.89	2.4351	.38652	.410656
0.40	1.4918	0.17372	0.670320	**0.90**	2.4596	0.39087	0.406570
0.41	1.5068	.17806	.663650	0.91	2.4843	.39521	.402524
0.42	1.5220	.18240	.657047	0.92	2.5093	.39955	.398519
0.43	1.5373	.18675	.650509	0.93	2.5345	.40389	.394554
0.44	1.5527	.19109	.644036	0.94	2.5600	.40824	.390628
0.45	1.5683	0.19543	0.637628	**0.95**	2.5857	0.41258	0.386741
0.46	1.5841	.19978	.631284	0.96	2.6117	.41692	.382893
0.47	1.6000	.20412	.625002	0.97	2.6379	.42127	.379083
0.48	1.6161	.20846	.618783	0.98	2.6645	.42561	.375311
0.49	1.6323	.21280	.612626	0.99	2.6912	.42995	.371577
0.50	1.6487	0.21715	0.606531	**1.00**	2.7183	0.43429	0.367879

TABLE 5 Exponential Functions (Continued)

x	e^x	$Log_{10}(e^x)$	e^{-x}	x	e^x	$Log_{10}(e^x)$	e^{-x}
1.00	2.7183	0.43429	0.367879	**1.50**	4.4817	0.65144	0.223130
1.01	2.7456	.43864	.364219	1.51	4.5267	.65578	.220910
1.02	2.7732	.44298	.360595	1.52	4.5722	.66013	.218712
1.03	2.8011	.44732	.357007	1.53	4.6182	.66447	.216536
1.04	2.8292	.45167	.353455	1.54	4.6646	.66881	.214381
1.05	2.8577	0.45601	0.349938	**1.55**	4.7115	0.67316	0.212248
1.06	2.8864	.46035	.346456	1.56	4.7588	.67750	.210136
1.07	2.9154	.46470	.343009	1.57	4.8066	.68184	.208045
1.08	2.9447	.46904	.339596	1.58	4.8550	.68619	.205975
1.09	2.9743	.47338	.336216	1.59	4.9037	.69053	.203926
1.10	3.0042	0.47772	0.332871	**1.60**	4.9530	0.69487	0.201897
1.11	3.0344	.48207	.329559	1.61	5.0028	.69921	.199888
1.12	3.0649	.48641	.326280	1.62	5.0531	.70356	.197899
1.13	3.0957	.49075	.323033	1.63	5.1039	.70790	.195930
1.14	3.1268	.49510	.319819	1.64	5.1552	.71224	.193980
1.15	3.1582	0.49944	0.316637	**1.65**	5.2070	0.71659	0.192050
1.16	3.1899	.50378	.313486	1.66	5.2593	.72093	.190139
1.17	3.2220	.50812	.310367	1.67	5.3122	.72527	.188247
1.18	3.2544	.51247	.307279	1.68	5.3656	.72961	.186374
1.19	3.2871	.51681	.304221	1.69	5.4195	.73396	.184520
1.20	3.3201	0.52115	0.301194	**1.70**	5.4739	0.73830	0.182684
1.21	3.3535	.52550	.298197	1.71	5.5290	.74264	.180866
1.22	3.3872	.52984	.295230	1.72	5.5845	.74699	.179066
1.23	3.4212	.53418	.292293	1.73	5.6407	.75133	.177284
1.24	3.4556	.53853	.289384	1.74	5.6973	.75567	.175520
1.25	3.4903	0.54287	0.286505	**1.75**	5.7546	0.76002	0.173774
1.26	3.5254	.54721	.283654	1.76	5.8124	.76436	.172045
1.27	3.5609	.55155	.280832	1.77	5.8709	.76870	.170333
1.28	3.5966	.55590	.278037	1.78	5.9299	.77304	.168638
1.29	3.6328	.56024	.275271	1.79	5.9895	.77739	.166960
1.30	3.6693	0.56458	0.272532	**1.80**	6.0496	0.78173	0.165299
1.31	3.7062	.56893	.269820	1.81	6.1104	.78607	.163654
1.32	3.7434	.57327	.267135	1.82	6.1719	.79042	.162026
1.33	3.7810	.57761	.264477	1.83	6.2339	.79476	.160414
1.34	3.8190	.58195	.261846	1.84	6.2965	.79910	.158817
1.35	3.8574	0.58630	0.259240	**1.85**	6.3598	0.80344	0.157237
1.36	3.8962	.59064	.256661	1.86	6.4237	.80779	.155673
1.37	3.9354	.59498	.254107	1.87	6.4883	.81213	.154124
1.38	3.9749	.59933	.251579	1.88	6.5535	.81647	.152590
1.39	4.0149	.60367	.249075	1.89	6.6194	.82082	.151072
1.40	4.0552	0.60801	0.246597	**1.90**	6.6859	0.82516	0.149569
1.41	4.0960	.61236	.244143	1.91	6.7531	.82950	.148080
1.42	4.1371	.61670	.241714	1.92	6.8210	.83385	.146607
1.43	4.1787	.62104	.239309	1.93	6.8895	.83819	.145148
1.44	4.2207	.62538	.236928	1.94	6.9588	.84253	.143704
1.45	4.2631	0.62973	0.234570	**1.95**	7.0287	0.84687	0.142274
1.46	4.3060	.63407	.232236	1.96	7.0993	.85122	.140858
1.47	4.3492	.63841	.229925	1.97	7.1707	.85556	.139457
1.48	4.3929	.64276	.227638	1.98	7.2427	.85990	.138069
1.49	4.4371	.64710	.225373	1.99	7.3155	.86425	.136695
1.50	4.4817	0.65144	0.223130	**2.00**	7.3891	0.86859	0.135335

TABLE 5 Exponential Functions (Continued)

x	e^x	$Log_{10}(e^x)$	e^{-x}	x	e^x	$Log_{10}(e^x)$	e^{-x}
2.00	7.3891	0.86859	0.135335	**2.50**	12.182	1.08574	0.082085
2.01	7.4633	.87293	.133989	2.51	12.305	1.09008	.081268
2.02	7.5383	.87727	.132655	2.52	12.429	1.09442	.080460
2.03	7.6141	.88162	.131336	2.53	12.554	1.09877	.079659
2.04	7.6906	.88596	.130029	2.54	12.680	1.10311	.078866
2.05	7.7679	0.89030	0.128735	**2.55**	12.807	1.10745	0.078082
2.06	7.8460	.89465	.127454	2.56	12.936	1.11179	.077305
2.07	7.9248	.89899	.126186	2.57	13.066	1.11614	.076536
2.08	8.0045	.90333	.124930	2.58	13.197	1.12048	.075774
2.09	8.0849	.90768	.123687	2.59	13.330	1.12482	.075020
2.10	8.1662	0.91202	0.122456	**2.60**	13.464	1.12917	0.074274
2.11	8.2482	.91636	.121238	2.61	13.599	1.13351	.073535
2.12	8.3311	.92070	.120032	2.62	13.736	1.13785	.072803
2.13	8.4149	.92505	.118837	2.63	13.874	1.14219	.072078
2.14	8.4994	.92939	.117655	2.64	14.013	1.14654	.071361
2.15	8.5849	0.93373	0.116484	**2.65**	14.154	1.15088	0.070651
2.16	8.6711	.93808	.115325	2.66	14.296	1.15522	.069948
2.17	8.7583	.94242	.114178	2.67	14.440	1.15957	.069252
2.18	8.8463	.94676	.113042	2.68	14.585	1.16391	.068563
2.19	8.9352	.95110	.111917	2.69	14.732	1.16825	.067881
2.20	9.0250	0.95545	0.110803	**2.70**	14.880	1.17260	0.067206
2.21	9.1157	.95979	.109701	2.71	15.029	1.17694	.066537
2.22	9.2073	.96413	.108609	2.72	15.180	1.18128	.065875
2.23	9.2999	.96848	.107528	2.73	15.333	1.18562	.065219
2.24	9.3933	.97282	.106459	2.74	15.487	1.18997	.064570
2.25	9.4877	0.97716	0.105399	**2.75**	15.643	1.19431	0.063928
2.26	9.5831	.98151	.104350	2.76	15.800	1.19865	.063292
2.27	9.6794	.98585	.103312	2.77	15.959	1.20300	.062662
2.28	9.7767	.99019	.102284	2.78	16.119	1.20734	.062039
2.29	9.8749	.99453	.101266	2.79	16.281	1.21168	.061421
2.30	9.9742	0.99888	0.100259	**2.80**	16.445	1.21602	0.060810
2.31	10.074	1.00322	.099261	2.81	16.610	1.22037	.060205
2.32	10.176	1.00756	.098274	2.82	16.777	1.22471	.059606
2.33	10.278	1.01191	.097296	2.83	16.945	1.22905	.059013
2.34	10.381	1.01625	.096328	2.84	17.116	1.23340	.058426
2.35	10.486	1.02059	0.095369	**2.85**	17.288	1.23774	0.057844
2.36	10.591	1.02493	.094420	2.86	17.462	1.24208	.057269
2.37	10.697	1.02928	.093481	2.87	17.637	1.24643	.056699
2.38	10.805	1.03362	.092551	2.88	17.814	1.25077	.056135
2.39	10.913	1.03796	.091630	2.89	17.993	1.25511	.055576
2.40	11.023	1.04231	0.090718	**2.90**	18.174	1.25945	0.055023
2.41	11.134	1.04665	.089815	2.91	18.357	1.26380	.054476
2.42	11.246	1.05099	.088922	2.92	18.541	1.26814	.053934
2.43	11.359	1.05534	.088037	2.93	18.728	1.27248	.053397
2.44	11.473	1.05968	.087161	2.94	18.916	1.27683	.052866
2.45	11.588	1.06402	0.086294	**2.95**	19.106	1.28117	0.052340
2.46	11.705	1.06836	.085435	2.96	19.298	1.28551	.051819
2.47	11.822	1.07271	.084585	2.97	19.492	1.28985	.051303
2.48	11.941	1.07705	.083743	2.98	19.688	1.29420	.050793
2.49	12.061	1.08139	.082910	2.99	19.886	1.29854	.050287
2.50	12.182	1.08574	0.082085	**3.00**	20.086	1.30288	0.049787

TABLE 5 Exponential Functions (Continued)

x	e^x	$\text{Log}_{10}(e^x)$	e^{-x}	x	e^x	$\text{Log}_{10}(e^x)$	e^{-x}
3.00	20.086	1.30288	0.049787	**3.50**	33.115	1.52003	0.030197
3.01	20.287	1.30723	.049292	3.51	33.448	1.52437	.029897
3.02	20.491	1.31157	.048801	3.52	33.784	1.52872	.029599
3.03	20.697	1.31591	.048316	3.53	34.124	1.53306	.029305
3.04	20.905	1.32026	.047835	3.54	34.467	1.53740	.029013
3.05	21.115	1.32460	0.047359	**3.55**	34.813	1.54175	0.028725
3.06	21.328	1.32894	.046888	3.56	35.163	1.54609	.028439
3.07	21.542	1.33328	.046421	3.57	35.517	1.55043	.028156
3.08	21.758	1.33763	.045959	3.58	35.874	1.55477	.027876
3.09	21.977	1.34197	.045502	3.59	36.234	1.55912	.027598
3.10	22.198	1.34631	0.045049	**3.60**	36.598	1.56346	0.027324
3.11	22.421	1.35066	.044601	3.61	36.966	1.56780	.027052
3.12	22.646	1.35500	.044157	3.62	37.338	1.57215	.026783
3.13	22.874	1.35934	.043718	3.63	37.713	1.57649	.026516
3.14	23.104	1.36368	.043283	3.64	38.092	1.58083	.026252
3.15	23.336	1.36803	0.042852	**3.65**	38.475	1.58517	0.025991
3.16	23.571	1.37237	.042426	3.66	38.861	1.58952	.025733
3.17	23.807	1.37671	.042004	3.67	39.252	1.59386	.025476
3.18	24.047	1.38106	.041586	3.68	39.646	1.59820	.025223
3.19	24.288	1.38540	.041172	3.69	40.045	1.60255	.024972
3.20	24.533	1.38974	0.040762	**3.70**	40.447	1.60689	0.024724
3.21	24.779	1.39409	.040357	3.71	40.854	1.61123	.024478
3.22	25.028	1.39843	.039955	3.72	41.264	1.61558	.024234
3.23	25.280	1.40277	.039557	3.73	41.679	1.61992	.023993
3.24	25.534	1.40711	.039164	3.74	42.098	1.62426	.023754
3.25	25.790	1.41146	0.038774	**3.75**	42.521	1.62860	0.023518
3.26	26.050	1.41580	.038388	3.76	42.948	1.63295	.023284
3.27	26.311	1.42014	.038006	3.77	43.380	1.63729	.023052
3.28	26.576	1.42449	.037628	3.78	43.816	1.64163	.022823
3.29	26.843	1.42883	.037254	3.79	44.256	1.64598	.022596
3.30	27.113	1.43317	0.036883	**3.80**	44.701	1.65032	0.022371
3.31	27.385	1.43751	.036516	3.81	45.150	1.65466	.022148
3.32	27.660	1.44186	.036153	3.82	45.604	1.65900	.021928
3.33	27.938	1.44620	.035793	3.83	46.063	1.66335	.021710
3.34	28.219	1.45054	.035437	3.84	46.525	1.66769	.021494
3.35	28.503	1.45489	0.035084	**3.85**	46.993	1.67203	0.021280
3.36	28.789	1.45923	.034735	3.86	47.465	1.67638	.021068
3.37	29.079	1.46357	.034390	3.87	47.942	1.68072	.020858
3.38	29.371	1.46792	.034047	3.88	48.424	1.68506	.020651
3.39	29.666	1.47226	.033709	3.89	48.911	1.68941	.020445
3.40	29.964	1.47660	0.033373	**3.90**	49.402	1.69375	0.020242
3.41	30.265	1.48094	.033041	3.91	49.899	1.69809	.020041
3.42	30.569	1.48529	.032712	3.92	50.400	1.70243	.019841
3.43	30.877	1.48963	.032387	3.93	50.907	1.70678	.019644
3.44	31.187	1.49397	.032065	3.94	51.419	1.71112	.019448
3.45	31.500	1.49832	0.031746	**3.95**	51.935	1.71546	0.019255
3.46	31.817	1.50266	.031430	3.96	52.457	1.71981	.019063
3.47	32.137	1.50700	.031117	3.97	52.985	1.72415	.018873
3.48	32.460	1.51134	.030807	3.98	53.517	1.72849	.018686
3.49	32.786	1.51569	.030501	3.99	54.055	1.73283	.018500
3.50	33.115	1.52003	0.030197	**4.00**	54.598	1.73718	0.018316

TABLE 5 Exponential Functions (Continued)

x	e^x	$\text{Log}_{10}(e^x)$	e^{-x}	x	e^x	$\text{Log}_{10}(e^x)$	e^{-x}
4.00	54.598	1.73718	0.018316	**4.50**	90.017	1.95433	0.011109
4.01	55.147	1.74152	.018133	4.51	90.922	1.95867	.010998
4.02	55.701	1.74586	.017953	4.52	91.836	1.96301	.010889
4.03	56.261	1.75021	.017774	4.53	92.759	1.96735	.010781
4.04	56.826	1.75455	.017597	4.54	93.691	1.97170	.010673
4.05	57.397	1.75889	0.017422	**4.55**	94.632	1.97604	0.010567
4.06	57.974	1.76324	.017249	4.56	95.583	1.98038	.010462
4.07	58.557	1.76758	.017077	4.57	96.544	1.98473	.010358
4.08	59.145	1.77192	.016907	4.58	97.514	1.98907	.010255
4.09	59.740	1.77626	.016739	4.59	98.494	1.99341	.010153
4.10	60.340	1.78061	0.016573	**4.60**	99.484	1.99775	0.010052
4.11	60.947	1.78495	.016408	4.61	100.48	2.00210	.009952
4.12	61.559	1.78929	.016245	4.62	101.49	2.00644	.009853
4.13	62.178	1.79364	.016083	4.63	102.51	2.01078	.009755
4.14	62.803	1.79798	.015923	4.64	103.54	2.01513	.009658
4.15	63.434	1.80232	0.015764	**4.65**	104.58	2.01947	0.009562
4.16	64.072	1.80667	.015608	4.66	105.64	2.02381	.009466
4.17	64.715	1.81101	.015452	4.67	106.70	2.02816	.009372
4.18	65.366	1.81535	.015299	4.68	107.77	2.03250	.009279
4.19	66.023	1.81969	.015146	4.69	108.85	2.03684	.009187
4.20	66.686	1.82404	0.014996	**4.70**	109.95	2.04118	0.009095
4.21	67.357	1.82838	.014846	4.71	111.05	2.04553	.009005
4.22	68.033	1.83272	.014699	4.72	112.17	2.04987	.008915
4.23	68.717	1.83707	.014552	4.73	113.30	2.05421	.008826
4.24	69.408	1.84141	.014408	4.74	114.43	2.05856	.008739
4.25	70.105	1.84575	0.014264	**4.75**	115.58	2.06290	0.008652
4.26	70.810	1.85009	.014122	4.76	116.75	2.06724	.008566
4.27	71.522	1.85444	.013982	4.77	117.92	2.07158	.008480
4.28	72.240	1.85878	.013843	4.78	119.10	2.07593	.008396
4.29	72.966	1.86312	.013705	4.79	120.30	2.08027	.008312
4.30	73.700	1.86747	0.013569	**4.80**	121.51	2.08461	0.008230
4.31	74.440	1.87181	.013434	4.81	122.73	2.08896	.008148
4.32	75.189	1.87615	.013300	4.82	123.97	2.09330	.008067
4.33	75.944	1.88050	.013168	4.83	125.21	2.09764	.007987
4.34	76.708	1.88484	.013037	4.84	126.47	2.10199	.007907
4.35	77.478	1.88918	0.012907	**4.85**	127.74	2.10633	0.007828
4.36	78.257	1.89352	.012778	4.86	129.02	2.11067	.007750
4.37	79.044	1.89787	.012651	4.87	130.32	2.11501	.007673
4.38	79.838	1.90221	.012525	4.88	131.63	2.11936	.007597
4.39	80.640	1.90655	.012401	4.89	132.95	2.12370	.007521
4.40	81.451	1.91090	0.012277	**4.90**	134.29	2.12804	0.007447
4.41	82.269	1.91524	.012155	4.91	135.64	2.13239	.007372
4.42	83.096	1.91958	.012034	4.92	137.00	2.13673	.007299
4.43	83.931	1.92392	.011914	4.93	138.38	2.14107	.007227
4.44	84.775	1.92827	.011796	4.94	139.77	2.14541	.007155
4.45	85.627	1.93261	0.011679	**4.95**	141.17	2.14976	0.007083
4.46	86.488	1.93695	.011562	4.96	142.59	2.15410	.007013
4.47	87.357	1.94130	.011447	4.97	144.03	2.15844	.006943
4.48	88.235	1.94564	.011333	4.98	145.47	2.16279	.006874
4.49	89.121	1.94998	.011221	4.99	146.94	2.16713	.006806
4.50	90.017	1.95433	0.011109	**5.00**	148.41	2.17147	0.006738

TABLE 5 Exponential Functions (Continued)

x	e^x	$\text{Log}_{10}(e^x)$	e^{-x}	x	e^x	$\text{Log}_{10}(e^x)$	e^{-x}
5.00	148.41	2.17147	0.006738	**5.50**	244.69	2.38862	0.0040868
5.01	149.90	2.17582	.006671	5.55	257.24	2.41033	.0038875
5.02	151.41	2.18016	.006605	5.60	270.43	2.43205	.0036979
5.03	152.93	2.18450	.006539	5.65	284.29	2.45376	.0035175
5.04	154.47	2.18884	.006474	5.70	298.87	2.47548	.0033460
5.05	156.02	2.19319	0.006409	**5.75**	314.19	2.49719	0.0031828
5.06	157.59	2.19753	.006346	5.80	330.30	2.51891	.0030276
5.07	159.17	2.20187	.006282	5.85	347.23	2.54062	.0028799
5.08	160.77	2.20622	.006220	5.90	365.04	2.56234	.0027394
5.09	162.39	2.21056	.006158	5.95	383.75	2.58405	.0026058
5.10	164.02	2.21490	0.006097	**6.00**	403.43	2.60577	0.0024788
5.11	165.67	2.21924	.006036	6.05	424.11	2.62748	.0023579
5.12	167.34	2.22359	.005976	6.10	445.86	2.64920	.0022429
5.13	169.02	2.22793	.005917	6.15	468.72	2.67091	.0021335
5.14	170.72	2.23227	.005858	6.20	492.75	2.69263	.0020294
5.15	172.43	2.23662	0.005799	**6.25**	518.01	2.71434	0.0019305
5.16	174.16	2.24096	.005742	6.30	544.57	2.73606	.0018363
5.17	175.91	2.24530	.005685	6.35	572.49	2.75777	.0017467
5.18	177.68	2.24965	.005628	6.40	601.85	2.77948	.0016616
5.19	179.47	2.25399	.005572	6.45	632.70	2.80120	.0015805
5.20	181.27	2.25833	0.005517	**6.50**	665.14	2.82291	0.0015034
5.21	183.09	2.26267	.005462	6.55	699.24	2.84463	.0014301
5.22	184.93	2.26702	.005407	6.60	735.10	2.86634	.0013604
5.23	186.79	2.27136	.005354	6.65	772.78	2.88806	.0012940
5.24	188.67	2.27570	.005300	6.70	812.41	2.90977	.0012309
5.25	190.57	2.28005	0.005248	**6.75**	854.06	2.93149	0.0011709
5.26	192.48	2.28439	.005195	6.80	897.85	2.95320	.0011138
5.27	194.42	2.28873	.005144	6.85	943.88	2.97492	.0010595
5.28	196.37	2.29307	.005092	6.90	992.27	2.99663	.0010078
5.29	198.34	2.29742	.005042	6.95	1043.1	3.01835	.0009586
5.30	200.34	2.30176	0.004992	**7.00**	1096.6	3.04006	0.0009119
5.31	202.35	2.30610	.004942	7.05	1152.9	3.06178	.0008674
5.32	204.38	2.31045	.004893	7.10	1212.0	3.08349	.0008251
5.33	206.44	2.31479	.004844	7.15	1274.1	3.10521	.0007849
5.34	208.51	2.31913	.004796	7.20	1339.4	3.12692	.0007466
5.35	210.61	2.32348	0.004748	**7.25**	1408.1	3.14863	0.0007102
5.36	212.72	2.32782	.004701	7.30	1480.3	3.17035	.0006755
5.37	214.86	2.33216	.004654	7.35	1556.2	3.19206	.0006426
5.38	217.02	2.33650	.004608	7.40	1636.0	3.21378	.0006113
5.39	219.20	2.34085	.004562	7.45	1719.9	3.23549	.0005814
5.40	221.41	2.34519	0.004517	**7.50**	1808.0	3.25721	0.0005531
5.41	223.63	2.34953	.004472	7.55	1900.7	3.27892	.0005261
5.42	225.88	2.35388	.004427	7.60	1998.2	3.30064	.0005005
5.43	228.15	2.35822	.004383	7.65	2100.6	3.32235	.0004760
5.44	230.44	2.36256	.004339	7.70	2208.3	3.34407	.0004528
5.45	232.76	2.36690	0.004296	**7.75**	2321.6	3.36578	0.0004307
5.46	235.10	2.37125	.004254	7.80	2440.6	3.38750	.0004097
5.47	237.46	2.37559	.004211	7.85	2565.7	3.40921	.0003898
5.48	239.85	2.37993	.004169	7.90	2697.3	3.43093	.0003707
5.49	242.26	2.38428	.004128	7.95	2835.6	3.45264	.0003527
5.50	244.69	2.38862	0.004087	**8.00**	2981.0	3.47436	0.0003355

TABLE 5   Exponential Functions (Continued)

x	e^x	$\text{Log}_{10}(e^x)$	e^{-x}
8.00	2981.0	3.47436	0.0003355
8.05	3133.8	3.49607	.0003191
8.10	3294.5	3.51779	.0003035
8.15	3463.4	3.53950	.0002887
8.20	3641.0	3.56121	.0002747
8.25	3827.6	3.58293	0.0002613
8.30	4023.9	3.60464	.0002485
8.35	4230.2	3.62636	.0002364
8.40	4447.1	3.64807	.0002249
8.45	4675.1	3.66979	.0002139
8.50	4914.8	3.69150	0.0002035
8.55	5166.8	3.71322	.0001935
8.60	5431.7	3.73493	.0001841
8.65	5710.1	3.75665	.0001751
8.70	6002.9	3.77836	.0001666
8.75	6310.7	3.80008	0.0001585
8.80	6634.2	3.82179	.0001507
8.85	6974.4	3.84351	.0001434
8.90	7332.0	3.86522	.0001364
8.95	7707.9	3.88694	.0001297
9.00	8103.1	3.90865	0.0001234
9.05	8518.5	3.93037	.0001174
9.10	8955.3	3.95208	.0001117
9.15	9414.4	3.97379	.0001062
9.20	9897.1	3.99551	.0001010
9.25	10405	4.01722	0.0000961
9.30	10938	4.03894	.0000914
9.35	11499	4.06065	.0000870
9.40	12088	4.08237	.0000827
9.45	12708	4.10408	.0000787
9.50	13360	4.12580	0.0000749
9.55	14045	4.14751	.0000712
9.60	14765	4.16923	.0000677
9.65	15522	4.19094	.0000644
9.70	16318	4.21266	.0000613
9.75	17154	4.23437	0.0000583
9.80	18034	4.25609	.0000555
9.85	18958	4.27780	.0000527
9.90	19930	4.29952	.0000502
9.95	20952	4.32123	0.0000477
10.00	22026	4.34294	0.0000454

Answers to
Selected Exercises

CHAPTER 1

Section 2, page 4

27. 2, 4   **29.** $2 \le a \le 8$ **31.** $-2 \le a \le 2$ **33.** all real a

Section 3, page 8

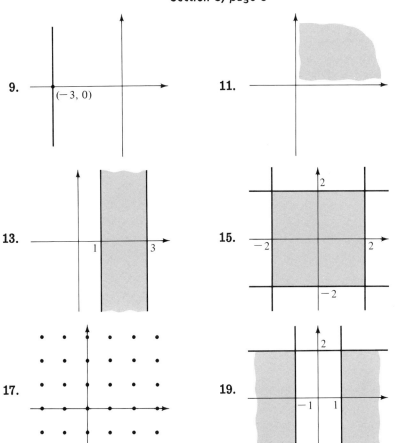

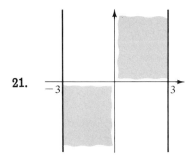

21.

23. $(\pm 1, \pm 1)$ **25.** $(9, 0), (0, 12)$ or $(12, 0), (0, 9)$

Section 4, page 13

1. $5, 9, 6, \dfrac{2}{x} + 5 = \dfrac{2 + 5x}{x}, 2x - 1$

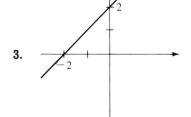

3.   **5.**

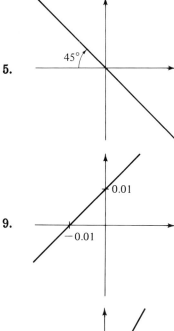

7.   **9.**

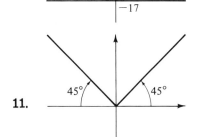

11.   **13.**

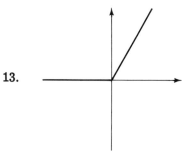

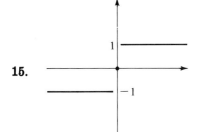

15.   **17.** all real x

19. all real x **21.** $x \neq \frac{3}{2}$ **23.** $x \neq \frac{5}{3}$ **25.** $x \geq 6$
27. $|x| \leq \frac{2}{3}$ **29.** $x \geq \frac{3}{2}$ **31.** $|x| \leq \frac{1}{2}$
33. all x such that $x \leq 1$ or $x \geq 4$

Section 5, page 15

1. $3x - 1, \ -6x - 2$ **3.** $x^2 - 2x + 1, \ -2x^3 + x^2$
5. No; their domains have no point in common.
7. $[f \circ g](x) = 3x - 5, \ [g \circ f](x) = 3x - 1$
9. $2x^2 + 4x + 2, \ -2x^2 - 1$ **11.** $-4x, \ -4x$ **13.** $9, 3$
15. $g(x)$ **17.** x **19.** $x + 1, 3$, etc.
21. No; $f(x)$ is defined only for $x \geq \frac{5}{2}$, but $g(x) \leq 1$.
23. Yes; $f[\frac{1}{2}(x_0 + x_1)] = \frac{1}{2}a(x_0 + x_1) + b$ and
        $\frac{1}{2}[f(x_0) + f(x_1)] = \frac{1}{2}[(ax_0 + b) + (ax_1 + b)]$
                              $= \frac{1}{2}a(x_0 + x_1) + b.$
25. $f[\frac{1}{2}(x_0 + x_1)] = 2/(x_0 + x_1) = 2f(x_0 + x_1).$

Section 6, page 22

1.
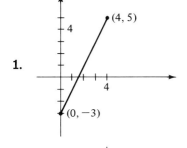

3.
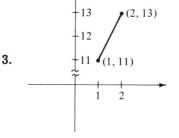

5.
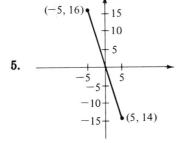

7.
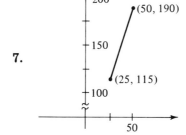

9.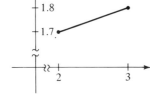

(different scales)

11.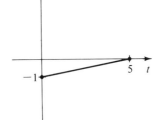

13.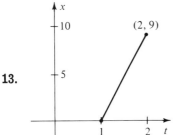

15.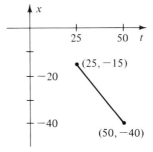

17. $\frac{4}{3}$ **19.** 0   **21.** 1   **23.** $\frac{3}{2}$ **25.** 1   **27.** $y = x + 1$, 1
29. $y = 3$, 3   **31.** $y = \frac{1}{2}x - 3$ **33.** $y = 2x$ **35.** $y = \frac{4}{3}x + \frac{4}{3}$
37. $y = x + \frac{1}{2}$ **39.** $y = -5x + 3.5$ **41.** 3, -7 **43.** -1, 7
45. x- 2, y- 3   **47.** x- $\frac{1}{2}$, y- $\frac{1}{3}$

Section 7, page 29

1.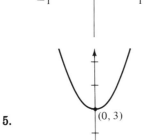

3.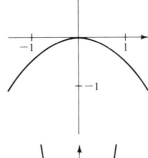

5.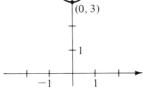

7.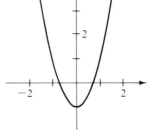

9.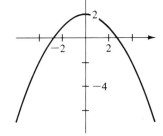

11.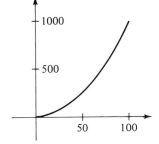

13.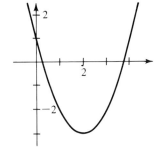

15.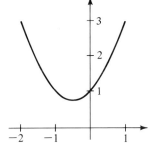

17.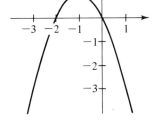

19.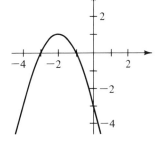

21.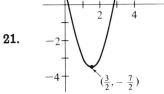

23.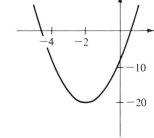

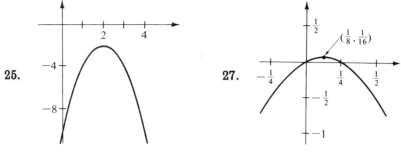

25.

27.

29. $(3/4, -8/9)$ **31.** $(-\frac{1}{2}, -\frac{17}{4})$ **33.** $(\frac{1}{2}, -\frac{7}{4})$ **35.** $(\frac{1}{4}, \frac{1}{8})$
37. When $x = 0$, then $y = a \cdot 0^2 + b \cdot 0 = 0$. **39.** $b = 0$

CHAPTER 2

Section 1, page 37

1. $(0, 3)$ **3.** $(2, -2)$ **5.** $(2, 12)$ **7.** $(3, 0)$ **9.** $(0, 0)$
11. $(1, 1)$ **13.** $(10, 4)$ **15.** $(18, 10)$ **17.** $(7, 3)$
19. $(-4, 4)$ **21.** $(1, -10)$ **23.** $a = -2, b = 5$
25. $\mathbf{u} = (2, 4), \mathbf{v} = (-2, 4)$

Section 2, page 42

1. $\mathbf{x} = (t, t); x = t, y = t; y = x$ **3.** $\mathbf{x} = (1, t); x = 1, y = t; x = 1$
5. $\mathbf{x} = (2 + 2t, 3 - t); x = 2 + 2t, y = 3 - t; x + 2y = 8$
7. $\mathbf{x} = (3 + 4t, 1 + 3t); x = 3 + 4t, y = 1 + 3t; 3x - 4y = 5$
9. $y = 0$ **11.** $x + y = 3$ **13.** $x = 1$ **15.** $3x - 2y = -7$
17. $y = 0$ **19.** $x - y = 1$ **21.** $2x + y = 5$
23. $3x - y = -4$ **25.** same **27.** same **29.** $(1, 2)$
31. $(1, 1)$ **33.** $(2, 3)$ **35.** $(-\frac{7}{5}, \frac{1}{5})$
37. Write $\mathbf{m} = \frac{1}{3}(\mathbf{u} + \mathbf{v} + \mathbf{w}) = \frac{1}{3}\mathbf{u} + \frac{2}{3}[\frac{1}{2}(\mathbf{v} + \mathbf{w})]$.
Hence $\mathbf{m}$ lies on the segment joining $\mathbf{u}$ to the midpoint of $\mathbf{vw}$, etc.
39. $7x - 4y = 0; 2x + y = 10; 16x - 7y = 10$ **41.** $y = -\frac{2}{3}x + c$.
43. the line parallel to L and passing through $\mathbf{x}_0 + \mathbf{c}$, where $\mathbf{x}_0$ is any point on L

Section 3, page 50

1. 6 **3.** 0 **5.** 3 **7.** 24
9. $\|\mathbf{v} + \mathbf{w}\|^2 = (\mathbf{v} + \mathbf{w}) \cdot (\mathbf{v} + \mathbf{w}) = \mathbf{v} \cdot \mathbf{v} + \mathbf{v} \cdot \mathbf{w} + \mathbf{w} \cdot \mathbf{v} + \mathbf{w} \cdot \mathbf{w}$
$= \|\mathbf{v}\|^2 + 2\mathbf{v} \cdot \mathbf{w} + \|\mathbf{w}\|^2$
11. $\|\mathbf{v} + \mathbf{w}\|^2 - \|\mathbf{v} - \mathbf{w}\|^2 = (\|\mathbf{v}\|^2 + 2\mathbf{v} \cdot \mathbf{w} + \|\mathbf{w}\|^2)$
$- (\|\mathbf{v}\|^2 - 2\mathbf{v} \cdot \mathbf{w} + \|\mathbf{w}\|^2) = 4\mathbf{v} \cdot \mathbf{w}$.
13. $\frac{1}{2}\pi$ **15.** $\cos \theta = 0.6, \ \theta \approx 0.93$ **17.** $\cos \theta = 0.6, \ \theta \approx 0.93$

19. If one vertex is **0**, the others are **u**, **v**, **u** + **v**, where $\|\mathbf{u}\| = \|\mathbf{v}\|$. The diagonals are **u** + **v** and a segment parallel to **u** − **v**. But $(\mathbf{u} + \mathbf{v}) \cdot (\mathbf{u} - \mathbf{v}) = \|\mathbf{u}\|^2 - \|\mathbf{v}\|^2 = 0$.

21. $(c, 9c)$ **23.** $(x, y) = (3 - 2t, 2 + 4t)$.

Section 4, page 58

1. $\frac{3}{10}\sqrt{10}\,x - \frac{1}{10}\sqrt{10}\,y = 0$ **3.** $\frac{1}{2}\sqrt{2}\,x - \frac{1}{2}\sqrt{2}\,y = \sqrt{2}$

5. $\frac{2}{5}\sqrt{5}\,x + \frac{1}{5}\sqrt{5}\,y = -\frac{1}{5}\sqrt{5}$ **7.** $\frac{1}{2}\sqrt{2}\,x + \frac{1}{2}\sqrt{2}\,y = \frac{3}{2}\sqrt{2}$

9. $\frac{3}{5}x - \frac{4}{5}y = 0$ **11.** $\frac{12}{13}x + \frac{5}{13}y = \frac{1}{13}$ **13.** $\frac{1}{5}\sqrt{5}$ **15.** $\frac{6}{5}$

17. $|b|/(a^2 + 1)^{1/2}$ **19.** 2 **21.** $\frac{1}{2}\sqrt{2}$ **23.** $\frac{23}{5}$ **25.** $\frac{4}{5}\sqrt{5}$

27. $\frac{1}{2}\pi$ **29.** $\cos\theta = \frac{4}{5}$, $\theta \approx 0.64$

31. $\cos\theta = \frac{1}{4}(\sqrt{2} + \sqrt{6})$, $\theta = \frac{1}{12}\pi \approx 0.26$

33. $y = -2x + 2$ **35.** $5x - 3y = 14$

37. Let **u** and **v** be points on the circle with center **0**. Then $\|\mathbf{u}\| = \|\mathbf{v}\|$ and the midpoint of **uv** is $\frac{1}{2}(\mathbf{u} + \mathbf{v})$. But $\frac{1}{2}(\mathbf{u} + \mathbf{v}) \cdot (\mathbf{v} - \mathbf{u}) = 0$.

39. Consider the line $\mathbf{x} \cdot \mathbf{m} - p = \mathbf{x} \cdot \mathbf{n} - q$. Its normal form is $\mathbf{x} \cdot \mathbf{u} = r$, where $\mathbf{u} = (\mathbf{m} - \mathbf{n})/\|\mathbf{m} - \mathbf{n}\|$ and $r = (p - q)/\|\mathbf{m} - \mathbf{n}\|$. It passes through the intersection $\mathbf{x}_0$ of given lines because $\mathbf{x}_0 \cdot \mathbf{m} - p = \mathbf{x}_0 \cdot \mathbf{n} - q = 0$. But $\mathbf{u} \cdot \mathbf{m} = -\mathbf{u} \cdot \mathbf{n} = (1 - \mathbf{m} \cdot \mathbf{n})/\|\mathbf{m} - \mathbf{n}\|$, so the angles between **u** and **m** and between **u** and −**n** are equal.

41. Let **u** and **w** be unit vectors in the directions from $\mathbf{v}_1$ to $\mathbf{v}_2$ and from $\mathbf{v}_1$ to $\mathbf{v}_3$. Then $\mathbf{u} = (\mathbf{v}_2 - \mathbf{v}_1)/a_3$ and $\mathbf{w} = (\mathbf{v}_3 - \mathbf{v}_1)/a_2$. Thus $\mathbf{p} - \mathbf{v}_1 = [(a_1\mathbf{v}_1 + a_2\mathbf{v}_2 + a_3\mathbf{v}_3) - (a_1 + a_2 + a_3)\mathbf{v}_1]/(a_1 + a_2 + a_3) = c(\mathbf{u} + \mathbf{w})$, where $c = a_2 a_3/(a_1 + a_2 + a_3)$. Hence $\mathbf{p} - \mathbf{v}_1$ bisects the angle at vertex $\mathbf{v}_1$, etc.

43. Let L be $\mathbf{x} \cdot \mathbf{m} = p$ and N be $\mathbf{x} \cdot \mathbf{n} = q$. Then $a = p/\mathbf{u} \cdot \mathbf{m}$ and $b = q/\mathbf{u} \cdot \mathbf{n}$ so $2/x = (\mathbf{u} \cdot \mathbf{m}/p) + (\mathbf{u} \cdot \mathbf{n}/q) = \mathbf{u} \cdot (p^{-1}\mathbf{m} + q^{-1}\mathbf{n})$. Therefore $\mathbf{x} \cdot (p^{-1}\mathbf{m} + q^{-1}\mathbf{n}) = 2$, a line unless $\mathbf{m} = \pm\mathbf{n}$, etc.

45. $\mathbf{p} \cdot \mathbf{u} = (\mathbf{x} + b\mathbf{v}) \cdot \mathbf{u} = b\mathbf{u} \cdot \mathbf{v}$ and $\mathbf{p} \cdot \mathbf{v} = (\mathbf{y} + a\mathbf{u}) \cdot \mathbf{v} = a\mathbf{u} \cdot \mathbf{v}$, hence $\mathbf{p} \cdot (\mathbf{y} - \mathbf{x}) = \mathbf{p} \cdot (b\mathbf{v} - a\mathbf{u}) = ab\mathbf{u} \cdot \mathbf{v} - ab\mathbf{u} \cdot \mathbf{v} = 0$. Therefore the line along **p** is the third altitude.

47. Let L_1 and L_2 be $\mathbf{x} \cdot \mathbf{n}_1 = 0$ and $\mathbf{x} \cdot \mathbf{n}_2 = 0$ and let M be $\mathbf{v} = \mathbf{x}_0 + t\mathbf{u}$. Then $\mathbf{p}_1 = \mathbf{v} - (\mathbf{v} \cdot \mathbf{n}_1)\mathbf{n}_1$ satisfies $\mathbf{p}_1 \cdot \mathbf{n}_1 = 0$ and $(\mathbf{p}_1 - \mathbf{v}) \cdot \mathbf{p}_1 = 0$, so it is the foot of the perpendicular. Likewise $\mathbf{p}_2 = \mathbf{v} - (\mathbf{v} \cdot \mathbf{n}_2)\mathbf{n}_2$, so $\mathbf{x} = \mathbf{v} - \frac{1}{2}(\mathbf{v} \cdot \mathbf{n}_1)\mathbf{n}_1 - \frac{1}{2}(\mathbf{v} \cdot \mathbf{n}_2)\mathbf{n}_2$. Set $\mathbf{v} = \mathbf{x}_0 + t\mathbf{u}$. Then $\mathbf{x} = \mathbf{k} + t\mathbf{w}$, where $\mathbf{k} = \mathbf{x}_0 - \frac{1}{2}(\mathbf{x}_0 \cdot \mathbf{n}_1)\mathbf{n}_1 - \frac{1}{2}(\mathbf{x}_0 \cdot \mathbf{n}_2)\mathbf{n}_2$ and $\mathbf{w} = \mathbf{u} - \frac{1}{2}(\mathbf{u} \cdot \mathbf{n}_1)\mathbf{n}_1 - \frac{1}{2}(\mathbf{u} \cdot \mathbf{n}_2)\mathbf{n}_2$ are constant vectors.

CHAPTER 3

Section 1, page 62

1. $(6, 4)$ **3.** $(5, -2)$ **5.** $(0, -8)$ **7.** $(-4, 5)$

9. $(-11, -5)$

11. $(\bar{x}_1 - \bar{x}_2)^2 + (\bar{y}_1 - \bar{y}_2)^2 = [(x_1 - h) - (x_2 - h)]^2$
$$+ [(y_1 - k) - (y_2 - k)]^2 = (x_1 - x_2)^2 + (y_1 - y_2)^2$$
13. $\bar{x} = x - h, \bar{y} = y - k$, where $3h - 2k = 1$
15. $\bar{x} = x + 1, \bar{y} = y$ **17.** $\bar{x} = x - \frac{1}{6}\pi, \bar{y} = y + 1$
19. $\bar{\mathbf{x}} \cdot \mathbf{n} = p - \mathbf{h} \cdot \mathbf{n}$

Section 2, page 67

1. $(x - 1)^2 + (y - 3)^2 = 36$ **3.** $(x + 4)^2 + (y - 3)^2 = 25$
5. $(x - 1)^2 + (y - 5)^2 = 26$ **7.** $(x + 5)^2 + (y - 2)^2 = 25$
9. $(x - \frac{3}{2})^2 + (y - 2)^2 = \frac{13}{4}$ **11.** $(x - a)^2 + (y \pm 3)^2 = 9$
13. $x^2 + y^2 - ax - by = 0$ **15.** circle, center $(2, 2)$, radius $2\sqrt{2}$
17. circle, center $(-1, -3)$, radius 6
19. circle, center $(\frac{1}{2}, -1)$, radius $\frac{1}{2}\sqrt{5}$
21. circle, center $(\frac{3}{4}, \frac{5}{4})$, radius $\frac{1}{4}\sqrt{26}$ **23.** $\frac{1}{2}(-1 \pm \sqrt{17}, 1 \pm \sqrt{17})$
25. $(1, 2)$, point of tangency   **27.** none
29. $\frac{1}{5}(6 \pm 4\sqrt{31}, 7 \mp 2\sqrt{31})$ **31.** $\frac{1}{8}(-21, \pm 3\sqrt{15})$ **33.** none

Section 3, page 72

1. $x = -1$ **3.** $y = x - \sqrt{2}$ **5.** $y = -\sqrt{3}x + 2$
7. $x = 0, y = \frac{3}{4}x$ **9.** $y - 1 = m(x + 5), m = \frac{2}{3}, -\frac{3}{2}$
11. distance between centers $=$ sum of radii: $2\sqrt{5} = \frac{3}{2}\sqrt{5} + \frac{1}{2}\sqrt{5}$.
13. $x_0 x + y_0 y = r^2$ is a line through (x_0, y_0) and perpendicular to the radius through (x_0, y_0).
15. $(\mathbf{x} - \mathbf{a}) \cdot (\mathbf{x} - \mathbf{b}) = \mathbf{x} \cdot \mathbf{x} - (\mathbf{a} + \mathbf{b}) \cdot \mathbf{x} + \mathbf{a} \cdot \mathbf{b} = c^2$. Now "complete the square" and rewrite as $\|\mathbf{x} - \frac{1}{2}(\mathbf{a} + \mathbf{b})\|^2 = c^2 + \frac{1}{4}\|\mathbf{a} - \mathbf{b}\|^2$.
17. quarter circle, radius 5 ft   **19.** concentric circle, radius $\sqrt{10}$

Section 4, page 81

1. $(0, 1)$ **3.** $(\frac{1}{2}\sqrt{3}, -\frac{1}{2})$ **5.** $(-\sqrt{2}, -\sqrt{2})$ **7.** $\{\sqrt{2}, \frac{1}{4}\pi\}$
9. $\{\sqrt{2}, \frac{3}{4}\pi\}$ **11.** $\{2, -\frac{1}{6}\pi\}$ **13.** $\theta = \frac{1}{4}\pi$
15. $r(\cos\theta + \sin\theta) = 1$ **17.** $r = -2a\cos\theta$ **19.** $r = 2\sin\theta$

21. 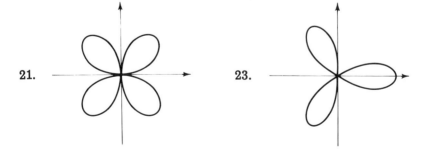   **23.**

25.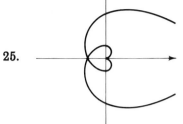

27.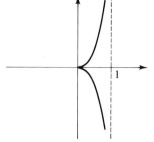

29.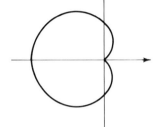

31.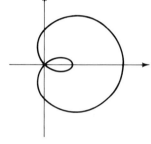

33.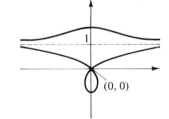

35. The formula follows from the law of cosines.

Section 5, page 86

1.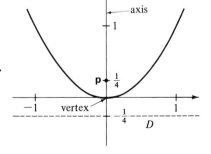

3.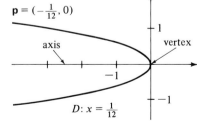

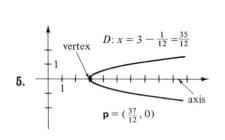

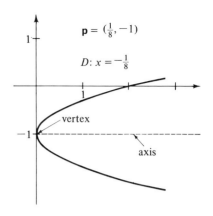

5.

7.

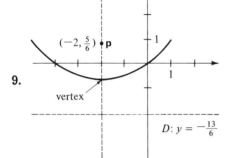

9.

11. $y = 3x^2$ **13.** $x - 1 = -(y - 2)^2$
15. $y + 3 = \frac{1}{16}(x - 2)^2$ **17.** $(-3, 9)$

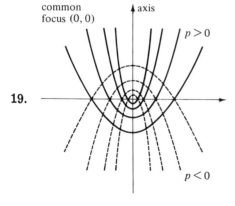

19.

21. Eliminate y: $x^2 = 4ay = 2x_0x - 4ay_0 = 2x_0x - x_0^2$.
Hence $(x - x_0)^2 = 0$, $x = x_0$, $y = x_0^2/4a$.

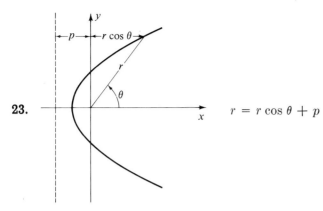

23. $r = r \cos \theta + p$

25.   Eliminate t: $(v_0{}^2 \cos^2 \alpha)y = (v_0{}^2 \sin \alpha \cos \alpha)x - 16x^2$, the equation of a parabola.

Section 6, page 91

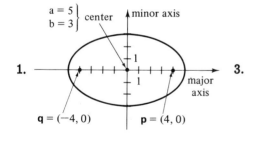

1.

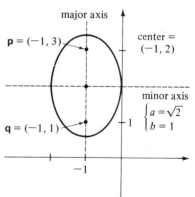

3.

5.   Write as $\dfrac{(x - 3)^2}{(\frac{1}{2}\sqrt{2})^2} + \dfrac{(y - 2)^2}{1^2} = 1$.

   Center $= (3, 2)$, $a = 1$, $b = \frac{1}{2}\sqrt{2}$, major axis $x = 3$, minor axis $y = 2$, **p, q** $= (3, 2 \pm \frac{1}{2}\sqrt{2})$

7. $\frac{1}{81}(x - 1)^2 + \frac{1}{4}(y - 4)^2 = 1$ **9.** $\frac{1}{25}(x - 5)^2 + \frac{1}{16}y^2 = 1$

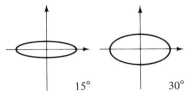

15°   30°

45°   60°

11. $\frac{1}{16}(x-1)^2 + \frac{1}{12}y^2 = 1$ **13.**

15. Describe the ellipse by $\mathbf{x} = (a\cos\theta, b\sin\theta)$. Then $x^2 + y^2 = (a^2 - b^2)$ $\cos^2\theta + b^2 \le (a^2 - b^2) + b^2 = a^2$, with "$=$" only if $\cos\theta = \pm 1$.

17. $e \approx 0.206$

19. An ellipse of half the size, with major diameter $\mathbf{0p}$, where $\mathbf{0}$ is the center of the given ellipse.

21.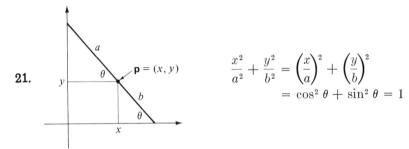

$$\frac{x^2}{a^2} + \frac{y^2}{b^2} = \left(\frac{x}{a}\right)^2 + \left(\frac{y}{b}\right)^2$$
$$= \cos^2\theta + \sin^2\theta = 1$$

23. $0 \le (c \pm x)^2 = c^2 + x^2 \pm 2cx < a^2 + x^2 \pm 2cx$
$$\le 2a^2 \pm 2cx = 2(a^2 \pm cx).$$

25. $a^2 + cx = \pm a\lambda$, but $a^2 + cx > 0$ and $a\lambda > 0$, hence $a^2 + cx = +a\lambda$. Likewise $a^2 - cx = +a\mu$.

Section 7, page 96

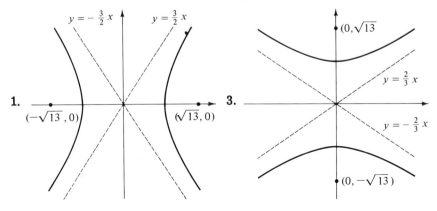

1.   **3.**

5.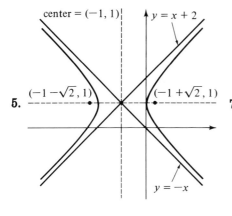

7.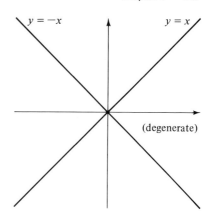

9.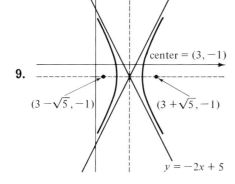

11. $-\frac{1}{9}x^2 + \frac{1}{16}y^2 = 1$

13. $\frac{1}{4}x^2 - \frac{1}{16}y^2 = 1$ **15.** $\frac{1}{3}(x-1)^2 - \frac{1}{3}y^2 = 1$

17.   Complete squares; the asymptotes are $y - \frac{1}{2}b = \pm(x - \frac{1}{2}a)$, two perpendicular lines.

19.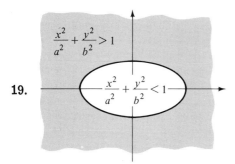

21.   Let the circles be $\|\mathbf{x} - \mathbf{p}\| = r$ and $\|\mathbf{x} - \mathbf{q}\| = s$, with $\|\mathbf{p} - \mathbf{q}\| \geq r + s$. The desired locus is $\|\mathbf{x} - \mathbf{p}\| - r = \|\mathbf{x} - \mathbf{q}\| - s$, that is, $\|\mathbf{x} - \mathbf{p}\| - \|\mathbf{x} - \mathbf{q}\| = r - s$.

23. $\|\mathbf{x}\| = r$, $\|\mathbf{x} - (2c, 0)\| = d$, and $d - r = \pm 2a$. By the law of cosines, $d^2 = r^2 + 4c^2 - 4rc \cos \theta$, $(d + r)(d - r) = d^2 - r^2 = 4c^2 - 4rc \cos \theta$. Replace $d - r$ by $\pm 2a$ and $d + r$ by $2(r \pm a)$; the result is $\pm ar + a^2 = c^2 - rc \cos \theta$, etc.

25. Set $[(x + c)^2 + y^2]^{1/2} + [(x - c)^2 + y^2]^{1/2} = 2k$. Multiply by $[\cdot \ \cdot \ \cdot]^{1/2} - [\cdot \ \cdot \ \cdot]^{1/2} = \pm 2a$: $[(x + c)^2 + y^2] - [(x - c)^2 + y^2] = \pm 4ak$, $4cx = \pm 4ak$, $k = \pm cx/a$.

27. $x^2 = a^2(1 + y^2/b^2) \geq a^2$, and $(a^2 + cx)(a^2 - cx) = a^4 - c^2x^2 \leq a^4 - c^2a^2 = a^2(a^2 - c^2) = -a^2b^2 < 0$.

29. Set $a^2 + cx = \pm a\lambda$ and $a^2 - cx = \epsilon a\mu$, where $\epsilon = +1$ or -1. Then $(a^2 + cx)(a^2 - cx) < 0$ by Ex. 27, hence $\pm \epsilon a^2 \lambda \mu < 0$. Therefore $\epsilon = \mp 1$.

Section 8, page 105

1. $\bar{x} = x \cos \alpha + y \sin \alpha$, $\bar{y} = -x \sin \alpha + y \cos \alpha$; $(x, y) \to (\bar{x}, \bar{y})$ by a rotation through $-\alpha$.

3. $x_1 x_2 + y_1 y_2 = \bar{x}_1 \bar{y}_1 + \bar{x}_2 \bar{y}_2$; this means inner product is unchanged by a rotation.

5. The polar angle of the point with respect to the rotated axes is $\theta - \alpha$.

7. $\alpha = \frac{3}{8}\pi$; $-\frac{1}{2}(\sqrt{2} - 1)\bar{x}^2 + \frac{1}{2}(1 + \sqrt{2})\bar{y}^2 = 1$

9. $\alpha = \frac{3}{8}\pi$; $\frac{1}{2}(1 + \sqrt{2})\bar{x}^2 - \frac{1}{2}(1 - \sqrt{2})\bar{y}^2 = 1$ **11.** $\alpha = \frac{1}{4}\pi$; ellipse

13. $\tan 2\alpha = \frac{1}{2}$; hyperbola   **15.** $\alpha = \frac{3}{8}\pi$; ellipse

17. $\alpha = \frac{1}{4}\pi$; parabola   **19.** $\tan 2\alpha = 6$; hyperbola

21. Add the formulas for $\bar{a}$ and $\bar{c}$ given in the text.

Section 9, page 106

CIRCLES AND LOCI

1. After simplification, the equation of the radical axis is $\mathbf{x} \cdot (\mathbf{b} - \mathbf{a}) = r^2 - s^2 + \|\mathbf{b}\|^2 - \|\mathbf{a}\|^2$, a line perpendicular to $\mathbf{b} - \mathbf{a}$.

3. The line passes through the point of tangency $\mathbf{x}_0$ because $\|\mathbf{x}_0 - \mathbf{a}\| = r$ and $\|\mathbf{x}_0 - \mathbf{b}\| = s$. It is also perpendicular to the line joining the centers (Ex. 1), hence it is the common tangent line.

5. $\|\mathbf{a} - \mathbf{b}\|^2 = r^2 + s^2$. For, let $\mathbf{x}_0$ be a point of intersection. Then $(\mathbf{x}_0 - \mathbf{a}) \cdot (\mathbf{x}_0 - \mathbf{b}) = 0$. Now compute $\|\mathbf{a} - \mathbf{b}\|^2 = \|(\mathbf{x}_0 - \mathbf{b}) - (\mathbf{x}_0 - \mathbf{a})\|^2 = $ etc.

7. $\mathbf{z} \cdot \mathbf{n} = p \neq 0$, and $\mathbf{z} = \mathbf{x}/\|\mathbf{x}\|^2$, hence $\mathbf{x} \cdot \mathbf{n} = p\|\mathbf{x}\|^2$, a circle.

9. Let $\mathbf{m} = \frac{1}{2}(\mathbf{x}_1 + \mathbf{x}_2)$ where $\mathbf{x}_i$ are the points of contact. Then $(\mathbf{x}_i - \mathbf{p}) \cdot \mathbf{x}_i = 0$ and $\|\mathbf{x}_i\|^2 = 1$, hence $\mathbf{x}_i \cdot \mathbf{p} = 1$ so $\mathbf{m} \cdot \mathbf{p} = 1$. But $\mathbf{m} = c\mathbf{p}$, so $c\mathbf{p} \cdot \mathbf{p} = 1$, $\mathbf{m} = \mathbf{p}/\|\mathbf{p}\|^2$.

11. Take C_i: $\|\mathbf{x} - \mathbf{c}_i\| = r_i^2$. The locus is $\|\mathbf{x} - \mathbf{c}_1\|^2 - a^2\|\mathbf{x} - \mathbf{c}_2\|^2 = r_1^2 - a^2 r_2^2$, a circle if $a \neq 1$, a line if $a = 1$.

PARABOLAS

1. Take C: $\|\mathbf{x}\| = r$ and L: $x = a$. The locus is $y^2 = (a^2 + r^2) - 2ax$, a parabola if $a \neq 0$, a pair of horizontal lines if $a = 0$.

3. Take P: $y = ax^2$. Then $y_1{}^2 = ax_1{}^2$, $y_2{}^2 = ax_2{}^2$, $x_1x_2 + y_1y_2 = 0$. Set $x_1 = t$. Then $\mathbf{x}_1 = (t, at^2)$, $\mathbf{x}_2 = (-1/a^2t, 1/a^3t^2)$. Set $\mathbf{x} = \frac{1}{2}\mathbf{x}_1 + \frac{1}{2}\mathbf{x}_2$, the midpoint. Then $\mathbf{x} = (x, y) = \frac{1}{2}(t - 1/a^2t, at^2 + 1/a^3t^2)$, so $2ax^2 = y - 1/a$, a parabola.

5. The line $y = mx + 1$ meets $4y = x^2$ where $x^2 - 4mx - 4 = 0$. The sum of the roots is $x_1 + x_2 = 4m$. Also $y_1 + y_2 = \frac{1}{4}(x_1{}^2 + x_2{}^2) = (mx_1 + 1) + (mx_2 + 1) = m(x_1 + x_2) + 2 = 4m^2 + 2$. The midpoint is $\mathbf{x} = (2m, 2m^2 + 1)$, that is, $x^2 = 2y - 2$.

7. By definition of a parabola, $\|\mathbf{x} - \mathbf{p}\| = y + p$, where the focus is $\mathbf{p} = (0, p)$. Therefore, the radius is $\frac{1}{2}(y + p)$. But the center is $\frac{1}{2}(\mathbf{x} + \mathbf{p}) = \frac{1}{2}(x, y + p)$, at distance $\frac{1}{2}(y + p)$ from the x-axis.

9. Take P: $y = ax^2$ and L: $y = mx$. Then $y = mx + b$ meets P where $ax^2 - mx - b = 0$. The sum of the roots is m/a, so the midpoint is $\mathbf{x} = (m/2a, y)$, that is, $x = m/2a$, a vertical line.

ELLIPSES

1. $x^2 + y^2 = 1$. Each point on the circle is represented, for if $-1 \leq y \leq 1$, then $yt^2 - 2t + y = 0$ has *real* roots, etc.

3. $\mathbf{x}_2 = c(-y_1, x_1)$, where $c^2(y_1{}^2/a^2 + x_1{}^2/b^2) = 1$. Hence

$$
\begin{aligned}
\|\mathbf{x}_1\|^{-2} + \|\mathbf{x}_2\|^{-2} &= \|\mathbf{x}_1\|^{-2}(1 + c^{-2}) \\
&= \|\mathbf{x}_1\|^{-2}(x_1{}^2a^{-2} + y_1{}^2b^{-2} + y_1{}^2a^{-2} + x_1{}^2b^{-2}) \\
&= \|\mathbf{x}_1\|^{-2}(a^{-2} + b^{-2})\|\mathbf{x}_1\|^2 = a^{-2} + b^{-2}.
\end{aligned}
$$

5. All foci are $(\pm c, 0)$. Suppose the ellipses for $\lambda_1 \neq \lambda_2$ meet at (x, y). Then $x^2/(\lambda_1 + c^2) + y^2/\lambda_1 = x^2/(\lambda_2 + c^2) + y^2/\lambda_2$, $x^2(\lambda_1 + c^2)^{-1}(\lambda_2 + c^2)^{-1} = -y^2/\lambda_1\lambda_2$, impossible. As $\lambda \to \infty$, the ellipses become larger and larger and more nearly circular ($e \to 0$). As $\lambda \to 0+$, the ellipses become very skinny and look more and more like the segment $y = 0$, $|x| \leq c$.

HYPERBOLAS

1. Start with $2xy = c^2$. Rotate by $-\frac{1}{4}\pi$ with $x = \frac{1}{2}\sqrt{2}\,(\bar{x} - \bar{y})$, $y = \frac{1}{2}\sqrt{2}\,(\bar{x} + \bar{y})$, obtaining $\bar{x}^2 - \bar{y}^2 = c^2$. This is a rectangular hyperbola with foci $(\pm c\sqrt{2}, 0)$. Rotate back; the foci go to $(\pm c, \pm c)$.

3. Take L and M to be the x- and y- axes, and take $\mathbf{p} = (x_0, y_0)$. A variable line through $\mathbf{p}$ is $y - y_0 = m(x - x_0)$. Then $(x, y) = \frac{1}{2}(\mathbf{a} + \mathbf{b}) = \frac{1}{2}(x_0 - (y_0/m), y_0 - mx_0)$. Eliminate m: $(x - \frac{1}{2}x_0)(y - \frac{1}{2}y_0) = \frac{1}{4}x_0y_0$, a hyperbola with center $\frac{1}{2}(x_0, y_0)$ and asymptotes parallel to the axes.

5. Use polar coordinates: $r(1 + e \cos \theta) = ep$. If $\mathbf{x}$ corresponds to θ, then $\mathbf{y}$ corresponds to $\theta + \pi$, so $\|\mathbf{x}\|^{-1} + \|\mathbf{y}\|^{-1} = (ep)^{-1}[(1 + e \cos \theta) + (1 - e \cos \theta)] = 2/ep$.

7. As $\lambda \to 0+$, the hyperbolas flatten towards the x-axis and the vertices approach $(\pm c, 0)$. The curves approach two infinite intervals: $y = 0$, $x \leq -c$ and $y = 0$, $x \geq c$. As $\lambda \to c^2-$, the hyperbolas broaden towards the y-axis.

9. Replacing θ by $\theta + \alpha$ allows us to suppose $\alpha = 0$. Set $t = \tan \theta$, $c = \tan \beta$. Then $(x, y) = (at, b(t + c)/(1 - ct))$ by the addition formula for tan. Eliminate t: $cxy + bx - ay = -abc$, $(x - a/c)(y + b/c) = -ab(c^2 + 1)/c^2 = -ab \csc^2 \beta$. The locus is a rectangular hyperbola with center $(a/c, -b/c)$ and asymptotes parallel to the coordinate axes.

CHAPTER 4

Section 2, page 113

1. $m = \frac{1}{4}$ 3. $m = -\frac{3}{2}$ 5. $m = 2$ 7. $m = \frac{1}{3}$ 9. $y = x$

11. $y = \frac{3}{2}x - 3$ 13. $y = x + 3$ 15. $y = 5x - 17$

17. $m = 1/(5280 \cdot 12) = 1/63360$ 19. like the line $y = 1$

Section 4, page 119

1. $2x$ 3. -4 5. 1 7. 3 9. 8 11. $6, 14, 22$

13. 13 15. 6 17. -32 19. $-12, 24, 2$

21. $-3, -3.5, -3.9, -3.999$ 23. $(3, 9)$ only

Section 5, page 122

1. $3x^2$ 3. 0 5. $0, 27, 27$ 7. 108 9. $48, 3a^2$

11. $7, 4.75, 3.31, 3.003001$ 13. $19, 15.25, 12.61, 12.006001$

15. $(-2, -8), (2, 8)$ 17. The line has slope -1; the curve has slope $3x^2 \geq 0$.   19. $0 < x < \frac{2}{3}$

Section 6, page 124

1. $y' = -1/x^2$ 3. $-1, -1, -1/a^2, -1/a^2$ 5. $-1/a^2, -a^2$

7. $-1/b^2$ 9. at $x = \pm\sqrt{2}$ 11. no; $-1/x^2 < 0$, but $3x^2 \geq 0$

13. $-1/110$

Section 7, page 126

1. $y = 4x - 4$ **3.** $y = -x - 2$ **5.** $y = -2x - 1$

7. $y = -\frac{1}{9}x - \frac{2}{3}$ **9.** $y = 10x - 25$ **11.** $y = \pm 8x - 16$

13. $y = 20x - 100$, $(0, -100)$, $(5, 0)$

15. $y = -81x - 18$, $(0, -18)$, $(-\frac{2}{9}, 0)$; $y = -81x + 18$, $(0, 18)$, $(\frac{2}{9}, 0)$

17. 2 **19.** $(0, -9)$ **21.** $y = -9x \pm 6$

Section 8, page 132

1. $3x^2 - 1/x^2$ **3.** $2x + 4$ **5.** $-1/(x + 1)^2$ **7.** $2(t - 8)$

9. $6x$ **11.** $3x^2 - 4x$ **13.** $6x^2 - 10x + 2$ **15.** $-2/(2x - 1)^2$

17. $72(36x - 2)$ **19.** $4\pi r + 2\pi$ **21.** $-(2x + 1)/x^2(x + 1)^2$

23. $(2x - 1)/x^2(x - 1)^2$ **25.** $-(x^2 + 4x + 2)/x^2(x + 1)^2$

27. $y = 9x - 15$ **29.** $y = -12x + 19$ **31.** 17.60 ohms/$^\circ$K

Section 10, page 139

1. $10x, 10$ **3.** $21x^2 + 8x - 3, 42x + 8$ **5.** $3P^2, 6P$

7. $3(x - 2)^2, 6(x - 2)$ **9.** $18x, 18$ **11.** $5, 17, 6, 6$ **13.** 8

15. $-3/(3t - 1)^2$ **17.** 23π **19.** 0 **21.** $0, \frac{2}{3}$

23. $\frac{1}{2}(1 - \sqrt[3]{2})$ **25.** -1 **27.** The tangents are $y = 2ax - a^2$ and $y = 2(a + 1)x - (a + 1)^2$; they intersect at $x = a + \frac{1}{2}$, $y = a^2 + a$. Eliminate a to find the relation $y = x^2 - \frac{1}{4}$.   **29.** $(-1, 5)$

CHAPTER 5

Section 2, page 146

1. concave up

3. concave down: $x < -1$; inflection point: $(-1, 0)$; concave up: $x > -1$

5. concave down: $x < 2$; inflection point: $(2, 4)$; concave up: $x > 2$

7. concave up: $x < 0$; inflection point: $(0, -5)$; concave down: $x > 0$

Section 4, page 152

1. 2 **3.** 4 **5.** $\frac{7}{4}$ **7.** 28 ft   **9.** 12

11. 4 hr after work starts   **13.** $r = \sqrt[3]{26/\pi}$ in., $h = 2r$ in.   **15.** 2

17. $32/(8 + 3\pi)$ in.

Section 5, page 159

1. $r = h = \sqrt[3]{V/\pi}$ **3.** $\frac{1}{2}a \times \frac{1}{2}b$

5. radius $= 1/16\pi$ mi $= 330/\pi$ ft, straight edge $= 1/16$ mi $= 330$ ft

7. $(1/2, \sqrt{2}/2)$ **9.** 1 unit   **11.** $2725.00

13. $100\sqrt{24} \approx 490$ mph

CHAPTER 6

Section 1, page 164

1. $1/(x + 1)^2$ **3.** $10/(2x + 5)^2$ **5.** $-\sin 2x$

Section 2, page 170

1. $f(x) = \frac{1}{2}x + c$ **3.** $y = -\frac{1}{2}x^2 + c$ **5.** $f(x) = \frac{1}{3}x^3 + c$

7. $y = 1/x + c$

Section 3, page 173

1. $ax + c$ **3.** $-\frac{1}{2}x^2 + c$ **5.** $\frac{4}{3}x^3 + \frac{1}{2}x^2 + c$

7. $4/x + c$ **9.** $\frac{1}{2}x^2 + x + c$ **11.** $x^3 + x^2 + x + c$

13. $\frac{2}{3}x^3 + 7/x + c$ **15.** $\frac{1}{3}(x + 4)^3 - 1/x + c$

17. $y = \frac{1}{2}x^2 - 5x + 13/2$ **19.** $y = x^3 - 2x^2 - 1/x + 19/2$

Section 4, page 176

1. 900, 914.4, 916 ft/sec

3. 10,500 ft, -80 ft/sec, $-80\sqrt{105} \approx -820$ ft/sec

5. $\frac{3}{4}$ sec, 16 ft/sec up or down (speed, not velocity)

7. (a) increasing for $t < 2$ or $t > 4$, decreasing for $2 < t < 4$; (b) increasing for $t > 3$, decreasing for $t < 3$; (c) 20 ft forward from 0 to 2 sec, 4 ft backwards from 2 to 4 sec, and 20 ft forward from 4 to 6 sec; total 44 ft

Section 5, page 180

1. $y = -8x^2 + 12$ **3.** $y = -16t^2 + 64t$

5. $y = \frac{1}{3}t^3 - \frac{1}{2}t^2 + 0.25t + 1.75$ **7.** 40 ft   **9.** 6 ft/sec^2

11. 26,500 ft   **13.** $300 + 3600 + 257\frac{1}{7} = 4157\frac{1}{7}$ ft

CHAPTER 7

Section 1, page 183

1. $\pi/3,\ 5\pi/6,\ -4\pi/3,\ 13\pi/6,\ -5\pi/2,\ 5\pi$
3. $\pi/4,\ -\pi,\ 3\pi/2,\ 7\pi/2,\ -3\pi/4,\ 11\pi/4$
5. $90°,\ -120°,\ 300°,\ 540°,\ -480°,\ 3000°$
7. $45°,\ -315°,\ 225°,\ -630°,\ 2340°,\ 720°$
13. $(\sqrt{2}/2,\ \sqrt{2}/2),\ (-\sqrt{2}/2,\ -\sqrt{2}/2),\ (-\sqrt{2}/2,\ \sqrt{2}/2)$
15. $(-1,0),\ (-1/2,\ -\sqrt{3}/2),\ (\sqrt{3}/2,\ 1/2)$ 17. $\pi/4,\ 3\pi/4$
19. $5\pi/6,\ 7\pi/6$ 21. $3\pi/2$ 23. $\pi/4,\ 5\pi/4$

Section 3, page 191

1. $\pi\cos\pi t$ 3. $-ab\sin ax$ 5. $\frac{1}{2}\pi\cos(\frac{1}{2}\pi\theta)$ 7. $1-\sin t$
9. $\dot{x}=\cos(t+t_0)$ 11. $2t-\sin t$ 13. $8x+12\cos 4x$
15. $-1/t^2+\sin t$ 17. $y=\sin t-1$ 19. $y=\sin x+1$
25. $\pi/2<t<3\pi/2$ 27. $(\frac{1}{3}\pi+2\pi k,\ \sqrt{3}/2)$
and $(-\frac{1}{3}\pi+2\pi k,\ -\sqrt{3}/2)$, where $k=0,\ \pm1,\ \pm2,\ \cdots$

Section 4, page 196

7. starts at $s=0$ and oscillates with period (time of complete cycle) 2π between $s=-2$ and $s=2$; also $v(t)=2\cos t$ and $a(t)=-2\sin t$
9. starts at $s=3$ and oscillates with period 2 between $s=-3$ and $s=3$; also $v(t)=-3\pi\sin\pi t$ and $a(t)=-3\pi^2\cos\pi t$
11. starts at $y=7$ and oscillates with period $2\pi/\omega=4\pi/\sqrt{g}$ sec between $y=3$ and 7; also $v(t)=-2\omega\sin\omega t$ and $a(t)=-2\omega^2\cos\omega t=-\frac{1}{2}g\cos\omega t$
13. The function is even.

Section 5, page 197

1. 0.472 3. -9.522 5. 0.123 7. 3.443
9. before: 0.735; after: 0.734 11. $0.855,\ 0.854$ 13. $1.061,\ 1.062$
15. $-0.006,\ +0.001$ 17. before: 20; after: 16 19. $16,\ 15$
21. $1,\ 2$

CHAPTER 8

Section 1, page 201

1. $1, 2, \frac{1}{4}, 8$ **3.** $27, \frac{1}{9}, 81, 3$ **5.** $3, \frac{1}{3}, 9, 1/81$ **7.** $37.83, 16.12$
9. $3.758, 0.08486$ **11.** $1, 125, \frac{1}{8}$ **13.** $4, 1/49, 4$ **17.** $x \geq 1$
19. $-\frac{3}{2} < x < 12$

Section 3, page 211

1. only if $c = 0$ **5.** $3e^{3x}$ **7.** $2e^{2x+1}$ **9.** $\frac{1}{2}(e^x - e^{-x})$
11. $3e^{3t} - 8e^{2t}$ **13.** $12e^{4x+1}$ **15.** $e^x + 2e^{-2x}$
17. $(\log_e 10)10^x$ **19.** $(\log_e 5)5^{x-1}$ **21.** $(4\log_e 10)10^{4x-1}$
23. $(2\log_e 10)(10^{2x} - 10^{-2x})$ **35.** $y = \frac{1}{2}e^{2x} + c$ **37.** $y = e^x + 1$
43. $y'' = y$, hence $y^{(58)} = y$

Section 4, page 214

1. $M = M_0 e^{-\lambda t}$, where $\lambda = \log 2/\log e^{3.64} \approx 0.1904$; about 5.77 days
3. $\log 2/\log e \approx 69.315\%$
5. $M = (3 \times 10^6)3^{t/2}$, $t = \log 4/\log 3 \approx 1.26$ hr **7.** $30(\frac{5}{6})^5 \approx 12.1$ in.
9. Let $a^{138.3} = 2$ and $b^{3.64} = 2$. Then $t = [\log(3/2)]/[\log(b/a)] \approx 2.2$ days.

CHAPTER 9

Section 1, page 217

1. $6x^2 - 2x$ **3.** $6e^{3x}$ **5.** $-3/(x + 2)^2$ **7.** $-5e^{-x} - 4\sin 4x$
9. $7e^{x+4} + 5e^{5x}$ **11.** 0

Section 2, page 221

1. $(x^2 + 2x)e^x$ **3.** $(-3x + 7)(x - 1)^3 e^{-3x}$
5. $\cos^2 x - \sin^2 x = \cos 2x$ **7.** $6(\sin 2x + 1)^2 \cos 2x$
9. $e^x(\sin x + x\sin x + x\cos x)$ **11.** $2^n n x^{n-1}$
13. $x\sin^2 x (2\sin x + 3x\cos x)$ **15.** $\frac{1}{2}e^{x/2}$ **17.** $-\frac{3}{2}x^{-5/2}$
19. $25(5x - 1)(3x + 1)$ **21.** $3(3x - 2)^2(x - 2)(15x - 22)$
23. $(x\cos x - \sin x)/x^2$

Section 3, page 225

1. $(1 - x)/e^x$ 3. $-x(x + 2)/(x^2 + x + 1)^2$ 5. $-12x/(x^2 + 1)^7$
7. $-2/(\sin x - \cos x)^2$ 9. $-(\cos 2x)^3(8x \sin 2x + 3 \cos 2x)/x^4$
11. $-1/[(x + 1)(x - 1)^3]^{1/2}$
13. $[(\sin x)^{m-1}/(\cos x)^{n+1}](m \cos^2 x + n \sin^2 x)$
15. $-(\sin x + x \cos x)/x^2 \sin^2 x$

Section 4, page 227

1. $3x^2 \cos x^3$ 3. $2e^{\sin 2x} \cos 2x$ 5. $5(x^3 + x - 3)^4 (3x^2 + 1)$
7. $(2ax + b)e^{ax^2+bx+c}$ 9. $e^x e^{e^x}$
11. $2[(x^3 + 2x)^5 + x^2][5(x^3 + 2x)^4 (3x^2 + 2) + 2x]$ 13. $2x(e^{x^2} - e^{-x^2})$

Section 5, page 228

1. 12   3. $4x^3$ 5. 4   7. $\frac{1}{3}$ 9. -1 11. $1/2\sqrt{2}$
13. $\sqrt[4]{2}/8$

Section 7, page 233

1. $-4/(2x - 1)^2$ 3. $-e^{1/x}/x^2$ 5. $e^{ax}(a \cos bx - b \sin bx)$
7. $(1 - x^2)^{-3/2}$ 9. $(\cos\sqrt{x/6})/(2\sqrt{6x})$
11. $(3x^3 - 2a^2x)/(x^2 - a^2)^{1/2}$ 13. $3k \sin^2 kx \cos kx$
15. $\sin(1/x) - [\cos(1/x)]/x$ 17. $-16/(8x - x^2)^{3/2}$
19. $(2x \cos 2x - 3 \sin 2x)/x^4$ 21. $(2x + 3)e^{-3/x}$
23. $-4 \sin x \cos x = -2 \sin 2x$ (note $y = \cos^2 x - \sin^2 x = \cos 2x$)
25. $3x^2(1 + e^{2x} - 2xe^{2x})/(e^{2x} + 1)^4$
27. $e^{-ax}(\sin bx - ax \sin bx + bx \cos bx)$
29. $-3 \sin u \cos u (1 + \cos^2 u)$, where $u = \frac{1}{2}x$ 31. $4/(e^x + e^{-x})^2$

CHAPTER 10

Section 1, page 238

1. 24π ft/sec   3. 4 ft/sec   5. 192 cm^3/sec   7. 8 ft^2/min
9. $640/\sqrt{65}$ mph   11. $\frac{3}{2}$ ft/sec   13. $10\sqrt{15/\pi}$ ft
15. $+10\pi$ ft^2/sec   17. 80 ft/min (don't use calculus)

Section 2, page 245

1. $1, -1$ **3.** $1, 1/e$ **5.** $1, -\frac{1}{3}$ **7.** $4/3, 2\sqrt{3}/3$
9. $4\sqrt{3}/9, 0$ **11.** $5/27$, no min   **13.** $4\pi, 0$

Section 3, page 253

1. $160 \times 53\frac{1}{3}$ **3.** width $= \sqrt[3]{10}$, height $= \frac{1}{2}\sqrt[3]{10}$
5. $\frac{1}{2}a, \frac{1}{2}b$ **7.** $x/2a + y/2b = 1$ **9.** 2048π in³
11. $y = -4x/\sqrt{3} + \frac{16}{3}$ **13.** 500 **15.** 6 ft from short post
17. Row to the point $\sqrt{3}$ miles upshore from the nearest point, then walk.
19. $3r$

CHAPTER 11

Section 3, page 263

1. 2   **3.** $45/2$ **5.** 9   **7.** 72   **9.** 2   **11.** 5   **13.** $e - 1$
15. $e^4 - 5$ **17.** $\frac{2}{3}$ **19.** 1

Section 4, page 268

1. $3/2$ **3.** 0   **5.** $\frac{1}{2}$ **7.** 2   **9.** $20/3$ **11.** $\frac{7}{2} - e^{-1}$
13. $\frac{1}{6}(b - a)^3$ **15.** $3/2$ **17.** $29/6$

Section 5, page 275

1. 1   **3.** $\frac{1}{3}$ **5.** 0   **7.** $16/3$ **9.** approx: $21/64$, exact: $\frac{1}{3}$
11. approx. ≈ 0.64395, exact: $2/\pi \approx 0.63662$ **13.** \$39
15. 0.326 in.   **17.** 1, 0   **19.** $e - 1, \frac{1}{2}(e + 1)$ **21.** $11/2, 11/2$

CHAPTER 12

Section 2, page 282

1. 36   **3.** 4   **5.** $\frac{36}{25}$ **7.** $2\sqrt{2}$ **9.** $2(e^2 + 1)$ **11.** $\frac{3}{2}$
13. $\frac{3}{2}$

Section 3, page 286

1. 6   **3.** $6/\pi$ **5.** $14/3$ **7.** 48   **9.** $\frac{1}{2}$ **11.** $8/\pi$
13. distance $= e - 2 + e^{-1}$, displacement $= e - 2 - e^{-1}$
15. distance $= 4\sqrt{2}$, displacement $= 0$

Section 4, page 288

1. 84 dyne-cm   **3.** 2500 ft-lb   **5.** 1, 4, 16 ft-lb

7. $(\frac{12}{43})(10^6)(5280)$, $(\frac{12}{23})(10^6)(5280)$ ft-lb

CHAPTER 13

Section 1, page 293

5. $\sqrt{26}$ **7.** $\sqrt{11}$ **9.** $5, \sqrt{13}, 2\sqrt{5}$ **13.** no

15. right angle at $(-1, 4, -7)$, area $6\sqrt{41}$ **17.** no   **19.** yes

Section 2, page 296

13. $y = -3$ **15.** $x + y - 2z = 0$

Section 3, page 299

11. $(x - 1)^2 + (y - 2)^2 + (z - 3)^2 = 16$

13. $(x - 2)^2 + (z - 4)^2 = 9$ **15.** $(x - 1)^2 + (z - 1)^2 = 2(y - 1)^2$

Section 6, page 310

1. 117π **3.** $4\pi/5$ **5.** 72π **7.** 102π **9.** $\frac{1}{4}\pi(e^8 + 4e^4 + 3)$

11. $\frac{1}{3}\pi h(R_0^2 + R_0 R_1 + R_1^2)$ **13.** $\frac{1}{3}\pi(a - h)^2(2a + h)$ **15.** $\pi h^3/6$

17. 8

Section 7, page 316

1. $\frac{1}{3}\pi$ **3.** 3π **5.** $176\pi/3$ **7.** does not apply   **9.** $15\pi/2$

11. $\frac{1}{3}(112)(\pi + 8)$ **13.** $(2/a)(e^{2ab} - 1)$

CHAPTER 14

Section 1, page 319

1. $x = \frac{1}{3}(y + 7)$ **3.** $x = \frac{1}{4}(y + 1)$

5. $x = (4y + 7)/(-y + 2), y \neq 2$ **7.** $x = (3y - 2)/(-y + 1), y \neq 1$

9. $x = -1/y, y \neq 0$ **11.** $x = \frac{1}{2}y^2 + 4, y > 0$

19. $f[g(x)] = x$; but $f[g(x)] = g(x)^3 + g(x)$

21. $f[f^{-1}(x)] = x$, so the answer is x

Section 2, page 326

1. $\frac{3}{5}x^{-4/5}$ **3.** $\frac{1}{4}(10^{1/4})x^{-3/4}$ **5.** $\frac{7}{6}(x^2 - x + 4)^{1/6}(2x - 1)$

7. $e^x(e^x - 2)\,(e^x + 1)^{1/2}(e^x - 1)^{-3/2}$ **9.** $e^2\sqrt{x}/\sqrt{x}$

11. $(p/8)\,(\sin x)^{(p/8)-1}(\cos x)$ **13.** $(1/7a)\,(x/a)^{-6/7}$ **15.** $-\frac{1}{5}x^{-6/5}$

Section 3, page 329

1. $a + 2$ **3.** $1/x$ **5.** $\frac{1}{2}$ **7.** 1 **9.** 2.99573

11. 0.67853 **13.** $2.48, -1.51, 5.52, 0.90$ **15.** 6

Section 4, page 333

1. $1/x$ **3.** $4/x$ **5.** $-1/x$ **7.** $\cot x$ **9.** 1

11. $1/x \ln x$ **13.** $[2/(x^2 + 1)] - [1/x^2]\ln(x^2 + 1)$

15. $2(\ln x)/x$ **17.** $[x(\ln x)\,(\ln \ln x)]^{-1}$ **19.** $-[x(\ln x)^2]^{-1}$

25. $-1/x^2 < 0$; concave downwards.

Section 5, page 335

1. $(3x^2/2)\,(x^3 + 2)^{-1/2}$ **3.** $6\left(\dfrac{x^2 + 4}{x + 7}\right)^6\left(\dfrac{2x}{x^2 + 4} - \dfrac{1}{x + 7}\right)$

5. $\frac{2}{3}(2x + 3)^{-2/3}(-6x^2 - 9x + 1)e^{-x^2}$ **7.** $x^{x-2}(x - 1 + x \ln x)$

9. $x^{1/x}(1 - \ln x)/x^2$ **11.** $(\ln 3)3^{\ln x}/x = (\ln 3)x^{\ln 3 - 1}$

13. $10^x \ln 10$ **15.** $\dfrac{e^x(x^3 - 1)}{\sqrt{2x + 1}}\left[1 + \dfrac{3x^2}{x^3 - 1} - \dfrac{1}{2x + 1}\right]$

Section 6, page 336

1. $\ln 5$ **3.** $\ln \frac{7}{4}$ **5.** $\frac{1}{2}\ln 7$ **7.** $\ln 2$ **9.** $\frac{1}{3}\ln 4$

11. $\ln(b/a) = \ln(a^{-1}/b^{-1})$ **13.** $\frac{1}{4}\ln 13$ **15.** $\frac{1}{4}\ln \frac{5}{3}$ **17.** $\frac{52}{3} + \ln 5$

19. $\displaystyle\int_a^{2a} dx/x = \ln 2a - \ln a = \ln 2$, for any $a > 0$

Section 7, page 340

1. ∞ **3.** 0 **5.** ∞ **7.** 0 **9.** 0 **13.** $e^a, a = 10^{10}$

15. In common logs, the inequality is $(\log x)^2/x < M^2 \cdot 10^{-10}$.

For $x > 10^{13}$, $(\log x)^2/x < 13^2 \times 10^{-13} = 1.69 \times 10^{-11} < M^2 \cdot 10^{-10}$.

Hence $x > 10^{13} \approx e^{29.9}$ works. **17.** $\max = e^{1/e} \approx 1.445$

Section 8, page 342

1. 0 **3.** $e - 1$ **5.** Set $x = u^3$; therefore, $u \to \infty$ as $x \to \infty$. Then the function is $e^u/u^{30} \to \infty$. **9.** no; try $x = 10^{10}$

11. (smallest) $x^3, e^x, 10^x, e^{10x}, e^{x^2}, e^{e^x}$ (largest)

CHAPTER 15

Section 1, page 347

1. π **3.** 1   **5.** 2   **7.** π **9.** π **11.** 2π **13.** odd

15. even   **17.** odd   **19.** none

21. no: for functions, even $\times$ odd = odd, odd $\times$ odd = even

Section 2, page 350

1. $\sin x = (1 + \cot^2 x)^{-1/2} = (\sec^2 x - 1)^{1/2}/\sec x$

3. $\cot^2 x = (\cos^2 x)/(1 - \cos^2 x)$

5. $\cos^4 x = \frac{1}{4}(\cos^2 2x + 2\cos 2x + 1)$

7. $\sin 15° = \sin(60° - 45°) = \sin 60° \cos 45° - \cos 60° \sin 45°$;
$\sin^2 15° = \frac{1}{2}(1 - \cos 30°)$

9. $1 - \cos x = 2\sin^2 \frac{1}{2}x,\ 1 + \cos x = 2\cos^2 \frac{1}{2}x$; divide.

11. $\sin x \cos y = \frac{1}{2}[\sin(x + y) + \sin(x - y)]$;
$\sin x \sin y = \frac{1}{2}[\cos(x - y) - \cos(x + y)]$

Section 3, page 352

1. $\frac{1}{3}\cos(x/3)$ **3.** $-3\cos^2 x \sin x$ **5.** $\cot 2x - 2x \csc^2 2x$

7. $\csc^2 x \cot x\,(2 - \csc^2 x)^{-1/2}$

9. $(-\frac{10}{3})\,(\cos^4 \frac{1}{3}x)\,(\sin \frac{1}{3}x)\,(1 + \cos^5 \frac{1}{3}x)$ **11.** $2(\cos x)/(1 - \sin x)^2$

13. $12x \sec^3(2x^2)\tan(2x^2)$

15. $-\sin x$; successive derivatives repeat in cycles of four

17. $dy/dx = -y\sqrt{y^2 - 1}$

19. $d(\ )/dx = 4\sec^4 x \tan x - 4\tan^3 x \sec^2 x$
$= 4\sec^2 x \tan x\,(\sec^2 x - \tan^2 x) = 4\sec^2 x \tan x$

21. $d(\ )/dx = 1 + \sec x \tan x - \sec^2 x = \sec x \tan x - \tan^2 x =$
$\tan x\,(\sec x - \tan x) = (\sin x/\cos x)\,(1 - \sin x)/\cos x$. But
$(1 - \sin x)/\cos^2 x = 1/(1 + \sin x)$

Section 4, page 358

3. $5\pi\sqrt{2}/36$ in²/sec; when the vertex angle is 90°

5. $(6 - 2\sqrt{6})\pi/3$ **7.** $(6 - \sqrt{3})$ ft; the angle at C is 120°

9. 4π in./min to the left   **10.** $(a^{2/3} + b^{2/3})^{3/2}$; this occurs when
$\tan^3 \theta = b/a$, found by minimizing the length $L = a \sec \theta + b \csc \theta$

11. In this case, $L^2 = (a \sec \theta + b \csc \theta)^2 + c^2$ so it is essentially the same
problem. Answer: $[(a^{2/3} + b^{2/3})^3 + c^2]^{1/2}$

Section 5, page 367

1. $\pi/4$ **3.** $\pi/3$ **5.** $\pi/2$ **7.** $4/5$ **9.** $\pi/2$

11.   Let $\theta = \arc \cos x$. Then $\cos \theta = x$ and $\cos 2\theta = 2 \cos^2 \theta - 1 = 2x^2 - 1$; hence, $2\theta = \arc \cos(2x^2 - 1)$.   **13.**   Use Ex. 12

Section 6, page 369

1. $1/(9 - x^2)^{1/2}$ **3.** $2x/(1 + x^4)$ **5.** $6(\arc \sin 3x)(1 - 9x^2)^{-1/2}$

7. $1/(1 + x^2)$ **9.** $1/(1 + x^2)$ **11.** $2 \arc \tan 2x$

Section 7, page 373

1. $(TB)^{1/2}$ ft   **3.** $\pi/3$ **5.** $\sqrt{7}/210$ rad/sec

Section 8, page 378

1. $11 \cosh 2x + 3 \sinh 2x$ **3.** $\cosh 2x = 2 \cosh^2 x - 1 = 2 \sinh^2 x + 1$

5.   Set $x = \tanh y = (e^y - e^{-y})/(e^y + e^{-y})$. Then $(1 + x)/(1 - x) = e^{2y}$; hence, $\frac{1}{2} \ln[(1 + x)/(1 - x)] = y = \tanh^{-1} x$.

7. $5 \cosh 5x$ **9.** 0 **11.** $e^{2x} \cosh x$

CHAPTER 16*

Section 2, page 384

1. $\sin 2x$ **3.** e^{x^2} **5.** $2(1 - x^2)^{1/2}$ **7.** $\frac{1}{4} \sin^4 x$

9. $-\frac{1}{2}(1 + x^2)^{-2}$ **11.** $-\sec x$ **13.** $\tan 5x$

15. $\ln(e^x + x^2 + 1)$ **17.** $\frac{2}{3}(4x^2 + 1)^{3/2}$ **19.** $e^{\sqrt{x}}$

Section 3, page 388

1. $(3x + 1)^6/18$ **3.** $(x^2 + 1)^4/8$ **5.** $\frac{1}{3} \sin 3x$

7. $(-\cos ax + \sin ax)/a$ **9.** $\frac{1}{3}e^{3x}$ **11.** $e^{2\sqrt{x}}$ **13.** $\frac{2}{5}(1 + 5x)^{1/2}$

15. $\frac{1}{4} \ln(1 + x^4)$ **17.** $\frac{1}{6} \ln^2|3x + 1|$ **19.** $\frac{1}{3}(5 - 3x)^{-1}$

21. $\frac{1}{2} \tan^4(x/2)$

---

*The constant of integration is always omitted.

Section 4, page 390

1. $\frac{2}{5}(x+3)^{3/2}(x-2)$ 3. $\frac{1}{3}(x-5)(2x+5)^{1/2}$

5. $\ln|x-1|-2(x-1)^{-1}-\frac{1}{2}(x-1)^{-2}$ 7. $2\sqrt{x}-2\ln(1+\sqrt{x})$

9. $\frac{4}{3}\ln(1+x^{3/4})$ 11. $\frac{1}{2}$ arc tan e^{2x} 13. $\frac{1}{5}$ arc tan$(5x+2)$

15. arc sin(x/a) 17. $\frac{1}{3}[x-(1/\sqrt{3})$ arc tan$(x\sqrt{3})]$

19. $\frac{1}{3}x^3-2x+2\sqrt{2}$ arc tan$(x/\sqrt{2})$ 21. $\frac{1}{2}[x^2-\ln(x^2+1)]$

Section 5, page 394

1. $\frac{49}{3}$ 3. $\frac{1}{2}(e^9-e)$ 5. $\frac{11}{36}$ 7. $2-\sqrt{2}$ 9. $2-2\ln\frac{3}{2}$

11. $\frac{1}{3}(16-9\sqrt{3})$

Section 6, page 399

1. x 3. $\frac{1}{5}\sin^5 x-\frac{1}{7}\sin^7 x$ 5. $\frac{1}{5}\cos^5 x-\frac{1}{3}\cos^3 x$

7. $\frac{1}{3}\sin 3x-\frac{2}{9}\sin^3 3x+\frac{1}{15}\sin^5 3x$

9. $\frac{1}{32}(\sin 4x+8\sin 2x+12x)$ 11. $\frac{1}{3}\tan^3 x-\tan x+x$

13. $(\sec^n kx)/kn$ 15. $\tan x+\sec x$ 17. 1   19. 0

21. $\frac{1}{2}$ arc tan $\frac{1}{2}(x+1)$ 23. arc sin $\frac{1}{3}(x-3)$

25. $-(4x-x^2)^{1/2}+2$ arc sin $\frac{1}{2}(x-2)$

27. $(1/2\sqrt{3})\ln|x^2-\frac{2}{3}+[(3x^4-4x^2+1)/3]^{1/2}|$

29. $(1/b)\ln|ax/(b-ax)|$

CHAPTER 17

Section 1, page 405

1. $\dfrac{1}{2}\left(\dfrac{1}{x-1}-\dfrac{1}{x+1}\right)$ 3. $1+\dfrac{1}{3}\left(\dfrac{4}{x-2}-\dfrac{1}{x+1}\right)$

5. $\dfrac{1}{2}\left(\dfrac{-1}{x+1}+\dfrac{4}{x+2}-\dfrac{3}{x+3}\right)$ 7. $1-\dfrac{2}{x^2+1}+\dfrac{1}{(x^2+1)^2}$

9. $\dfrac{1}{5}\left(\dfrac{2}{x-1}+\dfrac{-2x+3}{x^2+4}\right)$ 11. $\ln|(x-2)/(x-1)|$

13. $\ln|x^3/(x+1)^2|$ 15. $3\ln|x/(x^2+1)^{1/2}|+2$ arc tan x

17. $\frac{1}{169}\{\ln[(x^2+9)^2/(x-2)^4]-13/(x-2)-\frac{5}{3}$ arc tan$(x/3)\}$

19. $\frac{1}{2}x^2+\frac{1}{3}\ln|(x-1)/(x^2+x+1)^{1/2}|+(1/\sqrt{3})$ arc tan$(2x+1)/\sqrt{3}$

21. $\frac{1}{2}x^2-3x+8\ln|x+2|-\ln|x+1|$

23. $\frac{1}{17}[13\ln|x-3|+2\ln(x^2+2x+2)-$ arc tan$(x+1)]$

25. $\frac{1}{3}\ln|(2+\sin\theta)/(5+\sin\theta)|$

Section 2, page 409

1. $\ln[x + (1 + x^2)^{1/2}]$ **3.** $-\frac{1}{3}(8 + x^2)(4 - x^2)^{1/2}$

5. $-(16 - x^2)^{1/2}/(16x)$ **7.** $\ln|x + (x^2 + a^2)^{1/2}| - (x^2 + a^2)^{1/2}/x$

9. $\frac{1}{2}$ arc tan $x - \frac{1}{2}x/(1 + x^2)$

11. arg $\sinh(x/a) = \ln[x + (a^2 + x^2)^{1/2}] - \ln a$

13. $\frac{1}{2}x(a^2 + x^2)^{1/2} - \frac{1}{2}a^2$ arg $\sinh(x/a)$

Section 3, page 415

1. $\sin x - x \cos x$ **3.** $\frac{1}{4}e^{2x}(2x - 1)$ **5.** $\frac{2}{9}x^{3/2}(3 \ln x - 2)$

7. x arc tan $x - \frac{1}{2} \ln(1 + x^2)$ **9.** $\frac{1}{2}(1 + x^2)$ arc tan $x - \frac{1}{2}x$

11. $e^{2x}(2 \sin 3x - 3 \cos 3x)/13$ **13.** $x \sinh x - \cosh x$

15. $(x^2/a) \sin ax + (2x/a^2) \cos ax - (2/a^3) \sin ax$ **17.** 2

19. $(24 \ln 2 - 7)/9$ **21.** $10e - 5$

Section 4, page 419

1. Set $u = \ln^n x$, $v = x$, and integrate by parts.

3. Set $u = x^n$, $v = -\cos x$, and integrate by parts.

7. $(2 \times 4 \times 6)/(3 \times 5 \times 7) = \frac{16}{35}$ **9.** $\frac{1}{9} - \frac{1}{7} + \frac{1}{5} - \frac{1}{3} + 1 - \frac{1}{4}\pi$

Section 6, page 424

1. $(e^{-2x}/29)(-2 \sin 5x - 5 \cos 5x)$

3. $\frac{1}{64}[-4x(1 - 4x^2)^{3/2} + 2x(1 - 4x^2)^{1/2} + $ arc sin $2x]$

5. $\frac{1}{25}[5x - \sqrt{10}$ arc tan$(\frac{1}{2}x\sqrt{10})]$

7. $12(x^2 - 8) \sin \frac{1}{2}x - 2x(x^2 - 24) \cos \frac{1}{2}x$

9. $\dfrac{1}{10} \sqrt{10x^2 + 7} - \dfrac{6}{\sqrt{10}} \ln|x\sqrt{10} + \sqrt{10x^2 + 7}|$

$$+ \frac{2}{\sqrt{7}} \ln \left| \frac{\sqrt{7} + \sqrt{10x^2 + 7}}{x} \right|$$

11. $-\frac{1}{2}\pi$ **13.** $\frac{77}{325}(e^{3\pi} - 1)$ **15.** $\frac{3}{4} + 5 \ln \frac{7}{8}$

CHAPTER 18

Section 1, page 427

1. $n = 4: 3.8281; n = 10: 3.8325;$ exact: $\frac{23}{6} = 3.8333 \cdots$

3. $n = 4: 6.3230; n = 10: 6.3784;$ exact: $e^2 - 1 \approx 6.3891$

5. $n = 10: 0.49927; n = 100: 0.49999;$ exact: 0.5

7. $n = 20: 3.41674, n = 200: 3.41615;$ exact: $3 - \cos 2 \approx 3.41615$

9. $\Delta x = 0.5: 2.0817; \Delta x = 0.2: 2.0816,$ exact: $12 \log_{10} 12 - 10 - 2M \approx$ 2.0816

11. $\Delta x = 0.2: 1.09714; \Delta x = 0.01: 1.09861;$ exact: $\ln 3 \approx 1.09861$

13. $\Delta x = 0.2: 1.74146; \Delta x = 0.01: 1.74159;$ exact: $\sin 2 - 2 \cos 2 \approx$ 1.74160

15. $\Delta x = 0.2: 6.69284; \Delta x = 0.01: 6.69315;$ exact: $6 + \ln 2 \approx 6.69315$

Section 2, page 431

1. $n = 4: 10.000; n = 10: 9.440;$ exact: $9\frac{1}{3} = 9.333 \cdots$

3. $n = 10: 0.45931; n = 50: 0.45968;$ exact: $1 - \cos 1 \approx 0.45970$

5. $\Delta x = \pi/12: 0.78540; \Delta x = \pi/180: 0.78540$

7. $\Delta x = 0.1: 0.53333; \Delta x = 0.01: 0.53333$

9. $\Delta x = 0.1: 1.86326; \Delta x = 0.01: 1.86275$

11. $\Delta x = 0.1: 2.67663; \Delta x = 0.005: 2.53357$

13. rect: $2.3325;$ trap: $2.3350;$ exact: $2\frac{1}{3} = 2.3333 \cdots$

15. rect: $0.95685;$ trap: $0.95565;$ exact: $\cos 1 - \cos 2 \approx 0.95645$

17. 592.8 ft

Section 4, page 439

1. $y = 1, -x^2$ **3.** $y = 27(x - 2), (x - 3)^2(x + 6)$

5. $y = -3x - 2, 9(x + 1)^2/(3x + 4)$ **7.** $y = 1, \sin x - 1$

9. $(x - 3)(x + 6)$

Section 5, page 448

1. 1.71 **3.** -1.84 **5.** 3.162 **7.** -1.148 **9.** 0.540

11. 1.895

Section 6, page 454

7. $1 - x + \frac{1}{2}x^2 - \frac{1}{6}x^3$ **9.** $2 + 2x$

11. $-20(x - \pi/40) + \frac{1}{3}(4000)(x - \pi/40)^3$ **13.** $1 + 2x + 2x^2 + \frac{4}{3}x^3$

CHAPTER 19

Section 1, page 458

1. $\frac{1}{3}(2x^2 - 7x + 6)$ **3.** $\frac{1}{84}(-5x^2 + 63x - 106)$ **5.** $\frac{1}{3}(x + 7)$

7. $\frac{1}{2}(x^2 - 11x + 26)$ **9.** $\frac{1}{2}(-x + 4)$

11. $\frac{1}{6}(-x^3 + 3x^2 + 10x + 12)$ **13.** $\frac{1}{6}(-x^3 + 10x)$ **15.** $2x - 4$

17. $\frac{1}{6}(7x^3 + 27x^2 + 14x - 6)$ **19.** $\frac{1}{10}(-x^2 - 3x + 40)$

21. $\frac{1}{2}[(e-1)^2x^2 - (e-1)(e-3)x + 2]$ **23.** $-\frac{1}{6}(x^2 - 4x)$

25. $6x^3 - 11x^2 + 5x$ **27.** $\frac{1}{24}(-x^3 + 7x^2 + 6x)$ **29.** Estimate by
$s = \frac{1}{6}(t^3 + 21t^2 - 82t + 120)$. The minimum is $s \approx 7.70$ ft at $t \approx 1.74$ hr.

31. $\displaystyle\int_0^3 (-\frac{1}{2}x^3 + 2x^2 - x)\, dx = 3.375$

Section 2, page 461

1. $\frac{1}{12}(x^3 + 17x^2 + 18x - 24)$

3. $\frac{1}{48}(-x^3 + 18x^2 - 128x + 384)$

5. $\frac{1}{192}(-x^4 + 40x^3 - 212x^2 + 80x + 384)$

7. $\frac{1}{3}(x^3 - 6x^2 + 8x)$ **9.** $\frac{1}{2}(8x^2 - 18x + 9)$

11. $\displaystyle\int_{-1/2}^1 (-\frac{1}{3})(4x^3 - x)\, dx = -\frac{3}{16} = -0.1875$

13. $\frac{2}{3}(1 + 4e^{-4} + e^{-16}) \approx 0.72$

Section 3,* page 467

1. 136   **3.** 8.55   **5.** $-\frac{4}{45} \approx -0.09$ **7.** 1.22

9. 42.3266, 42.4301, 42.4387   **11.** 22.8784, 22.8664, 22.8654

13. $-4.1641, -2.5272, -2.3123$ **15.** 0.886227   **17.** 0.902570

---

*Answers from a computer depend on the computer, the compiler, and the algorithm used. Hence numerical answers may differ slightly from those given.

Section 4, page 471

1. Simpson: 1.65, Newton–Cotes: 1.64 **3.** 14.12, 14.10

5. -1.84, -1.81 **7.** 0.8517, 0.8456, 0.8490

9. 0.4930, 0.4931, 0.4931 **11.** 0.2040, 0.2141, 0.2133

13. Three-Eighths: $\frac{39}{8} = 4.875$ **15.** 5-pt. N-C: $\frac{116}{9} \approx 12.89$

17. Weddle: $\frac{63}{10} = 6.3$, 7-pt. N-C: $\frac{881}{140} \approx 6.293$

	Simp.	$\frac{3}{8}$	5-pt. N–C	7-pt. N–C	9-pt. N–C	Weddle
19.	0.684199	0.684038	0.684527	0.684286	0.683844	0.684327
21.	849.902	849.906	849.900	849.900	849.899	849.900
23.	238.000	230.250	237.422	246.114	218.351	244.200

Section 5, page 479

1. even **3.** odd **5.** even **7.** neither **9.** $x = -1$

11. $x = -1$ **13.** $x = \pi/4$ **15.** $x = 0$ **17.** $\int_1^2 (x^3 - 5x)\, dx$

19. 0 **21.** $\int_0^\pi \sin x\, dx = 2 \int_0^{\pi/2} \sin x\, dx$ **23.** $4 \int_0^{\pi/2} \sin^2 x\, dx$

25. $-2 \sin 4 \int_0^{4\pi} \cos \dfrac{x}{12}\, dx$

Section 6, page 486

1. hint: $1 - k^2 < 1 - k^2 \sin^2 \theta < 1$ **3.** $x^3 + 3x + 1 > 5$

5. $\sin^2 x < 1$ **7.** $3 + 2x > 2x$ **9.** $x^2 < x^2 + x + 1 < (x + 1)^2$

11. $9 < 3 + 2x < 13$ **13.** $1 < 1 + \sin^2 x < 2$

15. $\ln^2 2 < \ln^2 x < \ln^2 5$

17. $\int_0^{100} - \int_0^{10} = \int_{10}^{100} < e^{-10} \int_{10}^{100} dx = 90e^{-10} \approx .0041$

Section 7, page 492

1. Trapezoidal: $(\sin 1)/(12 \times 6^2) < 2 \times 10^{-3}$;

Simpson: $(\sin 1)/(180 \times 6^4) < 4 \times 10^{-6}$;

Three-Eighths: $(\sin 1)/(80 \times 6^4) < 9 \times 10^{-6}$

3. $\frac{1}{54} < 2 \times 10^{-2}$, $1/(45 \times 3^3) < 9 \times 10^{-4}$, $(20 \times 3^3)^{-1} < 2 \times 10^{-3}$

5. $(3^7 \times 1400)^{-1} < 4 \times 10^{-7}$, $11/(3^7 \times 1400) < 4 \times 10^{-6}$

7. $(9 \times 73e)/(2^9 \times 1400) < 3 \times 10^{-3}$,

$(10 \times 43e + 9 \times 73e/4)/(2^7 \times 1400) < 10^{-2}$

9. 7-point N–C (4 times) works. For $0 \le x \le 6$,

$|(x^2 e^{-x})^{(8)}| = |(x^2 - 16x + 56)e^{-x}| \le 6^2 + 16 \cdot 6 + 56 = 188 = M$,

$|\epsilon| \le 4(9/1400)\,(188)\,(1/4)^9 < 2 \times 10^{-5}$

11. $\dfrac{M}{12}\left(\dfrac{h}{10}\right)^2 (b - a) = \dfrac{1}{100}\left[\dfrac{M}{12}h^2(b-a)\right]$

17. for $2n + 1$ points: $h = (b-a)/2n$,

$$|\epsilon| \le n\left(\frac{Mh^5}{90}\right) = \frac{Mh^4}{90}(nh) = \frac{Mh^4}{180}(b-a)$$

19. $h = (b-a)/4n$, $|\epsilon| \le n\left(\dfrac{8Mh^7}{945}\right) = \dfrac{8Mh^6}{945}(nh) = \dfrac{2Mh^6}{945}(b-a)$

CHAPTER 20

Section 2, page 499

1. neither   **3.** both   **5.** below   **7.** above   **9.** both
11. $2r$ **13.** none   **15.** 2   **17.** 1
19. Let $x \in \mathbf{S}$. Then inf $\mathbf{S} \le x \le$ sup $\mathbf{S}$. Equal if and only if $\mathbf{S}$ consists of only one number.
21. First assume $B = $ sup $\mathbf{S}$. If $x \in \mathbf{S}$, then $x \le B$ because B is an upper bound. If $B_1 < B$, then B_1 is not an upper bound because B is the *least* upper bound. Hence $x > B_1$ for *some* $x \in \mathbf{S}$. Conversely, assume (1) and (2). By (1), B is an upper bound. By (2), no smaller number is an upper bound. Hence $B = $ sup $\mathbf{S}$.

Section 3, page 503

1. Only if the sequence is eventually constant, $x_n = L$ for all $n \ge N$.
3. 0   **5.** $\frac{3}{4}$ **7.** 0   **9.** 0   **11.** $\frac{1}{9}$
13. $n/10^n \to 0$ and all terms following $n/10^n$ are smaller. Hence $x_n \to 0$.

15. 1, 1.4, 1.41, 1.414, 1.4142, $\cdots$ has limit $\sqrt{2}$.

17. Suppose $x_n \to L < 0$. For $n \ge N$, we have $|x_n - L| < \frac{1}{2}|L|$, hence $x_n < L + \frac{1}{2}|L| = \frac{1}{2}L < 0$, a contradiction.

19. In either case the condition is $|L - x_n| < \epsilon$ for $n \ge N$.

21. Given ϵ, always choose N larger than the index of the last inserted or deleted term.

Section 4, page 509

1. Let $\epsilon > 0$. Choose N so $|x_n - L| < \epsilon$ for all $n \ge N$. Then $|y_j - L| < \epsilon$ for $j \ge N$ because $y_j = x_{n_j}$ and $n_j \ge j \ge N$.

3. Let $a_n/n \to L > 0$. For $n \ge N$ we have $a_n/n \ge \frac{1}{2}L$, so $a_n \ge \frac{1}{2}Ln$.

5. $\frac{1}{2}$ **7.** 0   **9.** 1   **11.** $\frac{1}{2}$ **13.** 1   **15.** 0   **17.** 3

19. Not necessarily. Try $a_n = (-1)^n$.

21. Not necessarily. Try $a_n = b_n = (-1)^n$.

23. Set $a^{1/n} = 1 + b_n$, where $0 < b_n$. Then $a = (1 + b_n)^n > 1 + nb_n$, so $b_n < (a - 1)/n$. Therefore $b_n \to 0$, $a^{1/n} \to 1$.

Section 5, page 515

1. $0 < x_n = x_{n-1}(3n - 2)/(3n - 1) < x_{n-1}$

3. $x_n = x_{n-1} + 1/(n!)^2 > x_{n-1}$ and $(n!)^2 \ge 2^{2(n-1)}$, etc. as in Example 5.3.

5. $x_0 < 5$. If $x_n < 5$, then $x_{n+1} = \sqrt{5x_n} < \sqrt{5 \cdot 5} = 5$, hence $x_n < 5$ for all n. Therefore $x_{n+1} = \sqrt{5x_n} > \sqrt{x_n \cdot x_n} = x_n$.

7. Let $\epsilon > 0$. Choose $N > 1/\epsilon$. Let m, $n \ge N$ with (say) $m > n$. Then

$$|x_m - x_n| = d_{n+1} \cdot 10^{-n-1} + \cdots + d_m \cdot 10^{-m} < 10^{-n}$$
$$\le 10^{-N} < N^{-1} < \epsilon.$$

9. Assume $|x_{n+1} - x_n| \le 2^{-n}$, which is true for $n = 1$. Then $|x_{n+2} - x_{n+1}| = \frac{1}{2}|x_{n+1} - x_n| < 2^{-n-1}$. Now use Ex. 8.

11. None; these are not *closed* intervals.

13. Yes, for example 0, 1, 0, 1, 0, 1, $\cdots$.

15. Suppose $x_{n_j} \to L$. Then $x_j \le x_{n_j} \le L$, so the sequence is bounded. Apply Theorem 5.1.

17. $(n + 2)n < (n + 2)n + 1 = (n + 1)^2$, hence $(n + 2)/(n + 1) < (n + 1)/n$. Assume $(n + 1)^n \le n^{n+1}$, which is true for $n = 3$. Then $[(n + 2)/(n + 1)]^{n+1} \le [(n + 1)/n]^{n+1} = (n + 1)[(n + 1)^n/n^{n+1}] \le n + 1$, hence $(n + 2)^{n+1} \le (n + 1)^{n+2}$.

19. It is true for $n = 2$. Assume for n; then $(1 + x)^{n+1} = (1 + x)(1 + x)^n \ge (1 + x)(1 + nx) = 1 + (n + 1)x + nx^2 \ge 1 + (n + 1)x$. The last $\ge$ is $>$ unless $x = 0$.

21. $b_{n-1}/b_n = [n^2/(n + 1)(n - 1)]^{n+1}n/(n + 1) = [1 + (n^2 - 1)^{-1}]^{n+1}n/(n + 1)$. By Bernoulli's inequality,

$$b_{n-1}/b_n > [1 + (n + 1)(n^2 - 1)^{-1}]n/(n + 1) = n^2/(n^2 - 1) > 1.$$

23. $x \in \bigcap\limits_{n=1}^{\infty} [a_n, b_n]$ if and only if $x \in [a_n, b_n]$ for all n, that is, if and only if $a_n \leq x$ and $x \leq b_n$ for all n, hence, if and only if sup $a_n \leq x$ and $x \leq$ inf b_n.

25.   Write $L = x + y$, where $x = b_{N-1}$ and $y = a_N \cdot 10^{-N} + a_{N+1}$ $10^{-(N+1)} + \cdots$. Then x is rational. To see that y is also rational, note that $(10^{N+P}y - 10^{N-1}y)$ is an integer. (Clear if you express y as a decimal.) Hence $y = (\text{integer})/(10^{N+P} - 10^{N-1})$, a rational number.

Section 6, page 521

1. $\frac{1}{2}$ **3.** $\frac{1}{5}$ **5.** 1   **7.** 0   **9.** 0

11.   Suppose $L \neq M$. Set $\epsilon = \frac{1}{2}|L - M| > 0$ and choose $\delta > 0$ so $|f(x) - L| < \epsilon$ and $|f(x) - M| < \epsilon$ for all x with $|x - c| < \delta$. Then $|L - M| \leq |L - f(x)| + |f(x) - M| < \epsilon + \epsilon = |L - M|$, impossible.

13.   Obvious if $a = 0$. Otherwise, if $\epsilon > 0$, make $|f(x) - L| < \epsilon/|a|$. Then $|af(x) - aL| < \epsilon$, etc.

15.   Follow Theorem 4.4.

17.   Suppose $f(x) \to L$ as $x \to c$. Then there exists $\delta > 0$ so that $|f(x) - L| < \frac{1}{2}$ for $|x - c| < \delta$. But there are both irrationals and rationals within δ of c, hence $|L| < \frac{1}{2}$ and $|1 - L| < \frac{1}{2}$, impossible.

19.   Let $\epsilon > 0$. Choose an integer $N > 1/\epsilon$. There are only a finite number of rationals p/q with $q \leq N$ (at most N^2 for example); choose δ so small that none is included in the set of x satisfying $0 < |x - c| < \delta$. Then $|f(x)| < \epsilon$ for any x, rational or irrational, in this set. Hence $\lim_{x \to c} f(x) = 0$.

21.   Suppose $f(x) \to L$ is false. Then for some $\epsilon > 0$, there is no $\delta > 0$ .... Choose x_n so $0 < |x_n - c| < 1/n$ and $|f(x_n) - L| \geq \epsilon$. Then $x_n \to c$ but $f(x_n) \to L$ is false.

23.   Suppose $f(x) \to L$ as $x \to c$. Let $\epsilon > 0$. Choose $\delta > 0$ so $|f(x) - L| < \frac{1}{2}\epsilon$ whenever $0 < |x - c| < \delta$. Then $|f(x) - f(x')| \leq |f(x) - L| + |f(x') - L| < \frac{1}{2}\epsilon + \frac{1}{2}\epsilon = \epsilon$ if $0 < |x - c| < \delta$ and $0 < |x' - c| < \delta$. Conversely, if $x_n \to c$, then $\{f(x_n)\}$ is a Cauchy sequence, hence converges. Apply Ex. 21.

25.   Suppose $\lim_{x \to c-} f(x) = \lim_{x \to c+} f(x) = L$. If $\epsilon > 0$, choose $\delta > 0$ so $|f(x) - L| < \epsilon$ for $c - \delta < x < c$ and $|f(x) - L| < \epsilon$ for $c < x < c + \delta$. Then $|f(x) - L| < \epsilon$ for $0 < |x - c| < \delta$. The converse is obvious.

27.   Repeat Def. 6.2 word for word, except replace $x > x_0$ by $x < x_0$ at the end.

29.   If $A > 0$ and $0 < x < 1/A^2$, then $1/\sqrt{x} > A$.

31.   The point is that $x > x_0 > 0$ if and only if $0 < 1/x < \delta = 1/x_0$.

33. 1   **35.** $\frac{3}{4}$ **37.** 0   **39.** $\frac{1}{2}$

Section 7, page 527

1. $||x| - |c|| \leq |x - c|$, etc.
3. $|(x^3 - 4x + 6) - (c^3 - 4c + 6)| = |(x^3 - c^3) - 4(x - c)| \leq |x^3 - c^3| - 4|x - c| \leq |x - c|(|x^2| + |cx| + |c^2| + 4)$. If $|x - c| < 1$, then $|x| < |c| + 1$, $|x^2| < (|c| + 1)^2$, so $|x^2| + |cx| + |c^2| + 4 < (|c| + 1)^2 + |c|(|c| + 1) + |c^2| + 4 = K$, a constant independent of x, for fixed c, etc.
5. $x^{1/3} - c^{1/3} = (x - c)/(x^{2/3} + x^{1/3}c^{1/3} + c^{2/3})$. First assume $c > 0$ and take $x > 0$. Then $|x^{1/3} - c^{1/3}| \leq |x - c|/c^{2/3}$, etc. because $x^{2/3} + x^{1/3}c^{1/3} + c^{2/3} > c^{2/3}$. $c < 0$ is similar. For $c = 0$, take $\delta = \epsilon^3$.
7. $|x \sin x^{-1}| \leq |x|$.
9. $|x^2 - z^2| = |x + z||x - z| \leq 6|x - z|$, so take $\delta = \frac{1}{6}\epsilon$, etc.
11. From $1 - 2|x| + x^2 = (1 - |x|)^2 \geq 0$, we deduce $|x|/(1 + x^2) \leq \frac{1}{2}$. Now we have $|1/(1 + x^2) - 1/(1 + z^2)| = |(z^2 - x^2)/(1 + x^2)(1 + z^2)| \leq |z - x|(|z| + |x|)/(1 + x^2)(1 + z^2) \leq |z - x|(\frac{1}{2}/(1 + x^2) + \frac{1}{2}/(1 + z^2)) \leq |z - x|$, etc.
13. Let $\delta > 0$, $x > 0$, $z > 0$, $|x - z| = \frac{1}{2}\delta$. Then $|x^3 - z^3| = |x^2 + xz + z^2||x - z| \geq z^2|x - z| = \frac{1}{2}\delta z^2 \to \infty$ as $z \to \infty$. Hence for any $\delta > 0$ given, $|x^3 - z^3| < \epsilon$ is impossible for *all* x, z such that $|x - z| < \delta$.
15. Take $\epsilon = f(c)$. Then there exists $\delta > 0$ such that $|f(x) - f(c)| < f(c)$ for $|x - c| < \delta$. Therefore $f(x) - f(c) > -f(c)$, $f(x) > 0$.
17. $||f(x)| - |f(c)|| \leq |f(x) - f(c)|$ etc.
19. No. $f(x) = g(x) = x$ on $(-\infty, \infty)$ is a counterexample.
21. $f_+ = \frac{1}{2}(f + |f|)$, $f_- = \frac{1}{2}(f - |f|)$.

Section 8, page 533

1. $f = $ const.   3. $f(x) = -x^2$ for $-1 < x < 1$
5. $f = $ const.; $f(x) = x$ is another
7. Set $h(x) = f(x) - g(x)$. Then $h(x) > 0$ for $x \in [a, b]$. Let $p = \inf h(x) = h(c_1) > 0$.
9. $f(7) = -7^4 + 7^2 - 1 < 0$, $f(8) = 8^2 - 1 > 0$.
11. $f(x) = x - 1 - 2^{-x}$. Then $f(1) = -\frac{1}{2} < 0$, $f(2) = 1 - \frac{1}{4} > 0$.
13. Set $g(x) = f(x) - x$. Then $g(0) \geq 0$ and $g(1) \leq 0$ so there is a root of $g(x) = 0$ in $[0, 1]$. The graphs of $y = f(x)$ and $y = x$ must cross.
15. $f(x) = x^n$ is continuous and strictly increasing on $[0, \infty)$ onto $[0, \infty)$. Its inverse function exists and is continuous by Theorem 8.4.
17. Let $a > 0$ and consider $g_a(x) = f(x + a) - f(x)$. This continuous function cannot have a zero on the subinterval of **D** where it is defined, hence it has constant sign, say $g_a(x) > 0$, $f(x + a) > f(x)$. We claim for each $b > 0$, that $g_b(x) > 0$. For consider $h(x) = f(c + x) - f(c)$, where c is fixed and $x \in [a, b]$ or $[b, a]$ if $b < a$. Then h has no zeros, hence has constant sign. But $h(a) = g_a(c) > 0$, and $h(b) = g_b(c)$.

Hence $g_b(x) > 0$, so $f(x + a) > f(x)$ whenever $a > 0$, and x and $x + a \in$ **D**.

21. If **S** is an interval, the condition is obviously satisfied. Suppose conversely that x, $z \in$ **S** and $x < y < z$ always implies $y \in$ **S**. *Case 1:* $a = \inf$ **S** and $b = \sup$ **S** exist. Let $a < x < b$. Then there are y and z in **S** such that $a < y < x < z < b$, by definition of inf and sup. Hence $x \in$ **S**. This means $(a, b) \subseteq$ **S** which easily implies **S** $= (a, b)$, $[a, b)$, $(a, b]$, or $[a, b]$. *Case 2:* $a = \inf$ **S** exists, but sup **S** doesn't exist. Then we prove similarly that $(a, \infty) \subseteq$ **S**, etc.

25. Consider f only on the closed interval $[0, p]$. It has a max and a min: $f(c_0) \le f(x) \le f(c_1)$ for $0 \le x \le p$. Now given *any* real x, choose n so $0 \le x - np < p$, that is, $n \le x/p < n + 1$. Then $f(x) = f(x - np)$ so $f(c_0) \le f(x) \le f(c_1)$.

27. By Ex. 25, $f(c_0) \le f(x) \le f(c_1)$. Set $g(x) = f(x + h) - f(x)$, a continuous function. Then $g(c_0) = f(c_0 + h) - f(c_0) \ge 0$ and $g(c_1) = f(c_1 + h) - f(c_1) \le 0$, so $g(x)$ has a zero. The result means that the graph of f has horizontal chords of every possible length.

CHAPTER 21

Section 1, page 539

1. The only doubtful point is 0. But $|f(x)/x| = |x| \to 0$ as $x \to 0$, so $f'(0) = 0$. For $x > 0$, $f'(x) = 2x$ and for $x < 0$, $f'(x) = -2x$. Therefore $f'(x) = 2|x|$ is continuous.

3. $f'(0) = 0$ and $f'(x) \ne 0$ if $x \ne 0$. If $y \ne 0$, then $y = f(x)$ for $x \ne 0$ and $g'(y) = 1/3x^2 = 1/3y^{2/3}$. However $g'(0)$ is not defined.

5. Yes; as $x \to 0$, $|[f(x) - f(0)]/(x - 0)| = |x \sin(1/x)| \le |x| \to 0$, so $f'(0) = 0$.

7. Apply Theorem 1.1 at $x = c + h$, and $x = c - h$, then subtract and let $h \to 0$:

$$\frac{f(c + h) - f(c - h)}{2h} = f'(c) + \frac{1}{2}[e(c + h) + e(c - h)] \to f'(c).$$

9. $x - 3$

11. Apply Theorem 1.1 to f and to $\pm g$, then add: $f(x) \pm g(x) = f(c) \pm g(c) + [f'(c) \pm g'(c)](x - c) + [e_1(x) \pm e_2(x)](x - c)$, where $e_1(x)$ comes from f and $e_2(x)$ from g. Clearly $e_1(x) \pm e_2(x) \to 0$ as $x \to c$, so the second part of Theorem 1.1 applies: $(f \pm g)'(c) = f'(c) \pm g'(c)$.

13. $y = f(c) + f'(c)(x - c)$. The error $e(x)$ $(x - c)$ measures the vertical distance between the graph of f and its tangent line at $x = c$.

Section 2, page 543

1. Suppose f has domain $[a, b]$ and $f'(a) > 0$. Then there exists $\delta > 0$ such that $f(x) > f(a)$ for $a < x < a + \delta$. *Proof:*   Take $\epsilon = f'(a)$ in the definition of derivative. Then there exists $\delta > 0$ such that

$$-f'(a) < \frac{f(x) - f(a)}{x - a} - f'(a)$$

for $a < x < a + \delta$, hence $f(x) > f(a)$.

3. Simply apply Theorem 2.1 to the function $g(x) = f(x) - \frac{9}{10}f'(c)\,(x - c)$, which satisfies $g'(c) = \frac{1}{10}f'(c) > 0$.

5. $\max f = 10 - 3a$ if $a \le 3$, $\max f = 1$ if $a > 3$; $\min f = 1$ if $a \le 0$, $\min f = 1 - \frac{1}{4}a^2$ if $0 < a < 6$, $\min f = 10 - 3a$ if $a \ge 6$.

7. If $x \ne c$, then $[f(x) - f(c)]/(x - c) \ge 0$. Take $\lim_{x \to c}$: $f'(c) \ge 0$.

9. $|f(x) - f(z)| = |f'(y)|\,|x - z| \le B|x - z|$. Given ϵ, take $\delta = \epsilon/B$.

11. $(\sqrt{x})' = 1/2\sqrt{x} < 1/20$ for $x > 100$, hence $\sqrt{101} - 10 = \sqrt{101} - \sqrt{100} = 1/2\sqrt{x} < 0.05$, so $\sqrt{101} < 10.05$. Obviously $\sqrt{101} > 10$.

13. If $x < z$, then $f(z) - f(x) = (z - x)f'(y)$. But $z - x > 0$ and $f'(y) \ge 0$, hence $f(z) \ge f(x)$.

15. Let $a < x < b$. By Theorem 2.9, $f(a) \le f(x) \le f(b) = f(a)$, hence $f(x) = f(a)$.

19. Set $g(x) = Bx - f(x)$. Then $g(b) = g(a)$ and $g'(x) \ge 0$, so $g(x)$ is a constant by Ex. 15.

21. Apply Theorem 2.4 to $g(x) = xf(x)$.

23. Apply Theorem 2.4 to $g(x) = e^{kx}f(x)$.

25. It reduces to the Mean Value Theorem.

27. Set

$$g(x) = \frac{a_0 x^{n+1}}{n + 1} + \frac{a_1 x^n}{n} + \cdots + a_n x.$$

Then $g(0) = g(1) = 0$ and $g'(x) = f(x)$. Apply Theorem 2.4.

29. Set $f(x) = (1 - x)e^x$. Then $f(x) > 0$ on $(-\infty, 1)$, $f(1) = 0$, $f(x) \to 0$ as $x \to -\infty$. Also $f'(x) = -xe^x$, so $f'(x) > 0$ for $x < 0$, $f'(0) = 0$, $f'(x) < 0$ for $0 < x \le 1$. This proves f has a maximum at $x = 0$, $f(x) \le f(0) = 1$, with equality only for $x = 0$.

31. Let $x \ne c$. By the Mean Value Theorem, $[f(x) - f(c)]/(x - c) = f'(y)$, where y is between c and x. Let $\epsilon > 0$. There is $\delta > 0$ such that $|f'(y) - L| < \epsilon$ for $0 < |y - c| < \delta$. If $0 < |x - c| < \delta$, then $0 < |y - c| < \delta$, so $|[f(x) - f(c)]/(x - c) - L| = |f'(y) - L| < \epsilon$. Therefore $[f(x) - f(c)]/(x - c) \to L$, so $f'(c) = L$.

33. Suppose $f'(a) < 0$ and $f'(b) > 0$ to be definite. By Exs. 1, 2, there is $x_0 > a$ with $f(x_0) < f(a)$ and $x_1 < b$ with $f(x_1) < f(b)$. Let $f(c)$ be the minimum of f on $[a, b]$. Then $f(c) \le f(x_0) < f(a)$, $f(c) \le f(x_1) < f(b)$, so $a < c < b$. By Theorem 2.3, $f'(c) = 0$.

35. No. For the given example, $f'(0) = 0$, $f'(x) = 2x \sin(1/x) - \cos(1/x)$ for $x \neq 0$, and as $x \to 0$, $f'(x)$ does not have a limit.

43. There is x_0 such that $f'(x) \geq 1$ for $x \geq x_0$. Then $f(x) - f(x_0) = f'(y)(x - x_0) \geq x - x_0$, so $f(x) \geq f(x_0) - x_0 + x \to \infty$.

45. $f(n + 1) - f(n) = f'(a_n)$ with $n < a_n < n + 1$. But $f(x + 1) - f(x) \to L - L = 0$, so $f'(a_n) \to 0$.

47. Assume $|f'(x)/e^x| \leq B$. By Theorem 2.10,

$$\left| \frac{f(x) - f(0)}{e^x - 1} \right| = \left| \frac{f'(y)}{e^y} \right| \leq B,$$

hence $|f(x)/e^x| \leq |f(0)/(e^x - 1)| + B \leq 2B$ for x sufficiently large, say $x \geq b$. Also $f(x)/e^x$ is continuous on $[0, b]$, hence bounded.

Section 3, page 553

1. True for $n = 1$. Suppose for some n that

$$\frac{d^n}{dx^n}(fg) = \sum_{j=0}^{n} \binom{n}{j} f^{(n-j)} g^{(j)}.$$

Then

$$\frac{d^{n+1}}{dx^{n+1}}(fg) = \sum_{j=0}^{n} \binom{n}{j} [f^{(n-j+1)} g^{(j)} + f^{(n-j)} g^{(j+1)}]$$

$$= \sum_{j=0}^{n} \binom{n}{j} f^{(n+1-j)} g^{(j)} + \sum_{j=1}^{n+1} \binom{n}{j-1} f^{(n+1-j)} g^{(j)}$$

$$= f^{(n+1)} g^{(0)} + \sum_{j=1}^{n} \left[\binom{n}{j} + \binom{n}{j-1} \right] f^{(n+1-j)} g^{(j)} + f^{(0)} g^{(n+1)}.$$

The result follows from

$$\binom{n}{j} + \binom{n}{j-1} = \binom{n+1}{j}.$$

3. The formula can be checked directly for $n = 1$ and $n = 2$. Next, set $f_n(x) = (d^n/dx^n)(x^{n-1} e^{1/x})$ and $g_n(x) = (-1)^n e^{1/x}/x^{n+1}$. From $f_n = (d^{n-1}/dx^{n-1})(d/dx)(x^{n-1} e^{1/x}) = (d^{n-1}/dx^{n-1})[(n-1)x^{n-2} e^{1/x} - x^{n-3} e^{1/x}]$ we find

$$f_n = (n-1)f_{n-1} - f'_{n-2} \qquad (n \geq 3).$$

By computing $g'_{n-2} = (-1)^n [e^{1/x}/x^{n+1}]'$ we also find

$$g_n = (n-1)g_{n-1} - g'_{n-2}.$$

If we assume $f_1 = g_1$, $f_2 = g_2$, $\cdots$, $f_{n-1} = g_{n-1}$ for some fixed $n \geq 3$, these formulas imply $f_n = g_n$, etc.

5. Write $f(c + x) - f(c - x) = 2xf'(c)$ and differentiate twice: $f'(c + x) + f'(c - x) = 2f'(c)$, $f''(c + x) - f''(c - x) = 0$. Hence

$$\frac{f''(c + x) - f''(c)}{x} = -\frac{f''(c - x) - f''(c)}{-x}.$$

As $x \to 0$, the left side approaches $f'''(c)$ and the right side $-f'''(c)$, hence $f'''(c) = 0$.

7. Let $x_1 < x_2 < \cdots < x_r$ be the distinct zeros, with multiplicities $m_1, \cdots, m_r$ so that $m_1 + \cdots + m_r = n$. There is a real zero of $f'(x)$ in each (x_j, x_{j+1}) $(j = 1, \cdots, r - 1)$. By Ex. 6, f' also has a zero of multiplicity $m_j - 1$ at x_j. Hence f' has at least $(r - 1) + (m_1 - 1) + \cdots + (m_r - 1) = n - 1$ real zeros. But $\deg f' = n - 1$, so f' has at most $n - 1$ real zeros.

9. $f(n + 1) - f(n) = f'(a_n)$ where $n < a_n < n + 1$ and $f'(a_n) \to A - A = 0$. Let $\epsilon > 0$. Choose x_0 so $|f'(a_n)| < \frac{1}{2}\epsilon$ and $|f''(x)| < \frac{1}{2}\epsilon$ for $a_n \geq x_0$ and $x \geq x_0$. If $x > x_0 + 1$, there is an a_n such that $|x - a_n| < 1$. Then $|f'(x) - f'(a_n)| = |x - a_n| |f''(y)| \leq |f''(y)| < \frac{1}{2}\epsilon$, so $|f'(x)| < |f'(a_n)| + \frac{1}{2}\epsilon < \epsilon$. Hence $f'(x) \to 0$.

11. Suppose f'' is continuous on (a, b) and $a < c < b$. Apply Theorem 3.2 to $x = c + 2h$ and $x = c + h$ and use these formulas in the desired quotient. The result is

$$\frac{f(c + 2h) - 2f(c + h) + f(c)}{h^2} = f''(c) + [4e(c + 2h) - 2e(c + h)],$$

which obviously converges to $f''(c)$ as $h \to 0$.

13. Let c be an interior point of the domain of f. Suppose f''' exists near c and is continuous at c. Then

$$f(x) = f(c) + f'(c)(x - c) + \tfrac{1}{2}f''(c)(x - c)^2 + \tfrac{1}{6}f'''(c)(x - c)^3 + e(x)(x - c)^3,$$

where $e(x) \to 0$ as $x \to c$.

15. From the formula analogous to that in Ex. 13 we have

$$f(x) = f(c) + [A + e(x)](x - c)^4,$$

where $A = \frac{1}{24}f^{(4)}(c) > 0$ and $e(x) \to 0$ as $x \to c$. Choose $\delta > 0$ so that $|e(x)| < A$ for $|x - c| < \delta$; then $A + e(x) > 0$ so $f(x) \geq f(c)$ for $|x - c| < \delta$, with equality only for $x = c$.

17. Let $a < x < z \leq b$. Apply Theorem 3.4 with z in place of b:

$$f(x) < f(a) + \frac{f(z) - f(a)}{z - a}(x - a).$$

Subtract $f(a)$ and divide by $x - a$: $g(x) < g(z)$, as required.

19. In the proof we have $g''(x) \geq 0$, so $g'(x) \geq 0$ for $c < x < b$ and $g'(x) \leq 0$ for $a < x < c$. If $c < x < b$, then $g(x) - g(c) = (x - c)g'(z) \geq 0$, etc.

21. By Theorem 3.4, if $f''(x) \geq 0$ for all x in (a, b), then $f(x) \leq 0$ on (a, b), contrary to hypothesis.

23. $(f + g)'' = f'' + g'' \geq 0$ **25.** $ff'' \geq f'^2 \geq 0$, so $f'' \geq 0$

29. $\frac{1}{6}$ **31.** -1 **33.** 1 **35.** 1 **37.** 0

39. 1 **41.** 0 **43.** e

45. If $a < x < y$, there exists a z with $x < z < y$ so that

$$\frac{f(x) - f(y)}{g(x) - g(y)} = \frac{f'(z)}{g'(z)} > 2A, \qquad \text{that is,} \qquad \frac{f(x)}{g(x)} > 2A \frac{1 - g(y)/g(x)}{1 - f(y)/f(x)}.$$

Since y is fixed, $g(x) \to \infty$, and $f(x) \to \infty$, we can choose $x_0 > a$ so that $f(x)/g(x) > A$ for $a < x < x_0$.

47. Set $h(x) = g(x) - f(x)$. Then $h(a) = h'(a) = \cdots = h^{(n-1)}(a) = 0$ and $h^{(n)}(x) \geq 0$ for $a < x < b$. For $n = 1$, the Mean Value Theorem yields $h(x) \geq 0$. In general, $h'(x)$ satisfies the given conditions for $n - 1$. Hence, by induction $h'(x) \geq 0$, so $h(x) \geq 0$.

Section 4, page 564

1. Let $a = x_0 < x_1 < \cdots < x_n = b$ be all of the partition points for $s_1(x)$ *and* for $s_2(x)$. Then $s_1(x) = A_i$ and $s_2(x) = B_i$ for $x_{i-1} < x < x_i$,

and $\displaystyle\int_a^b (s_1 + s_2)(x)\, dx = \sum_{i=1}^n (A_i + B_i)(x_i - x_{i-1}) = \sum A_i(x_i - x_{i-1}) +$

$\displaystyle\sum B_i(x_i - x_{i-1}) = \int_a^b s_1(x)\, dx + \int_a^b s_2(x)\, dx.$

3. If $\epsilon > 0$, choose s_1 so $|f(x) - s_1(x)| < \frac{1}{3}\epsilon/(b - a)$. Set $s(x) = s_1(x) - \frac{1}{3}\epsilon/(b - a)$ and $S(x) = s_1(x) + \frac{1}{3}\epsilon/(b - a)$, both step functions. We have $s(x) < f(x) < S(x)$ and $\displaystyle\int_a^b S(x)\, dx - \int_a^b s(x)\, dx = \frac{2}{3}\int_a^b \epsilon/(b - a)\, dx = \frac{2}{3}\epsilon < \epsilon$.

5. If $k = 0$ the result is obvious. *Case 1:* $k > 0$. Given $\epsilon > 0$, choose s and S so $s(x) \leq f(x) \leq S(x)$ and $\displaystyle\int_a^b (S - s)\, dx < \epsilon/k$. Then $ks(x) \leq kf(x) \leq kS(x)$ and $\displaystyle\int_a^b (kS - ks)\, dx < \epsilon$, so kf is integrable. *Case 2:* $k < 0$. Now choose s and S so $s(x) \leq f(x) \leq S(x)$ and $\displaystyle\int_a^b (S - s)\, dx < -\epsilon/k$. Then $kS(x) \leq kf(x) \leq ks(x)$ and $\displaystyle\int_a^b (ks - kS)\, dx = (-k)\int_a^b (S - s)\, dx < \epsilon$.

7. Given $\epsilon > 0$, choose s and S so $s(x) \leq f(x) \leq S(x)$ on $[a, b]$ and $\displaystyle\int_a^b (S - s)\, dx < \epsilon$. Then $s(x) \leq f(x) \leq S(x)$ on $[c, d]$ and $\displaystyle\int_c^d (S -$

$s)\ dx \leq \int_a^b (S - s)\ dx < \epsilon$ since $[c,\ d] \subseteq [a,\ b]$ and $S(x) - s(x) \geq 0$.
Therefore f is integrable on $[c,\ d]$.

9. Suppose $S_1(x) \geq S_2(x)$ so $S(x) = S_1(x)$. If $s_1(x) \geq s_2(x)$, then $s(x) = s_1(x)$ so $S(x) - s(x) = S_1(x) - s_1(x) \leq [S_1(x) - s_1(x)] + [S_2(x) - s_2(x)]$. If $s_2(x) \geq s_1(x)$, then $s(x) = s_2(x)$ so $S(x) - s(x) = S_1(x) - s_2(x) \leq S_1(x) - s_1(x) \leq [\ ] + [\ ]$. The case $S_2(x) \geq S_1(x)$ is similar. This proof shows that $S(x) - s(x) \leq \max\{S_1(x) - s_1(x),\ S_2(x) - s_2(x)\}$.

11. *Case 1:* g is a step function. Assume $g(x) \leq M$ on $[a,\ b]$. Given $\epsilon > 0$, there are s and S so $s(x) \leq f(x) \leq S(x)$ and $\int_a^b (S - s)\ dx < \epsilon/M$. Then $s(x)g(x) \leq f(x)g(x) \leq S(x)g(x)$, sg and Sg are step functions, and $\int_a^b (Sg - sg)\ dx \leq M \int_a^b (S - s)\ dx < M(\epsilon/M) = \epsilon$, hence fg is integrable. *Case 2:* f and g integrable. Then g is bounded, $g(x) \leq M$ on $[a,\ b]$. Given ϵ, s, S as before, sg and Sg are integrable by Case 1, $s(x)g(x) \leq f(x)g(x) \leq S(x)g(x)$, and $\int_a^b (Sg - sg)\ dx = \int_a^b (S - s)g\ dx \leq M \int_a^b (S - s)\ dx < M(\epsilon/M) = \epsilon$. By Ex. 10, fg is integrable.

13. If s is a step function and $s(x) \leq f(x)$, then $s(x) \leq 0$ so $\int_a^b s\ dx \leq 0$. Similarly, if $f(x) \leq S(x)$, then $S(x) \geq 1$, $\int_a^b S(x)\ dx \geq b - a$. Hence $\int_a^b (S - s)\ dx \geq b - a$.

15. We shall work with the upper sums T_n. The result for t_n follows by applying the result for T_n to $-f$. In any case we have

$$\int_a^b f\ dx = \sum_{i=1}^n \int_{x_{i-1}}^{x_i} f\ dx \leq \sum_{i=1}^n \int_{x_{i-1}}^{x_i} \sup\{f(x) \mid x_{i-1} \leq x \leq x_i\}\ dx$$

$$= \sum_{i=1}^n \frac{b - a}{n} \sup\{\ \} = T_n.$$

Case 1: f is a step function with partition points $a = z_0 < z_1 < \cdots < z_m \leq b$. Let $|f(x)| \leq B$. Given $\epsilon > 0$, choose an integer $N > 2mB(b - a)/\epsilon$. If $n \geq N$, then at most $2m$ of the intervals in the partition $a \leq x_0 < \cdots < x_n \leq b$ defining T_n contain a z_j; on these intervals $\sup\{f(x)\} \leq f(x) + B$. On all other $[x_{i-1},\ x_i]$, $\sup\{f(x)\} = f$. Therefore

$$T_n \leq \int_a^b f\ dx + {\sum}' B(x_i - x_{i-1}),$$

where Σ' is a sum over at most $2m$ terms. Therefore $\Sigma'B(x_i - x_{i-1}) = \Sigma'B(b - a)/n \leq 2mB(b - a)/n \leq 2mB(b - a)/N < \epsilon$. Consequently

$$\int_a^b f\, dx \leq T_n < \int_a^b f + \epsilon, \text{ that is, } \left| \int_a^b f\, dx - T_n \right| < \epsilon \text{ for all } n \geq N.$$

This proves $\lim T_n = \int_a^b f\, dx$. *Case 2:* f integrable. Given $\epsilon > 0$, choose a step function S so that $f(x) \leq S(x)$ and $\int_a^b S\, dx < \int_a^b f\, dx + \frac{1}{2}\epsilon$. Choose N so $T_n(S) < \int_a^b S\, dx + \frac{1}{2}\epsilon$ for all $n \geq N$. Clearly $T_n(f) \leq T_n(S)$ so we have

$$\int_a^b f\, dx \leq \int_a^b T_n(f)\, dx \leq \int_a^b T_n(S)\, dx$$
$$< \int_a^b S\, dx + \frac{1}{2}\epsilon < \int_a^b f\, dx + \epsilon.$$

This implies $T_n(f) \rightarrow \int_a^b f\, dx$.

17. *Case 1, g a step function:* Suppose $|f(x)| \leq A$ and $|g(x)| \leq B$, and the partition points for g are $a = z_0 < z_1 < \cdots < z_m = b$. Given $\epsilon > 0$, choose an integer $N > 8mAB(b - a)/\epsilon$. If $n \geq N$, then $f(z_i)g(w_i) = f(z_i)g(z_i)$ except for the at most $2m$ intervals (x_{i-1}, x_i) which include a point z_j. On these, $|f(z_i)g(w_i) - f(z_i)g(z_i)| = |f(z_i)|\, |g(w_i) - g(z_i)| \leq 2AB$, hence

$$\left| V_n - \frac{b - a}{n} \sum_{i=1}^n f(z_i)g(z_i) \right| \leq 2AB\, \frac{2m(b - a)}{n} \leq \frac{4ABm(b - a)}{N} < \frac{1}{2}\epsilon.$$

Since fg is integrable, we have $\left| \int_a^b fg\, dx - U_n(fg) \right| < \frac{1}{2}\epsilon$ for $n \geq N_1 \geq N$, hence $\left| \int_a^b fg\, dx - V_n \right| < \epsilon$ for all $n \geq N_1$. *Case 2, g integrable.* Given $\epsilon > 0$ we can find s and S such that $s(x) \leq g(x) \leq S(x)$ and $\int_a^b (fS - fs)\, dx < \frac{1}{3}\epsilon$. Clearly $V_n(f, s) \leq V_n(f, g) \leq V_n(f, S)$. By case 1, $V_n(f, s) \rightarrow \int_a^b fs\, dx$ and $V_n(f, S) \rightarrow \int_a^b fS\, dx$, hence $\left| V_n(f, s) - \int_a^b fs\, dx \right| < \frac{1}{3}\epsilon$ and $\left| V_n(f, S) - \int_a^b fS\, dx \right| < \frac{1}{3}\epsilon$ for $n \geq N$. Since also $\int_a^b fs\, dx \leq \int_a^b fg\, dx \leq \int_a^b fS\, dx$, it follows that $\left| V_n - \int_a^b fg\, dx \right| < \epsilon$ for all $n \geq N$.

19. Given $\epsilon > 0$, choose $n > b^2/\epsilon$. Partition $[0, b]$ by $x_i = ib/n$, $i = 0$, $1, \cdots, n$. Define a step function by $s(x) = x_{i-1}$ for $x_{i-1} \leq x < x_i$,

$s(b) = b$. Then $s(x) \le x \le s(x) + b/n$ for $0 \le x \le b$. Hence $\left| \displaystyle\int_0^b s\,dx \right.$

$\left. - \displaystyle\int_0^b x\,dx \right| < \displaystyle\int_0^b (b/n)\ dx = b^2/n < \epsilon$. But $\displaystyle\int_0^b s\,dx = \sum_{i=1}^{n} s(x_{i-1})$

$(x_i - x_{i-1}) = \Sigma_{i=1}^{n}\,[(i-1)b/n](b/n) = (b^2/n^2)\Sigma_{i=1}^{n}(i-1) = (b^2/n^2)$

$[n(n-1)/2] = \frac{1}{2}b^2(1 - 1/n)$. Hence $\left| \frac{1}{2}b^2(1 - 1/n) - \displaystyle\int_0^b x\,dx \right| < \epsilon$

for all n sufficiently large. Let $n \to \infty$. We find $\left| \frac{1}{2}b^2 - \displaystyle\int_0^b x\,dx \right| \le \epsilon$.

Since ϵ is arbitrary, $\displaystyle\int_0^b x\,dx = \frac{1}{2}b^2$.

21. Choose $c_1,\ c_2 \in [a,\ b]$ so $f(c_1) \le f(x) \le f(c_2)$ for $x \in [a,\ b]$. Then

$f(c_1)g(x) \le f(x)g(x) \le f(c_2)g(x)$, so $f(c_1)\displaystyle\int_a^b g\,dx \le \displaystyle\int_a^b fg\,dx \le$

$f(c_2)\displaystyle\int_a^b g\,dx$. If $\displaystyle\int_a^b g\,dx = 0$, this proves that $\displaystyle\int_a^b fg\,dx = 0$ and any

c works. Otherwise $\displaystyle\int_a^b g\,dx > 0$ and we have $f(c_1) \le \left[\displaystyle\int_a^b fg\,dx \right] \Big/$

$\left[\displaystyle\int_a^b g\,dx \right] \le f(c_2)$ and Theorem 20.8.2 provides c.

Section 5, page 568

1. By Theorem 5.1, $f(x) = (d/dx) \left(\displaystyle\int_a^x f(t)\,dt \right) = (d/dx)\,(0) = 0$.

3. $1/\sqrt{x^3 + 1}$ **5.** $-e^{-x^2}$ **7.** x or 0.

9. Apply integration by parts to f and G. Note that $G' = g$.

11. Set $F(x) = f(x + h) - f(x) - Bf'(x)$. Let $f(x_0) \ge f(x) \ge f(x_1)$ (by Ex. 20.8.25). Then $f'(x_0) = 0$ so $F(x_0) \le 0$ and $f'(x_1) = 0$ so $F(x_1) \ge 0$. By Ex. 10, $F(c) = 0$ for some c.

13. Set $c = \frac{1}{2}(a + b)$. Integration by parts yields $\displaystyle\int_a^b f(x)\,dx = \displaystyle\int_a^b (c - x)$

$f'(x)\,dx$, hence $\left| \displaystyle\int_a^b f(x)\,dx \right| \le M \displaystyle\int_a^b |c - x|\,dx = \frac{1}{4}M(b-a)^2$.

Section 6, page 573

1. $x = \ln s$ and $y = \ln t$, so $e^{x+y} = e^{\ln(st)} = st = e^x e^y$. Next $e^{x-y} = e^{\ln s - \ln t} =$ $e^{\ln(s/t)} = s/t = e^x/e^y$, and finally $nx = n \ln s = \ln s^n$ so $e^{nx} = s^n = (e^x)^n$.

3. Set $x = \ln s$, that is, $s = e^x$. Then $s \to \infty$ as $x \to \infty$, so $\lim_{x \to \infty} e^x/x^n = \lim_{s \to \infty} s/(\ln s)^n = \infty$.

5. Define $S(x)$ by $1 < \frac{5}{4} < \frac{6}{4} < \frac{7}{4} < \frac{8}{4} < \frac{9}{4} < \frac{10}{4} = 2.5$ with the values

$1,\ \frac{4}{5},\ \frac{4}{6},\ \cdots,\ \frac{4}{9}$. Then $1/x \le S(x)$ and $\displaystyle\int_a^b S\,dx = \frac{1}{4}(1 + \frac{4}{5} + \frac{4}{6} +$

$\frac{4}{7} + \frac{4}{8} + \frac{4}{9}) = \frac{1}{4} + \frac{1}{5} + \cdots + \frac{1}{9} = 2509/2520 < 1.$ Therefore $\int_1^{2.5} dx/x < 1$, $\ln 2.5 < 1$, $2.5 < e$.

7. By the Mean Value Theorem, $(\ln y - \ln x)/(y - x) = 1/z$, where $x < z < y$. Clearly $1/y < 1/z < 1/x$.

9. Set $f(x) = \ln x$ and $g(x) = \sqrt{x} - 1/\sqrt{x}$ for $x \geq 1$. We shall prove $f(x) < g(x)$ for $x > 1$. (When we have this we simply replace x by y/x to get Kepler's inequality.) First $f(1) = g(1) = 0$. It suffices to prove $f'(x) < g'(x)$ for $x > 1$, that is, $x^{-1} < \frac{1}{2}x^{-1/2} + \frac{1}{2}x^{-3/2}$, $2x^{1/2} < x + 1$. This is true because $0 < (\sqrt{x} - 1)^2$.

11. 1

13. Set $f(x) = (1 + 1/x)^{1+x}$. Then $f'(x) = f(x)g(x)$, where $g(x) = \ln(1 + 1/x) - 1/x$. We must prove $g(x) < 0$ for $x > 0$. Now $g'(x) = 1/x^2(x + 1) > 0$ for $x > 0$, so $g(x)$ is steadily increasing. But $g(x) \to 0$ as $x \to \infty$, hence $g(x) < 0$ for $x > 0$. The simplest way to find $\lim_{x \to \infty} f(x)$ is to write $f(x) = (1 + 1/x)(1 + 1/x)^x$. Clearly $1 + 1/x \to 1$, and $(1 + 1/x)^x \to e$ by Theorem 6.7.

15. e^a 17. $\ln \ln x$

Section 7, page 579

1. Set $g(x) = \arctan y$, where $y = 2x/(1 - x^2)$. Then $g(0) = 0$ and $g'(x) = 2/(1 + x^2) = (2 \arctan x)'$. Therefore $g(x) = 2 \arctan x$ for $-1 < x < 1$. For $x > 1$ we observe that $\lim_{x \to 1+} g(x) = -\frac{1}{2}\pi$ so $g(x) = 2 \arctan x - \pi$ for $x > 1$. Similarly $g(x) = 2 \arctan x + \pi$ for $x < -1$.

3. The relation is true if $y = 0$, so we may assume $y \neq 0$. Fix y and set $f(x) = \arctan [(x + y)/(1 - xy)]$ and $g(x) = \arctan x + \arctan y$. Then $f'(x) = g'(x)$ by direct calculation, so $f(x) = g(x) + \text{const.}$ wherever f and g are continuous. The discontinuity occurs at $x = 1/y$. *Case 1:* $y > 0$. Then $f(0) = g(0)$ so $f(x) = g(x)$ for $-\infty < x < 1/y$. Since $\lim_{x \to \infty} f(x) = \arctan(-1/y) = \arctan y - \frac{1}{2}\pi$ by Ex. 2 and $\lim_{x \to \infty} g(x) = \frac{1}{2}\pi + \arctan y$, we also have $f(x) = g(x) - \pi$ for $1/y < x < \infty$. *Case 2:* $y < 0$. We find similarly that $f(x) = g(x)$ for $1/y < x < \infty$ and $f(x) \to \arctan y + \frac{1}{2}\pi$ and $g(x) \to -\frac{1}{2}\pi + \arctan y$ as $x \to -\infty$, so $f(x) = g(x) + \pi$ for $-\infty < x < 1/y$.

5. By the Mean Value Theorem,

$$\frac{\sin x - \sin(2n + 1)\pi}{x - (2n + 1)\pi} = \cos y,$$

where y is between $(2n + 1)\pi$ and x. If $x \to (2n + 1)\pi$, then $y \to (2n + 1)\pi$. Since $\cos y$ is continuous, we get $\cos(2n + 1)\pi$ for the limit. The sine is treated similarly.

7. In Ex. 3 we obtained $\arctan[(x + y)/(1 - xy)] = \arctan x + \arctan y$ if $y > 0$ and $xy < 1$. Set $x = \frac{1}{2}$, $y = \frac{1}{3}$.

9. Set $x = \frac{1}{5}$ and $y = \frac{1}{8}$ in Ex. 3. Then use Ex. 8.

11. Apply the inequality of Ex. 10 to the formula of Ex. 8:

$$2\frac{\frac{1}{3}}{1 + (\frac{1}{3})^2} + \frac{\frac{1}{7}}{1 + (\frac{1}{7})^2} < \frac{1}{4}\pi < \frac{2}{3} + \frac{1}{7}.$$

13. By Lhospital's rule, $\lim (\sin x)/x = \lim \cos x = 1$.

15. $(\sin x)/(1 + \cos x) = [2t/(1 + t^2)]/[2/(1 + t^2)] = t.$

Index

10. $\displaystyle\int \sin^2 ax\, dx = \frac{x}{2} - \frac{\sin 2ax}{4a}$

11. $\displaystyle\int \cos^2 ax\, dx = \frac{x}{2} + \frac{\sin 2ax}{4a}$

12. $\displaystyle\int \sin^n ax\, dx = -\frac{\sin^{n-1} ax \cos ax}{na} + \frac{n-1}{n}\int \sin^{n-2} ax\, dx$

13. $\displaystyle\int \cos^n ax\, dx = \frac{\cos^{n-1} ax \sin ax}{na} + \frac{n-1}{n}\int \cos^{n-2} ax\, dx$

14. $\displaystyle\int \sin ax \cos bx\, dx = -\frac{\cos(a+b)x}{2(a+b)} - \frac{\cos(a-b)x}{2(a-b)} \qquad (a \neq \pm b)$

15. $\displaystyle\int \sin ax \sin bx\, dx = \frac{\sin(a-b)x}{2(a-b)} - \frac{\sin(a+b)x}{2(a+b)} \qquad (a \neq \pm b)$

16. $\displaystyle\int \cos ax \cos bx\, dx = \frac{\sin(a-b)x}{2(a-b)} + \frac{\sin(a+b)x}{2(a+b)} \qquad (a \neq \pm b)$

17. $\displaystyle\int x \sin ax\, dx = \frac{\sin ax}{a^2} - \frac{x \cos ax}{a}$

18. $\displaystyle\int x \cos ax\, dx = \frac{\cos ax}{a^2} + \frac{x \sin ax}{a}$

19. $\displaystyle\int x^n \sin ax\, dx = -\frac{x^n \cos ax}{a} + \frac{n}{a}\int x^{n-1} \cos ax\, dx$

20. $\displaystyle\int x^n \cos ax\, dx = \frac{x^n \sin ax}{a} - \frac{n}{a}\int x^{n-1} \sin ax\, dx$

21. $\displaystyle\int \tan ax\, dx = -\frac{1}{a}\ln|\cos ax|$

22. $\displaystyle\int \cot ax\, dx = \frac{1}{a}\ln|\sin ax|$

23. $\displaystyle\int \tan^2 ax\, dx = \frac{1}{a}\tan ax - x$

24. $\displaystyle\int \cot^2 ax\, dx = -\frac{1}{a}\cot ax - x$

25. $\displaystyle\int \tan^n ax\, dx = \frac{\tan^{n-1} ax}{(n-1)a} - \int \tan^{n-2} ax\, dx \qquad (n > 1)$

26. $\displaystyle\int \cot^n ax\, dx = -\frac{\cot^{n-1} ax}{(n-1)a} - \int \cot^{n-2} ax\, dx \qquad (n > 1)$